GROUND WATER CONTAMINATION

ISBN 0-13-013840-1

90000

9 780130 138408

GROUND WATER CONTAMINATION

TRANSPORT AND REMEDIATION

Second Edition

Philip B. Bedient
Rice University

Hanadi S. Rifai
University of Houston

Charles J. Newell
Groundwater Services, Inc.

Prentice Hall PTR
Upper Saddle River, NJ 07458
http://www.phptr.com

Library of Congress Cataloging-in-Publication Data

Bedient, Philip B., 1948-
    Ground water contamination : transport and remediation / Philip B. Bedient, Hanadi s. Rifai,
      Charles J. Newell. -- 2nd ed.
      p.   cm.
    Includes bibliographical references and index.
    ISBN 0-13-013840-1
    1. Groundwater--Pollution. 2. Groundwater--Quality--Management.
    I. Rifai, H.S. II. Newell, Charles J. III. Title.
    TD426.B44 1999
    628.1'68--dc21   99-38305
                                                   CIP

Editorial/production supervision: *Vincent Janoski*
Acquisitions editor: *Bernard Goodwin*
Marketing manager: *Lisa Konzelmann*
Manufacturing manager: *Alan Fischer*
Editorial assistant: *Diane Spina*
Cover design director: *Jerry Votta*

Published by Prentice Hall PTR
Prentice-Hall, Inc.
Upper Saddle River, NJ 07458

Prentice Hall books are widely used by corporations and government agencies
for training, marketing, and resale.

The publisher offers discounts on this book when ordered in bulk quantities.
For more information, contact: Corporate Sales Department, Phone: 800-382-3419;
Fax: 201-236-7141; E-mail: corpsales@prenhall.com; or write: Prentice Hall PTR,
Corp. Sales Dept., One Lake Street, Upper Saddle River, NJ 07458.

Printed in the United States of America
10 9 8 7 6 5 4 3 2 1

ISBN   0-13-013840-1

Prentice-Hall International (UK) Limited, London
Prentice-Hall of Australia Pty. Limited, Sydney
Prentice-Hall Canada Inc., Toronto
Prentice-Hall Hispanoamericana, S.A., Mexico
Prentice-Hall of India Private Limited, New Delhi
Prentice-Hall of Japan, Inc., Tokyo
Prentice-Hall Singapore Pte. Ltd., Singapore
Editora Prentice-Hall do Brasil, Ltda., Rio de Janeiro

C O N T E N T S

4 SOURCES AND TYPES OF GROUNDWATER CONTAMINATION 75

5 HYDROGEOLOGIC SITE INVESTIGATIONS 113

by Robert S. Lee and John A. Connor

6 CONTAMINANT TRANSPORT MECHANISMS 159

7   CONTAMINANT FATE PROCESSES   203

by Joseph B. Hughes

8   MODELING BIODEGRADATION AND NATURAL ATTENUATION   237

9   FLOW AND TRANSPORT IN THE UNSATURATED ZONE   289

by Manar El-Beshry

PREFACE

The 1970s ushered in a new decade of environmental awareness in response to major air pollution and water quality problems throughout the country. One of the primary missions of the newly formed Environmental Protection Agency (EPA) was to define, maintain, and protect the quality of the nation's surface waters and subsurface aquifers. The field of environmental engineering was in its infancy, but hydrologists, civil and environmental engineers, hydrogeologists and other scientists were needed to provide the necessary expertise and engineering designs for water pollution control of surface waters.

By the late 1970s, the discovery of hazardous wastes at sites such as Love Canal in New York, the Denver Arsenal in Colorado, and a number of chlorinated organics sites in California and Arizona ushered in a new era in hazardous waste site problems. In the early 1980s, a large number of major disposal sites were discovered associated with industrial and military practices. These sites had been in place for decades. As a result, literally thousands of studies of active and abandoned waste sites and spills were conducted, as required by Resource Conservation and Recovery Act (RCRA) and the Superfund legislation administered by EPA, all designed to protect ground water quality (Chapter 14). During this time, hydrogeologists and consulting engineers were collecting samples, characterizing geology, analyzing data, and remediating hazardous waste sites with respect to ground water contamination. More than 1500 hazardous waste sites were eventually placed on the National Priorities List and thousands of other sites still remaining to be cleaned up.

By 1985, leaking underground fuel tanks became one of the most ubiquitous of all subsurface contamination issues. In addition, chlorinated hydrocarbon sites were recognized as some of the most difficult to remediate due to the presence of newly discovered non-aqueous phase liquids (NAPLs). But as these sites and others were being investigated and remediation systems were being designed and installed across the country, it became clear by 1989 that many of these systems were not working to cleanup aquifers to drinking water standards. By the early 1990s, EPA and the National Research Council found that the nation was wasting large sums of money on ineffective remediation systems, such as pump and treat (see Chapter 13).

Along with the maturing of environmental engineering and related ground water fields in the eighties, attention to hazardous waste problems has greatly expanded the scope and emphasis of traditional ground water investigations. Contaminant transport in the subsurface is of paramount importance and encompasses physical, chemical, and biological mechanisms which affect rates of migration, degradation, and ultimate remediation. In the nineties, many of the these complex transport mechanisms were evaluated at actual field sites or in supporting laboratory studies.

After all of the efforts spent on analyzing and remediating soluble contaminant plumes, scientists and engineers in the nineties and beyond 2000 must be prepared to deal with more complex problems. These include source zone areas with non-aqueous phase liquids (NAPLs), residual oils, and vapors in the unsaturated zone. LNAPLs, which float on the water table, and DNAPLs, which sink to the bottom of an aquifer, can leach contamination for decades to shallow ground water aquifers. Specialized remediation schemes, which might involve a variety of methods for a mixture of chemicals, must now be evaluated in complex ground water settings. The old concept of simply pumping out the contaminated ground water does not effectively work to return an aquifer to useful condition. Rather, new and emerging methods and models must be considered in order to address and possibly control complex NAPL source zones.

The second edition of our textbook has been written to better address the scientific and engineering aspects of subsurface contaminant transport and remediation in ground water. This book contains traditional emphasis on site characterization and hydrogeologic evaluation, but with an orientation to the engineering analysis and modeling of complex field problems, compared to other texts written primarily for hydrogeologists. The current text is a departure from past efforts in that it is written from both a theoretical and practical viewpoint with engineering methods and transport theory applied directly to hazardous waste site investigation. Entire chapters are included on biodegradation, soil vapor transport, contaminant transport modeling, and site remediation. A number of new case studies have been added that illustrate the various evaluation schemes and emerging remediation techniques.

This second edition is designed for hydrologists, civil, environmental, and chemical engineers, hydrogeologists, and other decision makers in the ground water field who are or will be involved in the evaluation and remediation of the nation's ground water. However, the field of ground water contamination has changed rapidly in recent years (since 1994) as new remediation techniques are being researched in laboratories and at many field sites nationwide. Any modern student of the topic must keep a watchful eye on the literature, which reports both results and breakthroughs on a monthly basis. We hope this text will provide the fundamentals for understanding and incorporating new approaches into the more traditional methods developed in site investigations of the past two decades.

The legal framework of ground water legislation under RCRA and Superfund has provided significant guidance and funding for many of the ground water studies which have been performed to date. These comprehensive legal instruments set into motion an entire industry devoted to the identification, characterization, and remediation of hazardous waste sites throughout the U.S. As a result of billions of dollars allocated for remedial investigations and studies in the past 20 years, thousands of engineers and scientists now form the core of the ground water and remediation industry. During this time, college and university programs quickly added ground water flow and transport courses to their traditional fields of civil and environmental engineering and geology. And professional groups, such as the Assn. of Ground Water Scientists and Engineers, saw their memberships grow in response to the challenge of education and technology transfer.

Our new revision was written in response to the tremendous demand in the college classroom and in the environmental industry for a modern engineering approach to ground water contamination problems of the nineties and beyond. Any practicing hydrologist or engineer today must understand mechanisms of ground water flow (Chapters 2 and 3), sources of contamination (Chapter 4), site investigations (Chapter 5), and contaminant transport (Chapters 6 and 7). In addition, biodegradation (Chapters 7 and 8), modeling approaches (Chapter 10), NAPL impacts in source areas and plumes (Chapters 11), natural attenuation (Chapter 12), and emerging remediation schemes (Chapter 13) are covered. In the second edition, Chapters 4, 7, 8, 9, 11, 12, and 13 have been completely rewritten to better reflect current trends and ideas. Many new examples and case studies have been added based on emerging methods from the current literature, A new chapter on natural attenuation and risk assessment has been added, along with detailed discussions of emerging remediation methods such as surfactant and co-solvent soil flushing for sites contaminated with residual oils. The organization is described in more detail in Chapter 1.

For more information about software that relates to the book, updates, or to communicate with the primary author, please visit Prentice-Hall's website at http://www.pren-hall.com or http://www.rice.edu/envi.

ACKNOWLEDGMENTS

Any textbook represents the evolution of ideas and concepts with input from a variety of colleagues, students, and friends over a long period of time. We would particularly like to thank reviewers of the original manuscript for their helpful guidance and numerous suggestions, especially Dr. Robert Borden. Special thanks are due to personnel and researchers at the EPA Robert S. Kerr Environmental Research Lab in Ada, Oklahoma who supported and contributed to our research for more than a decade. The National Center for Ground Water Research, headed by Dr. Herb Ward, provided the mechanism for exchange of ideas. We would like to thank the Shell Foundation for support through the years as part of Dr. Bedient's Shell Distinguished Chair in Environmental Science. Most recently, the U.S. Air Force and SERDP/EPA funded activities at Hill Air Force Base in Utah provided an interdisciplinary study site for the evaluation of new remediation technologies, some of which are described in the text.

Many Rice University staff and students contributed significantly to the new edition of the text. Joseph Hughes, Manar El-Beshry, Robert Lee, and Anthony Holder contributed important new sections to the second edition. Emily Hall, AnnMarie Spexet, Michelle Truesdale, and Jude Benavides contributed to final editing. Susan Hickman and Michelle Truesdale handled new figure designs, and Christina Walsh organized the revised figures and final layout for the second edition. AnnMarie Spexet did a great job with figure design, indexing, revised homework problems, and helped develop the solutions manual. Anthony Holder did a superb job of final text and figure editing, placement, and computer linkage. Cory Deveney was responsible for the revised cover for the new edition. Finally, the authors are deeply indebted to Emily Hall for taking on the enormous challenge of typing, format layout, and editing the newly revised manuscript. Without her daily commitment to the overall success of the project, the revision would not have been completed on time and with such style.

CHAPTER 1

INTRODUCTION TO GROUND WATER CONTAMINATION

1.1 THE HYDROLOGIC CYCLE

The definition of **hydrology** includes the study of storage and movement of water in streams and lakes on the surface of the earth, as well as in ground water aquifers in the subsurface. An **aquifer** represents a geological unit, which can store and supply significant quantities of water for a variety of uses. Many shallow and deep aquifers have been investigated and identified as having elevated levels of contaminants from releases that may have occurred decades ago. Modern hydrology encompasses both flow and water quality transport aspects of the water cycle.

Figure 1.1 shows the various components of the hydrologic cycle, including both natural processes and manmade or engineered processes and transport pathways. These concepts are covered in detail in modern texts on hydrology (Bedient and Huber, 1992; Gupta,

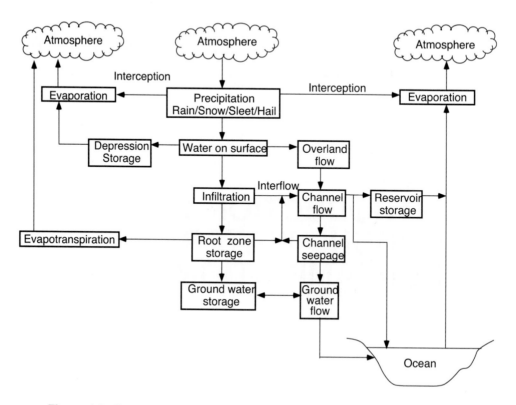

Figure 1.1 Components of the hydrologic cycle.

1989, Chow et al., 1988). Atmospheric water and solar energy provide the main inputs for the generation of precipitation, which falls over the land and oceans. Rainfall can infiltrate into the soil system, percolate to deeper ground water, evaporate from detention areas, transpire through vegetation back to the atmosphere, or runoff to the nearest stream or river. Infiltrating water is the main source of recharge to the root zone and ground water aquifers below. Rivers can also recharge aquifers or can act as discharge points for aquifer outflows. The ocean is the ultimate receptor of surface and ground water contributions from surrounding land areas, and provides the main source of water for evaporation back to the atmosphere.

Manmade changes to the cycle have been recorded since the beginning of civilization. They include changes in infiltration patterns and evaporation due to land development, changes in runoff and evaporation patterns due to reservoir storage, increases in streamflow due to channelization and piping, and changes in ground water levels due to pumping of aquifers. Since the 1930s, hydrologists traditionally have spent much time and effort designing alterations to the natural hydrologic cycle for man's use. Such alterations include providing surface or ground water supplies for industrial, agricultural, and municipal needs; providing water treatment for drinking water and the disposal of wastewater; meeting water supply needs through building of dams and reservoirs or drilling of water supply well fields; providing drainage and flood control via channelization and dams; and providing water quality and recreational benefits through development and maintenance of reservoirs and stream corridors.

Due to the complexity of the hydrologic cycle shown in Figure 1.1, not all of the transport pathways and storage elements can be measured easily, and some components can be determined only indirectly as unknowns in the overall hydrologic water balance equation. Infiltration and evaporation are often computed as losses from the system and are not usually measured directly. Precipitation rates and stream levels can be directly measured by rainfall and stream gages that have been located within a particular watershed being studied. Ground water levels and flow rates are measured from wells installed into aquifers with screens across the permeable zones. In complex geological settings, multiple layers are monitored for water and contaminant levels. Methods include use of flow meters within the well casing and electronic water level meters. Pumps and individual bailers are used to collect water samples for the analysis of water quality levels in wells.

Overall water balances for a watershed or ground water basin can be computed if the above hydrologic data is available. Computer methods have been developed beginning in the 1970s to assist the hydrologist in watershed analysis, ground water assessment, and hydrologic design. Surface water aspects of the hydrologic cycle are usually covered in modern hydrology texts such as Viessman et al. (1989), Chow et al. (1988), and Bedient and Huber (1992).

1.2 GROUND WATER HYDROLOGY

Ground water is an important source of water supply for municipalities, agriculture, and industry. Figure 1.2 indicates the percentage of various types of ground water use in the United States through 1995. Primary users are agriculture, municipalities, industry, and rural areas where alternate surface supplies are inadequate. Agricultural irrigation use is clearly the largest category. Figure 1.3 depicts ground water use relative to total water use for each state in the continental United States, indicating that western and midwestern areas are more dependent on ground water aquifers than are states in the east and northeast.

Ground water hydrology has traditionally included the characterization of aquifers, application of Darcy's law for ground water flow through porous media, infiltration into soils, and flow in shallow and deep aquifer systems. More advanced topics include the mechanics of well flow in radial coordinates for single or multiple well systems. Techniques for the analysis of aquifer characteristics using slug tests, pump tests, or tracer tests are a major part of ground water investigations. The prediction of flow rates and directions in confined (under pressure) and unconfined (water table) aquifers is the starting point for understanding ground water contamination issues. The **water table** in a shallow aquifer is defined as the level to which water will rise in a dug well under atmospheric conditions. The **piezometric** surface is the level to which water rises in a confined aquifer under pressure (see Chapter 2).

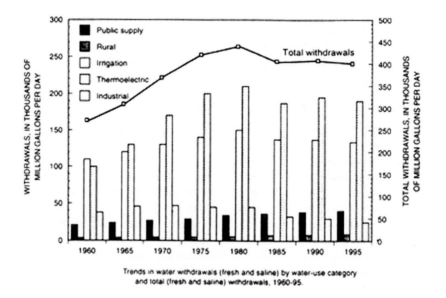

Trends in water withdrawals (fresh and saline) by water-use category
and total (fresh and saline) withdrawals. 1960-95.

Figure 1.2 Trends in water withdrawals (fresh and saline) by water use category and total (fresh and saline) withdrawals, 1960-95.   Source USGS, 1995.

Ground water hydrology is of great importance because of the use of aquifer systems for water supply and because of the threat of contamination from leaking hazardous waste sites, which occur at or below the ground surface. Recently, more attention has been given to the connection between the unsaturated zone and shallow aquifers just below the water table as it relates to migration of contaminants from the surface or from buried tanks, pipes, or waste ponds. Properties of the porous media and subsurface geology govern both the rate and direction of ground water flow in any aquifer system. The injection or accidental spill of hazardous wastes into an aquifer or the pumping of the aquifer for water supply may alter the natural hydrologic flow patterns. In order for the hydrologist, hydrogeologist, civil engineer, or environmental engineer to obtain a full understanding of the mechanisms that lead to ground water contamination from spills or continuous leaks, it is necessary to address first the properties of ground water flow and well mechanics, as covered in Chapters 2 and 3.

Geological aspects of ground water, sometimes referred to as hydrogeology, are of importance to understanding ground water flow and the fate and transport of contaminants in the subsurface. Regional geological aspects have been covered in detail in books by Freeze and Cherry (1979), Fetter (1994), and Domenico and Schwartz (1998) and will be addressed in this text only to a limited basis. One useful generalization is the concept of ground water regions, which are geographical areas of similar occurrence of ground water. Meinzer (1923), considered the father of modern hydrogeology in the United States, proposed a classification

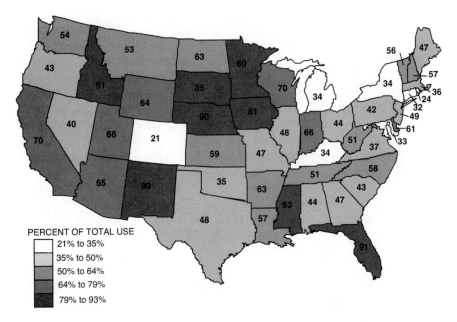

Figure 1.3 Ground water use as a percent of total water use, 1985. Source Solley, et al., 1988.

system based on 21 different ground water provinces. Thomas (1952) devised the system based on 10 ground water regions, and Heath (1984) revised Thomas' system to include 15 different regions. Heath based his system on five features of ground water systems:

1. The components of the system and their arrangement;

2. The nature of the water-bearing openings of the dominant aquifer or aquifers with respect to whether they are of primary or secondary origin;

3. The mineral composition of the rock matrix of the dominant aquifers with respect to whether it is soluble or insoluble;

4. The water storage and transmission characteristics of the dominant aquifer or aquifers; and

5. The nature and location of recharge and discharge areas.

The various regions for the United States are shown in Figure 1.4 and are based on the DRASTIC system (Aller et al, 1987).

Each of the above regional geologic categories is unique in its own right and important to understanding the underlying stratigraphy that may be impacting the transport of contaminants in the subsurface. Extensive studies exist on each of the regions from the United States Geological Survey or from State Geological Surveys, but some areas have been more inten-

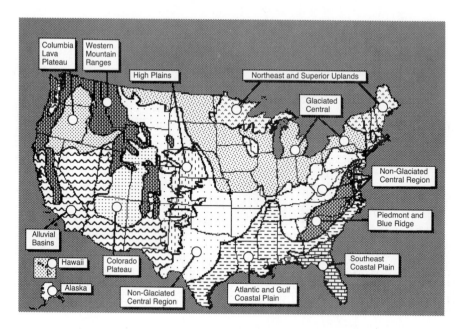

Figure 1.4 Ground water regions of the United States. Source Newell, et al., 1990.

sively evaluated than others. In many cases of practical interest, the first few shallow layers of sand or silty sand (5m to 50 m depth) may be the only zones of concern from a contamination and remediation standpoint. These relatively shallow zones may not have been evaluated by qualified hydrogeologists in a consistent manner, which has led to significant errors in the prediction of flow rates and contaminant impacts associated with some hazardous waste sites.

The revised text presents detailed methods and examples of hydrogeological site investigations in shallow and deep ground water in Chapter 5, as well as various remediation methods that can be used at hazardous waste sites in Chapters 12 and 13. It is important for students and professionals alike to understand the relationship between the regional geological setting and the local, shallow stratigraphy surrounding a waste site. Often, the overall regional setting has very little to do with shallow aquifers near the surface (within 20 m), which are often the main pathways for contaminant migration in the subsurface. However, an understanding of the regional setting is important to evaluate the extent to which the aquifer is used for water supply.

1.3 GROUND WATER CONTAMINATION AND TRANSPORT

The occurrence of ground water contamination and the quality of ground water have become major issues since the discovery of numerous hazardous waste sites in the late seventies.

Waste sites such as Love Canal in New York, the Denver Arsenal in Colorado, and Hughes Plant 44 in Arizona are three examples where hazardous wastes have created serious ground water contamination problems for decades to come. Over 1500 sites nationwide were on the National Priority List from EPA. Sources of ground water contamination are widespread as shown in Figure 1.5 and include thousands of accidental spills, landfills, surface waste ponds, underground storage tanks, above ground tanks, pipelines, injection wells, land application of wastes and pesticides, septic tanks, radioactive waste disposal sites, salt water intrusion, and acid mine drainage.

An engineering hydrologist today must be able to address mechanisms of ground water flow, contaminant transport, biodegradation and sorption, pure phase impacts in source areas and plumes, and remediation schemes. This text is designed to assist engineering and science students, hydrogeologists, and other professionals in dealing with these major processes in ground water, not always covered in earlier texts in a comprehensive way.

A review of ground water flow in the subsurface, including well mechanics, is required before one can make any progress toward explaining or predicting contamination processes. Chapter 2 provides a working knowledge of methods that have been developed to predict rates of flow according to Darcy's Law, and directions of movement in aquifer systems. Chapter 3

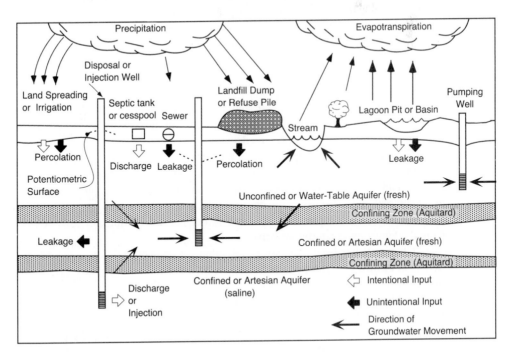

Figure 1.5 How waste disposal practices contaminate the ground water system.

follows with coverage of steady and unsteady well mechanics and a review of standard aquifer tests (pump tests, slug tests, tracer tests) for determining hydraulic conductivity (permeability) in the field. A number of homework problems and examples are also included on ground water flow and well mechanics.

Sources of ground water contamination are widespread and include thousands of accidental spills, landfills, surface waste ponds, underground storage tanks, pipelines, injection wells, land application of wastes and pesticides, septic tanks, radioactive waste disposal, salt water intrusion, and acid mine drainage. These various sources are described in more detail in Chapter 4, which has been greatly expanded for the second edition. The main contaminants of concern still include petroleum hydrocarbons such as benzene, toluene, and xylene; chlorinated organics such as perchloroethylene (PCE), trichloroethylene (TCE) and its associated daughter products; heavy metals such as lead, zinc, and chromium, and certain inorganic salts. A section on organic chemicals is also included.

Sampling and monitoring methods (direct and indirect) have advanced significantly over the past two decades with vast improvements in microelectronics and low level organic chemical analyses. Cone penetrometers, push technology, and specialized multi-level samplers are routinely used as part of site investigations. Data collection and monitoring methods, and the preparation of site work plans for hydrogeologic investigations are described in Chapter 5, which has been updated for the second edition.

Chapter 6 introduces discussion of contaminant transport processes, theory, and equations, including mechanisms of advection, dispersion, and adsorption. These are still considered some of the most important mechanisms in that they all contribute to the spatial and temporal changes in concentration often observed in plumes. These processes also are important for natural attenuation of plumes in aquifer systems. Many examples and analytical methods are presented in this chapter, and tracer results from the Borden Landfill and studies at Otis Air Force Base are highlighted. A number of homework problems are included to reinforce the concepts that are presented.

Chapter 7 is a new chapter on contaminant fate processes and covers topics such as adsorption, abiotic transformation, volatilization and biodegradation associated with organic contaminants. Chapter 8 on biodegradation modeling has been greatly expanded to include new examples and a discussion of new models that apply to fuel contaminants and chlorinated solvents. Both chapters address modern mechanisms of transport that relate directly to natural attenuation in aquifer systems.

Chapter 9 has been extensively rewritten for the new edition and presents a concise treatment of flow and transport in the unsaturated zone. This zone has received major attention with the discovery in the 1980s and early 1990s that soil vapor extraction (SVE) is a viable remediation method for many fuel spill sites. Both analytical and numerical modeling approaches for SVE systems are presented along with detailed examples. A major SVE case study is depicted in Chapter 13.

Chapter 10 describes modern approaches to numerical modeling of ground water flow and transport systems, including a detailed treatment of finite difference methods. A number of the standard models used in the industry are presented in detail with examples on their application at field sites. Modeling approaches have become even more important in recent years as budgets have shrunk for the collection of data and the drilling of extensive monitoring well networks. New visualization tools have greatly improved our ability to set up and use models to assist in data collection and decision making.

Chapter 11 covers nonaqueous phase liquids (NAPLs) in the subsurface, an important topic which has received considerable attention in the past decade as it relates to the remediation of hazardous waste sites (EPA, 1992; National Research Council, 1994: Pankow and Cherry, 1996). NAPLs, which can provide a source of continuing contamination for decades, are often associated with fuel leaks and chlorinated organic contaminants. Special treatment of source areas contaminated with NAPLs cannot be overlooked, and in earlier years led to the selection of ineffective remediation methods at many sites. The presence of DNAPL at a site may represent the most difficult problem to cleanup due to vertical migration associated with dense, often chlorinated, solvents and organics. Figure 1.6 presents the current conceptual model for what happens to a typical LNAPL hydrocarbon spill in the subsurface. It is now widely recognized that understanding NAPLs transport and remediation may be the most important ground water problem of the nineties. Figure 1.7 indicates the transport mecha-

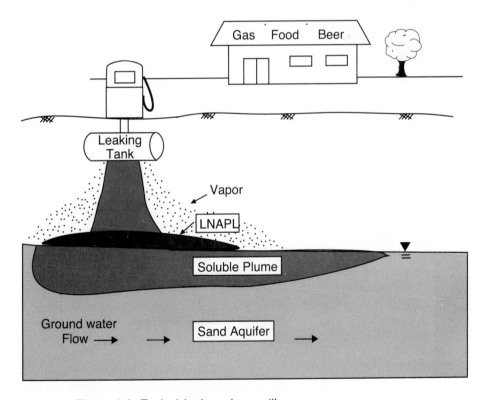

Figure 1.6 Typical hydrocarbon spill.

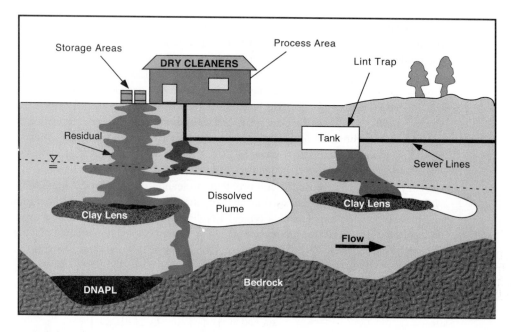

Figure 1.7 Transport mechanisms associated with DNAPLs at a chlorinated solvent site.

nisms associated with DNAPL at a typical dry cleaner site where chlorinated solvents have been used.

A relatively new approach for managing ground water plumes, natural attenuation, is reviewed in Chapter 12. With this approach, plume history, geochemical indicators, and ground water modeling are used to demonstrate that naturally occurring processes such as dispersion, sorption, dilution, and, most importantly, biodegradation, are effective at controlling plume migration. Methods for evaluating natural attenuation data are presented along with a summary of natural attenuation protocols and guidance documents. An overview of a related plume management approach, risk-based corrective action (RBCA) is also provided in Chapter 12. Under RBCA, a risk assessment is performed for the ground water pathway, and the data are used to develop cleanup standards that are protective of human health and the environment. Depending on the location of receptors and hydrogeologic and source conditions, the cleanup standards either will be higher than existing concentrations (indicating no active remediation is required) or will be more stringent than existing concentrations (indicating that either active remediation, containment, or institutional controls will be required).

Chapter 13 covers ground water remediation and design, which has experienced the greatest change since 1994, the publication of the first edition of the book. The chapter has been largely redone, with emphasis on those methods that have emerged as the clear winners in the list of possible active remediation techniques. New examples are included and older examples have been updated and improved with new data and ideas relating to cleanup and natural attenuation. Barrier systems, funnel and gate, and treatment walls are described in detail in the revised edition. Emerging methods for soil flushing with surfactants and co-solvents are highlighted for DNAPL extraction tested at Hill Air Force Base.

Chapter 14 reviews the important legal measures relating to ground water contamination that have arisen due to legislation, which has guided the EPA's mission to protect ground water quality in the United States. Federal legislation such as the Safe Drinking Water Act (SDWA, 1974), the Resource Conservation Recovery Act (RCRA, 1976), the Clean Water Act (1977), the Toxic Substances Control Act (TSCA, 1976), and the Comprehensive Environmental Response, Compensation, and Liability Act (CERCLA, 1980) provide a complex and comprehensive group of laws to protect the quality of ground water. Together, these laws have created an entire industry devoted to the evaluation and remediation of ground water.

1.4 EVOLUTION OF GROUND WATER INFORMATION

A number of classic textbooks in the ground water field have been written over the past thirty years. The field of ground water hydrology has expanded greatly since the first American textbook by Tolman (1937). Todd's (1959) text, *Ground Water Hydrology*, stood as a classic in the field for many years and was updated with a new edition in 1980. DeWiest's text in 1965 and Davis and DeWiest in 1966 further advanced the subject with their books on geohydrology and hydrogeology. Bear's texts written in 1972 and 1979 were departures from earlier approaches and emphasized the hydraulics of ground water, providing a very theoretical development of flow and transport in both the saturated and unsaturated zone for engineers, hydrologists, and hydrogeologists. In 1979, Freeze and Cherry's *Ground Water* quickly replaced others as the standard in the ground water field for more than a decade. Their chapters on transport, chemical properties, and contamination are still of great use even today. The new book by Pankow and Cherry (1996) provides a modern and comprehensive coverage of DNAPLs and chlorinated solvents.

There has been an explosion of literature in the past two decades, and there are numerous new sources of information and data in the ground water hydrology area. The United States Geological Survey (USGS) has primary responsibility for the collection of ground water data and evaluation of these data in terms of impacts on water supply, water quality, water depletion, and potential contamination. Studies performed by engineering consultants for EPA and for industry during the remedial investigation or feasibility study of RCRA and Superfund sites also provide a useful description of applied methods in ground water. Other primary sources of information are state environmental and water resources agencies, the American Geophysical Union, and the National Ground Water Association. Journals such as Water Resources Research, Ground Water, Journal of Hydrology, the ASCE Journal of Environmental Engineering, and Environmental Science and Technology are major resources for exchange of information.

The current text is a departure from past efforts in that it is written from both a theoretical and an engineering viewpoint with hydrologic and transport theory applied to hazardous waste site characterization, transport modeling, and remediation. For the first time, chapters on numerical methods and discussions of model applications to actual field sites exist alongside discussions of advection, adsorption, dispersion, chemical reaction, and biodegradation. Chapters on monitoring, hydrogeologic site characterization, and remediation are included along with detailed case studies that illustrate the various techniques currently being applied.

1.5 GROUND WATER REMEDIATION

The discovery of hazardous wastes at Love Canal in Niagara, New York, and at numerous other sites across the United States brought to light a new era in hazardous waste issues and problems. During the **hazardous waste decade** of the 1980s, hydrologists, hydrogeologists, civil and environmental engineers, and other scientists were involved in characterizing, evaluating, and remediating hazardous waste sites with respect to ground water contamination. The field of ground water has seen a virtual explosion in the number of remedial investigation studies related to the thousands of abandoned and active hazardous waste disposal sites and leaking tanks across the United States. One of the main objectives of this text is to provide engineers and scientists with a modern treatment of remediation methods currently being practiced, but with an eye towards the future.

Emerging new technologies are rapidly coming into place as we learn more about some of the failures of the past. Earlier pump and treat systems, which did not consider the presence of NAPLs in source zones, have not cleaned aquifers to the required levels. Many of the original systems worked adequately for a period of time, but after they were turned off, many sites had contaminant levels return to even higher values than before remediation. There have been success stories as well, with the discovery that many fuel (BTEX) plumes are limited in their extent due to natural attenuation processes. It is now widely recognized that EPA has given up the objective of trying to remediate shallow aquifers to drinking water standards. The actual use of these aquifers is now being considered in the overall evaluation of remedial options.

Chapters 11, 12, and 13 in the revised text address some of the above issues in detail, but the reader is cautioned that ground water remediation is a rapidly changing and dynamic industry. For example, the use of treatment walls and funnel and gate systems and soil flushing technologies were barely in existence in 1993, and have emerged as useful new approaches today. Natural attenuation is more accepted than ever before for certain types of plumes. Preferred remedial methods have changed dramatically just in the past five years, and the general literature should be consulted for the latest results on emerging new methods.

REFERENCES

Aller, L., T. Bennett, J. Lehr, R. J. Petty, G. and Hackett, DRASTIC: A standardized system for evaluating ground water pollution potential using hydrogeologic settings. U.S. EPA. EPA-600/2-87-035, 1987.

Bear, J., *Dynamics of Fluids in Porous Media*, New York, American Elsevier, 1972.

Bear, J., *Hydraulics of Ground Water*, New York, McGraw-Hill, 1979.

Bedient, P. B., W. C. and Huber, *Hydrology and Floodplain Analysis*, 2nd ed., Boston, Addison-Wesley, 1992.

CERCLA (Comprehensive Environmental Response, Compensation, and Liability Act or Superfund), 40 C.F.R. Part 300, 1980.

Chow, V. T., D. R. Maidment, L. W. and Mays, *Applied Hydrology*, New York, McGraw-Hill, 1988.

CWA (Clean Water Act), 40 C.F.R. Parts 100-140, 1977.

Davis, S. N., and R. J. M. DeWiest, *Hydrogeology*, New York, John Wiley, 1966.

De Marsily, G., *Quantitative Hydrogeology*, Orlando, FL, Academic Press, Inc., Harcourt Brace Jovanovich, 1986.

DeWiest, R. J. M., *Geohydrology*, New York, John Wiley and Sons, 1965.

Domenico, P. A. F. W. and Schwartz, *Physical and Chemical Hydrogeology*, 2nd ed., New York, John Wiley and Sons, 1998.

Fetter, C.W., *Applied Hydrogeology*, 3rd ed., Columbus, OH, Merrill Publishing Company, 1994.

Freeze, R. A., J. A. and Cherry, *Ground Water*, Englewood Cliffs, NJ, Prentice-Hall, 1979.

Heath, R. C., *Ground water Regions of the United States*. U.S. Geol. Survey Water Supply Paper 2242, 1984.

Meinzer, O. E., Outline of ground water in hydrology with definitions: U.S. Geol. Survey Water Supply Papers, 494, 1923.

National Research Council, *Alternatives for Ground Water Cleanup*, Washington, DC, National Academy Press, 1994.

Newell, C. J., J. F. Haasbeek, P. B. and Bedient, 1990, "OASIS: A Graphical Decision Support System for Groundwater Contaminant Modeling," *Ground Water*, 28: 224-234

Pankow, James F., and John A. Cherry, *Dense Chlorinated Solvents and other DNAPLs in Groundwater,* Portland, OR, Waterloo Press, 1996.

Pye, V. I., R. Patrick, and J. Quarles, *Ground Water Contamination in the United States*, Philadelphia, PA, University of Pennsylvania Press, 1987.

SDWA (Safe Drinking Water Act), 40 C.F.R. Parts 141-147, 1974.

Solley, W. B., C. F. Merk, and R. R. Pierce, 1988, "Estimated Water Use in the United States in 1985," *U.S. Geological Survey Circular 1004.*

Thomas, H. E., "Ground Water Regions of the United States—Their Storage Facilities." U.S. 83rd Congress, *The Physical and Economic Foundation of Natural Resources*, vol 3. 1952

Todd, D. K., *Ground Water Hydrology*, 2nd ed., New York, John Wiley and Sons, 1980.

Tolman, C. F., *Ground Water*, New York, McGraw-Hill, 1937.

TSCA (Toxic Substance Control Act), 40 C.F.R. Parts 712-799, 1976.

U.S. Environmental Protection Agency, *Evaluation of Ground-Water Extraction Remedies: Phase II*, Volume1 Summary Report, EPA OERR 9355.4-05, Washington, D.C., February, 1992.

Viessman, W., Jr., G. L. Lewis, and J. W. Knapp, *Introduction to Hydrology*, 3rd ed., New York, Harper & Row, 1989.

C H A P T E R   2

GROUND WATER HYDROLOGY

2.1 INTRODUCTION

This chapter is devoted to the properties of ground water including the definition of aquifer systems and the parameters that can be used to characterize them. Porosity, hydraulic conductivity, storage coefficient, and hydraulic gradient are all important in determining the rate and direction of ground water flow. Governing equations of ground water flow are introduced and solved for simple flow systems in confined and unconfined aquifers. Flow nets are useful representations of streamlines and equipotential lines in two dimensions, and provide a graphical picture of ground water heads and gradients of flow. The chapter ends with an introduction to the unsaturated zone, which lies above the water table up to the soil root zone.

2.2 PROPERTIES OF GROUND WATER

2.2.1 Vertical Distribution of Ground Water

Ground water can be characterized according to vertical distribution as defined by Todd (1980). Figure 2.1 indicates the main divisions of subsurface water, and the **water table** generally divides the unsaturated zone from the saturated ground water zone. The **soil water zone**, which extends from the ground surface down through the major root zone, varies with soil type and vegetation, but is usually a few feet in thickness. The amount of water present in the soil water zone depends primarily on recent exposure to rainfall, infiltration, and vegetation. **Hygroscopic** water is a film of water tightly held by surface forces, and remains adsorbed to the surface of soil grains, while gravitational water drains through the soil under the influence of gravity.

The **unsaturated zone (vadose zone)** extends from the surface to the water table through the root zone, intermediate zone, and the capillary zone (see Figure 2.1). **Capillary water** is held by surface tension forces just above the **water table**, which is defined as the level to which water will rise in a well drilled into the saturated zone. Thickness of the unsaturated zone may vary from a few feet for high water table conditions to hundreds of feet (meters) in arid regions of the country, such as Arizona or New Mexico. Unsaturated zone water is held in place by surface forces, and infiltrating water passes downward towards the water table as gravitational flow, subject to retardation by capillary forces.

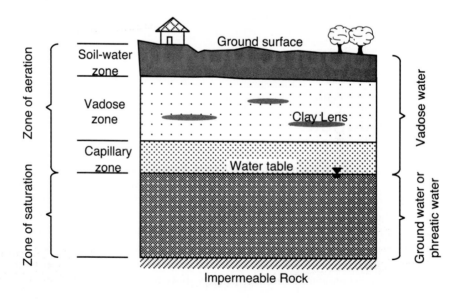

Figure 2.1 Vertical zones of subsurface water.

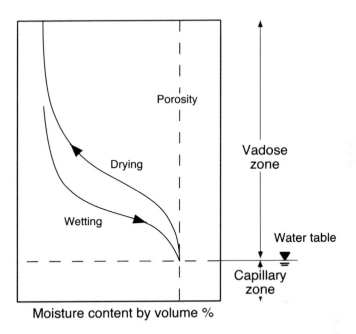

Figure 2.2 Typical soil-moisture relationship.

The capillary zone, or fringe, extends from the water table up to the limit of capillary rise, which varies inversely with the pore size of the soil and directly with the surface tension. The capillary forces at work are related to the meniscus between the gas phase and the liquid phase, as in the case of a small straw inserted into a pan of water. Capillary rise can range from 2.5 cm for fine gravel to more than 200 cm for silt (Todd, 1980). Just above the water table almost all pores contain capillary water, and the water content decreases with height depending on the type of soil. A typical soil moisture curve is shown in Figure 2.2, where the amount of moisture in the vadose zone generally decreases with vertical distance above the water table. Soil moisture curves vary with soil type and with the wetting cycle; more details on the unsaturated zone are contained in Section 2.7 and Chapter 9. A more detailed treatment is available from Guymon (1994).

In the **saturated zone**, which occurs beneath the water table, the **porosity** is a direct measure of the water contained per unit volume, expressed as the ratio of the volume of voids to the total volume. Porosity averages about 25% to 35% for most aquifer systems. Also, ground water flows according to Darcy's Law, which relates velocity to gradient and hydraulic conductivity, in the saturated zone (Section 2.3). Only a portion of the water can be removed from the saturated zone by drainage or by pumping from a well. **Specific yield** is defined as the volume of water released from an unconfined aquifer per unit surface area per unit head decline in the water table. Fine-grained materials yield little water whereas coarse-grained materials provide significant water and thus serve as aquifers. In general, specific yields for unconsolidated formations fall in the range of 7% to 25%.

2.2.2 Aquifer Systems

An **aquifer** can be defined as a formation that contains sufficient saturated permeable material to yield significant quantities of water to wells or springs. Aquifers are generally areally extensive and may be overlain or underlain by a confining bed, defined as a relatively impermeable material. Figure 2.3 shows some typical examples of confined aquifers, which have relatively impermeable confining units above, such as clay or silt, and are under pressure. An **aquitard** is a low permeability stratum, such as a sandy clay unit, that may leak water vertically to adjacent aquifers.

Aquifers can be characterized by the porosity of a rock or soil, expressed as the ratio of the volume of voids V_v to the total volume V. Porosity may also be expressed by

$$n = \frac{V_v}{V} = 1 - \frac{\rho_b}{\rho_m} \tag{2.1}$$

where ρ_m is the density of the grains and ρ_b is the **bulk density**, defined as the oven-dried mass of the sample divided by its original volume. Table 2.1 shows a range of porosities (6% to 46%) for a number of aquifer materials. In practice, the porosity of an aquifer is usually assumed to be about 30%, assuming that there are no fractures present. Fractured rock such as limestone is more complex and can have much lower porosities in the range of 1% to 10%. Figure 2.4 shows the theoretical maximum porosity of 47.65% associated with cubic packing of spheres, and the lowering effect of adding smaller grains into the void space.

Unconsolidated geologic materials are normally classified according to their size and distribution. Standard soil classification based on particle size is shown in Table 2.2. Particle sizes are measured by mechanically sieving grain sizes larger than 0.05 mm and measuring rates of settlement for smaller particles in suspension. A typical particle size distribution graph is plotted in Figure 2.5, where a fine sand has a more uniform distribution than an alluvium which includes a range of particle sizes. The value of the **uniformity coefficient**, defined as D_{60}/D_{10}, indicates the relative sorting of the material, and takes on a low value for the fine sand compared to the alluvium. The texture of a soil is defined by the relative proportions of sand, silt and clay present in the particle size analysis and can be expressed most easily on a triangle diagram of soil textures (see any soils textbook). For example, a soil with 30% clay, 60% silt, and 10% sand is referred to as a silty clay loam.

Most aquifers can be considered as underground storage reservoirs that receive recharge from rainfall or from a river system. Water flows out of an aquifer due to gravity drainage according to water level gradients or to pumping from extraction wells. An aquifer may be classified as **unconfined** if the water table exists under atmospheric pressure, as defined by levels in shallow wells. A **confined** aquifer is one that is overlain by a relatively impermeable unit such that the aquifer is under pressure and the pressure level rises above the confined unit. A **leaky confined** aquifer represents a stratum that allows water to flow

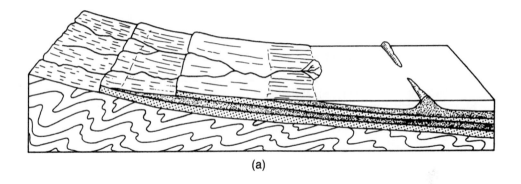

(a)

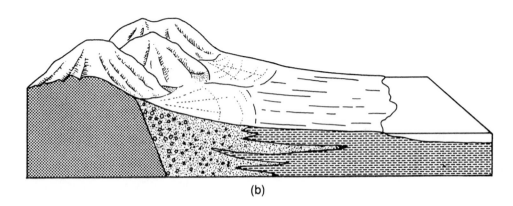

(b)

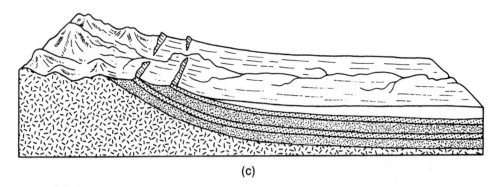

(c)

Figure 2.3 Confined aquifers are created when aquifers are overlain by confining beds. (a) Confined aquifers created by alternating aquifers and confining units deposited on regional dip. (b) Confined aquifers created by deposition of alternating layers of permeable sand and gravel and impermeable silts and clays deposited in intermontane basins. (c) Confined aquifer created by upwarping of beds by intrusions. Source: C.W. Fetter, Applied hydrology, 2/E. Reprinted with the permission of Prentice-Hall, Inc.

TABLE 2.1   Representative values of porosity

Material	Porosity (%)	Material	Porosity (%)	Material	Porosity (%)
Gravel, coarse	28†	Sandstone, medium	37	Claystone	43
Gravel, medium	32†	Limestone	30	Shale	6
Gravel, fine	34†	Dolomite	26	Till, predominantly silt	34
Sand, coarse	39	Dune sand	45	Till, predominantly sand	31
Sand, medium	39	Loess	49	Tuff	41
Sand, fine	43	Peat	92	Basalt	17
Silt	46	Schist	38	Gabbro, weathered	43
Clay	42	Siltstone	35	Granite, weathered	45
Sandstone, fine	33				

† These values are for repacked samples, all others are undisturbed. Source: Morris and Johnson, 1967.

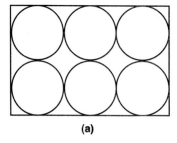   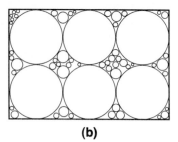

      (a)   (b)

Figure 2.4 (a) Cubic packing of spheres of equal diameter with a porosity of 47.65%. (b) Cubic packing of spheres with void spaces occupied by grains of smaller diameter, resulting in a much lower overall porosity.

from above through a confining zone into the underlying aquifer. A **perched aquifer** is where an unconfined water zone sits on top of a clay lens, separated from the main aquifer below.

Figure 2.6 shows a vertical cross section illustrating typical characteristics of unconfined and confined aquifers. An unconfined aquifer is usually identified at a field site by drilling bore holes and wells to shallow depths, as described below and in Chapter 5. A confined aquifer (artesian) is one that is identified by a confining unit at depth, and the water level (elevation plus pressure head) that is under pressure, and rises above the confining unit. If the water level rises above the land surface, a flowing well or spring results and is referred to as **an artesian well** or spring.

TABLE 2.2 Soil classification based on particle size

Material	Particle Size (mm)
Clay	<0.004
Silt	0.004-0.062
Very fine sand	0.062-0.125
Fine sand	0.125-0.25
Medium sand	0.25-0.5
Coarse sand	0.5-1.0
Very coarse sand	1.0-2.0
Very fine gravel	2.0-4.0
Fine gravel	4.0-8.0
Medium gravel	8.0-16.0
Coarse gravel	16.0-32.0
Very coarse gravel	32.0-64.0

Source: Morris and Johnson, 1967

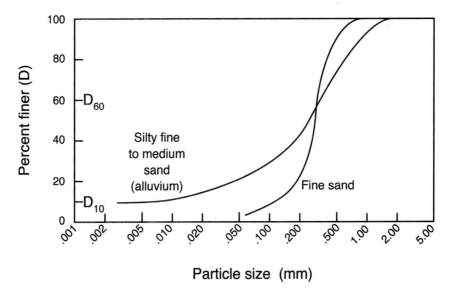

Figure 2.5 Particle-size distribution for two geologic samples.

A recharge area supplies water to a confined aquifer, and such an aquifer can convey water from the recharge area to locations of natural or artificial discharge. The **piezometric sur-face** (or **potentiometric surface**) of a confined aquifer is the hydrostatic pressure level of water in the aquifer, defined by the water level that occurs in a lined penetrating well. It should be noted that a confined aquifer will become unconfined when the piezometric sur-

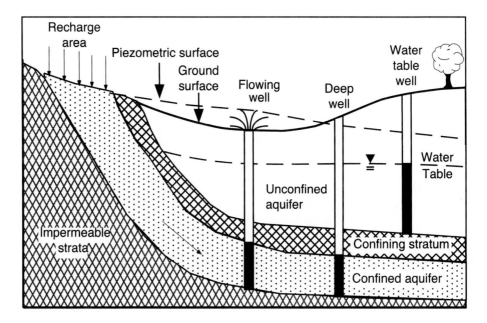

Figure 2.6 Schematic cross-section of unconfined and confined aquifers. Black areas indicate screened zones.

face falls below the bottom of the upper confining bed. Contour maps and profiles can be prepared for the water table elevation for an unconfined aquifer, or the piezometric surface for a confined aquifer. These **equipotential lines** are described in more detail in Section 2.6. Once determined from a series of wells in an aquifer, orthogonal lines can be drawn to indicate the general direction of ground water flow, in the direction of decreasing head (Figure 2.7).

A parameter of some importance relates to the water-yielding capacity of an aquifer. The **storage coefficient** S is defined as the volume of water that an aquifer releases from or takes into storage per unit surface area per unit change in piezometric head. For a confined aquifer, values of S fall in the range of 0.00005 to 0.005, indicating that large pressure changes produce small changes in the storage volume. For unconfined aquifers, a change in storage volume is expressed simply by the product of the volume of aquifer lying between the water table at the beginning and end of a period of head change, and the average specific yield of the formation. Thus, the storage coefficient for an unconfined aquifer is approximately equal to the specific yield, typically in the range of 0.07 to 0.25.

A vertical hole, which is extended into an aquifer at depth, is referred to as a **well**, and the steel or PVC plastic pipe which extends from the surface to the screened zone is called the **casing**. Wells are either drilled or pushed into the subsurface with specialized GeoProbe equipment (Chapter 5). Wells are used for pumping of water and contaminants, injection of water or disposal of chemicals, water level observation, and water quality sam-

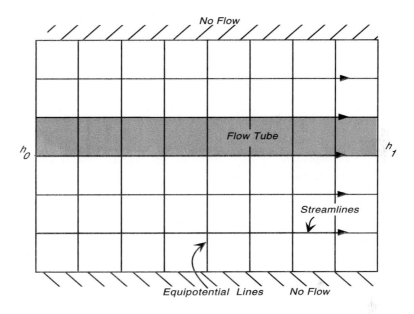

Figure 2.7 Simple flow net.

pling. The portion of the well that is open to the aquifer is **screened** to prevent aquifer ma
terial from entering the well. The annular space around the screen is often filled with sand or
gravel to minimize hydraulic resistance to flow. The annulus is usually cemented up to the
surface with a material such as bentonite clay to protect against contamination of the well
from surface leakage. Details on well construction and development methods are presented in
Chapter 5.

2.3 GROUND WATER MOVEMENT

2.3.1 Darcy's Law

The movement of ground water is well understood by hydraulic principles reported in 1856
by Henri Darcy, who investigated the flow of water through beds of permeable sand. Darcy
advanced one of the most important laws in hydrology—that the flow rate through porous
media is proportional to the head loss and inversely proportional to the length of the flow
path. Darcy's Law serves as the basis for present-day knowledge of ground water flow and
well hydraulics, and for the derivation of governing ground water flow shown in the equations in Section 2.4.

Figure 2.8 depicts the experimental setup for determining head loss through a sand column, with **piezometers** located a distance L apart. Total energy for this system can be expressed by the Bernoulli equation

$$\frac{p_1}{g} + \frac{v_1^2}{2g} + z_1 = \frac{p_2}{g} + \frac{v_2^2}{2g} + z_2 + h_1 \tag{2.2}$$

where

  p = pressure
  γ = specific weight of water
  v = velocity
  z = elevation
  h_1 = head loss

Because velocities are very small in porous media, velocity heads may be neglected, allowing head loss to be expressed as

$$h_1 = \left(\frac{p_1}{\gamma} + z_1\right) - \left(\frac{p_2}{\gamma} + z_2\right) \tag{2.3}$$

It follows that the head loss is independent of the inclination of the column. Darcy related flow rate to head loss and length of column through a proportionality constant referred to as K, the **hydraulic conductivity**, a measure of the ability of the porous media to transmit water. Darcy's Law can be stated thus:

$$v = -\frac{Q}{A} = -K\frac{dh}{dL} \tag{2.4}$$

The negative sign indicates that flow of water is in the direction of decreasing head. The Darcy velocity that results from Eq. (2.4) is an average discharge velocity, v, through the entire cross section of the column. The actual flow is limited to the pore space only, so that the seepage velocity v_s is equal to the Darcy velocity divided by porosity:

$$v_s = \frac{Q}{nA} \tag{2.5}$$

Thus, actual seepage velocities are usually much higher (by a factor of 3 or 4) than the Darcy velocities. Seepage velocity is used later in the text for all transport calculations.

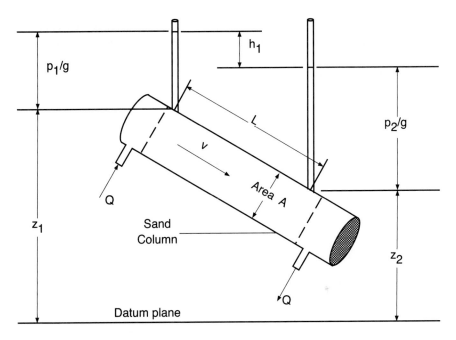

Figure 2.8 Head loss through a sand column.

It should be pointed out that Darcy's law applies to laminar flow in porous media, and experiments indicate that Darcy's law is valid for Reynolds numbers ($R = \rho vd/\mu$) less than 1 and perhaps as high as 10. This represents an upper limit to the validity of Darcy's law, which turns out to be applicable in most ground water systems. Deviations can occur near heavily pumped wells and in fractured aquifer systems, such as limestone, where flow is primarily along the fractures.

2.3.2 Hydraulic Conductivity

The hydraulic conductivity (K) of a soil or rock depends on a variety of physical factors and is an indication of an aquifer's ability to transmit water. Thus, sand aquifers have K values many orders of magnitude larger than clay units. Typical values for aquifers would be 10^{-2} cm/sec for sand, 10^{-4} cm/sec for silt, and 10^{-7} cm/sec for clay. Table 2.3 indicates representative values of hydraulic conductivity for a variety of materials. As can be seen, K can vary over many orders of magnitude in an aquifer system that contains several different types of material. Thus, velocities and flow rates can also vary over the same range, as expressed by Darcy's law.

The term **transmissivity** is often used in the description of ground water hydraulics applied to confined aquifers. It is defined as the product of K and the **saturated thickness** of the aquifer b. Hydraulic conductivity is usually expressed in m/day (ft/day) and transmissivity T is expressed in m^2/day (ft^2/day). An older unit for T that is still reported in some applications is gal/day/ft. The **intrinsic permeability** (k) of a rock or soil is a property of the medium only, independent of fluid properties. Intrinsic permeability can be related to hydraulic conductivity K by

$$K = k\left(\frac{\rho g}{\mu}\right)$$
(2.6)

where

μ = dynamic viscosity

ρ = fluid density

g = gravitational constant.

Intrinsic permeability k has units of m^2 or darcy (where 1 darcy = 0.987 μm^2); k is often used in the petroleum industry, whereas K is primarily used in ground water hydrology for categorizing aquifer systems.

TABLE 2.3   Representative values of hydraulic conductivity

Material	Hydraulic Conductivity (cm/sec)		
UNCONSOLIDATED SEDIMENTARY DEPOSITS			
Gravel	3	to	3×10^{-2}
Coarse sand	6×10^{-1}	to	9×10^{-5}
Medium sand	5×10^{-2}	to	9×10^{-5}
Fine sand	2×10^{-2}	to	2×10^{-5}
Silt, loess	2×10^{-3}	to	1×10^{-7}
Till	2×10^{-4}	to	1×10^{-10}
Clay	5×10^{-7}	to	1×10^{-9}
Unweathered marine clay	2×10^{-7}	to	8×10^{-11}
SEDIMENTARY ROCKS			
Karst limestone	2	to	1×10^{-4}
Limestone and dolomite	6×10^{-4}	to	1×10^{-7}
Sandstone	6×10^{-4}	to	3×10^{-8}
Shale	2×10^{-7}	to	1×10^{-11}
CRYSTALLINE ROCKS			
Permeable basalt	2	to	4×10^{-5}
Fractured igneous and metamorphic	3×10^{-2}	to	8×10^{-7}
Basalt	4×10^{-5}	to	2×10^{-9}
Unfractured igneous and metamorphic	2×10^{-8}	to	3×10^{-12}
Weathered granite	3×10^{-4}	to	5×10^{-3}

Note on units: 1 m/sec = 1×10^2 cm/sec = 1.04×10^5 darcy

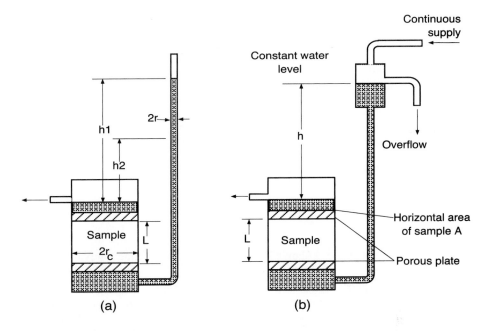

Figure 2.9 Permeameters for measuring hydraulic conductivity of geologic samples. (a) falling head. (b) constant head.

2.3.3 Determination of Hydraulic Conductivity

Hydraulic conductivity in saturated zones can be determined by a number of techniques in the laboratory as well as in the field. **Constant head** and **falling head permeameters** are used in the laboratory for measuring K and are described in detail below. They provide only a rough indication of field values since only small core samples are usually collected and analyzed from a limited number of locations at a site.

A permeameter (Figure 2.9) is used in the laboratory to measure K by maintaining flow through a small column of material and measuring flow rate and head loss. For a constant head permeameter, Darcy's law can be directly applied to find K, where V is volume flowing in time t through a sample of area A, length L, and with constant head h:

$$K = \frac{VL}{Ath} \tag{2.7}$$

The falling head permeameter test consists of measuring the rate of fall of the water level in the tube or column and noting

$$Q = \pi r^2 \frac{dh}{dt} \qquad (2.8)$$

Darcy's law can be written for the sample as

$$Q = \pi r_c^2 K \frac{h}{L} \qquad (2.9)$$

After equating and integrating,

$$K = \frac{r^2 L}{r_c^2 t} \ln \left(\frac{h_1}{h_2} \right) \qquad (2.10)$$

where L, r, and r_c are as shown in Figure 2.9 and t is the time interval for water to fall from h_1 to h_2.

At a typical field site, **pump tests**, **slug tests**, and **tracer tests** are the preferred methods for determination of K. Pump tests and tracer tests provide estimates of average K over a large area of aquifer, based on the size of the test. Pump tests use the constant removal of water and the measurement of head change to estimate K. The slug test for shallow wells involves the measurement of decline or recovery of the water level in the well through time. Slug tests are used to estimate K around an individual well or boring. These tests are described in more detail in Chapter 3 under the general heading of well hydraulics.

Tracer tests involve controlled injection of inorganic and organic tracers (chloride, bromide, and selected organics) and the temporal measurement of concentrations and water levels in wells that are positioned in the direction of ground water flow. Average seepage velocities can be determined by analyzing the resulting curves in space and time, and K values can be computed from Darcy's Law (Figure 2.10). Major tracer tests were implemented at a number of sites in the 1980s and are described in Chapter 6.

The pump test involves the constant removal of water from a single well and observations of water level declines at several adjacent wells. In this way, an integrated K value for a portion of the aquifer is obtained. Field methods generally yield significantly different values of K from those in corresponding permeameter tests performed on cores removed from the aquifer. Thus, field tests are preferable for the accurate determination of aquifer parameters (Chapter 3).

2.3.4 Anisotropic Aquifers

Most real geologic systems tend to have variations in one or more directions due to the processes of deposition and layering that can occur. In the typical field situation in alluvial deposits, the hydraulic conductivity in the vertical direction Kz is often less than the value in

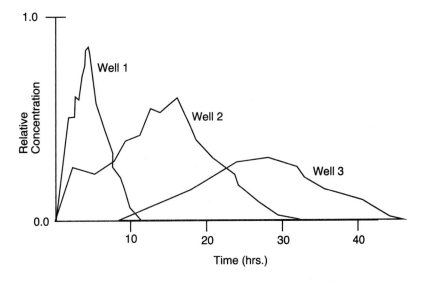

Figure 2.10 Tracer test results.

the horizontal direction K_x. For the case of a two-layered aquifer of different K in each layer and different thicknesses, we can apply Darcy's law to horizontal flow to show

$$K_x = \frac{K_1 z_1 + K_2 z_2}{z_1 + z_2} \tag{2.11}$$

or, in general,

$$K_x = \frac{\Sigma K_i z_i}{\Sigma z_i} \tag{2.12}$$

where

$K_i = K$ in layer i

z_i = thickness of layer i

For the case of vertical flow through two layers, q_z is the same flow per unit horizontal area in each layer:

$$dh_1 + dh_2 = \left(\frac{z_1}{K_1} + \frac{z_2}{K_2} \right) q_z \tag{2.13}$$

but

$$dh_1 + dh_2 = \left(\frac{z_1 + z_2}{K_z}\right)q_z \tag{2.14}$$

where K_z is the hydraulic conductivity for the entire system. Setting Eqs. (2.13) and (2.14) equal to each other, we have

$$K_z = \frac{z_1 + z_2}{\left(z_1 / K_1\right) + \left(z_2 / K_2\right)} \tag{2.15}$$

or, in general,

$$K_z = \frac{\Sigma z_i}{\Sigma z_i / K_i} \tag{2.16}$$

Ratios of K_x to K_z usually fall in the range of 2 to 10 for alluvium, with values up to 100 where clay layers exist. Many real field sites have spatial and vertical variations in K that can be addressed only by statistical methods or modeling methods. In actual application to layered systems, it is usually necessary to apply ground water flow models that can properly handle complex geologic strata through numerical simulation. Various flow and transport modeling techniques are described in Chapters 6 and 10.

2.3.5 Flow Nets

Darcy's law was originally derived in one dimension, but because many ground water problems are really two- or three-dimensional, graphical methods are available for the determination of flow rate and direction. A specified set of **streamlines** and **equipotential lines** can be constructed for a given set of boundary conditions to form a **flow net** (Figures 2.7 and 2.11) in two dimensions.

Equipotential lines are prepared based on observed water levels in wells penetrating an **isotropic** aquifer. Flow lines are then drawn orthogonally to indicate the direction of flow. For the flow net of Figure 2.11, the hydraulic gradient i is given by

$$i = \frac{dh}{ds} \tag{2.17}$$

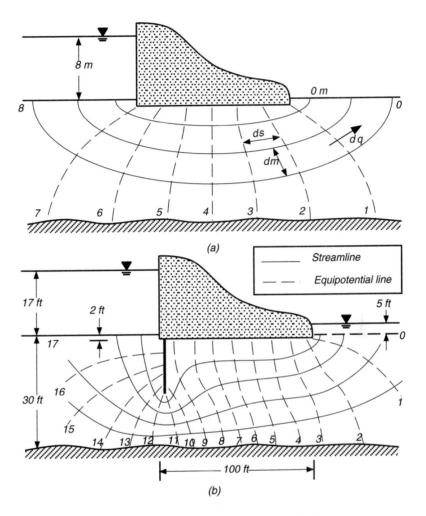

Figure 2.11 (a) Flow net for a simple dam section. (b) Flow net for a complex dam section.

and constant flow q per unit thickness between two adjacent flow lines is

$$q = K \frac{dh}{ds} dm \qquad (2.18)$$

If we assume $ds = dm$ for a square net, then for n squares between two flow lines over which total head is divided $(h = H/n)$ and for m divided flow channels,

$$Q' = mq = \frac{KmH}{n}$$ (2.19)

where

Q' = flow per unit width,

K = hydraulic conductivity of the aquifer,

M = number of flow channels,

n = number of squares over the direction of flow, and

H = Total head loss in direction of flow.

Flow nets are useful graphical methods to display streamlines and equipotential lines. Since no flow can cross an impermeable boundary, streamlines must parallel it. Also, streamlines are usually horizontal through high K material and vertical through low K material because of refraction of lines across a boundary between different K media. It can be shown that

$$\frac{K_1}{K_2} = \frac{\tan\theta_1}{\tan\theta_2}$$ (2.20)

where θ_1 and θ_2 are angles that the velocity vectors make with the normal to the boundary between two materials.

Flow nets can be used to evaluate the directions of flow as a function of different boundary conditions, and the effects of pumping on ground water levels and directions of flow. Figure 2.12 depicts an x–y contour map of water levels resulting from heavy pumping near a source zone in the Atlantic coastal plain. Directions of flow are perpendicular to the equipotential lines, which are lines of constant head. Figure 2.13 shows a flow net for a single well pumping from a uniform flow field.

Example 2.1 FLOW NET COMPUTATION

Compute the total flow seeping under the dam in Figure 2.11a, where width is 20 m and K = 10^{-5} m/sec. Equation (2.19) is used to provide flow per unit width. From the figure $m = 4$, $n = 8$, $H = 8$m, and K is given above.

Solution

$$Q' = \frac{(10^{-5} \text{ m / sec})(4)(8\text{m})}{8}$$

$$= 4 \times 10^{-5} \text{ m}^2 / \text{sec} = 3.46 \text{ m}^2 / \text{day}$$

Total flow $Q = 3.46$ m²/day (20m) = 69.1 m³/day

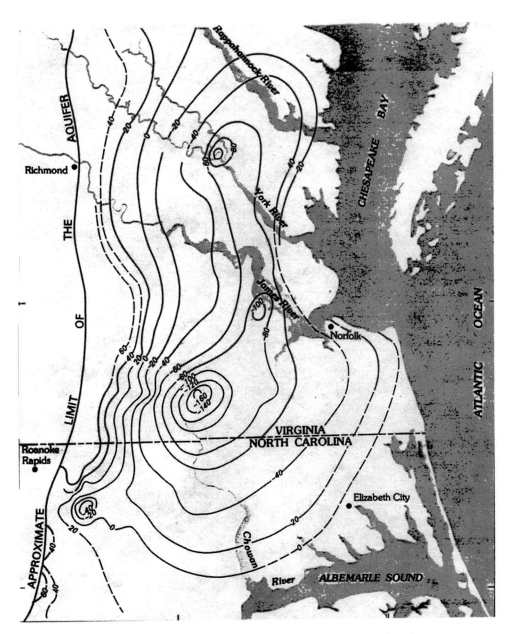

Figure 2.12 Potentiometric surface of lower aquifer in the Atlantic Coastal Plain.

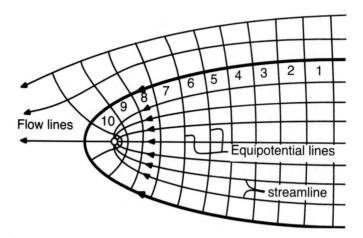

Figure 2.13 Flow net.

2.4 GENERAL FLOW EQUATIONS

The governing flow equations for ground water are derived in most of the standard texts in the field (Bear, 1979; Todd, 1980; Domenico and Schwartz, 1998). The equation of continuity from fluid mechanics is combined with Darcy's law in three dimensions to yield a partial differential equation of flow in porous media, as shown in the next section. Both steady-state and transient flow equations can be derived. Mathematical solutions for specific boundary conditions are well known for the governing ground water flow equation. For complex boundaries and heterogeneous systems, numerical computer solutions must be used (Chapters 9 and 10).

2.4.1 Steady-State Saturated Flow

Consider a unit volume of porous media called an elemental control volume. The law of conservation of mass requires that

(Mass flux in – Mass flux out) = (change in Mass per time)

For steady-state conditions, the right-hand side is zero, and the equation of continuity becomes

$$-\frac{\partial}{\partial x}\left(\rho v_x\right) - \frac{\partial}{\partial y}\left(\rho v_y\right) - \frac{\partial}{\partial z}\left(\rho v_z\right) = 0 \qquad (2.21)$$

The units of ρv are mass/area/time as required. For an incompressible fluid, $\rho(x,y,z)$ = constant, and ρ can be divided out of Eq. (2.21). Substitution of Darcy's law for v_x, v_y, and v_z yields

$$\frac{\partial}{\partial x}\left(K_x \frac{\partial h}{\partial x}\right) + \frac{\partial}{\partial y}\left(K_y \frac{\partial h}{\partial y}\right) + \frac{\partial}{\partial z}\left(K_z \frac{\partial h}{\partial z}\right) = 0 \qquad (2.22)$$

For an isotropic, homogeneous medium, $K_x = K_y = K_z = K$ and can be divided out of the equation to yield

$$\frac{\partial^2 h}{\partial x^2} + \frac{\partial^2 h}{\partial y^2} + \frac{\partial^2 h}{\partial z^2} = 0 \qquad (2.23)$$

Equation (2.23) is called Laplace's equation and is one of the best-understood partial differential equations. The solution is $h = h(x,y,z)$, the hydraulic head at any point in the flow domain. In two dimensions, the solution is equivalent to the graphical flow nets described in Section 2.3.5. If there were no variation of h with z, then the equation would reduce to two terms on the left-hand side of Eq. (2.23).

2.4.2 Transient Saturated Flow

The transient equation of continuity for a confined aquifer becomes

$$-\frac{\partial}{\partial x}\left(\rho v_x\right) - \frac{\partial}{\partial y}\left(\rho v_y\right) - \frac{\partial}{\partial z}\left(\rho v_z\right) = \frac{\partial}{\partial t}\left(\rho n\right) = n\frac{\partial \rho}{\partial t} + \rho\frac{\partial n}{\partial t} \qquad (2.24)$$

The first term on the right-hand side of Eq. (2.24) is the mass rate of water produced by an expansion of water under a change in ρ. The second term is the mass rate of water produced by compaction of the porous media (change in n). The first term relates to the compressibility of the fluid β and the second term to the aquifer compressibility α.

Compressibility and effective stress are discussed in detail in Freeze and Cherry (1979) and Domenico and Schwartz (1998), and will only be briefly reviewed here. According to Terzaghi (1925), the total stress acting on a plane in a saturated porous media is due to the sum of the weight of overlying rock and fluid pressure. The portion of the total stress not borne by the fluid is the effective stress σ_e. Since total stress can be considered constant in most problems, the change in effective stress is equal to the negative of the pressure change in the media, which is related to head change by $dp = \rho\, g dh$. Thus, a decrease in hydraulic head or pressure results in an increase in effective stress, since $d\sigma_e = -dp$.

The compressibility of water β implies that a change in volume occurs for a given change in stress or pressure, and is defined as $(-dV/V)/dp$, where dV is volume change of a given mass of water under a pressure change of dp. The compressibility is approximately constant at $4.4 \times 10^{-10} m^2/N$ for water at usual ground water temperatures.

The compressibility of the porous media or aquifer, α, is related to vertical consolidation for a given change in effective stress, or $\alpha = (db/b)/d\sigma_e$, where b is the vertical dimension. From laboratory studies, α is a function of the applied stress and is dependent on previous loading history. Clays respond differently than sands in this regard, and compaction of clays is largely irreversible for a reduced pressure in the aquifer compared to the response in sands. Land surface subsidence is a good example of aquifer compressibility on a regional scale where clays have been depressured over time.

Freeze and Cherry (1979) indicate that a change in head will produce a change in ρ and n in Eq. (2.24), and the volume of water produced for a unit head decline is S_s, the specific storage. Theoretically, one can show that specific storage is related to aquifer compressibility and the compressibility of water by

$$S_s = \rho g(\alpha + n\beta),$$

(2.25)

and the mass rate of water produced (right-hand side of Eq. (2.24) is $S_s(\partial h/\partial t)$. Equation (2.24) becomes, after substituting Eq. (2.25) and Darcy's law,

$$\frac{\partial}{\partial x}\left(K_x \frac{\partial h}{\partial x}\right) + \frac{\partial}{\partial y}\left(K_y \frac{\partial h}{\partial y}\right) + \frac{\partial}{\partial z}\left(K_z \frac{\partial h}{\partial z}\right) = S_s \frac{\partial h}{\partial t}$$

(2.26)

For homogeneous and isotropic media,

$$\frac{\partial^2 h}{\partial x^2} + \frac{\partial^2 h}{\partial y^2} + \frac{\partial^2 h}{\partial z^2} = \frac{S_s}{K}\frac{\partial h}{\partial t}$$

(2.27)

For the special case of a horizontal confined aquifer of thickness b,

$S = S_s b$ where S is the storativity or storage coefficient

$T = Kb$

and

$$\nabla^2 h = \frac{S}{T}\frac{\partial h}{\partial t}$$ in two dimensions.

(2.28)

Solution of Eq. (2.28) requires knowledge of S and T to produce $h(x,y)$ over the flow domain. The classical development of Eq. (2.28) was first advanced by Jacob (1940) along with considerations of storage concepts. More advanced treatments consider the problems of a fixed elemental control volume in a deforming media (Cooper, 1966), but these are unnecessary considerations for most practical problems.

2.5 DUPUIT EQUATION

For the case of unconfined ground water flow, Dupuit (1863) developed a theory that allows for a simple solution based on several important assumptions:

1. The water table or free surface is only slightly inclined.
2. Streamlines may be considered horizontal and equipotential lines, vertical.
3. Slopes of the free surface and hydraulic gradient are equal.

Figure 2.14 shows the graphical example of Dupuit's assumptions for essentially one-dimensional flow. The free-surface from $x = 0$ to $x = L$ can be derived by considering Darcy's law and the governing one-dimensional equation. The Dupuit approach neglects any vertical components of flow and reduces a complex 2-D problem to a one-dimensional problem which can be easily solved. For steady state flow, the discharge through the system must be constant and requires the free surface to be a parabola. Example 2.2 demonstrates the derivation of the Dupuit equations.

Example 2.2   DUPUIT EQUATION

Derive the equation for one-dimensional flow in an unconfined aquifer using the Dupuit assumptions (Figure 2.14).

Solution. Darcy's law gives the one-dimensional flow per unit width as

$$q = -Kh\frac{dh}{dx}$$

where h and x are as defined in Figure 2.14. At steady state, the rate of change of q with distance is zero, or

$$\frac{d}{dx}\left(-Kh\frac{dh}{dx}\right) = 0$$

$$-\frac{K}{2}\frac{d^2h^2}{dx^2} = 0$$

which implies that,

$$\frac{d^2h^2}{dx^2} = 0$$

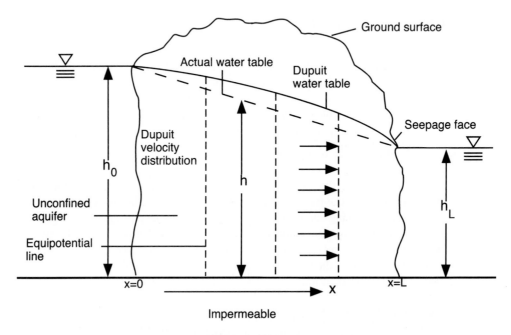

Figure 2.14 Steady flow in an unconfined aquifer between two water bodies with vertical boundaries.

Integration yields

$$h^2 = ax + b$$

where a and b are constants. Setting the boundary condition $h = h_0$ at $x = 0$, we can solve for b,

$$b = h_0^2$$

Differentiation of $h^2 = ax + b$ allows us to solve for a,

$$a = 2h \frac{dh}{dx}$$

From Darcy's law,

$$h \frac{dh}{dx} = -\frac{q}{K}$$

so, by substitution

$$h^2 = h_0^2 - \frac{2qx}{K}$$

Setting $h = h_L$ at $x = L$ and neglecting flow across the seepage face yields

$$h_L^2 = h_0^2 - \frac{2qL}{K}$$

Rearrangement gives

$$\boxed{q = \frac{K}{2L}\left(h_0^2 - h_L^2\right) \qquad \text{Dupuit Equation}}$$

Then the general equation for the shape of the parabola is

$$\boxed{h^2 = h_0^2 - \frac{x}{L}\left(h_0^2 - h_L^2\right) \qquad \text{Dupuit Parabola}}$$

The derivation of the Dupuit equations in Example 2.2 does not consider recharge to the aquifer. For the case of a system with recharge, the **Dupuit parabola** will take the mounded shape shown in Figure 2.15. The point where $h = h_{max}$ is known as the **water divide**. At the water divide, $q = 0$ since the gradient is zero. Example 2.3 derives the Dupuit equation for recharge and illustrates the use of the water divide concept.

Example 2.3 DUPUIT EQUATION WITH RECHARGE W [L/T]

Two rivers located 1000 m apart fully penetrate an aquifer (Figure 2.15). The aquifer has a K value of 0.5 m/day. The region receives an average rainfall of 15 cm/yr and evaporation is about 10 cm/yr. Assume that the water elevation in River 1 is 20 m and the water elevation in River 2 is 18 m. Determine the daily discharge per meter width into each river.

The Dupuit equations with recharge W becomes:

$$h^2 = h_0^2 + \frac{\left(h_L^2 - h_0^2\right)}{L}x + \frac{Wx}{K}(L - x) \qquad \text{Dupuit Parabola.}$$

This equation will give the shape of the Dupuit parabola shown in Figure 2.15. If $W = 0$, this equation will reduce to the parabolic equation found in Example 2.2, and

$$\boxed{q = \frac{K}{2L}\left(h_0^2 - h_L^2\right) + W\left(x - \frac{L}{2}\right)}$$

This equation will give the shape of the Dupuit parabola shown in Figure 2.15. If $W = 0$, this equation will reduce to the parabolic equation found in Example 2.2, and

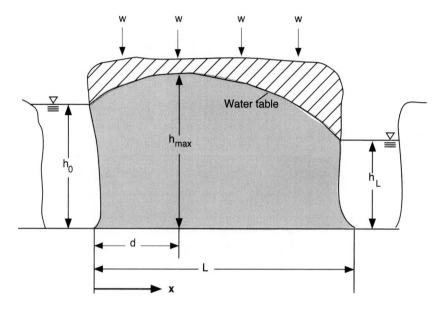

Figure 2.15 Dupuit parabola with recharge.

$$q = \frac{K}{2L}\left(h_0^2 - h_L^2\right) + W\left(x - \frac{L}{2}\right)$$

Given

$L = 1000$ m,

$K = 0.5$ m/day,

$h_0 = 20$ m,

$h_L = 18$ m, and

$W = 5$ cm/yr $= 1.369 \times 10^{-4}$ m/day.

For discharge into River 1, set $x = 0$ m:

$$q = \frac{K}{2L}\left(h_0^2 - h_L^2\right) + W\left(0 - \frac{L}{2}\right)$$

$$= \frac{0.5\,\text{m/day}}{(2)(1000\text{m})}\left(20^2\,\text{m}^2 - 18^2\,\text{m}^2\right) + \left(1.369 \times 10^{-4}\,\text{m/day}\right)(-1000\text{m}/2)$$

$$q = -0.05\,\text{m}^2/\text{day}$$

The negative sign indicates that flow is in the opposite direction from the x direction. Therefore,

$$q = 0.05 \text{ m}^2 / \text{day into river 1}$$

For discharge into River 2, set $x = L = 1000$ m:

$$q = \frac{K}{2L}\left(h_o^2 - h_L^2\right) + W\left(L - \frac{L}{2}\right)$$

$$= \frac{0.5\text{m} / \text{day}}{(2)(1000\text{m})}\left(20^2\,\text{m}^2 - 18^2\,\text{m}^2\right) + \left(1.369 \times 10^{-4}\,\text{m} / \text{day}\right)\left(1000\text{m} - \frac{1000\text{m}}{2}\right)$$

$$q = 0.087 \text{ m}^2 / \text{day into river 2}$$

By setting $q = 0$ at the divide and solving for x_d, the water divide is located 361.2 m from the edge of River 1 and is 20.9 m high.

2.6 STREAMLINES AND EQUIPOTENTIAL LINES

The formal mathematical definition of the flow net can be derived using the equation of continuity for steady, incompressible, isotropic flow in two dimensions. The concept of velocity potential and a stream function was presented concisely by De Wiest (1965) in a classic text on geohydrology. The continuity equation states

$$\frac{\partial u}{dx} + \frac{\partial v}{\partial y} = 0$$

The governing steady-state flow equation is

$$\nabla^2 h = \frac{\partial^2 h}{\partial x^2} + \frac{\partial^2 h}{\partial y^2} = 0 \tag{2.29}$$

The **velocity potential** ϕ is a scalar function and can be written

$$\phi\left(x, y\right) = \pm K\left(z + p/\gamma\right) + c \tag{2.30}$$

where K and c are assumed constant. From Darcy's law in two dimensions,

$$u = \frac{\partial \phi}{\partial x}, \quad v = \frac{\partial \phi}{\partial y} \qquad (2.31)$$

Using Eq. (2.29) in two dimensions, we have

$$\nabla^2 \phi = \frac{\partial^2 \phi}{\partial x^2} + \frac{\partial^2 \phi}{\partial y^2} = 0 \qquad (2.32)$$

where $\phi(x,y)$ = constant represents a family of equipotential curves on a two-dimensional surface. It can be shown that the **stream function** $\psi(x,y)$ = constant is orthogonal to $\phi(x,y)$ = constant and that both satisfy the equation of continuity and Laplace's equation. The stream function $\psi(x,y)$ is defined by

$$u = \frac{\partial \psi}{\partial y} \qquad v = -\frac{\partial \psi}{\partial x} \qquad (2.33)$$

Combining Eqs. (2.31) and (2.33), the Cauchy-Riemann equations become

$$\frac{\partial \phi}{\partial x} = \frac{\partial \psi}{\partial y} \qquad \frac{\partial \phi}{\partial y} = -\frac{\partial \psi}{\partial x} \qquad (2.34)$$

It can further be shown that ψ also satisfies Laplace's equation

$$\nabla^2 \psi = \frac{\partial^2 \psi}{\partial x^2} + \frac{\partial^2 \psi}{\partial y^2} = 0 \qquad (2.35)$$

Example 2.4 STREAMLINES AND EQUIPOTENTIAL LINES

Prove that ψ and ϕ are orthogonal for isotropic flow, given Figure 2.16, where $V = (u,v)$ is a velocity vector tangent to ψ_2. Show that flow between two streamlines is constant.

Solution. We can write for the slope of the streamline

$$\frac{v}{u} = \frac{dy}{dx} = \tan \alpha$$

and

$$v\,dx - u\,dy = 0$$

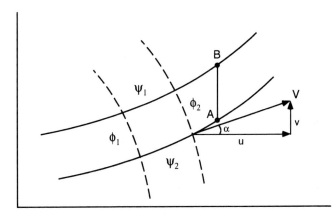

Figure 2.16 Streamlines and equipotential lines.

Since

$$u = \frac{d\psi}{dy} \qquad\qquad v = -\frac{d\psi}{dx}$$

then

$$\frac{d\psi}{dx}dx + \frac{d\psi}{dy}dy = 0$$

or $d\psi(x,y) = 0$. The total differential equals zero, and $\psi(x,y) = $ constant, as required by the stream function. The ϕ_1 and ϕ_2 lines represent equipotential lines and can be represented by the total differential

$$d\phi = \frac{\partial \phi}{\partial x}dx + \frac{\partial \phi}{\partial y}dy = 0$$

Substituting for $\partial\phi/\partial x$ and $\partial\phi/\partial y$ from Darcy's law produces $udx + vdy = 0$, which can be solved for

$$\frac{dy}{dx} = -\frac{u}{v}, \qquad \text{the slope of the equipotential line.}$$

Thus, since the two slopes are negative inverses of one another, equipotential lines are normal to streamlines for a homogeneous isotropic system. The system of orthogonal lines forms a flow net, as described earlier in this chapter.

Consider the flow crossing a vertical section AB between streamlines ψ_1 and ψ_2. The discharge across the section is designated Q, and it is apparent from fluid mechanics that

$$Q = \int_{\psi_2}^{\psi_1} u \, dy$$

$$= \int_{\psi_2}^{\psi_1} d\psi$$

$$= \psi_1 - \psi_2$$

Thus, the flow between streamlines is constant, and the spacing between streamlines reveals the relative magnitude of flow velocities between them. Once either streamlines or equipotential lines are determined in a domain, the other can be evaluated from the Cauchy-Riemann equations Eq. (2.34). Thus,

$$\psi = \int \left(\frac{\partial \phi}{\partial x} dy - \frac{\partial \phi}{\partial y} dx \right)$$

and

$$\phi = \int \left(\frac{\partial \psi}{\partial y} dx - \frac{\partial \psi}{\partial x} dy \right)$$

Example 2.5   FLOW FIELD CALCULATION

A flow field is defined by $u = 2x$ and $v = -2y$. Find the stream function and potential function for this flow and sketch the flow net.

Solution. For this example define

$$d\psi = -v \, dx + u \, dy$$
$$d\phi = -u \, dx - v \, dy$$

Continuity requires that

$$\frac{\partial u}{\partial x} + \frac{\partial v}{\partial y} = 2 - 2 = 0$$

The stream function becomes

$$d\psi = -v \, dx + u \, dy = 2y \, dx + 2x \, dy$$

or

$$\psi = 2xy + C_1$$

where C_1 is a constant. The velocity potential ϕ exists if flow is irrotational and $\partial v / \partial x - \partial u / \partial y = 0$, which is satisfied in this case. Thus,

$$d\phi = -udx - vdy = -2xdx + 2ydy$$

$$\phi = -(x^2 - y^2) + C_2$$

One can sketch the flow field by substituting values of ψ into the expression $\psi = 2xy$. For $\psi = 60$, $x = 30/y$ and for $\phi = 60$ we have $x = \pm\sqrt{y^2 - 60}$. Figure 2.17 shows the flow field for the case of flow in a corner.

2.7 UNSATURATED FLOW AND THE WATER TABLE

Hydraulic conductivity $K(\theta)$ in the unsaturated zone above the water table relates velocity and hydraulic gradient in Darcy's law. **Moisture content** θ is defined as the ratio of the volume of water to the total volume of a unit of porous media. To complicate the analysis of unsaturated flow, the moisture content θ and the hydraulic conductivity K are functions of the capillary suction ψ. Also, it has been observed experimentally that the θ–ψ relationships differ significantly for different types of soil. Figure 2.2 shows the characteristic drying and wetting curves that occur in soils which are draining water or receiving infiltration of water. The nonlinear nature of these curves greatly complicates analyses in the unsaturated zone (see Figure 9.1).

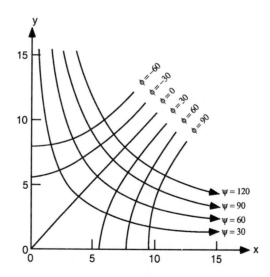

Figure 2.17 Flow net for flow in a corner.

The **water table** defines the boundary between the unsaturated and saturated zones and is defined by the surface on which the fluid pressure P is exactly atmospheric, or $P = 0$. Hence, the total hydraulic head $h = \psi + z$, where $\psi = P/\rho g$, the pressure head. For saturated ground water flow, θ equals the **porosity** n of the sample, defined as the ratio of volume of voids to total volume of sample; for unsaturated flow above a water table, $\theta < n$.

Darcy's law is used with the unsaturated value for K and can be written

$$v = -K(\theta)\frac{\partial h}{\partial z} \qquad\qquad (2.36)$$

where

v = Darcy velocity,

z = depth below surface,

h = potential or head = $z + \psi$,

ψ = tension or suction,

$K(\theta)$ = unsaturated hydraulic conductivity, and

θ = volumetric moisture content.

Near the water table, a capillary fringe can occur where ψ is a small negative pressure corresponding to the air entry pressure. This capillary zone is small for sandy soils but can be up to two meters in depth for fine grained soils. By definition, pressure head is negative (under tension) at all points above the water table and is positive for points below the water table. The value of ψ is greater than zero in the saturated zone below the water table and equals zero at the water table. Soil physicists refer to $\psi < 0$ as the tension head or capillary suction head, and it can be measured in the laboratory or field by an instrument called a tensiometer.

To summarize the properties of the unsaturated zone as compared to the saturated zone, Freeze and Cherry (1979) state that for the unsaturated zone:

1. It occurs above the water table and above the capillary fringe.
2. The soil pores are only partially filled with water; the moisture content θ is less than the porosity n.
3. The fluid pressure P is less than atmospheric; the pressure head ψ is less than zero.
4. The hydraulic head h must be measured with a tensiometer.
5. The hydraulic conductivity K and the moisture content θ are both functions of the pressure head ψ.

More details on the unsaturated zone can be found in Chapter 9, where both flow and transport in the unsaturated zone are described along with applications of analytical and numerical methods, and in Guymon (1994).

SUMMARY

Chapter 2 has presented mechanisms of ground water flow in the subsurface. Aquifer characteristics such as hydraulic conductivity, hydraulic gradient and porosity are defined and used in governing equations of flow. Both steady-state and transient saturated flow equations are derived for confined and unconfined aquifers. The Dupuit equation is derived and applied to seepage examples. Flow net theory is derived and several applications are presented for local ground water problems. The chapter ends with a brief introduction to the unsaturated zone.

REFERENCES

Bear, J., *Hydraulics of Ground Water,* New York, McGraw-Hill Book Company, 1979.

Cooper, H. H., Jr., "The Equation of Ground Water Flow in Fixed and Deforming Coordinates," *J. Geophys. Res.,* vol. 71, pp. 4785-4790, 1966.

DeWiest, R. J. M., *Geohydrology,* New York, John S. Wiley and Sons, 1965.

Domenico, P. A., and Schwartz, F. W., *Physical and Chemical Hydrogeology,* 2nd ed., New York, John S. Wiley & Sons, 1998.

Fetter. C. W., *Applied Hydrogeology*, 2nd ed., Columbus, OH, Merrill Publishing Co., 1988.

Freeze, R. A., and Cherry, J. A., *Ground Water*, Englewood Cliffs, NJ, Prentice-Hall, 1979.

Guymon, G.L., *Unsaturated Zone Hydrology*, Englewood Cliffs, NJ, Prentice Hall, 1994.

Jacob, C. E., "On the Flow of Water in an Elastic Artesian Aquifer," Trans. Am. Geophys. Union, vol. 2, pp. 574-586, 1940.

Todd, D. K., *Ground Water Hydrology*, 2nd ed., New York, John Wiley and Sons, 1980.

Terzaghi, K., Erdbaumechanic auf Bodenphysilischer Grundlage. Franz Deuticke, Vienna, 1925.

C H A P T E R   3

GROUND WATER FLOW AND WELL MECHANICS

3.1 STEADY-STATE WELL HYDRAULICS

The case of steady flow to a well implies that the variation of head occurs only in space and not in time. The governing equations of flow presented in Section 2.4 can be solved for pumping wells in unconfined or confined aquifers under steady or unsteady conditions. Boundary conditions must be kept relatively simple and aquifers must be assumed to be homogeneous and isotropic in each layer. More complex geometries can be handled by numerical simulation models in two or three dimensions (Chapters 8, 9 and 10).

3.2 STEADY ONE-DIMENSIONAL FLOW

For the case of ground water flow in the x-direction in a confined aquifer, the governing equation becomes

$$\frac{d^2h}{dx^2} = 0 \qquad (3.1)$$

and has the solution

$$h = -\frac{vx}{K} + h_0 \qquad (3.2)$$

where $h = 0$ and $x = 0$ and $dh/dx = -v/K$, according to Darcy's law. This states that head varies linearly with flow in the x–direction.

The case of steady one-dimensional flow in an unconfined aquifer was presented in Section 2.5 using Dupuit's assumptions. The resulting variation of head with x is called the Dupuit parabola and represents the approximate shape of the water table for relatively flat slopes. In the presence of steep slopes near wells, the Dupuit approximation may be in error, and more sophisticated computer methods should be used.

3.3 STEADY RADIAL FLOW TO A WELL—CONFINED

The drawdown curve or cone of depression varies with distance from a pumping well in a confined aquifer (Figure 3.1). The flow is assumed two-dimensional for a completely penetrating well in a homogeneous, isotropic aquifer of unlimited extent. For horizontal flow, the above assumptions apply, and Q at any radius r equals, from Darcy's law,

$$Q = -2\pi r b K \frac{dh}{dr} \qquad (3.3)$$

for steady radial flow to a well. Integrating after separation of variables, with $h = h_w$ at $r = r_w$ at the well, yields

$$Q = 2\pi K b \frac{h - h_w}{\ln(r / r_w)} \qquad (3.4)$$

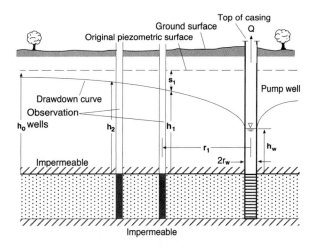

Figure 3.1 Radial flow to a well penetrating an extensive confined aquifer.

Equation (3.4) shows that h increases indefinitely with increasing r, yet the maximum head is h_0 for Figure 3.1. Near the well, the relationship holds and can be rearranged to yield an estimate for transmissivity T

$$T = Kb = \frac{Q}{2\pi(h_2 - h_1)} \ln\frac{r_2}{r_1} \tag{3.5}$$

by observing heads h_1 and h_2 at two adjacent observation wells located at r_1 and r_2, respectively, from the pumping well. In practice, it is often necessary to use unsteady-state analyses because of the long times required to reach steady state.

Example 3.1   DETERMINATION OF K AND T IN A CONFINED AQUIFER

A well is constructed to pump water from a confined aquifer. Two observation wells, OW–1 and OW–2, are constructed at distances of 100 m and 1000 m, respectively. Water is pumped from the pumping well at a rate of 0.2 m^3/min. At steady state, drawdown s' is observed as 2 m in OW–2 and 8 m in OW–1. Determine the hydraulic conductivity K and transmissivity T if the aquifer is 20 m thick.

Solution. Given

$$Q = 0.2 \text{ m}^3/\text{min},$$
$$r_2 = 1000 \text{ m},$$
$$r_1 = 100 \text{ m},$$

$$s'_2 = 2 \text{ m},$$
$$s'_1 = 8 \text{ m},$$
$$b = 20 \text{ m}.$$

Equation (3.5) gives

$$T = Kb = \frac{Q}{2\pi(h_2 - h_1)} \ln\left(\frac{r_2}{r_1}\right)$$

Knowing that $s'_1 = h_0 - h_1$ and $s'_2 = h_0 - h_2$, we have

$$T = Kb = \frac{Q}{2\pi(s'_1 - s'_2)}\left[\ln\left(\frac{r_2}{r_1}\right)\right] = \frac{0.2\text{m}^3/\text{min}}{(2\pi)(8\text{m} - 2\text{m})} \ln\left(\frac{1000\text{m}}{100\text{m}}\right)$$

$$T = 0.0122\text{m}^2/\text{min} = 2.04\text{cm}^2/\text{sec}$$

Then,

$$K = T/b = \frac{(2.04\text{cm}^2/\text{sec})}{(20\text{m})(100\text{cm}/1\text{m})}$$

$$\boxed{K = 1.02 \times 10^{-3}\text{cm}/\text{sec}}$$

3.4 STEADY RADIAL FLOW TO A WELL—UNCONFINED

Applying Darcy's law for radial flow in an unconfined, homogeneous, isotropic, and horizontal aquifer and using Dupuit's assumptions (Figure 3.2),

$$Q = -2\pi r K h \frac{dh}{dr} \tag{3.6}$$

Integrating, as before,

$$Q = \pi K \frac{h_2^2 - h_1^2}{\ln(r_2/r_1)} \tag{3.7}$$

Solving for K,

$$K = \frac{Q}{\pi\left(h_2^2 - h_1^2\right)} \ln \frac{r_2}{r_1}$$ (3.8)

where heads h_1 and h_2 are observed at adjacent wells located distances r_1 and r_2 from the pumping well, respectively.

Example 3.2 DETERMINATION OF K IN AN UNCONFINED AQUIFER

A fully penetrating well discharges 75 gpm from an unconfined aquifer. The original water table was recorded as 35 ft. After a long time period the water table was recorded as 20 ft MSL in an observation well located 75 ft away and 34 ft MSL at an observation well located 2000 ft away. Determine the hydraulic conductivity of this aquifer in ft/s.

Solution. Given

$$Q = 75 \text{ gpm,}$$
$$r_2 = 2000 \text{ ft,}$$
$$r_1 = 75 \text{ ft,}$$
$$h_2 = 34 \text{ ft, and}$$
$$h_1 = 20 \text{ ft.}$$

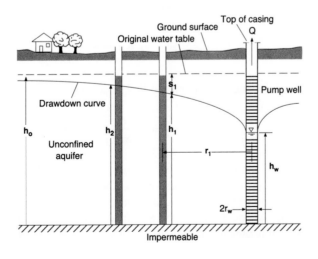

Figure 3.2 Radial flow to a well penetrating an extensive unconfined aquifer.

Equation (3.8) gives

$$K = \frac{Q}{\pi\left(h_2^2 - h_1^2\right)} \ln\left(\frac{r_2}{r_1}\right)$$

$$= \frac{(75\text{gpm})\left(0.134\text{ft}^3 / \text{gal}\right)(1\text{min} / 60\text{sec})}{(\pi)\left(34^2\,\text{ft}^2 - 20^2\,\text{ft}^2\right)} \ln \frac{2000\text{ft}}{75\text{ft}}$$

$$\boxed{K = 2.32 \times 10^{-4}\,\text{ft/s}}$$

3.5 WELL IN A UNIFORM FLOW FIELD

A typical problem in well mechanics involves a well pumping from a uniform flow field (Figure 3.3). A vertical section and plan view indicate the sloping piezometric surface and the resulting flow net. The ground water divide between the region that flows to the well and the region flowing by the well can be found from

$$-\frac{y}{x} = \tan\left(\frac{2\pi K b i}{Q} y\right) \tag{3.9}$$

Equation (3.9) results from the superposition of radial and one-dimensional flow field solutions, where i is the original piezometric slope (gradient). It can be shown that

$$y_L = \pm \frac{Q}{2 K b i} \tag{3.10}$$

as $x \to \infty$, and the stagnation point (no flow) occurs at

$$x_S = -\frac{Q}{2\pi K b i}, \quad y = 0 \tag{3.11}$$

Equations (3.10) and (3.11) may be applied to unconfined aquifers for cases of relatively small drawdowns, where b is replaced by h_0, the average saturated aquifer thickness. An important application of the well in a uniform flow field involves the evaluation of pollution sources and impacts on downgradient well fields and the potential for pumping and capturing a plume as it migrates downgradient. Chapter 13 addresses capture zone methods in more detail.

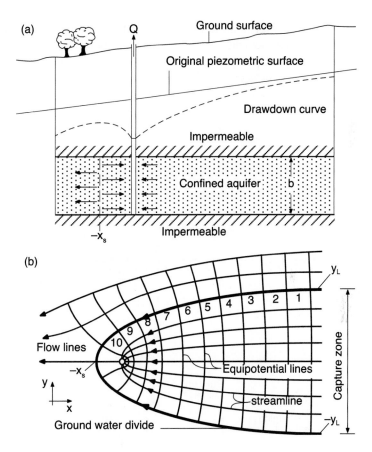

Figure 3.3 Flow to a well penetrating a confined aquifer having a sloping-plane piezometric surface. (a) vertical section. (b) Plan view.

3.6 MULTIPLE-WELL SYSTEMS

For multiple wells with drawdowns that overlap, the principle of superposition can be used. Drawdown at any point in the area of influence of several pumping wells is equal to the sum of drawdowns from each well in a confined aquifer.

Because Laplace's equation is linear, the superposition of drawdown effects is found by simple addition. Linear superposition is generally valid only for confined aquifers, since T does not change with drawdown. Thus, drawdown at any point in the area of influence of several pumping wells is equal to the sum of drawdown from each well. The above methods can be used for evaluating the effect of multiple wells in dewatering applications, well field effects, and for the case of unsteady well hydraulics. Several of the homework problems and example 3.6 demonstrate the use of linear superposition and well flow near boundaries.

The same principle applies for well flow near a boundary. Figure 3.4 shows the case for a well pumping near a fixed head stream, and Figure 3.5 shows an impermeable boundary. **Image wells** placed on the other side of the boundary at a distance x_w can be used to represent the equivalent hydraulic condition. In one case, the image well is recharging at the

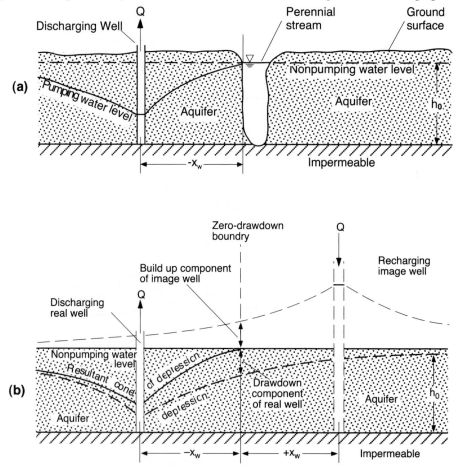

Figure 3.4 Sectional views. (a) Discharging well near a perennial stream. (b) Equivalent hydraulic system in an aquifer of infinite areal extent. Aquifer thickness h_0 should be very large compared with resultant drawdown near real well. Source: Ferris, et al., 1962.

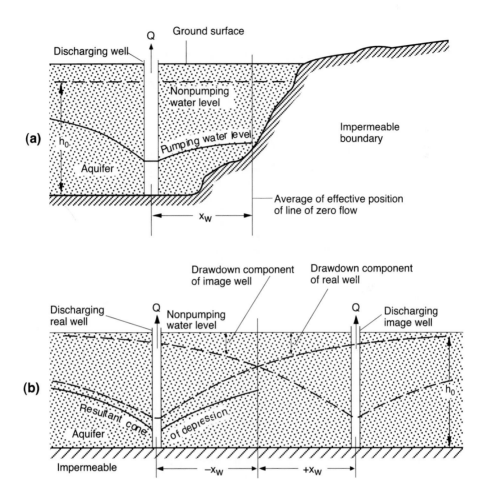

Figure 3.5 Sectional views. (a) Discharging well near an impermeable boundary. (b) Equivalent hydraulic system in an aquifer of infinite areal extent. Aquifer thickness h_0 should be very large compared with resultant drawdown near real well. Source: Ferris, et al., 1962.

same rate Q, and in another case it is pumping at rate Q. The summation of drawdowns from the original pumping well and the image well provides a correct boundary condition at distance x_w from the well. Thus, the use of image wells allows an aquifer of finite extent to be transformed into an infinite aquifer so that closed-form solution methods can be applied. Figure 3.6 shows a flow net for a pumping well and a recharging image well and indicates a line of constant head between the two wells. The steady-state drawdown s' at any point (x,y) is given by

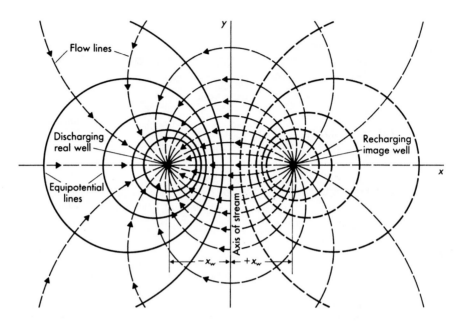

Figure 3.6 Flow net for a discharging real well and a recharging image well. Source: Ferris, et al,1962.

$$s' = \frac{Q}{4\pi T} \ln \frac{(x + x_w)^2 + (y - y_w)^2}{(x - x_w)^2 + (y - y_w)^2} \qquad (3.12)$$

where $(\pm x_w, y_w)$ are the locations of the recharge and discharge wells (DeWiest, 1965). For the case shown in Figure 3.6, $y_w = 0$.

3.7 UNSTEADY WELL HYDRAULICS

3.7.1 The Theis Method of Solution

Because a well penetrating a confined aquifer of infinite extent is pumped at a constant rate, a drawdown occurs radially extending from the well. The rate of decline of head times the storage coefficient summed over the area of influence equals the discharge. The rate of decline decreases continuously as the area of influence expands. The governing ground water flow equation (see Eq. (2.27)) in plane polar coordinates is

$$\frac{\partial^2 h}{\partial r^2} + \frac{1}{r}\frac{\partial h}{\partial r} = \frac{S}{T}\frac{\partial h}{\partial t} \qquad (3.13)$$

where

h = head

r = radial distance

S = storage coefficient, and

T = transmissivity

Theis (1935) obtained a solution for Eq. (3.13) by assuming that the well is a mathematical sink of constant strength and by using boundary conditions $h = h_0$ for $t = 0$ and $h \rightarrow h_0$ as $r \rightarrow \infty$ for $t \geq 0$:

$$s' = \frac{Q}{4\pi T}\int_u^\infty \frac{e^{-u}}{u}du = \frac{Q}{4\pi T}W(u) \qquad (3.14)$$

where s' is drawdown, Q is discharge at the well, and

$$u = \frac{r^2 S}{4Tt} \qquad (3.15)$$

Equation (3.14) is known as the nonequilibrium, or Theis equation. The integral is written as $W(u)$ and is known as the exponential integral, or well function, which can be expanded as a series:

$$W(u) = -0.5772 - \ln(u) + u - \frac{u^2}{2\cdot 2!} + \frac{u^3}{3\cdot 3!} - \frac{u^4}{4\cdot 4!} + \cdots \qquad (3.16)$$

The equation can be used to obtain aquifer constants S and T by means of pumping tests at fully penetrating wells. It is widely used because a value of S can be determined, only one observation well and a relatively short pumping period are required, and large portions of the flow field can be sampled with one test.

The assumptions inherent in the Theis equation should be included since they are often overlooked:

1. The aquifer is homogeneous, isotropic, uniformly thick, and of infinite areal extent.

2. Prior to pumping, the piezometric surface is horizontal.

3. The fully penetrating well is pumped at a constant rate.

4. Flow is horizontal within the aquifer.

5. Storage within the well can be neglected.

6. Water removed from storage responds instantaneously with a declining head.

These assumptions are seldom completely satisfied for a field problem, but the method still provides one of the most useful and accurate techniques for aquifer characterization. The complete Theis solution requires the graphical solution of two equations with four unknowns:

$$s' = \frac{Q}{4\pi T} W(u) \tag{3.17}$$

$$\frac{r^2}{t} = \left(\frac{4T}{S}\right) u \tag{3.18}$$

The relation between $W(u)$ and u must be the same as that between s' and r^2/t because all other terms are constants in the equations. Theis suggested a solution based on graphical superposition. Example 3.3 indicates how a plot of $W(u)$ vs. u, called a **type curve**, is superimposed over observed time-drawdown data while keeping the coordinate axes parallel. The two plots are adjusted until a position is found by trial, such that most of the observed data fall on a segment of the type curve. Any convenient point is selected, and values of $W(u)$, u, s' and r^2/t are used in Eqs. (3.17) and (3.18) to determine S and T (see Figure 3.7).

It is also possible to use Theis's solution for the case where several wells are sampled for drawdown simultaneously near a pumped well. Distance-drawdown data are then fitted to the type curve similar to the method just outlined.

Example 3.3   DETERMINATION OF T AND S BY THE THEIS METHOD

A fully penetrating well in a 25 m thick confined aquifer is pumped at a rate of 0.2 m³/s for 1000 min. Drawdown is recorded vs. time at an observation well located 100 m away. Compute the transmissivity and storativity using the Theis method.

Solution. A plot of s' vs. r^2/t is made on log-log paper. This is superimposed on a plot of $W(u)$ versus u, which is also on log-log paper. A point is chosen at some convenient point on the matched curve, and values for s', r^2/t, $W(u)$ and u are read (see Figure 3.7 and the accompanying Tables 3.1 and 3.2).

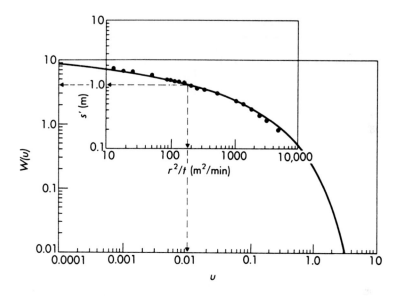

Figure 3.7 Theis curve compared to measured data.

TABLE 3.1 Radial flow to a well penetrating an extensive confined aquifer

Time (min)	s' (m)	Time (min)	s' (m)	Time (min)	s' (m)
1	0.11	20	0.71	90	1.11
2	0.20	30	0.82	100	1.15
3	0.28	40	0.85	200	1.35
4	0.34	50	0.92	400	1.55
6	0.44	60	1.02	600	1.61
8	0.50	70	1.05	800	1.75
10	0.54	80	1.08	1000	1.80

From the plot,

$$r^2/t = 180 \text{ m}^2/\text{min}$$
$$s' = 1.0 \text{ m}$$
$$u = 0.01$$
$$W(u) = 4.0$$

TABLE 3.2 Calculated values for the Well function

u	W(u)	u	W(u)	u	W(u)	u	W(u)	u	W(u)
1 e-10	22.45	2 e-08	17.15	3 e-06	12.14	4 e-04	7.25	5 e-02	2.47
2	21.76	3	16.74	4	11.85	5	7.02	6	2.3
3	21.35	4	16.46	5	11.63	6	6.84	7	2.15
4	21.06	5	16.23	6	11.45	7	6.69	8	2.03
5	20.84	6	16.05	7	11.29	8	6.55	9	1.92
6	20.66	7	15.9	8	11.16	9	6.44	1 e-01	1.823
7	20.5	8	15.76	9	11.04	1 e-03	6.33	2	1.223
8	20.37	9	15.65	1 e-05	10.94	2	5.64	3	0.906
9	20.25	1 e-07	15.54	2	10.24	3	5.23	4	0.702
1 e-09	20.15	2	14.85	3	9.84	4	4.95	5	0.56
2	19.45	3	14.44	4	9.55	5	4.73	6	0.454
3	19.05	4	14.15	5	9.33	6	4.54	7	0.374
4	18.76	5	13.93	6	9.14	7	4.39	8	0.311
5	18.54	6	13.75	7	8.99	8	4.26	9	0.26
6	18.35	7	13.6	8	8.86	9	4.14	1 e+00	0.219
7	18.2	8	13.46	9	8.74	1 e-02	4.04	2	0.049
8	18.07	9	13.34	1 e-04	8.63	2	3.35	3	0.013
9	17.95	1 e-06	13.24	2	7.94	3	2.96	4	0.004
1 e-08	17.84	2	12.55	3	7.53	4	2.68	5	0.001

Equation (3.17) gives

$$s' = \frac{Q}{4\pi T} W(u)$$

$$T = \frac{Q\,W(u)}{4\pi s'}$$

$$T = \frac{\left(0.2\,\text{m}^3/\text{sec}\right)(4.0)}{(4\pi)(1.0\text{m})}$$

$$\boxed{T = 6.37 \times 10^{-2}\,\text{m}^2/\text{sec}}$$

Equation (3.18) gives

$$\frac{r^2}{t} = \frac{4Tu}{S}$$

$$S = \frac{4Tu}{r^2/t}$$

$$= \frac{(4)(6.37 \times 10^{-2} \, \text{m}^2/\text{sec})(0.01)}{(180 \text{m}^2/\text{min})(1\,\text{min}/60\,\text{sec})}$$

$$\boxed{S = 8.49 \times 10^{-4}}$$

3.7.2 Cooper-Jacob Method of Solution

Cooper and Jacob (1946) noted that for small values of r and large values of t, the parameter u in Eq. (3.16) becomes very small so that the infinite series can be approximated by

$$s' = \frac{Q}{4\pi T}\left[-0.5772 - \ln\left(\frac{r^2 S}{4Tt}\right)\right] \tag{3.19}$$

Further rearrangement and conversion to decimal logarithms yields

$$s' = \frac{2.30Q}{4\pi T}\log\left(\frac{2.25Tt}{r^2 S}\right) \tag{3.20}$$

Thus, a plot of drawdown s' vs. logarithm of t forms a straight line, as shown in Figure 3.8. A projection of the line to $s' = 0$, where $t = t_0$, yields

$$0 = \frac{2.3Q}{4\pi T}\log\left(\frac{2.25Tt_0}{r^2 S}\right) \tag{3.21}$$

and it follows that, since log (1) = 0,

$$S = \frac{2.25Tt_0}{r^2} \tag{3.22}$$

Finally, by replacing s' by $\Delta s'$, where $\Delta s'$ is the drawdown difference of data per log cycle of t, Eq. (3.20) becomes

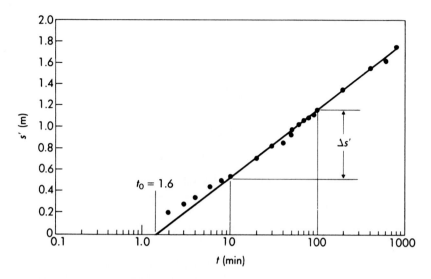

Figure 3.8 Cooper-Jacob method of analysis.

$$T = \frac{2.3Q}{4\pi\Delta s'} \tag{3.23}$$

The Cooper-Jacob method first solves for T with Eq. (3.23) and then for S with Eq. (3.22) and is applicable for small values of u (less than 0.01). Calculations with the Theis method were presented in Example 3.3, and the Cooper-Jacob method is used in Example 3.4.

Example 3.4   DETERMINATION OF T AND S BY THE COOPER-JACOB METHOD

Using the data given in Example 3.3, determine the transmissivity and storativity of the 25 m thick confined aquifer using the Cooper-Jacob method.

Solution. Values of s' and t are plotted on semilog paper with the t-axis logarithmic (see Figure 3.4). A line is fitted through the later time periods and is projected back to a point where $s' = 0$. This point determines t_0. $\Delta s'$ is measured over one log cycle of t.

From the plot,

$$t_0 = 1.6 \text{ min}$$
$$\Delta s' = 0.65 \text{ m}$$

Equation (3.23) gives

$$T = \frac{2.3Q}{4\pi\Delta s'}$$

$$= \frac{(2.3)(0.2\text{m}^3/\text{sec})}{(4\pi)(0.65\text{m})}$$

$$\boxed{T = 5.63 \times 10^{-2}\,\text{m}^2/\text{sec}}$$

Equation (3.22) gives

$$S = \frac{2.25Tt_0}{r^2}$$

$$= \frac{(2.25)(5.63 \times 10^{-2}\,\text{m}^2/\text{sec})(1.6\text{min})(60\text{sec}/1\text{min})}{(100\,\text{m})^2}$$

$$\boxed{S = 1.22 \times 10^{-3}}$$

3.7.3 Slug Tests

Slug tests involve the use of a single well for the determination of aquifer formation constants. Rather than pumping the well for a period of time, as described above, a volume of water is suddenly removed or added to the well casing and observations of recovery or drawdown are noted through time. By careful evaluation of the drawdown curve and knowledge of the well screen geometry, it is possible to derive K or T for an aquifer.

Typical procedure for a slug test requires use of a rod of slightly smaller diameter than the well casing or a pump to evacuate the well casing. The simplest slug test method in a piezometer was published by Hvorslev (1951), who used the recovery of water level over time to calculate hydraulic conductivity of the porous media. Hvorslev's method relates the flow $q(t)$ at the piezometer at any time to the hydraulic conductivity and the unrecovered head distance, $H_0 - h$ in Figure 3.9, by

$$q(t) = \pi r^2 \frac{dh}{dt} = FK(H_0 - h) \tag{3.24}$$

where F is a factor that depends on the shape and dimensions of the piezometer intake. If $q = q_0$ at $t = 0$, then $q(t)$ will decrease toward zero as time increases. Hvorslev defined the basic time lag

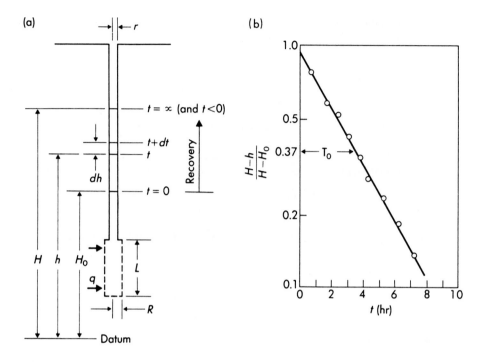

Figure 3.9 Hvorslev piezometer test.   (a) Geometry.   (b) Method of analysis.

$$T_0 = \frac{\pi r^2}{FK}$$

and solved Eq. (3.24) with initial conditions $h = H_0$ at $t = 0$. Thus

$$\frac{H - h}{H - H_0} = e^{-t/T_0} \qquad\qquad (3.25)$$

By plotting recovery $(H - h)/(H - H_0)$ vs. time on semilog graph paper, we find that $t = T_0$, where recovery equals 0.37 (Figure 3.9). For piezometer intake length divided by radius (L/R) greater than 8, Hvorslev has evaluated the shape factor F and obtained an equation for K.

$$K = \frac{r^2 \ln(L/R)}{2LT_0} \qquad\qquad (3.26)$$

Several other slug test methods have been developed by Cooper et al. (1967) and Papadopoulos et al. (1973) for confined aquifers. These methods are similar to Theis's in that a curve-matching procedure is used to obtain S and T for a given aquifer. A family of type curves $H(t)/H_0$ vs. Tt/r_c^2 was published for five values of the variable α, defined as $(r_s^2/r_c^2)S$ in Figure 3.10. Papadopoulos et al. (1973) added five additional values of α. The solution method is graphical and requires a semilogarithmic plot of measured $H(t)/H_0$ vs. t, where H_0 is the assumed initial excess head. The data are then curve-matched to the plotted type curves by horizontal translation until the best match is achieved (Figure 3.10), and a value of α is selected for a particular curve. The vertical time axis t, which overlays the vertical axis for $Tt/r_c^2 = 1.0$ is selected, and a value of T can then be found from $T = 1.0\, r_s^2/t_1$. The value of S can be found from the definition of α. The use of the method is representative of the formation only in the immediate vicinity of the test hole and should be used with caution.

The most commonly used method for determining hydraulic conductivity in ground water investigations is the Bouwer and Rice (1976) slug test. While it was originally designed for unconfined aquifers, it can be used for confined or stratified aquifers if the top of the screen is some distance below the upper confining layer. The method is based on the following equation:

$$K = \frac{r_c^2 \ln(R_e / r_w)}{2L_e} \frac{1}{t} \ln \frac{y_0}{y_t} \tag{3.27}$$

where

r_c	=	radius of casing,
y_0	=	vertical difference between water level inside well and water level outside at $t = 0$,
y_t	=	vertical difference between water level inside well and water table outside (drawdown) at time t,
R_e	=	effective radial distance over which y is dissipated, and varying with well geometry,
r_w	=	radial distance of undisturbed portion of aquifer from centerline (usually thickness of gravel pack),
L_e	=	length of screened, perforated, or otherwise open section of well, and
t	=	time.

In the above equation, y and t are the only variables. Thus, if a number of y and t measurements are taken, they can be plotted on semi-logarithmic paper to give a straight line. The slope of the best-fitting straight line will provide a value for $[\ln(y_0/y_t)]/t$. All the other parameters in the above equation are known from well geometry, and K can be calculated. A point to note is that drawdown on the ground water table becomes increasingly sig-

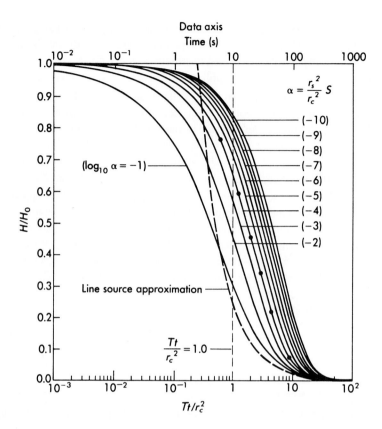

Figure 3.10 Papadopoulos slug test type curves. Source: Papadopoulos, et al., 1973. © 1973 American Geophysical Union.

nificant as the test progresses, and the points will begin to deviate from the straight line for large t and small y. Hence, only the straight line portion of the data must be used in the calculation for K.

Example 3.5. SLUG TEST METHOD

A screened, cased well penetrates a confined aquifer. The casing radius is 5 cm and the screen is 1 m long. A gravel pack 2.5 cm wide surrounds the well and a slug of water is injected that raises the water level by 0.28 m. The change in water level with time is as listed in the following table. Given that R_e is 10 cm, calculate K for the aquifer (see Figure 3.11a).

Solution. Data for y vs. t are plotted on semi-log paper as shown in Figure 3.11b. The straight line from $y_0 = 0.28$ m to $y_t = 0.001$ m covers 2.4 log cycles. The time

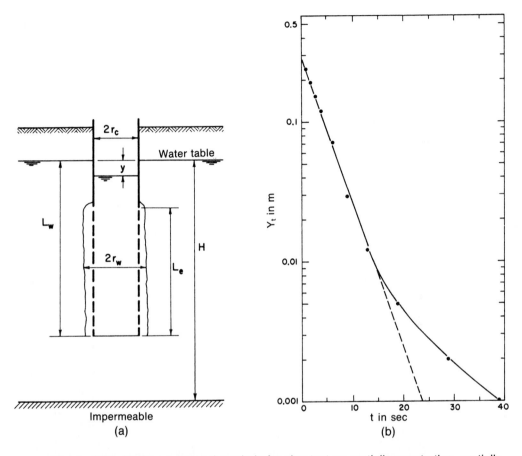

Figure 3.11 (a) Geometry and symbols for slug test on partially penetrating, partially screened well in an unconfined aquifer with gravel pack and/or developed zone around screen. (b) Graph of log Y_t versus t for slug test on well in Salt River bed, 27th Avenue, Phoenix, AZ. Source: Bouwer and Rice, 1976.© American Geophysical Union.

increment between the two points is 24 seconds. To convert the log cycles to natural log, a factor of 2.3 is used. Thus, $1/t \ln(y_0 / y_t) = 2.3 \times 2.4 / 24 = 0.23$. Using this value in the Bouwer and Rice equation gives

$$K = \frac{(5\text{cm})^2 \ln(10\text{cm} / 7.5\text{cm})}{2 \times 100\text{cm}} (0.23\text{sec}^{-1})$$

and

$$K = 8.27 \times 10^{-3} \text{ cm/s}$$

t (sec)	y_t (m)
1	0.24
2	0.19
3	0.16
4	0.13
6	0.07
9	0.03
13	0.013
19	0.005
20	0.002
40	0.001

Example 3.5 indicates how slug tests are applied to field data. It should be noted that slug tests are often used at hazardous waste sites since large volumes of contaminated water do not have to be dispersed, as in the case of a pump test. However, the pump test generally gives a better picture of overall hydraulic conductivity than does the slug test at a site.

3.7.4 Radial Flow in a Leaky Aquifer

Leaky aquifers represent a unique and complex problem in well mechanics. When a leaky aquifer is pumped, as shown in Figure 3.12, water is withdrawn both from the lower aquifer and from the saturated portion of the overlying aquitard. By creating a lowered piezometric surface below the water table, ground water can migrate vertically downward and then move horizontally to the well. While steady-state conditions in a leaky system are possible, a general nonequilibrium analysis for unsteady flow is more applicable and more often occurs in the field. When pumping starts from a well in a leaky aquifer, drawdown of the piezometric surface can be given by

$$s' = \frac{Q}{4\pi T} \mathrm{W}\left(u, \frac{r}{B}\right) \qquad (3.28)$$

where the quantity r/B is given by

$$\frac{r}{B} = \frac{r}{\sqrt{T/(K'/b')}}$$

where T is transmissivity of the aquifer, K' is vertical hydraulic conductivity of the aquitard, and b' is thickness of the aquitard. Values of the function $\mathrm{W}(u, r/B)$ have been tabulated by Hantush (1956) and have been used by Walton (1960) to prepare a family of type curves, shown in Figure 3.13. Equation (3.28) reduces to the Theis equation for $r/B = 0$. The method of solution for the leaky aquifer works in the same way as the Theis solution with a super-

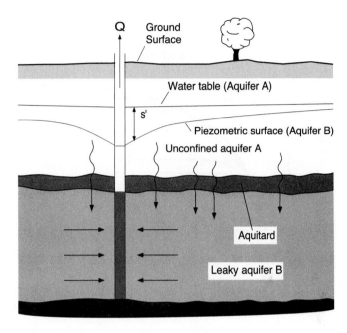

Figure 3.12 Well pumping from a leaky aquifer.

position of drawdown data on top of the leaky type curves. A curve of best fit is selected, and values of W, $1/u$, s', and t are found, which allows T and S to be determined. Finally, based on the value of r/B, it is possible to calculate K' and b'.

In general, leaky aquifers are much more difficult to deal with than confined or unconfined systems. But the method just described does provide a useful tool for evaluating leaky systems analytically. For more complex geologies and systems with lenses, a three-dimensional computer simulation may be employed to properly represent ground water flow. These types of models are described in detail in Chapter 10.

Example 3.6 APPLICATION OF THEIS

A 375-m square excavation is to be dewatered by the installation of four wells at the corners. Point A is in the middle and Point B is on one side equidistant from two of the wells. For an allowable pumping period of 24 hours, determine the pumping rate required to produce a minimum drawdown of 4 m everywhere within the limits of the excavation. The confined aquifer has a transmissivity of 2×10^{-4} m^2/s and a storage factor of 7×10^{-5}.

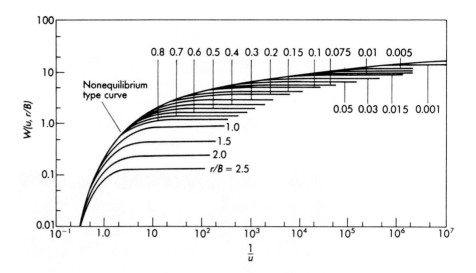

Figure 3.13 Type curves for analysis of pumping test data to evaluate storage coefficient and transmissivity of leaky aquifers. Source: Walton, 1960.

Solution. By symmetry, we expect the maximum drawdown to be at either A or B, so we must determine which of them is limiting. We will use the Theis equations (below) to determine the flow rate Q necessary to create a 4 m drawdown at A and B.

$$s = \left(\frac{Q}{4\pi T}\right) W(u), \quad \text{and} \quad u = \frac{r^2 S}{4Tt}$$

a) Determine the required pumping rate for 4 m drawdown at A. Using r, S, T, and t, find u with the second equation above, then determine $W(u)$ from Table 3.2, and solve the first equation for Q.

$$r = \sqrt{2}\,\frac{375}{2} = 265 \text{ m}$$

$$u = \frac{(265\text{m})^2 (7 \times 10^{-5})}{(4)(2 \times 10^{-4}\,\text{m}^2/\text{sec})(24\text{hr})(3600\text{sec}/\text{hr})} = 0.071$$

$$W(u) = 2.14$$

and each well contributes 25%,

$$Q = \frac{1}{4}\frac{s}{W(u)}(4\pi T) = \frac{(4\text{m})}{(4)(2.14)}(4)(\pi)(2 \times 10^{-4}\text{m}^2 / \text{sec})$$

$$Q = 1.17 \times 10^{-3} \text{ m}^3/\text{s} = 4.23 \text{ m}^3/\text{hr for each well}$$

b) Determine drawdown at B using the flowrates calculated above. Drawdown at B is a combination of two wells 187.5 m from B and two wells at $r = \sqrt{187.5^2 + 375^2}$ m = 419 m from B. For the closer two wells:

$$u = \frac{(187.5\text{m})^2(7 \times 10^{-5})}{(4)(2 \times 10^{-4}\text{m}^2 / \text{sec})(24\text{hr})(3600\text{sec} / \text{hr})} = 0.036$$

$$W(u) = 2.79$$

and the drawdown produced by the closer two wells is:

$$s = 2\frac{(1.17 \times 10^{-3}\text{m}^3 / \text{sec})}{(4)(\pi)(2 \times 10^{-4}\text{m}^2 / \text{sec})}(2.79) = 2.60 \text{ m}$$

For the two farther wells,

$$u = \frac{(419\text{m})^2(7 \times 10^{-5})}{(4)(2 \times 10^{-4}\text{m}^2 / \text{sec})(24\text{hr})(3600\text{sec} / \text{hr})} = 0.18 \Rightarrow W(u) = 1.34$$

$$s = 2\frac{(1.17 \times 10^{-3}\text{m}^3 / \text{sec})}{(4)(\pi)(2 \times 10^{-4}\text{m}^2 / \text{sec})}(1.34) = 1.25 \text{ m}$$

Summing over all four wells, the total drawdown at B = 2.60 + 1.25 = 3.85 m. Thus, the drawdown at B is less than at A, so requiring a 4 m drawdown at B will automatically meet the criteria at Point A, and over the entire site. Since s and Q are linearly related, multiplying the above calculated Q by (4 m/3.85 m) will give us a drawdown of 4 m at B. Therefore $Q = 4.4$ m³/hr will keep the construction site dry.

SUMMARY

Chapter 3 has provided a review of well mechanics under both steady-state and transient conditions. The principle of superposition was applied for multiple well systems and image well problems. The Theis method of solution was derived and several examples are shown. Slug test methods for single wells are covered in detail. Well mechanics solutions are important in the application of pump tests and capture zones, which are discussed in more detail in Chapters 10 and 13.

REFERENCES

American Water Works Association, AWWA Standard for Deep Wells, AWWA-A100-66, Denver, Colorado, 1967.

Bedient, P. B., and W. C. Huber, *Hydrology and Floodplain Analysis*, 2nd ed., Reading, MA , Addison-Wesley, 1992.

Bouwer, H., and R. C. Rice, "A Slug Test for Determining Hydraulic Conductivity of Unconfined Aquifers with Completely or Partially Penetrating Wells," *Water Resources Res.* 12:423-428, 1976.

Campbell, M. D., and J. H. Lehr, Water Well Technology, New York, McGraw-Hill, , 1973.

Cooper, H. H., Jr., J. D. Bredehoeft, and I. S. Papadopoulos, "Response of a Finite-Diameter Well to an Instantaneous Charge of Water," *Water Resour. Res.*, vol. 3, pp. 263—269, 1967.

Cooper, H. H., Jr., and C. E. Jacob, "A Generalized Graphical Method for Evaluating Formation Constants and Summarizing Well Field History," Trans. Am. Geophys. Union, vol. 27, pp. 526-534, 1946.

DeWiest, R. J. M., *Geohydrology*, New York, John Wiley and Sons, Inc., 1965.

Ferris, J. G., D. B. Knowles, R. H. Browne, and R. W. Stallman, *Theory of Aquifer Tests*, U.S. Geological Survey Water Supply Paper 1536-E, 1962.

Freeze, R. A., and J. A. Cherry, *Ground Water*, Englewood Cliffs, New Jersey, Prentice-Hall, 1979.

Hantush, M. S., "Analysis of Data from Pumping Tests in Leaky Aquifers," *J. Geophys. Res.*, vol. 69, pp. 4221-4235, 1956.

Hvorslev, M. J., Time Lag and Soil Permeability in Ground Water Observations, U.S. Army Corps of Engineers Waterways Exp. Sta. Bull. 36, Vicksburg, Mississippi, 1951.

Papadopoulos, I. S., J. D. Bredehoeft, and H. H. Cooper, Jr., "On the Analysis of Slug Test Data," *Water Resour. Res.*, vol. 9, no. 4, pp. 1087-1089, 1973.

Theis, C. V., "The Relation Between the Lowering of the Piezometric Surface and the Rate and Duration of Discharge of a Well Using Ground-Water Storage," Trans. Am. Geophys. Union, vol. 16, pp. 519-524, 1935.

Walton, W. C., Leaky Artesian Aquifer Conditions in Illinois, Illinois State Water Surv. Rept. Invest. 39, Urbana, Illinois, 1960.

C H A P T E R   4

SOURCES AND TYPES OF GROUND WATER CONTAMINATION

4.1 INTRODUCTION

Humans have been exposed to hazardous substances dating back to prehistoric times when they inhaled noxious gases from volcanoes and in cave dwellings. Pollution problems started in the industrial sector with the production of dyes and other organic chemicals developed from the coal tar industry in Germany during the 1800s. In the 1900s the variety of chemicals and chemical wastes increased drastically from the production of steel and iron, lead batteries, petroleum refining, and other industrial practices. During that time radium and chromic wastes began to create serious problems as well. The World War II era ushered in massive production of wartime products that required use of chlorinated solvents, polymers, plastics, paints, metal finishing, and wood preservatives. Very little was known about the environmental impacts of many of these chemical wastes until much later.

The Love Canal hazardous waste site attracted major public attention in 1979 and heralded the hazardous waste decade of the 1980s. The site in Niagara Falls, New York, had received 20,000 metric tons of chemical waste containing at least 80 different chemicals and was creating serious environmental impacts on nearby residents. By 1989 state and federal governments had spent $140 million to clean up the site and relocate the residents. Several other sites during the 1980s also received national attention including the Stringfellow Acid Pits near Riverside, California; the Valley of the Drums in Kentucky; the Brio and Motco chemical waste sites in Houston, Texas; the dioxin contamination at Times Beach, Missouri, and at the Vertac facility in Arkansas. Many of the above sites and dozens of others all across the United States became the subject of major environmental investigations and remediation studies under Superfund. In addition, many of the largest sites came under private or federal litigation starting in about 1986 to the present.

No hazardous waste site is more famous at the national level than the one created by poor industrial practices in Woburn, Massachusetts, where tannery wastes back to 1850 and chlorinated chemicals were dumped. The claim was made that chlorinated chemicals contaminated two drinking water wells in the small community, and may have resulted in the deaths of a number of children living in the area. The dispute over which company was responsible for the contamination of the wells resulted in a major lawsuit, a major site investigation, and the recent best-selling book and motion picture, *A Civil Action* (Harr, 1995).

This chapter describes most of the significant chemical threats to ground water quality from various sources of contamination. In a 1984 report, *Protecting the Nation's Groundwater from Contamination*, the Office of Technology Assessment (OTA 1984) listed more than 30 different potential sources of contamination. Table 4.1 lists the major sources of ground water contamination and divides them into six major categories. Section 305(b) of the Federal Clean Water Act requires states to submit reports to the EPA on sources and types of ground water contamination. In 1988 the *National Water Quality Inventory — 1988 Report to Congress* (USEPA 1990) presented the data on the relative importance of various sources of contamination and various types of contaminants. State inventories showed that more than half the states and territories listed underground storage tanks, septic tanks, agricultural activities, municipal landfills, and abandoned hazardous waste sites as major threats to ground water. Other sources that were listed include industrial landfills, injection wells, regulated hazardous waste sites, land application, road salt, salt water intrusion, and brine pits from oil and gas wells. The highest priority rankings were given to underground storage tanks, abandoned waste sites, agricultural activity, septic tanks, surface impoundments, and municipal landfills.

Table 4.2 provides a list of major organic contaminants according to the Environmental Protection Agency (EPA). This is the target list of 126 priority pollutants defined by EPA for their contract laboratory program. The volatile compounds are determined by standard EPA method 624, the semivolatiles by method 625, and pesticides and PCBs by method 608.

TABLE 4.1 Sources Of Ground Water Contamination

CATEGORY I	CATEGORY II	CATEGORY III
Sources designed to discharge substances	Sources designed to store, treat, and/or dispose of substances; discharge through unplanned release	Sources designed to retain substances during transport or transmission
Subsurface percolation (e.g., septic tanks and cesspools) Injection wells Land application	Landfills Open dumps Surface impoundments Waste tailings Waste piles Materials stockpiles Above ground storage tanks Under ground storage tanks Radioactive disposal sites	Pipelines Materials transport and transfer

CATEGORY IV	CATEGORY V	CATEGORY VI
Sources discharging as consequence of other planned activities	Sources providing conduit or inducing discharge through altered flow patterns	Naturally occurring sources whose discharge is created and/or exacerbated by human activity
Irrigation practices Pesticide applications Fertilizer applications Animal feeding operations De-icing salts applications Urban runoff Percolation of atmospheric pollutants Mining and mine drainage	Production wells Other wells (non-waste) Construction excavation	Ground water – surface water interactions Natural leaching Salt-water intrusion/ brackish water upcoming

Office of Technology Assessment, 1984

Figures 4.1 and 4.2 indicate the priority rankings of the sources and of the various contaminants as reported to Congress in 1990. Each section of this chapter discusses how the major sources of contamination may degrade ground water quality and provides the latest information about the scope of the problem. Figure 4.3 shows the various mechanisms of ground water contamination associated with some of the major sources, which include chemical and fuel storage tanks, septic tanks, municipal landfills, and surface impoundments. A wide variety of organic and inorganic chemicals have been identified as potential contaminants in ground water. These include inorganic compounds such as nitrates, brine, and various trace metals; synthetic organic chemicals such as fuels, chlorinated solvents, and pesticides; radioactive contaminants associated with defense sites; and pathogens.

Large quantities of organic compounds are manufactured and used by industry, the federal government, agriculture, and municipalities. They have created the greatest potential for ground water contamination, as described later in this chapter. One such group is the soluble aromatic hydrocarbons associated with petroleum fuels or lubricants. The group includes benzene, toluene, ethyl benzene, and various xylene isomers (BTEX) often associated with petroleum spills. Chlorinated hydrocarbons such as tetrachloroethylene (PCE) and

TABLE 4.2. Environmental Protection Agency List of Priority Pollutants

Base-Neutral Extractables

Acenaphthene	Diethyl phthalate
Acenaphthylene	Dimethyl phthalate
Anthracene	2,4-Dinitrotoluene
Benzidine	2,6-Dinitrotoluene
Benzo[a]anthracene	Di-n-octyl phthalate
Benzo[b]fluoranthene	1,2-Diphenylhydrazine
Benzo[k]fluoranthene	Fluoranthene
Benzo[ghi]perylene	Fluorene
Benzo[a]pyrene	Hexachlorobenzene
Bis(2-chloroethoxy) methane	Hexachlorobutadiene
Bis(2-chloroethyl) ether	Hexachlorocyclopentadiene
Bis(2-chloroisopropyl) ether	Hexachloroethane
Bis(2-ethylhexyl) phthalate	Indeno[1,2,3-cd] pyrene
4-Bromophenyl phenyl ether	Isophorone
Butyl benzyl phthalate	Naphthalene
2-Chloronaphthalene	Nitrobenzene
4-Chlorophenyl phenyl ether	N-Nitrosodimethylamine
Chrysene	N-Nitrosodiphenylamine
Dibenzo[a,h] anthracene	N-Nitrosodi-n-propylamine
Di-n-butyl phthalate	Phenanthrene
1,2-Dichlorobenzene	Pyrene
1,3-Dichlorobenzene	2,3,7,8-Tetrachlorodibenzo-p-dioxin
1,4-Dichlorobenzene	1,2,4-Trichlorobenzene
3,3'-Dichlorobenzidine	

Pesticides

Aldrin	Dieldrin	PCB-1016[a]
α-BHC	α-Endosulfan	PCB-1221[a]
β-BHC	β-Endosulfan	PCB-1232[a]
γ-BHC	Endosulfan sulfate	PCB-1242[a]
δ-BHC	Endrin	PCB-1248[a]
Chlordane	Endrin aldehyde	PCB-1254[a]
4,4'-DDD	Heptachlor	PCB-1260[a]
4,4'-DDE	Heptachlor epoxide	Toxaphene
4,4'-DDT		[a] not pesticides

Organic compounds are subdivided into four categories according to the method of analysis

TABLE 4.2. Environmental Protection Agency List of Priority Pollutants

Volatiles

Acrolein	1,1-Dichloroethylene
Acrylonitrile	trans-1,2-Dichloroethylene
Benzene	1,2-Dichloropropane
Bis(chloromethyl) ether	cis-1,3-Dichloropropene
Bromodichloromethane	trans-1,3-Dichloropropene
Bromoform	Ethylbenzene
Bromomethane	Methylene chloride
Carbon tetrachloride	Styrene
Chlorobenzene	1,1,2,2-Tetrachloroethane
Chloroethane	1,1,2,2-Tetrachloroethene
2-Chloroethyl vinyl ether	Toluene
Chloroform	1,1,1-Trichloroethane
Chloromethane	1,1,2-Trichloroethane
Dibromochloromethane	Trichloroethylene
Dichlorodifluoromethane	Trichlorofluoromethane
1,1-Dichloroethane	Vinyl chloride
1,2-Dichloroethane	Xylene

Acid Extractables

p-Chloro-m-cresol	2-Nitrophenol
2-Chlorophenol	4-Nitrophenol
2,4-Dichlorophenol	Pentachlorophenol
2,4-Dimethylphenol	Phenol
4,6-Dinitro-o-cresol	2,4,6-Trichlorophenol
2-4-Dinitrophenol	Total phenols

Inorganics

Antimony	Chromium	Nickel
Arsenic	Copper	Selenium
Asbestos	Cyanide	Silver
Beryllium	Lead	Thallium
Cadmium	Mercury	Zinc

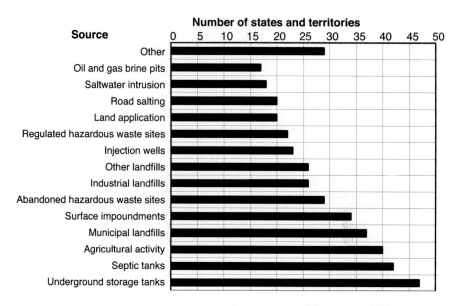

Figure 4.1 Frequency of various contamination sources considered by states and territories of the United States to be major threats to ground water quality.

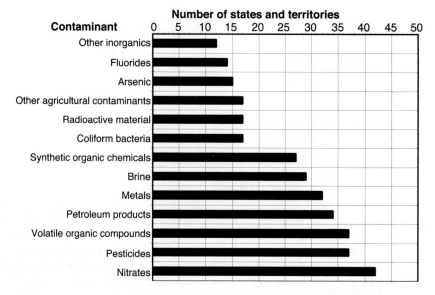

Figure 4.2 Frequency of various contaminants considered by states and territories of the United States to be major threats to ground water quality.

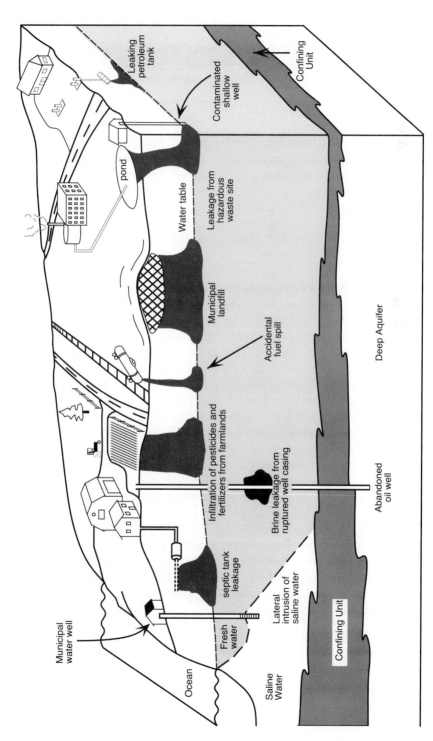

Figure 4.3 Mechanisms of ground water contamination.

TABLE 4.3 Typical Organic Compounds Found in Ground Water

Ground water contaminant

Acetone	Methylene chloride
Benzene	Naphthalene
bis-(2-ethylhexyl)phthalate	Phenol
Chlorobenzene	Tetrachloroethene
Chloroethane	Toluene
Chloroform	1,2-trans-Dichloroethane
1,1-Dichloroethane	1,1,1-Trichloroethane
1,2-Dichloroethane	Trichloroethene
Di-n-butyl phthalate	Vinyl chloride
Ethyl benzene	Xylene

trichloroethylene (TCE) have been used for metal degreasing and for solvents, cleaners, dry cleaning fluids, paint removers, and printing inks.

Table 4.3 lists some of the more common organic compounds found in ground water along with their important properties. These compounds can generally be divided into categories: fuels and derivatives (BTEX), PAHs, alcohols, and ketones; halogenated aliphatics (trichloroethylene); halogenated aromatics (chlorobenzene); and polychlorinated biphenyls (PCBs). Chapter 7 presents more details on the properties and degradation pathways for fuels and chlorinated organics in ground water. The above compounds have been discharged to the environment in a number of ways over the years, beginning largely after World War II. While fuel contamination was recognized in the late 1980s as a major ground water problem associated with underground storage tanks, it has largely been replaced in the 1990s by chlorinated organic problems associated with industrial and military sites. Some of the largest underground contaminant plumes in the United States are located west of the Mississippi River, and involve chlorinated organics, which have migrated several miles in a number of cases.

The inorganic compounds occur in nature and may come from natural as well as man-made sources. Metals from mining, industry, metal finishing, wastewater, agriculture, and fossil fuel burning can present serious problems in ground water. Table 4.4 lists some of the more important trace metals occurring in ground water. Chromium may represent one of the most important metals because of its occurrence and mobility at a number of industrial sites that have impacted ground water.

TABLE 4.4 Examples of Trace Metals Occurring in Ground Water

Aluminum	Copper	Selenium
Antimony	Gold	Silver
Arsenic	Iron	Strontium
Barium	Lead	Thallium
Beryllium	Lithium	Tin
Boron	Manganese	Titanium
Cadmium	Mercury	Uranium
Chromium	Molybdenum	Vanadium
Cobalt	Nickel	Zinc

4.2 UNDERGROUND STORAGE TANKS

Underground tanks are ubiquitous in the environment. While most often associated with gasoline service stations, these tanks are also used by small and large industries, agriculture, governmental agencies, and private homes for storage of products. In general, fuels, oils, hazardous chemicals and solvents, and chemical waste products have been stored in below-ground tanks. The Office of Technology Assessment estimated in 1984 the number of storage tanks, both abandoned and in use, at approximately 2.5 million. A recent EPA survey (1990) found that 47 states indicated major ground water contamination from faulty underground tanks.

Many of the tanks were originally installed in the 1950s and 1960s and some are still in use today or have been abandoned or forgotten. Underground tanks can leak due to internal or external corrosion of the metal. Leaks can occur through holes in the tank or in associated piping and valves. In a recent survey of motor fuel storage tanks, the EPA found that 35% of the estimated 800,000 such tanks leaked. Steel tanks are being replaced by fiberglass tanks but faulty piping and subsequent leaks still occur. Figure 4.4 shows a typical double wall tank and leak detection system, a possible solution to the problems resulting from leaking tanks. Obviously, such systems are more expensive than older tanks and they have yet to be tested over time, but EPA and the individual states are involved in a major program to replace older tanks and to upgrade leak-detection systems.

The state of Texas alone was spending millions per year for investigation and cleanup of leaking underground storage tanks estimated at more than 5,000 in number. The remediation of underground storage tank plumes was a major focus of hydrogeologic assessments in the U.S. in the late 1980s and early 1990s. One of the most studied underground storage tank incidents in the U.S. was a fuel spill at the U.S. Coast Guard Station at Traverse City, Michigan. The spill of aviation gas and jet fuel resulted in a plume of contamination more than 1 mile long and 500 ft wide, which polluted about 100 shallow municipal water wells.

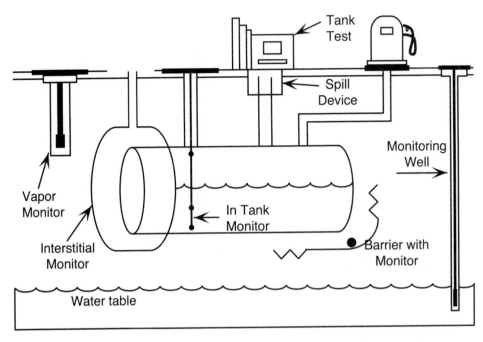

Figure 4.4 Typical double-walled tank and leak detection system.

The site has been the subject of extensive evaluation and remediation study, and more detail is provided in Chapters 8 and 13.

A different view of the true impact of underground storage tanks began to emerge in the mid 1990s when it became apparent that complete cleanups to EPA drinking water standards would not be affordable at many sites. In addition, two reports were written, one in California and one in Texas, which analyzed and reviewed in detail hundreds of leaking underground storage tank sites in an effort to draw general conclusions on rate and extent of ground water contamination. The California report (Lawrence Livermore National Laboratory, 1995) and the Texas report (Bureau of Economic Geology, 1997) both found that the median length of the ground water plume from typical UST sites was between 101 ft and 130 ft for California and between 190 ft and 260 ft for Texas. Thus, the size of the ground water impact at UST sites is much smaller than originally thought, due to processes of dilution and natural aerobic biodegradation of fuel components. Physical transport mechanisms associated with UST leaks and natural biodegradation issues are covered in more detail in Chapters 8 and 12.

4.3 LANDFILLS

Landfills today may be built with elaborate leak prevention systems, but most, particularly the older ones, are simply large holes in the ground filled with waste and covered with dirt. Originally designed to reduce the air pollution and unsightly trash that accompanied open dumping and burning, landfills became the disposal method for every conceivable type of waste. However, many were poorly designed and are leaking liquids or leachate, which have contaminated surrounding shallow ground water. According to EPA reports, there are approximately 2,395 open dumps and 24,000 to 36,000 closed or abandoned landfills in the U.S., and EPA estimates that 12,000 to 18,000 municipal landfills may contain hazardous wastes. In addition, there are an estimated 75,000 on-site industrial landfills. Materials placed in many of these landfills include garbage, trash, debris, sludge, incinerator ash, foundry waste and hazardous substances. Liquid hazardous wastes can no longer be legally disposed of in municipal landfills.

Many older landfills were located based on convenience rather than hydrogeologic study and consequently have been situated in environmentally sensitive marshlands, abandoned mines, gravel and sand pits, and sink holes. The disposal technology simply involved filling the hole with liquid and solid wastes, compacting with a bulldozer, and then covering with a layer of soil. As rainwater infiltrates through the top of a typical landfill, water levels increase inside the landfill creating a mounded condition, and leaching of inorganic and organic contaminants into the ground water can occur (Figure 4.5a). Thus, in many settings, thelandfill acts like a surface impoundment that may be loaded with hazardous organic and inorganic materials. A number of older landfills have become famous study sites over the years and include the Borden landfill in Canada, the subject of extensive hydrogeologic and transport studies beginning in the early 1980s (Chapters 6 and 7). Other landfills and burial areas that were filled with hazardous waste and caused serious off-site problems include Love Canal in New York; Lone Pine landfill in New Jersey (Zheng et al., 1991); and the Vertac site in Arkansas.

Extensive siting, engineering, hydrologic, and hydrogeologic designs are required for the permitting of municipal and industrial landfills today. Modern landfills have leachate collection systems to control the migration of contaminants so they can be collected and transported off-site to a water treatment plant. A landfill must have a properly designed and constructed liner to minimize vertical migration, and a low-permeability cover to minimize off-site impacts. Many of the landfills built from the 1950s through the 1970s contained no liners or leachate collection systems, and have had serious leakage problems. Hazardous waste landfills are now regulated under the Resource Conservation and Recovery Act, and open dumps are no longer possible under Subtitle D of RCRA (see Chapter 14). Figure 4.5.b depicts the various design features of a modern hazardous waste landfill.

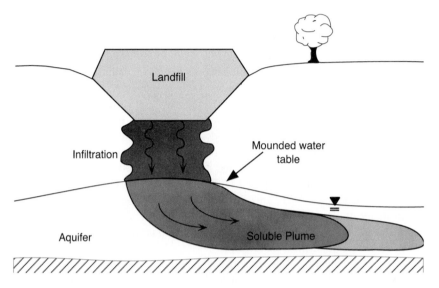

Figure 4.5a. Typical landfill with mounded water table.

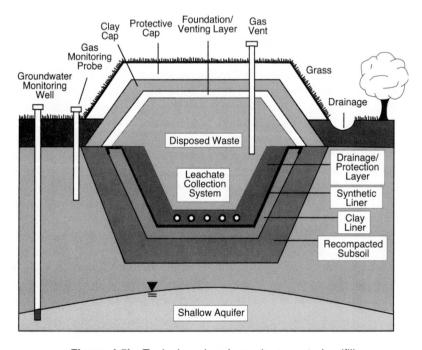

Figure 4.5b Typical modern hazardous waste landfill.

4.4 SURFACE IMPOUNDMENTS

Surface impoundments are often called pits, ponds, or lagoons. Ranging in size from a few square feet to several thousand acres, surface impoundments serve as disposal or temporary storage sites for hazardous and nonhazardous wastes. They are designed to accept purely liquid wastes, or mixed solids and liquids that separate in the impoundment. Chemical wastes in the impoundment are either treated and discharged to the environment, allowed to infiltrate the soil, or evaporate to the atmosphere. Prior to the passage of RCRA, liquid hazardous wastes were also discharged into pits that may have been lined or unlined with clay or other liner membranes.

Surface impoundments are commonly used by municipal wastewater and sewage treatment operations for settling of solids, biological oxidation, and chemical treatment. They are also used by animal feedlots and farms, and by many industries including oil and gas, mining, paper, and chemical operations. Water from surface impoundments may be discharged to streams and lakes. Many surface impoundments have been found to leak (Figure 4.6) and create large contaminated zones in the subsurface. The most famous case is the Rocky Mountain Arsenal near Denver, which discharged nerve gas and pesticides into unlined evaporation ponds from 1942 until 1956. Contamination of nearby wells was detected in the early 1950s when irrigated crops died and ground water contamination extended over an eight-mile region. The ground water under the Rocky Mountain Arsenal has been found more recently to contain many synthetic organic contaminants associated with the manufacture of nerve gas and pesticides (Konikow and Thompson, 1984). It is estimated that the cleanup of contaminated soil and ground water at the arsenal will ultimately cost more than $1 billion.

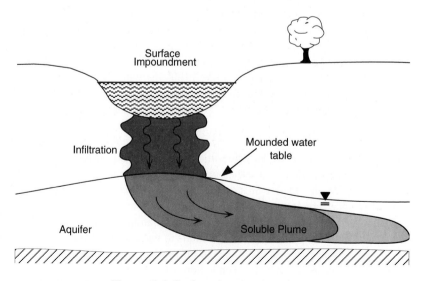

Figure 4.6 Surface impoundment leak.

In 1982 EPA identified over 180,000 waste impoundments including 37,000 munici-pal, 19,400 agricultural, 27,912 industrial, 25,000 mining, and 65,688 brine pits for oil and gas (EPA 1982). Of the industrial sites evaluated, 95% were within one mile of drinking water wells, 70% were unlined and 50% were on top of aquifers. Thus, impoundments repre-sent a major and continuing source for migration of organic and inorganic chemicals to ground water by often causing a mounded condition in the subsurface. Most industrial sites where contamination problems have occurred have one or more impoundments located on site.

Discharge of water with chlorinated solvents into impoundments at Plant 44 near Tuc-son, Arizona contributed to one of the largest chlorinated ground water plumes in the U.S. The contaminants impacted water supply wells and created a ground water plume over six miles long in the downgradient direction (Section 13.9.1).

4.5 WASTE DISPOSAL INJECTION WELLS

Injection wells are used to discharge liquid hazardous waste, brine, agricultural and urban runoff, municipal sewage, aquifer recharge water, and fluids used in solution mining and oil recovery into the subsurface. Every year in the United States millions of tons of toxic, haz-ardous, radioactive, and other liquid wastes are dumped directly into the subsurface through thousands of waste disposal wells. This practice, most commonly utilized by the chemical, petroleum, metals, minerals, aerospace, and wood-preserving industries, has contaminated ground water in over 20 states.

Injection wells can cause ground water contamination if the fluid enters a drinking wa-ter aquifer due to poor well design, faulty construction, or inadequate understanding of the geology. Wastewater can migrate vertically upward into a drinking water aquifer through cracks, fault zones, or abandoned well casings. Figure 4.7 shows a typical deep well injec-tion of liquid waste. Normally, such wells are designed to have pressure gages and monitor-ing wells to detect any leak or fracture problems with the injection. Injection wells are now regulated under the Underground Injection Control Program of the Safe Drinking Water Act. The RCRA amendments of 1984 prohibit the underground injection of certain hazardous wastes.

The injection wells that pose the greatest threat to ground water include agricultural wells, septic system wells, brine injection wells, and deep wells for hazardous waste. An additional concern is that wastes that have been disposed of earlier may migrate into drinking water aquifers due to fractures and faults in abandoned casings (Figure 4.8). The injection fluid is under pressure and creates a zone of influence that extends beyond the well casing (Chapter 3). If abandoned oil wells or deteriorating well casings are in the immediate area, they can possibly provide vertical conduits to water supply aquifers that reside above.

A serious problem that exists in oil-producing states is the disposal of brine waters via surface pits or injection wells. Ten gallons of salt water are produced and brought to the sur-face for every gallon of oil pumped out of the ground. The brine waters are often rein-

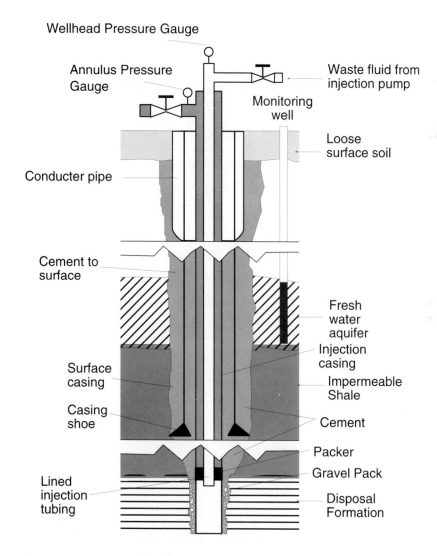

Figure 4.7 Deep well injection of liquid wastes.

jected into wells, and in some cases, have contaminated nearby aquifer systems or surface streams. The problem is particularly acute where aquifers can transport the salt water over large distances. Many of these problem sites were developed decades ago (1940s and 1950s) before modern technology for proper brine control and disposal was introduced.

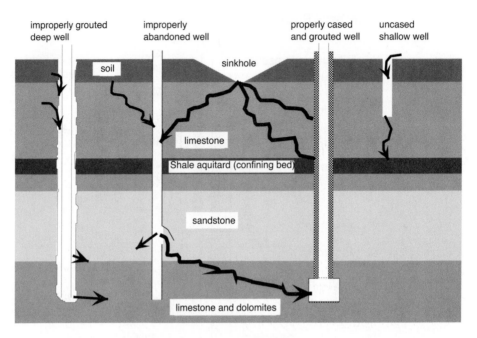

Figure 4.8 Aquifer contamination through improperly constructed or abandoned wells.

4.6 SEPTIC SYSTEMS

Approximately 22 million septic systems are operating in the United States today, and about one-half million new systems are installed every year. These systems serve nearly thirty percent of the nation's population.

Septic systems generally are composed of a septic tank and a drain field into which effluent flows from the tank (Figure 4.9). Within the tank, physical processes separate the inflow into sludge (which accumulates on the bottom of the tank), wastewater, and scum (which forms on top of the wastewater). Once a tank reaches a certain percentage of its capacity, the sludge and scum, called septage, must be pumped out, so the tank will continue to function properly.

Serious system failures are usually quite evident because wastes will surface and flood the drainage field (not only causing an odor, but also exposing people to pathogenic bacteria and viruses). Unfortunately, we cannot see or smell contaminants from underground systems that leach into aquifers. Years may pass before contamination emanating from poorly designed systems is detected. Septic systems discharge a variety of organic and inorganic compounds including BOD, COD, TSS, fecal coliform bacteria, nitrates and nitrites, ammonia

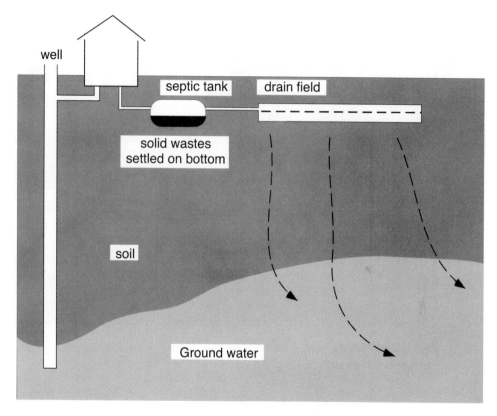

Figure 4.9 A typical septic system.

and phosphorus. Synthetic organic chemicals such as TCE, benzene, and methylene chloride may also be discharged to the subsurface.

Commercial and industrial septic systems present unique and potentially more severe problems to ground water contamination than do domestic systems due to the hazardous nature of the wastes disposed of in these systems. Chemicals including nitrates, heavy metals such as lead, copper, and zinc, and certain synthetic organic chemicals, such as benzene, PCE, TCE, and chloroform are dumped into such systems. The EPA has identified several commercially used septic systems as sources of chemical contamination at sites around the nation designed for cleanup under the federal Superfund law.

In addition, many small businesses including dry cleaners, hardware stores, restaurants, service stations, and laboratories contaminate ground water through commercial septic systems. A number of dry cleaner sites in Texas and California were recently identified as major sources for PCE contamination in the subsurface. At many of the sites, the sources include leaks at the surface, but also leaks into the sanitary sewer system, which then leaked NAPLs into shallow ground water. There is evidence that the PCE then biodegraded into TCE and

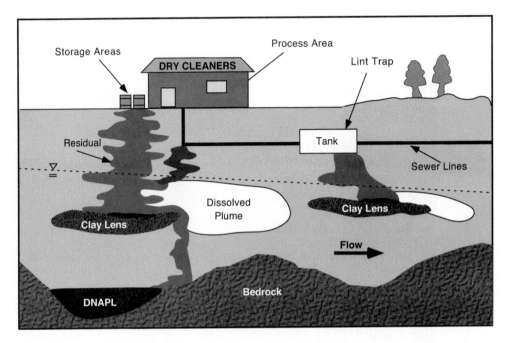

Figure 4.10 Routes of migration that can occur from leaks and faulty equipment at a typical dry cleaner operation.

DCE contaminants in creating off-site plumes. Figure 4.10 depicts the routes of migration that can occur from leaks and faulty equipment at a typical dry cleaner operation.

4.7 AGRICULTURAL WASTES

Pesticides were first identified in ground water less than ten years ago, but now over 35 states report ground water contaminated by pesticides. Recent limited ground water monitoring efforts are only beginning to tell the story of decades of often indiscriminate pesticide use. Pesticides have been widely used for many purposes such as weed control, insecticides, fungicides, and defoliants. There are 50,000 different pesticide products in the U.S. composed of 600 active ingredients. They are used on agricultural fields, on golf courses, lawns and gardens, roadsides, parks, home foundations, and in wood products. They can contaminate ground water through migration through the soil to the water table. Many in use today are biodegradable to some extent. More than 65% of pesticides are applied by aerial spraying and pose a special problem. (Rachel Carson's *Silent Spring*, published in 1962, is a classic book that exposed the serious problem of pesticide use in the U.S.)

Fertilizers from agriculture can also provide a major source of elevated nutrient levels to the subsurface. Nitrogen, potassium, and phosphorous are the three basic fertilizers, but nitrogen represents over half of the total used and is the most likely to leach to ground water, while phosphorous is not very mobile and does not pose a significant threat to ground water. The use of nitrogen on U.S. agricultural lands increased 38% from 1975 to 1981, bringing the total to over 10 million metric tons. In a recent USGS survey, 20% of the sample had a nitrate concentration of over 3 mg/L, and 6% had a nitrate concentration exceeding EPA's 10mg/L limit for drinking water. Nitrates represent the most frequently reported contaminant considered a major threat to ground water quality according to the *National Water Quality Inventory 1988*, but nitrates are also generated in septic tank wastes and in urban runoff.

The production of millions of tons of manure by agricultural sources annually contaminates underlying aquifers with nitrogen, bacteria, viruses, hormones, and salts. Although ground water can be contaminated by relatively small livestock operations if they are located above porous soils, the most obvious threat stems from animal feedlots, where dense livestock populations are confined to small areas. Facilities that treat or dispose of animal wastes likewise pose a threat to local ground water.

Modern irrigation practices can lead to salt contamination and high levels of TDS in underlying aquifers. Irrigation water contains small quantities of salt which, because they are not transpired by crops or evaporated from soil, build up within the soil and eventually leach into ground water. Irrigation return flows that eventually reach rivers and streams may also contribute to ground water contamination, especially in arid areas. In arid and semi-arid areas of the country, excess irrigation water is applied to rid the root zone of potentially crop-devastating salt buildup. Though it may maintain crop productivity, this practice degrades underlying ground water supplies, and is a major problem in the western U.S.

Agricultural sources of contamination to ground water have generally been ignored under hazardous waste legislation, but as urban sprawl continues to expand into former agricultural areas, pesticide, salt, and nitrate issues may again become important in the future.

4.8 LAND APPLICATION AND MINING

Land application is a treatment and disposal method also called land treatment and land farming. The practice involves spreading waste sludges and wastewater generated by public treatment works, industrial operations such as paper, pulp and textile mills, tanneries and canneries, livestock farms, and oil and gas exploration and extraction operations. Wastewater is applied primarily by a spray irrigation system, while sludge from wastewater plants is generally applied to soil as a fertilizer. Oily wastes from refining operations have been land farmed in soil to be broken down by soil microbes. If properly designed and operated, land application recycles nutrients and waters to the soil and aquifer.

Over 20 states reported land application as a major threat to ground water. Contamination occurs when heavy metals, toxic chemicals, nitrogen, and pathogens leach to underlying aquifers. This occurs if the sludge or waste water has not received adequate pretreatment or if the depth to ground water has not been properly considered. In some cases the hazardous materials do not degrade in the subsurface. For example, 40% of California's hazardous wastes were treated by land farming practices. The land application of hazardous wastes has received major attention from EPA in recent years and is no longer an approved technology in most aquifer settings.

The construction techniques, products, and by-products of mining operations have been serious threats to the quality and quantity of nearby aquifers for decades. Surface and underground mining may disrupt natural ground water flow patterns and create the potential for acid mine drainage to seep from the mine. Millions of acres of U.S. land have been mined for coal, copper, uranium, and other minerals. Mine tailings and associated pits also create serious problems as water comes in contact with metals and other wastes. Inactive and abandoned mines as well as active mines can be steady and serious sources of contamination; there are an estimated 67,000 inactive or abandoned mines in the United States.

4.9 RADIOACTIVE CONTAMINANTS

The massive production of radioactive isotopes by weapons and nuclear reactors since World War II has been accompanied by increasing concern about environmental and health effects. The top secret "Manhattan Project", which resulted in the first atomic bomb, created a huge industry for the research, manufacture, and testing of nuclear weapons that, of course, continued into the late 1980s. The legacy of the Cold War has been a nuclear weapons complex that spreads from one coast to the other, and includes some of the most contaminated sites on the planet. At its peak, the complex consisted of 16 major facilities, including vast reservations of land in Nevada, Idaho, Washington, and South Carolina. Figure 4.11 depicts the various sites around the U.S., and indicates some of the processes carried out at the sites, now owned and controlled by the Department of Energy, originally set up in 1977.

Radionuclides are unstable isotopes of elements, including fission products of heavy nuclei such as uranium and plutonium and naturally occurring isotopes such as carbon-14. Large quantities of radioactive wastes have been produced by the nuclear weapons industry in the U.S. The ultimate disposal of radioactive wastes has caused major controversy regarding the widespread use of nuclear power.

Radionuclides emit ionizing radiation in the form of alpha particles, beta particles, and gamma rays. Gamma rays are the most damaging and are a form of electromagnetic radiation, like X-rays, though more energetic. The decay of a specific radionuclide follows a first order decay law, which can be expressed $C = C_0 e^{-\lambda t}$, where C is the activity at time t, C_0 is the initial activity at time 0, and λ, the decay coefficient, is related to the half-life by $t_{1/2} = 0.693/\lambda$. The half-life is defined as the time during which 50% of a given number of radioactive atoms will decay. First-order decay is described in more detail in Chapter 6. Table 4.5 summarizes the major natural and artificial radionuclides typically encountered in water and their associated half-lives.

Figure 4.11 U.S. map of various nuclear sites.

TABLE 4.5 Radionuclides in Water

Radionuclide	Half-life
Naturally occurring and from cosmic reactions	
Carbon 14	5730 years
Silicon 32	~300 years
Potassium 40	~1.4 X10^9 years
Naturally occurring from 238U series	
Radium 226	1620 years
Lead 210	21 years
Thorium 230	75,200 years
Thorium 234	24 days
From reactor and weapons fission	
Strontium 90	28 years
Iodine 131	8 days
Cesium 137	30 years
Barium 140	13 days
Zirconium 95	65 days
Cerium 141	33 days
Strontium 89	51 days
Ruthenium 103	40 days
Krypton 85	10.3 years
Cobalt 60	5.25 years
Manganese 54	310 days
Iron 55	2.7 years
Plutonium 239	24,300 years

The nuclear industry is currently the main generator of radioactive contaminants. Potential sources occur in uranium mining and milling, fuel fabrication, power plant operation, fuel reprocessing and waste disposal. The disposal of civilian radioactive wastes and uranium mill tailings is licensed under the Nuclear Regulatory Commission. High level radioactive wastes from nuclear power plants are currently in temporary storage but will eventually go into an underground repository such as the one planned for Yucca Mountain, Nevada. Low level wastes and medical wastes are currently buried in shallow landfills.

Unless radioactive wastes are properly handled in well-designed sites, the potential for migration to ground water exists. The most serious problems with radioactive contamination exist at a number of facilities including Oak Ridge, Tennessee; the Hanford Site in Washington State; the Savannah River Site in Georgia; and the Idaho National Engineering Laboratory. The Hanford Site contains a ground water plume of tritium that is more than 12 miles long and 8 miles wide and flows into the Columbia River. Figure 4.12 shows barrels of transuranic waste that contain traces of plutonium, located at the East Burial Grounds at the Savannah River Site. More than 300,000 barrels of these wastes are stored around the country. These and other associated nuclear weapons facilities are the subject of massive environmental studies and remediation efforts for both ground water and soils or building contamination.

Figure 4.12 Barrels of transuranic waste. Source: DOE, 1995.

The health hazards associated with radiation leaks are well known but the risks are difficult to assess at low levels of exposure. Even though the Department of Energy is spending large sums of money to address environmental problems, the true impact of radioactive waste disposal may not be known for decades. An excellent review of the environmental legacy of the nuclear weapons industry can be found in a 1995 DOE report, "Closing the Circle on the Splitting of the Atom."

4.10 MILITARY SOURCES OF CONTAMINATION

According to the Citizen's Clearinghouse for Hazardous Waste, the U.S. military branches may be the largest generators of hazardous waste in the country, producing over 1 billion pounds per year, more than that produced by the top five civilian chemical companies combined. Numerous spills, leaks, and landfills have been discovered on military bases throughout the country and are the subject of intense investigation and remediation efforts. The U.S. Air Force alone estimates more than 4,300 waste sites and spills on more than 100 of their bases. Some of these military sites are currently on the EPA national priority list as Superfund sites. Many of the sites have contaminant plumes associated with all of the contaminants already discussed, including fuels, chlorinated solvents, trace metals, and other organics.

One of these air force sites is Plant 44 in Tucson, Arizona, where missiles and guidance systems were manufactured, and planes were repaired and painted. The operations at the site created a TCE and chromium plume of contamination that extends six miles in length and half a mile in width, and flows through the city of Tucson. Many of the water supply wells for the city have been contaminated with TCE and associated daughter products, and have been taken out of service over the years. The site has been the subject of major site investigations, remediation, and evaluation involving the air force, EPA, and the Tucson Airport authority. The Hughes Plant 44 site is currently being remediated with a one of the largest pump and treat systems in the U.S., designed to withdraw and treat up to 5000 gal/min of water from the aquifer located over 100 ft below the surface. This site is described in more detail in Chapter 10.

Hill Air Force Base (AFB) in Utah has several areas of environmental damage, including Operable Unit 1 (OU 1), a former chemical disposal pit/fire training area. This base is one of the premier repair facilities for the U.S. Air Force, and over the years, massive dumping of chlorinated solvents and fuels has occurred at several locations on base. One area on the base had a significant BTEX plume, which impacted an area of housing in the downgradient direction. The area of OU 2 was severely contaminated with DNAPL near the base boundary and was the subject of extensive testing of surfactant remediation techniques in 1996⁻97 (Hirasaki et al., 1998). Finally, a major soil vapor extraction test was demonstrated at the base, and is described in more detail in Chapter 9 (El Beshry et al., 1998). The extensive contamination and the security of a military installation at Hill AFB provided an ideal site where many experiments involving advanced remediation methods could be tested.

In the summer of 1996, nine individual cells were constructed within a contaminated NAPL zone of the shallow aquifer at the site (Bedient et al., 1999). The area at OU 1 is contaminated with a light nonaqueous phase mixture of chlorinated solvents and fuel hydrocarbons, which are present in residual and free phase across the site. Nine enhanced aquifer remediation technologies were demonstrated in side-by-side tests at the Hill AFB site. The demonstrations were performed inside 3 m x 5 m cells isolated from the surrounding shallow aquifer by steel sheet piling. The technologies demonstrated were designed to manipulate the solubility, mobility, and volatility of the contaminants in order to enhance the aquifer remediation over a standard "Pump-and-Treat" system. Over 80,000 samples of water and soil were collected as part of tracer tests, soil flushing demonstrations, and routine characterization efforts at OU 1.

Hill AFB's OU 1 site was chosen because all nine technologies could be demonstrated side-by-side, within a similar hydrogeology with similar contamination levels. To facilitate comparisons among the nine technologies being demonstrated, the cell instrumentation, characterization, and basic study methodology were standardized prior to the beginning of field work. Each of the studies was conducted in a test cell designed to separate the test area from the surrounding environment. The demonstrated technologies facilitated contaminant removal through dissolution, emulsification, or mobilization in ground water or through volatilization and enhanced bioremediation when air delivery systems were used. In some cases, this was the first time that remediation approach had been demonstrated in the field. More details and results from surfactant (Sabatini et al., 1999) and cosolvent (Rao et al., 1997) tests are described in the advanced remediation section of Chapter 13.

4.11 CLASSIFICATION OF ORGANIC COMPOUNDS

In the past 20 years, organic compounds in ground water have come to be recognized as one of the major threats to human health. This section will introduce some of the major classes and some of the most important compounds found in ground water. More detailed coverage on organic compounds in ground water can be found in Pankow and Cherry (1996), Manahan (1991), Sawyer et al. (1994), Schwarzenbach et al. (1993), and Fetter (1999).

Organic chemistry deals with the chemistry of carbon compounds; carbon is a unique element in that it forms four covalent bonds and is capable of bonding to other carbon atoms, with single, double, or triple bonds. It is this characteristic of carbon that gives rise to the possibility of great diversity in the physical and chemical properties of organic compounds. The simplest organic compounds are hydrocarbons consisting of carbon and hydrogen alone. The traditional approach to classifying organic compounds involves defining functional groups, which include a simple combination of two or more of the following atoms: C, H, O, S, N, P. Domenico and Schwartz (1998) present a condensed scheme of classification consisting of 16 major classes (Table 4.6) and is a useful approach for organizing organic contaminants in ground water. Elements such as O, N, S, P, H, and Cl can bond

TABLE 4.6 Classification of Organic Compounds

1. Miscellaneous Nonvolatile Compounds

2. Halogenated Hydrocarbons

Aliphatic   Aromatic

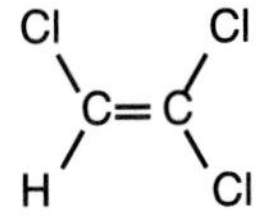

Trichloroethylene   Chlorobenzene

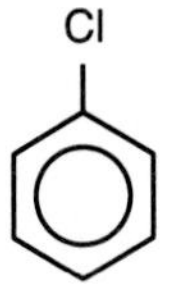

3. Amino Acids

Basic Structure   Aspartic acid

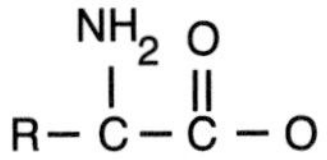

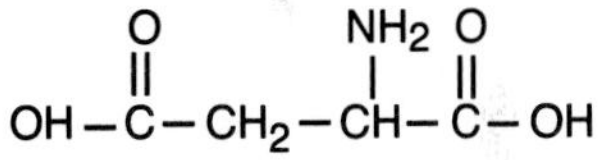

4. Phosphorous Compounds

Basic Structure   Malathion

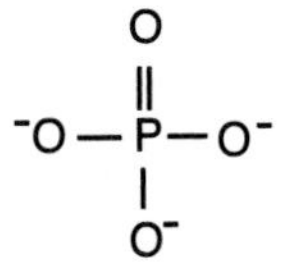

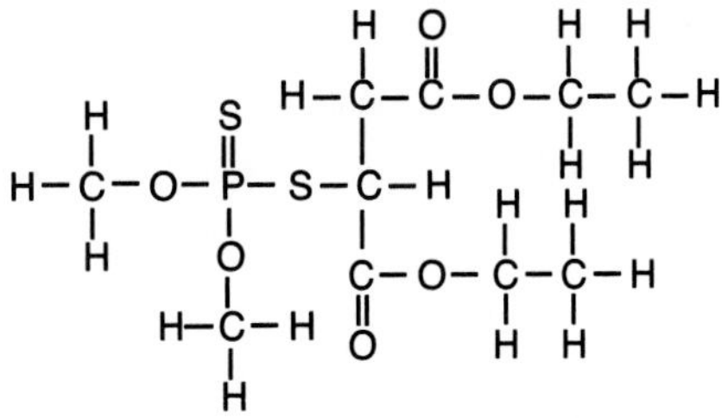

5. Organometallic Compounds

Tetraethyllead

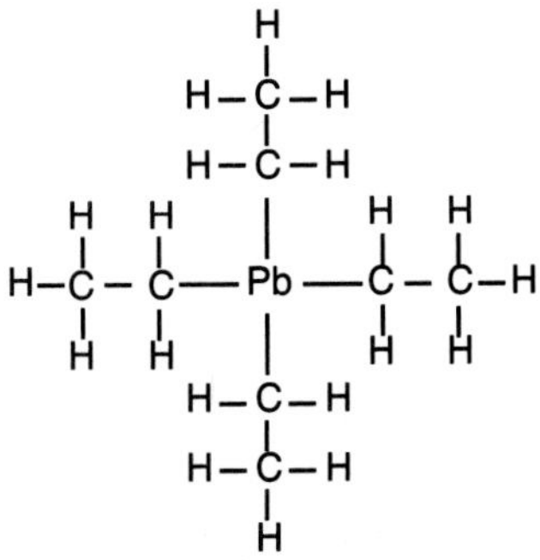

6. Carboxylic Acid

Basic Structure

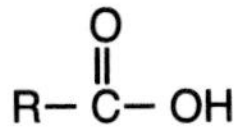

Acetic acid

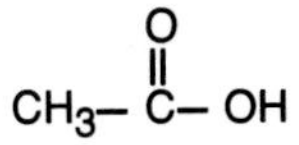

TABLE 4.6 Classification of Organic Compounds (continued)

7. Phenols

Basic Structure	Cresol

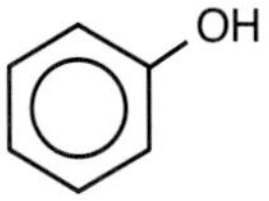

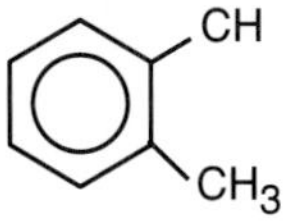

8. Amines

Basic Structure

Aromatic	Aliphatic

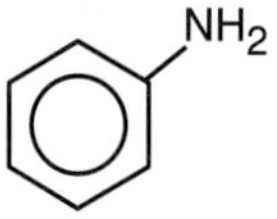

$CH_3-\overset{\overset{\displaystyle CH_3}{|}}{N}-H$

Dimethylamine

9. Ketones

Basic Structure	Acetone

$R-\overset{\overset{\displaystyle O}{\|}}{C}-R'$ $CH_3-\overset{\overset{\displaystyle O}{\|}}{C}-CH_3$

10. Aldehydes

Basic Structure	Formaldehyde

$R-\overset{\overset{\displaystyle O}{\|}}{C}-H$ $H-\overset{\overset{\displaystyle O}{\|}}{C}-H$

11. Alcohols

Basic Structure	Methanol
$R-OH$	CH_3-OH

12. Esters

Basic Structure	Vinyl acetate

$R-\overset{\overset{\displaystyle O}{\|}}{C}-OR'$ $H_2C=CH-O-\underset{\underset{\displaystyle O}{\|}}{C}-CH_3$

13. Ethers

Basic Structure	1,4-Dioxane
$C-O-C$	

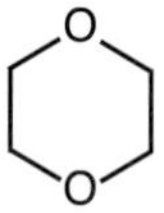

14. Polynuclear Aromatic Hydrocarbons

Phenanthrene

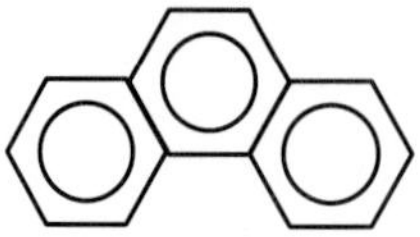

TABLE 4.6 Classification of Organic Compounds (continued)

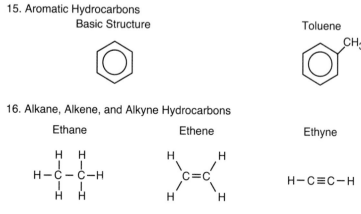

15. Aromatic Hydrocarbons
    Basic Structure
                                Toluene

16. Alkane, Alkene, and Alkyne Hydrocarbons
    Ethane   Ethene   Ethyne

R = aliphatic backbone

with carbon at any of four locations. Other groups such as OH and CH_3 can also bond with carbon to form many other compounds of interest. Hydrocarbons can be divided into aromatics, which contain a benzene ring, and aliphatics, which are compounds of C and H that are linked to a straight or branched carbon chain.

4.11.1 Aliphatic Hydrocarbons

The aliphatic hydrocarbons with more than one carbon atom can be classified as alkanes (single bonds), alkenes (double bonds) or alkynes (triple bonds). Straight chain alkanes include methane (CH_4), ethane (H_3CCH_3), propane ($H_3CCH_2CH_3$), butane, pentane, and hexane. These compounds are known as saturated hydrocarbons or paraffins. Alkanes can also have branched chains creating isomers with the same formula but with different properties. They conform to the general formula C_nH_{2n+2}, where n is the number of carbon atoms. Cycloalkanes are characterized by a ring structure that contains single C–C bonds such as cyclopropane and cyclohexane.

4.11.2 Aromatic Hydrocarbons

Aromatic hydrocarbons are compounds with a molecular structure based on that of the benzene ring, C_6H_6. These compounds are a major constituent of petroleum and related products. Typical benzene-related compounds are shown in Figure 4.13 where the benzene molecule consists of six carbon and six hydrogen atoms in a cyclical form. The ring in the center represents a delocalized cloud of electrons. The carbon atoms in benzene are also capable of bonding to functional groups, and isomerism is possible. Nomenclature includes numbering the ring from 1 to 6 starting at the top of the ring. More than one functional group may

Name	Structure	Molecular Weight	Solubility in Water	Soil-Water Partition Coefficient
Benzene		78.11	1780 mg/L	97
Toluene	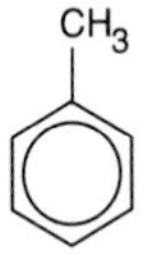	92.1	500 mg/L	242
Xylene, ortho	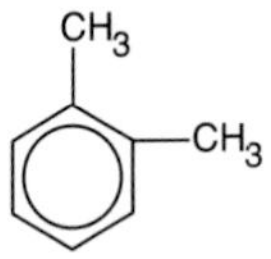	106.17	170 mg/L	363
Xylene, meta	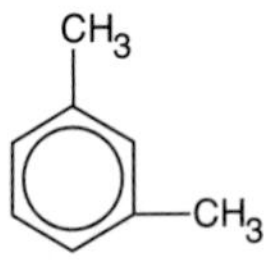	106.17	173 mg/L	182
Xylene, para		106.17	200 mg/L	331
Ethyl benzene	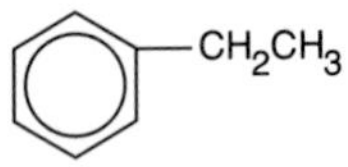	106.17	150 mg/L	622

Figure 4.13 Benzene related compounds.

result in *ortho-*, *meta-*, or *para-* isomers, as in the case of xylene, which contains two methyl groups (Figure 4.10).

When several of the benzene rings are joined together, polycyclic aromatic hydrocarbons (PAH), such as naphthalene (2 benzene rings), phenanthrene (3 benzene rings), and benzo-a-pyrene (5 benzene rings) are formed. Figure 4.14 shows several of the important PAH's in ground water. These compounds are found in petroleum products, asphalt, coal tar, creosote and result from the incomplete combustion of fossil fuels. If the benzene ring is joined to another group, it may be referred to as a functional group, phenyl, and in combination with chlorine these compounds are called polychlorinated biphenyls (PCBs). They are extremely resistant to chemical, thermal, or biological degradation and tend to persist in the

Name	Structure	Molecular Weight	Solubility in Water	Soil-Water Partition Coefficient
Naphthalene	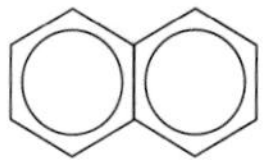	128.16	31.7 mg/L	1300
Acenaphthene	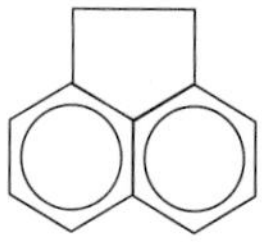	154.21	7.4 mg/L	2580
Ancenaphthylene	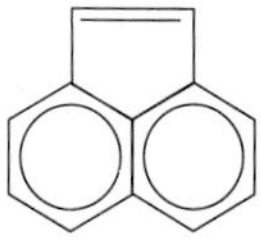	152.2	3.93 mg/L	3814
Fluorene	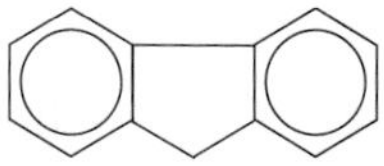	166.2	1.98 mg/L	5835
Fluoranthene	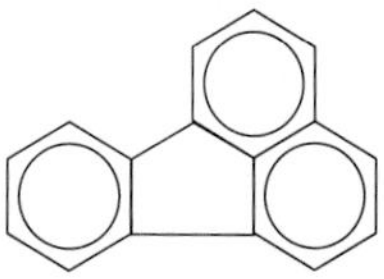	202	0.275 mg/L	19000
Phenanthrene	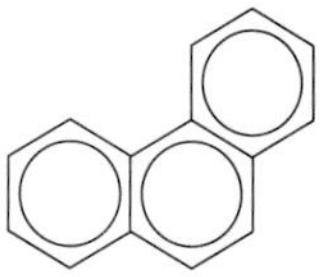	178.23	1.29 mg/L	23000
Anthracene	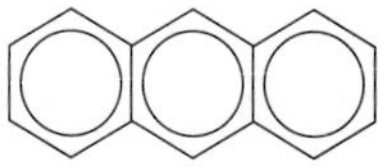	178.23	0.073 mg/L	26000

Figure 4.14 Structure and properties of some polycyclic aromatic hydrocarbons (PAHs).

environment. Because of human health and environmental effects, the manufacture of PCBs was banned in the U.S. in 1977. PCBs associated with the energy industry comprise some of the most serious contaminants to soils and ground water.

Alkenes are unsaturated hydrocarbons and have a carbon-carbon double bond with the general formula C_nH_{2n}, and include such compounds as ethene and propene, also called ethylene and propylene. Alkenes are referred to as olefins or the ethylene series. If functional groups are present, their position is indicated by the carbon atom to which they are bonded, and structural isomers can exist. Many of the chlorinated solvents (such as trichlorothylene) are of great concern as ground water contaminants at industrial sites. The acetylene series (alkynes) have triple bonds between two adjacent carbon atoms.

Phenols are characterized by a benzene ring with one attached hydroxyl group. They originate in ground water mostly as contaminants from industrial wastes or biocides. Phenol is a common ground water contaminant due to its many industrial uses and can also occur naturally with decomposing organic matter. Cresols have a methyl group and OH attached to the benzene ring and are used for the coal tar refining and for wood preservation. For example, lysol is a mixture of cresols and is sold as a household disinfectant. Chlorophenols are used as wood and leather preservatives and as antimildew agents. Phenol, in general, has acute toxic effects on bacteria and has been used as a disinfectant and germacide. Pentachlorophenol has been found at a number of creosote wood preserving sites and represents a highly toxic and nonbiodegradable compound.

Benzene is a carcinogen and inhaled benzene is readily absorbed by blood and is strongly taken up by fatty tissues. Benzene can be converted to phenol by an oxidation reaction in the liver that is responsible for the unique toxicity of benzene, which involves damage to bone marrow, and is known to cause leukemia. Benzene is also a skin irritant and can affect the central nervous system. Toluene is classified as moderately toxic and is much less toxic than benzene because it is readily excreted from the body. (Manahan, 1991).

4.11.3 Alcohols

Alcohols have one or more OH groups, are miscible with water, and have the potential for significant mobility; however, they are readily biodegraded. Alcohols are considered the primary oxidation product of hydrocarbons. At many industrial sites, alcohols are discharged into ground water and can act as solvents for other organics. Common alcohols include methanol (CH_3OH), ethanol (C_2H_5OH), 1-propanol, and isopropyl (C_3H_7OH). Selected alcohols are being used experimentally as cosolvents to help solubilize NAPLs from the subsurface. Aldehydes are the oxidation products of primary alcohols, and ketones are the oxidation products of secondary alcohols.

4.11.4 Halogenated Hydrocarbons

Halogenated hydrocarbons are one of the largest and most important groups of contaminants found in ground water. This group consists of both aliphatic and aromatic subclasses and is characterized by the presence of one or more halogen atoms (Cl, Br, F). Included in the aliphatic group are solvents such as methylene chloride, chloroform, tetrachloroethylene (PCE), trichloroethylene (TCE), 1,2 dichloroethylene (1,2 DCE), and vinyl chloride. Many of the halogenated ethenes have been found in large quantities in ground water, associated with industrial sites where solvents, cleansers, and degreasers were used. Many of these compounds in the halogenated group are biodegradation products from other chlorinated compounds in the production of plastics (Chapter 7 and Figure 4.15).

The aromatic group of chlorinated pesticides includes DDD, DDE, DDT, and 2,4-D and 2,4,5-T compounds. The latter two are herbicides and were used as defoliants in Vietnam. Dioxin (2,3,7,8-dioxin), an extremely toxic organic to humans, is a byproduct contaminant of 2,4,5-T production, and has been found at sites where chlorinated organics were burned. Organic phosphorus pesticides include malathion, which is toxic to insects but not to mammals.

The specific toxicity of halogenated hydrocarbons varies with the compound but most affect the central nervous system. Carbon tetrachloride, for example, is a systemic poison that affects the nervous system, the intestinal tract, liver and kidneys. Over the years the FDA compiled a grim record of toxic effects and eventually banned its household use in 1970. Vinyl chloride has been used widely in the production of PVC materials and exposure can affect the central nervous system, respiratory system, liver, blood and lymph systems. Most notably, vinyl chloride is a carcinogen. The dichlorobenzenes are irritants that affect the respiratory system, liver, skin and eyes, through inhalation or contact. Polychlorinated biphenyls (PCBs) have been widely used in the electrical industry as hydraulic fluids in transformers. They represent extremely persistent environmental pollutants with a strong tendency to undergo bioaccumulation in lipid tissue (Manahan, 1991).

The use and disposal of chlorinated solvents by industries involved in electronics manufacturing, metal degreasing, engine repair, paint stripping, and plastics have created a number of serious chlorinated organics plumes, especially in the western U.S. The Hughes Plant 44 Superfund site in Arizona is an example of a site seriously contaminated with halogenated hydrocarbons (see Chapter 10).

4.11.5 Other Organic Compounds

Table 4.6 indicates other classes of organic compounds. Esters are the result of the combination of an alcohol with a carboxylic acid. Esters are used as flavorings, perfumes, solvents and paints. One important class of esters is the phthalates, which are used to improve the flexibility of various plastics. Ethers have an oxygen atom strongly bonded between two carbon atoms and thus have relatively low toxicities.

Organic compounds that contain nitrogen are common in industry and are used for the manufacturing of explosives. Aniline and diphenylamine are aromatic compounds that contain nitrogen in aromatic rings. Trinitrotoluene (2,4,6-TNT) is the main ingredient of military explosives, and has been reported as a soil contaminant in areas where munitions are manufactured.

Name	Structure	Uses and Other Sources
Trichloromethane (chloroform)	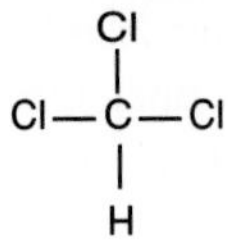	Liquid used in manufacture of anesthetics, pharmaceuticals, fluorocarbon refrigerants and plasics. Used as solvent and insecticide. Formed from methane when chlorinating drinking water.
Vinyl chloride (chloroethene)	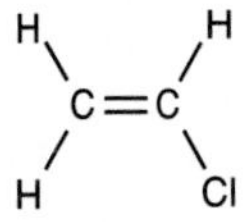	Gas used in the manufacture of polyvinyl chloride. End product of microbial degradation of chlorinated ethenes.
Chloroethane	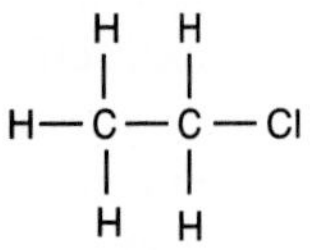	Liquid used to manufacture tetraethyl lead. Degradation product of chlorinated ethanes.
1,2-Dichloroethane	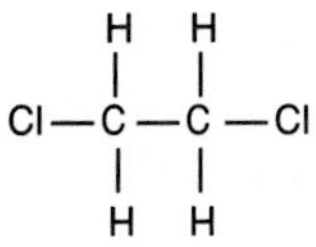	Liquid used to manufacture vinyl chloride. Degradation product of trichloroethane.
Trichloroethene (Trichloroethylene)	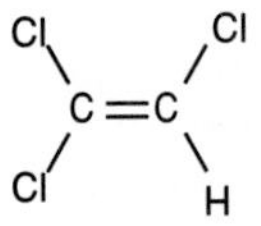	Solvent used in dry cleaning and metal degreasing. Organic synthesis. Degradation product of tetrachloroethene.
Tetrachloroethene (perchloroethene) (perchloroethylene)	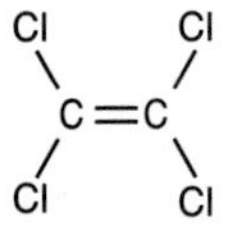	Solvent used in dry cleaning and metal degreasing. Used to remove soot from industrial boilers. Used in manufacture of paint removers and printing inks.
1,2-Dibromo-3-chloropropane (DBCP)	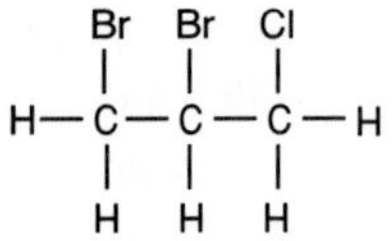	Soil fumigant to kill nematodes. Intermediate in organic synthesis.
o-Dichlorobenzene (1,2-dichlorobenzene)	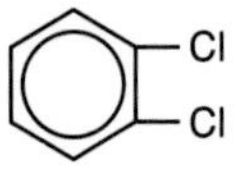	Chemical intermediate. Solvent. Fumigant and insecticide. Used for industrial odor control. Found in sewage form odor control chemicals used in toilets.

Figure 4.15 Chlorinated organics found in hazardous waste.

The above review of organic compounds has been very brief and is not designed to address details contained in texts on organic or environmental chemistry. More details on organic compounds, their degradation, and reactions in ground water can be found in Sawyer, McCarty, and Parkin (1994), Pankow and Cherry (1996), Fetter (1999), and Manahan (1991). Chapter 7 presents important chemical reactions, adsorption processes, and biodegradation mechanisms that affect organic contaminants in the subsurface.

4.12 INORGANIC COMPOUNDS IN GROUND WATER

The quality of water is a direct result of the reactions that occur between sources of contamination and other compounds that it may contact. In ground water, chemistry and chemical processes are important primarily because ground water is in contact with soil and rocks that contain a variety of minerals. In addition, the carbon and the nitrogen cycles contribute greatly to the quality of ground water. For instance, rainfall may come in contact with high levels of carbon dioxide in the atmosphere and become acidic. There is potential for this acidic water to infiltrate to ground water and dissolve minerals as it encounters them. Because of the processes that affect it, ground water naturally contains dissolved inorganic ions. A list of major and minor inorganic constituents and trace metals of ground water is presented in Table 4.7.

TABLE 4.7 Dissolved Constituents in Ground Water Classified According to Relative Abundance.

Major Constituents (greater than 5 mg/L)	
Bicarbonate	Magnesium
Calcium	Silicon
Carbonic Acid	Sodium
Chloride	Sulfate

Minor Constituents (0.1–5.0 mg/L)	
Boron	Nitrate
Carbonate	Potassium
Fluoride	Strontium
Iron	

Trace Constituents (less than 0.1 mg/L)	
Aluminum	Lithium
Antimony	Manganese
Arsenic	Molybdenum
Barium	Nickel
Beryllium	Phosphate
Bromide	Radium
Cadmium	Selenium
Cesium	Silver
Chromium	Tin
Copper	Uranium
Iodine	Zinc
Lead	

Chemical parameters of particular importance to ground water constituents and contaminants include solubility product, pH, and oxidation-reduction reactions (Chapter 7). More detailed information may be found in Freeze and Cherry (1979), Domenico and Schwartz (1998), and Fetter (1999), or in Environmental Chemistry texts such as Manahan (1991) or Sawyer, McCarty, and Parkin (1994).

Of the inorganic contaminants in ground water, those of greatest concern are nitrates, ammonia, and trace metals. Nitrates in ground water originate from nitrate sources on land and are associated with fertilizers and the disposal of sewage waste, especially associated with faulty septic tanks. Feedlots are also a major source of nitrate in ground water, especially in rural areas. Nitrate concentrations are not limited by solubility constraints, resulting in high mobility of nitrates in ground water. It has been known since 1940 that ground waters containing high nitrate levels could cause methemoglobinemia in infants, and based on data from the mid-western U.S., EPA set the limit for nitrate–N not to exceed 10 mg/L in public water supplies.

Arsenic, cadmium, chromium, lead, zinc, and mercury are metal pollutants of major concern in ground water. Most of them arise from industrial practices and discharges from mining, metal plating, plumbing, coal, gasoline, and pesticide related industries. Many of these metals are very toxic to humans, especially cadmium, lead, and mercury. Cadmium and zinc are common water and sediment pollutants in areas associated with industrial installations. A major source of lead comes from leaded gasoline and lead piping. Mercury is associated with discarded batteries, laboratory products, and lawn fungicides. Arsenic is produced through phosphate mining and is a by-product of copper, gold, and lead refining.

These metals are of concern in ground water due to their unique acid-base and solubility characteristics in aerobic systems. Metals occur as cations in ground water of low pH and have a greater mobility in acidic waters. Mobility tends to decrease as the solid phase is approached. Mobility of metals is also increased by complexation of ions, and nearly all the trace metals in ground water are influenced by redox conditions, especially when complexation occurs. Heavy metals are particularly toxic in their chemically combined forms and some, notably mercury, are toxic in the elemental form.

Chromium is perhaps the most mobile of all metals in ground water, and contaminant plumes have been identified and sampled at a number of industrial facilities where metal plating was a predominant activity. A classic plume on Long Island, New York, was reported and modeled by Wilson and Miller (1978). More recently the U.S. Air Force Hughes Plant 44 Site in Tucson, Arizona had a major chromium plume migrating more than 150 ft below the surface in a sand and gravel aquifer, but most of it was remediated via a pump and treat system.

4.13 A TYPICAL INDUSTRIAL WASTE SITE

A typical abandoned industrial site, which has source areas that are leaking organic contaminants, is shown in Figure 4.16. Possible source areas consist of a process area for chemicals

and wastes, drum storage areas, an old drum burial area, an unlined landfill for solid and liquid wastes, surface pits, an injection well for liquid wastes and brines, and leaking industrial
sewer lines. A great deal of effort was expended in the 1980s searching aerial photographs,
state permit records, and ground water quality records to find active and abandoned industrial
waste sites. Many of the older or abandoned sites that were eventually put on the Superfund
list resembled the site shown in Figure 4.16. The presence of surface pits or impoundments,
drums stored above ground, distressed vegetation from contaminated runoff, and fish kills in
surface streams were all indicators of a serious problem at the site.

Source areas often leaked out organic and hazardous contaminants into shallow subsurface aquifers. Because of the slow rate of velocity in ground water compared to surface water
(ft/day vs. ft/sec), it can take years or decades for contaminant plumes to migrate from a
source area to a receptor off-site where contamination is first observed.

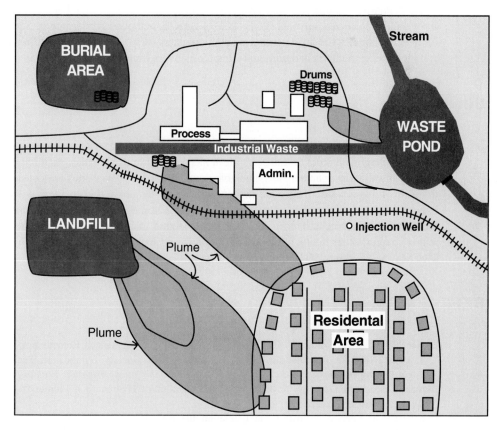

Figure 4.16 Typical contaminated industrial site.

Plumes of contamination are often associated with leaking drums, landfills, burial areas, ponds, and leaking pipe systems. Oftentimes, these plumes can extend for hundreds or thousands of feet from the source area, and impact neighborhoods, commercial areas, or receiving streams. Note the ground water plumes emanating from the process area, the landfill, and the drum storage areas. In the 1980s, these plumes became the subject of intense investigation and remedial activity, designed to cleanup shallow aquifers that had been contaminated with organics. Many of the hazardous waste sites were discovered when contaminant plumes finally arrived at receptor wells or impacted surface streams.

Mechanisms of transport in the subsurface include vertical migration through the unsaturated zone, advection and dispersion in the saturated zone, adsorption to soils, and possibly biodegradation under the right chemical conditions (see Chapters 6, 7 and 8). The most commonly found organic contaminants in ground water from industrial sites include the most mobile and soluble of the compounds listed in Table 4.3 and Table 7.1 in Chapter 7. These primarily include the fuel aromatics (benzene, toluene, ethyl benzene, and the xylenes), and chlorinated solvents (PCE, TCE, 1,2-DCE, and others described in Section 4.11). Chapter 5 addresses the investigation of contaminated sites and describes drilling, sampling, and monitoring methods in detail, and Chapter 6 covers transport mechanisms in detail.

SUMMARY

Chapter 4 has reviewed the main sources and types of ground water contamination. In particular, underground storage tanks, septic tanks, agricultural activities, municipal landfills, military installations, nuclear sites, and abandoned hazardous waste sites are considered major threats to ground water. These are described in some detail in the chapter, with examples indicated for each of the major source categories. The nomenclature and characteristics of the most common organic and inorganic compounds found in ground water are addressed briefly in this chapter; other major references on organic and inorganic compounds include Sawyer, McCarty, and Parkin (1994), Pankow and Cherry (1996), and Fetter (1999).

REFERENCES

Bedient, P. B., A. W. Holder, C. G. Enfield, and A. L. Wood, "Enhanced Remediation Demonstrations at Hill AFB: Introduction," in American Chemical Society Symposium Series Volume, *Field Testing of Innovative Subsurface Remediation and Characterization Technologies*, 1999

Bureau of Economic Geology, "Extent, Mass, and Duration of Hydrocarbon Plumes from LPSTs in Texas," Austin, Texas, 1997.

Department of Energy, "Closing the Circle on the Splitting of the Atom," Washington, DC, 1995.

Domenico, P. A. and F. W. Schwartz, *Physical and Chemical Hydrogeology*, 2nd Ed., New York, John Wiley and Sons, 1998.

El-Beshry, M. Z., J. S. Gierke, and P. B. Bedient, "Comparison of Predictions of a 3-Dimensional Numerical Simulator to Data from a Full-Scale Soil Vapor Extraction System at a Jet-Fuel Contaminated Site," submitted to the *ASCE Journal of Environmental Eng.*, May 1998.

Fetter, C.W., *Applied Hydrogeology,* 3rd ed. Columbus, OH, Merrill Publishing Company, 1994.

Fetter, C.W., *Contaminant Hydrogeology,* 2nd Ed., Upper Saddle River, NJ, Prentice Hall, 1999.

Freeze, R. A., and J. A. Cherry, *Groundwater*, Englewood Cliffs, NJ, Prentice-Hall, 1979.

Harr, Jonathan, *A Civil Action,* New York, First Vintage Books, 1996.

Hirasaki. G. J., C. A. Miller, R. Szafranski, J. B. Lawson, and N. Akiya, "Surfactant Foam Process for Aquifer Remediation," SPE paper no. 37257, presented at the SPE International Symposium on Oil Field Chemistry, Houston, TX, February 18-21,1997.

Jorgensen, E. P., Ed., *The Poisoned Well*, Chapter 3, Washington, D.C., Island Press, 1989.

Konikow, L. F., D. W. Thompson, "Groundwater Contamination and Aquifer Reclamation at the Rocky Mountain Arsenal, Colorado," *Studies in Geophysics, Groundwater Contamination*, Washington, D.C., National Academy Press, 1984.

Lawrence Berkeley Laboratories, California LUFT Historical Case Analyses, 1995.

Manahan, S. E., *Environmental Chemistry*, 5th ed., Chelsea, MI, Lewis Publishers, 1991.

Office of Technology Assessment (OTA), *Protecting the Nation's Groundwater from Contamination*, Report, 1984.

Pankow, J. F., *Aquatic Chemistry Concepts*, Chelsea, MI, Lewis Publishers, 1991.

Pankow, J. F. and J. A. Cherry, *Dense Chlorinated Solvents*, Canada, Waterloo Press, 1996.

Rao, P. S. C., M. D. Annable, R. K. Sillan, D. Dai, K. Hatfield, W. D. Graham, A. L. Wood, and C. G. Enfield, "Field-Scale Evaluation of In Situ Cosolvent Flushing for Enhanced Aquifer Remediation," *Water Resources Res.*, 33 (12), 2673–2686, 1997.

Sabatini, D. A., J. H. Harwell, and R. C. Knox, "Surfactant Selection Criteria for Enhanced Subsurface Remediation," Brusseau et al., eds., *Innovative Subsurface Remediation: Field Testing of Physical, Chemical and Characterization Technologies,* ACS Symposium Series, in press, 1999.

Sawyer, C. N., P. L. McCarty, and G. F. Parkin, *Chemistry for Environmental Engineering*, 4th Ed., New York, McGraw Hill, 1994.

Schwarzenbach, R. P., P. M. Gschwend, and D. M. Imboden, Environmental Organic Chemistry, New York, John S. Wiley and Sons, 1993.

U.S. EPA, the National Water Quality Inventory - 1988 Report to Congress, 1990.

Wilson, J. D. and P. J. Miller, April, "Two-Dimensional Plume in Uniform Ground-Water Flow," *Journal of the Hydraulics Division,* 1978.

Zheng, C. and G. D. Bennett, *Applied Contaminant Transport Modeling: Theory and Practice,* New York, Van Nostrand Reinhold, 1995.

CHAPTER 5

HYDROGEOLOGIC SITE INVESTIGATIONS

ROBERT S. LEE
JOHN A. CONNOR

5.1 INTRODUCTION

The purpose of hydrogeologic site investigations is to characterize soil and ground water pollution problems in sufficient detail to facilitate design of a cost-effective corrective action program. For this purpose, the site investigation entails measurement of the physical parameters that control subsurface contaminant transport at a given site. Geologic, hydrologic, and chemical data must be acquired and integrated to define the nature and extent of soil and ground water contamination and the potential for migration of contaminants within the natural ground water flow system. To the extent practical, the remedy should be anticipated at the outset of an investigation so that design-basis information necessary for development of the corrective action program is obtained in a timely and cost-effective manner.

The preceding chapters of this book have reviewed the general principles of ground water occurrence and flow within geologic formations and the nature of the most common ground water contaminants. In this chapter, the engineering procedures involved in the acquisition and interpretation of ground water flow and contaminant information will be addressed. The following sections outline a systematic approach to planning and implementing soil and ground water contamination studies and summarize engineering standards for data evaluation and presentation.

5.2 DEVELOPMENT OF CONCEPTUAL SITE MODEL

Hydrogeologic processes are, by nature, complex, due to the heterogeneities of geologic formations and the transient effects of aquifer recharge and discharge phenomena. Additional complexity arises from the presence of contaminants that may be irregularly distributed in, and reacting with, subsurface formations and ground water. Consequently, detailed characterization of contaminant distribution and transport patterns throughout every inch of an aquifer system is impractical. From an engineering perspective, our objective is therefore to define subsurface contaminant transport processes to the degree necessary to allow us to design effective measures for control or reversal of these processes, as needed to protect public health and the environment.

Ultimately, protection of drinking water resources may require us to extract or "mine" the contaminated ground water mass from the affected aquifer. Therefore, it is helpful to approach a ground water contaminant delineation study in much the same manner as prospecting for hydrocarbons or precious metals. We do not need to know each twist and turn of every minor "ore" seam, but we do want to know how wide and how deep the play runs and, because our "ore" is a fluid, which way it is moving and how fast.

The hydrogeologic site investigation is the procedure by which we develop our understanding or our "working model" of contaminant plume migration within the ground water flow regime. In all cases, this model of the subsurface environment is constructed of three principal components of information:

1. **Geology**: the physical framework within which subsurface fluids collect and flow;
2. **Hydrology**: the movement of fluids through this physical framework; and
3. **Chemistry**: the nature of the chemical constituents that are entrained in this flow system and the chemical and physical interactions between the contaminants and the subsurface formation and ground water that may be occurring.

We build our model of the site by systematically addressing each of these principal components in turn. First, we must characterize the stratigraphic profile beneath the site and identify those strata serving as potential conduits for fluid flow and the geologic features that may influence the movement and accumulation of nonaqueous phase liquids (NAPLs). Second, we must measure the fluid hydraulic head distribution within the zone of saturation to determine the actual rate and direction of ground water movement through these conduits. Third, water samples are collected and analyzed to map the lateral and vertical extent of contaminant migration within the ground water flow regime.

There is significant overlap in the acquisition of these three classes of data, and in practice, they are collected simultaneously. For example, a soil boring may be drilled to characterize the geology of the site; it provides soil samples for laboratory analysis of contaminant concentration; and it may be converted to a monitoring well to permit collection of ground water samples and hydrologic data. A well designed site investigation will maximize the relevant information collected during each step of the work program. It is then the job of the project engineer or scientist to sort this information into a meaningful and accurate picture of subsurface ground water flow and contaminant transport processes.

5.3 STRATEGY FOR HYDROGEOLOGIC SITE INVESTIGATIONS

5.3.1 Overview and General Considerations

As a practical matter, site investigation workplans usually represent a compromise between the ideal of knowing as much as possible about a site and the realities imposed by a finite budget. For the purpose of economy and efficiency, every field and laboratory measurement conducted during the investigation must contribute to the conceptual model of the site. The key is to design a work program that provides the necessary data by making the maximum use of the available resources.

To achieve project objectives in a cost-effective manner, a clear strategy for mapping the contaminant zones must be established prior to commencement of field or laboratory work. At the outset, all available site information concerning subsurface geology, ground water flow, and the nature, extent, and timing of the contaminant release should be assembled to guide the selection of sampling locations. Data quality objectives and appropriate sampling and testing technologies must be identified to ensure collection of data that meet not only the engineering, but also the regulatory requirements of the project.

As a basis for a site investigation strategy, all subsurface contaminant problems should be viewed as two distinct zones of contamination: (1) contaminant source materials and contaminated soils in the unsaturated soil (or rock) zone; and (2) nonaqueous phase liquids (NAPLs) and/or ground water containing dissolved contaminants within the zone of saturation (Figure 5.1). For practical purposes, we can define the vertical boundary between these two zones as the surface of the uppermost water bearing unit beneath the site (e.g., a water-saturated stratum with hydraulic conductivity, $K \geq 1 \times 10^{-4}$ cm/sec). These two zones differ significantly in terms of their operant mechanisms of contaminant transport and the requisite corrective actions, and therefore should be addressed individually in the course of the hydrogeologic site investigation.

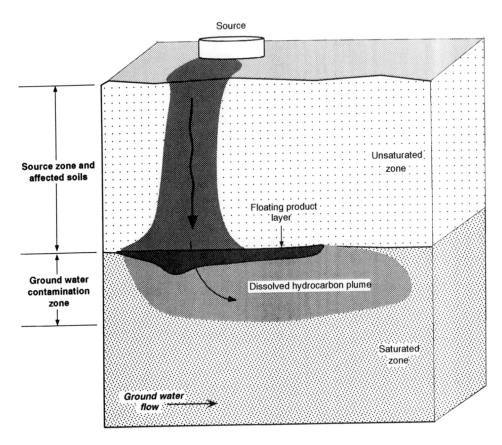

Figure 5.1 Zones of contamination for two-stage site investigation approach.

5.3.2 Unsaturated Source Zone Characteristics

Most incidents of hazardous chemical release to the subsurface environment occur as surface spills of products or wastes or leachate percolation from the base of waste landfills, surface impoundments, or material stockpiles. As the wetting front percolates downward through the unsaturated soil (or rock) zone underlying the source area, a significant portion of the contaminant mass may be retained in the unsaturated soil matrix due to the effects of filtration, sorption, or capillary retention. For many years thereafter, this contaminated soil can serve as a source of continuing contaminant release to stormwater flowing across the site surface or percolating downward through the unsaturated soil zone to the depth of underlying ground water.

Depending on the size and geological characteristics of this residual source zone and the nature and concentration of the contaminants, protection of surface water and ground water resources could involve either complete excavation and removal of the contaminated soils, capping of the site to minimize rainfall contact and precipitation, or contaminant extraction by means of in-situ soil venting or rinsing. To support design of appropriate corrective measures, the hydrogeologic site investigation must therefore address the full lateral and vertical extent of residual contaminants within the unsaturated soil zone and the potential for future release of contaminants to local water resources.

5.3.3 Ground Water Plume Characteristics

Dissolved contaminants contained in waste leachate fluids penetrating to the depth of ground water occurrence will become entrained in the natural ground water flow system and spread laterally and vertically in accordance with local ground water flow gradients (Figure 5.1). Free-phase liquid contaminants may be subject to an additional "density gradient" with light non-aqueous phase liquids (LNAPLs, such as gasoline) floating atop the zone of saturation and collecting in the structural highs of confined water-bearing units. Alternatively, dense non-aqueous phase liquids (DNAPLs) can percolate downward through the water-bearing stratum to perch and spread atop underlying confining units (Chapter 11).

In all cases, ground water contamination problems are fluid problems. The contaminant enters the ground water system as a fluid and can therefore be removed or controlled as a fluid. Unlike contamination within the unsaturated soil zone, excavation and removal of the soil or rock mass from the zone of ground water contamination is neither practical nor necessary. The hydrogeologic site investigation must therefore provide definitive information on the current lateral and vertical extent of dissolved and free-phase contaminants within the ground water, as well as the hydraulic processes controlling contaminant migration.

5.3.4 Two-Stage Site Investigation Approach

In practice then, the hydrogeologic site investigation proceeds as a two-stage process: (1) delineate the unsaturated source zone, comprised of the chemical waste or product mass and the associated contaminated soils within the unsaturated soil column, and (2) investigate the presence and extent of contaminant migration within the underlying ground water system. Step-by-step strategies for implementation of these source zone and ground water contamination delineation studies are outlined below and illustrated on Figures 5.2 – 5.4.

Procedures for Unsaturated Source Zone Characterization. The objectives of the source zone characterization study are to locate the site of the release, identify the contaminants of concern and determine their concentrations, and delineate the source material or unsaturated soil mass that may act as a continuing source of contaminant release to surface water or underlying ground water. The principal steps required for delineation of the source zone are illustrated in Figure 5.2 and listed below.

As shown on the task flowchart, to commence the delineation study, available chemical information regarding the suspected source of the subsurface release (e.g., waste or product spill) must be compiled to provide a basis for design of the laboratory testing program. If

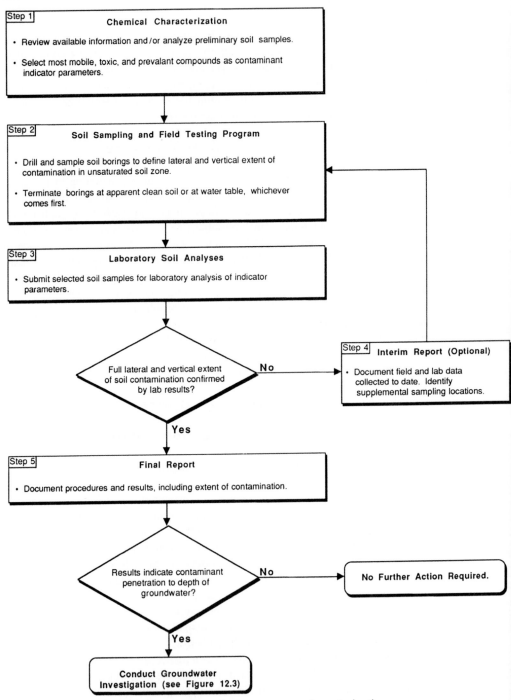

Figure 5.2 Procedures for source zone characterization.

such information is unavailable or inadequate, representative contaminated soil samples should be collected from the release site and analyzed for a broad suite of chemical compounds, as appropriate, to identify the principal contaminants of concern. Appropriate laboratory indicator parameters and field testing procedures should then be selected on the basis of the prevalence, mobility, and toxicity of the principal constituents identified.

In Step 2 of the source delineation, a field sampling and testing program is conducted to define the apparent lateral and vertical extent of contamination within the unsaturated soil zone. At each soil sampling location, sampling and field testing should be conducted continuously with depth until either clean soil or ground water infiltration is encountered. As discussed in Section 5.4, typical field test methods for hydrocarbon contamination include organic vapor headspace analyses and various colorimetric indicator tests.

To confirm the apparent lateral and vertical extent of contamination observed in the field, samples of the uppermost "clean" soils encountered at each sampling location should be submitted for laboratory analysis of indicator parameter content (see Step 3, Figure 5.2). Representative samples from within the contamination zone should also be submitted for analysis of total and leachable contaminant indicator concentrations in order to characterize contaminant mass and mobility.

Delineation of the contaminated soil zone is an iterative process, often requiring two or more field and laboratory cycles for completion. Should the results of the source zone investigation show contaminants to have penetrated to the depth of underlying ground water at concentrations exceeding relevant cleanup standards, a ground water contamination study will also be required.

Procedures for Ground Water Contaminant Plume Delineation. The objective of a ground water contaminant investigation is to determine the presence and extent of dissolved or free-phase contaminants, as well as the likely rate and direction of contaminant migration within the ground water flow system. Principal steps to be followed are shown on Figures 5.3 and 5.4.

As indicated on the task flowchart, the ground water investigation must be preceded by identification and characterization of all potential source zones in the study area. A detection monitoring program, involving installation of 1 to 3 ground water sampling points at each known or suspected source location, should then be completed to identify all sites of hazardous constituent release to ground water.

Ground water plume delineation should be conducted in a step-wise procedure in order to minimize the number of ground water sampling points required. First, based upon the suspected age of the release and the lateral ground water seepage velocity determined during the detection monitoring study, estimate the potential length of the contaminant plume (i.e., seepage rate × time = length) and space sampling points accordingly along the plume axis to locate the actual downgradient boundary. Second, to define the width of the contaminant plume, complete additional sampling points on 1 or 2 lines running transverse to the plume axis. Finally, to determine the vertical limit of contaminant migration, collect and analyze ground water samples from "nested" sampling points (i.e., samples collected in close lateral proximity, e.g., < 10 ft distance, but from different discrete depths within the water-bearing unit).

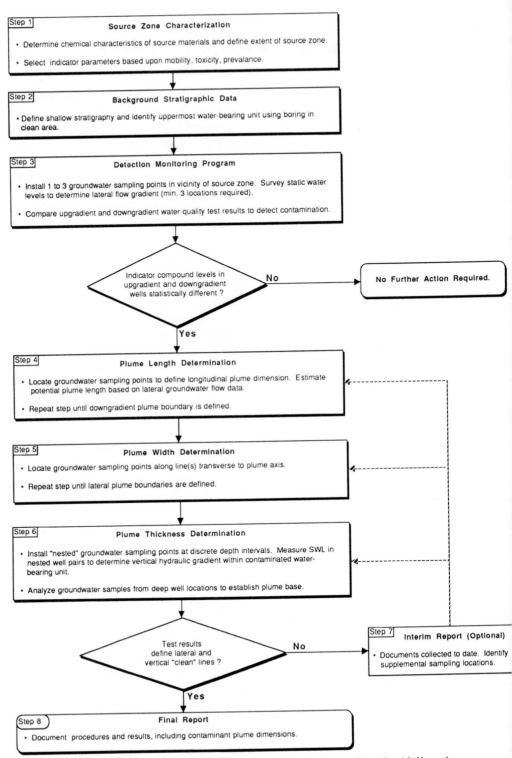

Figure 5.3 Procedures for ground water contaminant plume detection/delineation.

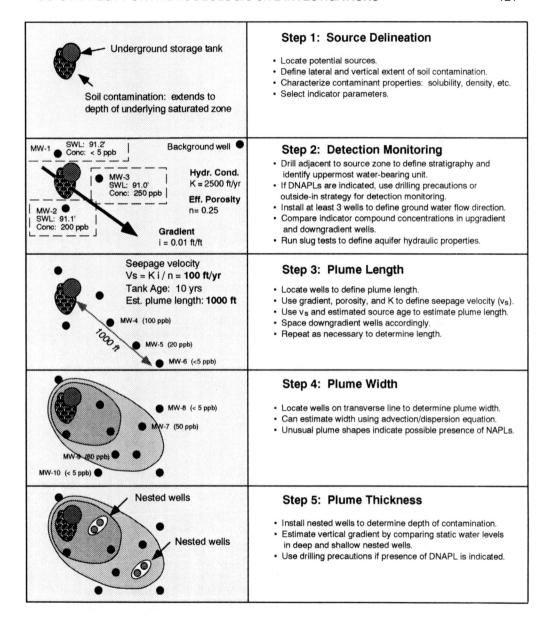

Step 1: Source Delineation

- Locate potential sources.
- Define lateral and vertical extent of soil contamination.
- Characterize contaminant properties: solubility, density, etc.
- Select indicator parameters.

Step 2: Detection Monitoring

- Drill adjacent to source zone to define stratigraphy and identify uppermost water-bearing unit.
- If DNAPLs are indicated, use drilling precautions or outside-in strategy for detection monitoring.
- Install at least 3 wells to define ground water flow direction.
- Compare indicator compound concentrations in upgradient and downgradient wells.
- Run slug tests to define aquifer hydraulic properties.

Step 3: Plume Length

- Locate wells to define plume length.
- Use gradient, porosity, and K to define seepage velocity (v_s).
- Use v_s and estimated source age to estimate plume length.
- Space downgradient wells accordingly.
- Repeat as necessary to determine length.

Step 4: Plume Width

- Locate wells on transverse line to determine plume width.
- Can estimate width using advection/dispersion equation.
- Unusual plume shapes indicate possible presence of NAPLs.

Step 5: Plume Thickness

- Install nested wells to determine depth of contamination.
- Estimate vertical gradient by comparing static water levels in deep and shallow nested wells.
- Use drilling precautions if presence of DNAPL is indicated.

Figure 5.4 Typical work program for ground water plume delineation.

If the contaminant plume is found to extend through the full thickness of the upper-most water-bearing unit, sampling and analysis of ground water from the next underlying water-bearing stratum may be necessary to establish the vertical limit of contamination. In such case, it is critical that any observation points penetrating the confining layer separating the upper and lower water-bearing strata be completed in a manner not providing an artificial conduit for contaminant migration. Appropriate protective measures are discussed in Section 5.4.

5.4 DEVELOPMENT OF A DETAILED SITE INVESTIGATION WORKPLAN

Prior to commencing the hydrogeologic site investigation, the specific field and laboratory tasks required to implement the site investigation strategy described above should be identified and appropriate resources allocated. Preplanning activities should include specification of the number, location, and depth of soil and ground water samples to be collected; sampling procedures and associated equipment requirements; field safety protocol; and field and laboratory test methods. The proposed sampling plan should be reviewed in advance to ensure that the information obtained will be adequate to meet the geologic, hydrologic, and chemical data objectives of the source characterization or ground water plume detection/delineation study.

To provide a technical basis for planning of the site investigation, available site information must be compiled and reviewed to define the general location and duration of the suspected release, the probable contaminants of concern, and general stratigraphic conditions. Typical sources of information include site operating records, regulatory agency records, employee interviews, historical aerial photographs, published geologic references, prior foundation studies or hydrogeologic site investigation reports.

5.4.1 Project Objectives

Both the source zone investigation and the ground water plume investigation should be approached in a step-by-step manner. In addition, the project engineer or scientist must clearly anticipate the end point of the site investigation, as well as actions to be taken in the event that unexpected site conditions are encountered. For example, is the purpose of the sampling merely to confirm the presence or absence of a specific compound or to delineate its full extent? If ground water is encountered during a source characterization study, will a sample be collected for the purpose of contaminant detection?

It is not necessary or even advisable to complete a full hydrogeologic site investigation in one step. Rather, it will generally prove more economical to conduct the project in a phased manner with each work stage having a predefined objective and end point.

Based upon available information, a preliminary plan should be developed regarding the number, location, and depth of samples required to meet the project objectives. All proposed drilling locations should be staked and cleared in advance for the presence of buried utilities. Appropriate sample collection and handling procedures must be specified and relevant equipment provided in working order. Sample kits containing the sample containers and preservatives required for the specified analytical methods should be ordered from the laboratory.

The field supervisor should be provided with a written copy of the sampling plan and project safety plan, specifying project objectives, proposed sampling locations, field test procedures, and laboratory analyses, as well as the basis for modification of the proposed workplan during implementation. General guidelines for design of the field program are provided below.

5.4.2 Design of Unsaturated Source Zone Characterization Study

General guidelines regarding the number, location, and depth of sampling points required for a source zone characterization study are as follows:

Number and Location of Samples. For initial chemical characterization of the residual waste materials or affected soil zone, analysis of one to four samples collected from known contaminated areas will generally suffice. To define the lateral limits of the source zone, samples can either be located on a rough grid pattern across the suspected contaminant area or completed on a "step-out" pattern, whereby samples are collected at even distances along lines extending radially from the known source area until clean soil conditions are encountered.

To minimize the number of samples required for the source zone delineation, the field program should be focused on establishing the "clean line" (i.e., the perimeter of the contaminant area), rather than defining variations in contaminant concentrations within the source zone. In general, "clean" soil conditions will correspond either to (1) the natural background concentrations of the contaminant compounds occurring in site soils or (2) other cleanup standards established by the state or federal regulatory authority.

Sampling Depth. At each sampling location, soil samples should be collected continuously to the depth of clean soil conditions or to the depth of ground water occurrence, whichever comes first. However, care must be taken not to puncture confining layers (i.e., clay, shale, or other low-permeability strata) which might be serving as a "safety net" against downward migration of contaminants beneath the source zone. For this purpose, at sites where soil contamination may extend beyond the depth of the surface soil stratum, it is advisable to drill at least one "background" soil boring at a known clean location to define site stratigraphy prior to drilling through the contaminant zone.

Sampling and Field Testing Methods. Initial chemical characterization of the source zone materials will typically involve collection of wastes, spilled products, or affected soils for laboratory analyses of a broad range of hazardous chemical constituents potentially associated with the site. Thereafter, sample analyses may be limited to key indicator parameters, including the use of various field tests (such as organic vapor analyses or colorimetric methods). Hand augers may be used to collect soil samples at depths less than 5 ft below grade. For delineation of large contaminant areas or buried waste sites, backhoes are effective to depths of 10 to 15 ft. In general, direct-push soil probing devices or conventional drilling rigs represent the most cost-effective means of soil sample collection at depths greater than 10 ft.

5.4.3 Ground Water Plume Detection/Delineation Studies

General guidelines regarding the number, location, and depth of sampling points required for a plume study are as follows:

Number and Location of Samples. For the purpose of a plume detection study, a minimum of three monitoring wells or piezometers are required to establish the lateral hydraulic flow gradient in the uppermost water-bearing stratum underlying the source area. Water quality measurements from upgradient sampling locations should be compared to data from downgradient locations to confirm the presence or absence of ground water contamination. The strategy for lateral and vertical delineation of the contaminant plume is outlined on Figure 5.4.

Sampling Depth. Wells should be screened within the uppermost water-bearing stratum underlying the suspected source area. Good practice calls for limiting the length of the well screen to no more than 15 ft to minimize potential dilution of dissolved or free-phase contaminants. Consequently, in thick aquifers, installation of "nested" wells (i.e., adjacent wells screened at different depth intervals) may be required at selected locations to define the vertical limit of contaminant migration. To detect free-phase contaminants, well screens should be positioned to intersect either the top (for floating fluids) or the base (for sinking fluids) of the water-bearing stratum. If, upon completion of the plume delineation in the uppermost aquifer unit, sampling of deeper, underlying water-bearing units is required, special care must be taken to avoid inadvertent interconnection of contaminated and uncontaminated layers.

Ground Water Investigation Methods. Drilling and sampling of monitoring wells provides information on site stratigraphy, static water level elevations, and water quality. Consequently, wells are a common component of most ground water detection/delineation studies. However, as discussed in Section 5.4, many other site investigation technologies can be employed to obtain discrete-depth ground water samples or supplementary information regarding site stratigraphy or aquifer hydraulics. The utility of these alternate methods depends on the specific type of information required to complete the "picture" of the ground water contamination problem.

5.4.4 Laboratory Specifications

The appropriate analytical method to be employed for measurement of a specific contaminant or group of contaminants in a soil or ground water sample depends both upon the level of contamination anticipated and the detection limit required. In order to demonstrate "clean" conditions, an analytical method having a detection limit less than the anticipated cleanup standard must be employed. For example, to show that benzene concentrations in a ground water sample are less than the U.S. Primary Drinking Water Standard for this contaminant (i.e., 5 μg/L), a gas-chromatography (GC) or gas-chromatography mass spectroscopy (GCMS) method, providing part-per-billion (ppb) sensitivity, must be employed. However, gross delineation of plumes and characterization of total contaminant mass can be accomplished to a large extent using less sensitive analytical methods (e.g., part-per-million sensitivity level).

Procedures for selection of laboratory samples and the specific analytical methods to be employed must be defined in advance of sample collection. For each test method specified, appropriate sample containers and preservatives must be obtained and arrangements made for completion of the laboratory analysis within the holding time specified under EPA protocol. Detailed information regarding test methods applicable to soil and ground water samples is provided in EPA Publication SW-846 (EPA, 1986).

5.4.5 Data Evaluation and Report Specifications

The project workplan should define what the final product of the study will be, including the specific determinations to be made, the procedures to be employed to make such determinations (e.g., statistical analyses, calculations, etc.), and the manner in which such findings will be presented (e.g., cross-sections, data plots, etc.). The proposed field and laboratory plan should be reviewed to ensure that the data required for completion of the final report will be obtained and properly recorded during the work program.

5.5 DATA COLLECTION METHODS

5.5.1 General Considerations

Traditionally, the methods employed in hydrogeologic site investigations have been those originally developed for the geotechnical, water well, and petroleum industries. Equipment and techniques have been refined to accommodate the special requirements associated with defining the extent of contaminant plumes. New technologies for environmental site investigations are continuously being developed. Many new techniques offer significant cost advantages over more conventional methods, and have gained wide acceptance among regulators. To assist investigators in selection of appropriate field sampling and testing methods, the U.S. EPA maintains a site on its web page (www.epa.gov) in which a wide variety technologies are described and evaluated, with links to other sources of information.

Information concerning the nature of the geologic materials, the occurrence of ground water, and the presence or absence of contaminants in soil and ground water beneath a site can be obtained by both direct observation, that is, collection and analysis of soil and ground water samples, and by indirect means, such as geophysical measurements and in-situ chemical sensing. Use of such indirect methods of assessing site conditions can reduce the cost of the investigation and in some cases can also replace subjective description with more readily comparable numerical data. However, geophysical instrumentation can produce identical responses from a variety of conditions, and a unique and definitive interpretation of the data is often not possible. In-situ chemical data are typically semi- or quasi-quantitative, and may not be considered definitive of site conditions by regulatory agencies. Therefore, such indirect measurements should be, at a minimum, calibrated against, and or confirmed by, "direct" data obtained from soil and ground water samples collected on site.

The following sections describe methods for the acquisition of geologic, hydrologic, and soil and ground water quality (chemical) data. The emphasis is on the more conventional techniques, employing direct observation and measurement of soil and ground water samples. Techniques employing indirect measurement of soil and water properties are treated more briefly, but their value should not be discounted. Use of indirect sampling methods in environmental assessments is an evolving field, and improvements in data quality and cost-effectiveness are likely to continue make such techniques increasingly common in the future.

5.5.2 Project Safety

Safety considerations should figure prominently into all drilling and sampling plans. A project health and safety plan meeting the requirements of 29 CFR §1910.120 is required by federal regulations (OSHA) for all investigations of hazardous waste sites. The plan should be distributed to and reviewed by all project personnel prior to project start-up. Prior to commencement of any drilling operation, the locations must be cleared for underground utilities.

5.5.3 Documentation of Site Conditions

Documentation of field sampling procedures and observations is a critically important aspect of the hydrogeologic site investigation. Without reliable records, the results of field sampling program may be of no value. Therefore, all measurements and relevant observations must be clearly and legibly recorded either in field logbooks or on data collection forms. Subjective observations, a necessary component of the field record should be made in the most precise, unambiguous language possible. In addition to the sample measurements and descriptions, the log should record any site conditions that could affect the observations or measurements, and any deviations from the established scope of work or sampling protocols.

5.6 GEOLOGIC DATA ACQUISITION

5.6.1 Direct Observation Methods

The essential geologic data required in all hydrogeologic site investigations is a description of the principal stratigraphic units underlying the site, including their thickness, lateral continuity, and water-bearing properties. This is most commonly assessed by direct examination of soil or rock samples collected from core borings. Soil samples collected during this process are also typically submitted for analysis of potential contaminants.

On sites underlain by unconsolidated materials and where drilling depths are shallow (100 ft or less), the collection of core samples from soil borings is a generally cost-effective method of collecting geologic data. In areas underlain by consolidated rock, where site conditions require investigation at greater depths, and where the cost of disposal of investigation-derived wastes (IDWs) is high due to classification of these materials as hazardous wastes, the collection of core samples is more costly and may be augmented or replaced in part by cone penetrometer testing, or surface or borehole geophysical methods, which are described below.

5.6.2 Drilling Methods

A variety of drilling methods are employed during hydrogeologic site investigations. Selection of the drilling method depends on such factors as drilling depth, nature of the geologic formations under investigation, and the specific purpose of the boring, that is, lithologic sampling, soil sampling for chemical analysis, and/or well installation. An additional consideration is the volume of drill cuttings and fluids that are produced, especially at sites where these investigation-derived wastes (IDWs) must be disposed as a hazardous waste.

This summary is intended to be only a brief introduction to the most common drilling methods used in the environmental industry. Driscoll (1986) presents detailed descriptions of drilling techniques used in the water well industry generally. Scalf et al. (1981) includes a description of drilling techniques which focuses on environmental applications.

In conducting environmental site investigations, the introduction of foreign materials into the borehole is generally undesirable due to the possibility of reaction with the geologic media or ground water, which may affect the results of laboratory analysis of soil or ground water samples. Even when a potable water source is used in the preparation of drilling fluids, chlorine may react with naturally occurring organic material in the soil to produce detectable concentrations of trihalomethane compounds (such as chloroform and dichlorobromomethane) in the ground water. Therefore, drilling is frequently performed "dry," that is, without the use of drilling fluids or "mud." Drilling dry also allows identification of the depth of the first occurrence of ground water. When ground water is first encountered, drilling operations should be halted long enough to observe whether or not water rises in the borehole, to determine whether ground water is confined or unconfined. Some drill rigs are equipped for both wet and dry drilling methods and can be switched from auger drilling above the water table to wet-rotary below it. Dry drilling is most commonly performed using either solid-flight or hollow-stem augers as described in the following paragraphs.

Solid Flight Auger Drilling. Solid flight augers consist of sections of solid rod with a continuous ramp of upward spiraling "flights" welded around it (Figure 5.5). The auger sections (each typically 5 ft in length) are pinned together as drilling proceeds. As the drill-stem is rotated, cutting teeth on the lead auger dig into the formation and the loosened soil rides up the flights to the ground surface. The "string" of auger sections is "tripped" out of the hole at each soil sample interval, and samples are collected by hydraulically pushing a thin-walled steel sampling tube ("Shelby tube") or driving "split-spoon" sampler with a percussion hammer, into the underlying undrilled formation. The drill string is then "tripped" back into the hole, and drilling proceeds to the next sample point.

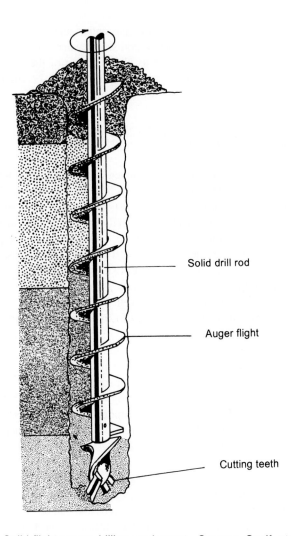

Figure 5.5 Solid-flight auger drilling equipment. Source: Scalf, et al., 1981.

Solid-flight augers are effective in cohesive soils above the saturated zone. Because of the tendency for borehole walls to collapse when the drill string is tripped in and out of the hole, solid flight augers are not useful in loose soils or below the water table and are not generally suitable for monitoring well installation.

Hollow Stem Auger Drilling. Hollow-stem augers are another type of flight auger, but instead of being welded to a solid rod, the flights are welded around a hollow pipe (Figure 5.6), The lead auger is fitted with cutting bits located around the circumference of its

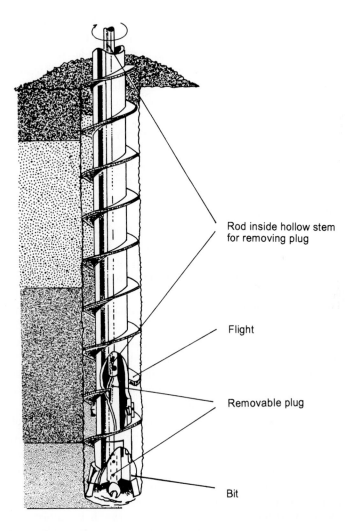

Rod inside hollow stem
for removing plug

Flight

Removable plug

Bit

Figure 5.6 Hollow-stem auger drilling and soil sampling equipment. Source: Scalf, et al., 1981.

base. During drilling, a center rod equipped with a pilot bit is lowered inside the auger, and the center rod and hollow-stem are rotated together.

As drilling proceeds, loosened soil rides up the outer ramp of auger flights as with the solid flight auger. A plug, positioned above the bit, prevents soil from traveling up the inside of the hollow-stem. When the sample interval is reached, the center rod, plug, and bit are removed, and the soil sampling tool is lowered inside the hollow-stem, which remains in the borehole to prevent collapse of the walls. The sampling tool, typically a split-spoon or

Shelby tube sampler, is then pushed or driven into the soil ahead of the auger. If a monitoring well is to be installed, the well screen and riser can also be lowered within the hollow stem, which provides a temporary casing, as described later.

Under favorable conditions, hollow-stem auger can be used to depths exceeding 150 feet. However, at depths below about 50 ft, drilling and soil sampling slow down considerably. At greater depths, in harder formations, and in flowing sand conditions, wet rotary is a more effective method.

Wet Rotary Drilling. During wet rotary drilling, a dense drilling fluid or "mud" is pumped down a hollow drill pipe and through holes or "jets" located above the teeth of the drill bit (Figure 5.7). As the fluid is pumped down the hole, drill cuttings are circulated up the borehole to the surface. The drilling mud also cools the drill bit, exerts hydrostatic pressure on the formation, and forms a thin coating or "mudcake" on the borehole wall, which keeps the unconsolidated aquifer material from collapsing and closing the borehole during soil sampling and well installation. In environmental applications, the drilling mud is most commonly prepared from powdered, additive-free bentonite (a mixture of dense clay minerals of volcanic origin) and potable water. During soil sample collection, the drill stem may be removed from the hole and the drill bit replaced with either a split-spoon or Shelby tube sampler.

Wet rotary drilling is effective in environments where auger drilling is not practical, including hard, consolidated formations, such as well cemented sandstones or shales, and very loose, flowing sand formations. In general, drilling and soil sample collection by wet rotary are faster than in hollow-stem operation, particularly as drilling depth increases. Because the borehole does not need to accommodate the auger, a smaller diameter hole may be drilled by wet rotary than with hollow-stem, which can reduce the volume of soil cuttings; however, more fluid wastes are generated due to the use of drilling mud.

Air Rotary Drilling. Formations such as vesicular basalts and highly fissured or cavernous limestones, are frequently drilled by air rotary methods. Air rotary drilling operates on the same principle as wet-rotary. Direct circulation of compressed air down the drill string and through the bit raises cuttings to the surface in small-diameter boreholes without introducing water from the surface. As formation water is blown out of the borehole along with drill cuttings, identification of the upper-most water-bearing zone is possible.

Sonic Drilling. Sonic drilling, also known as vibratory or "rotosonic" drilling, is a relatively new method that has been used in unconsolidated formations and soft of fractured rock to maximum depths of close to 500 ft. The drill bit is advanced into the subsurface by high-frequency vibrations transmitted through a rotating drill pipe. A temporary casing string advanced simultaneously keeps the hole open during drilling. Soil samples are collected from within the casing as the hole is advanced. Upon reaching the required depth, the well is set within the casing, which is subsequently extracted. Sonic drilling is faster than hollow-stem auger and comparable to mud rotary drilling, and it produces less drilling wastes than either auger or wet rotary drilling. To date, the use of sonic drilling has been limited in part by its higher cost relative to more conventional methods.

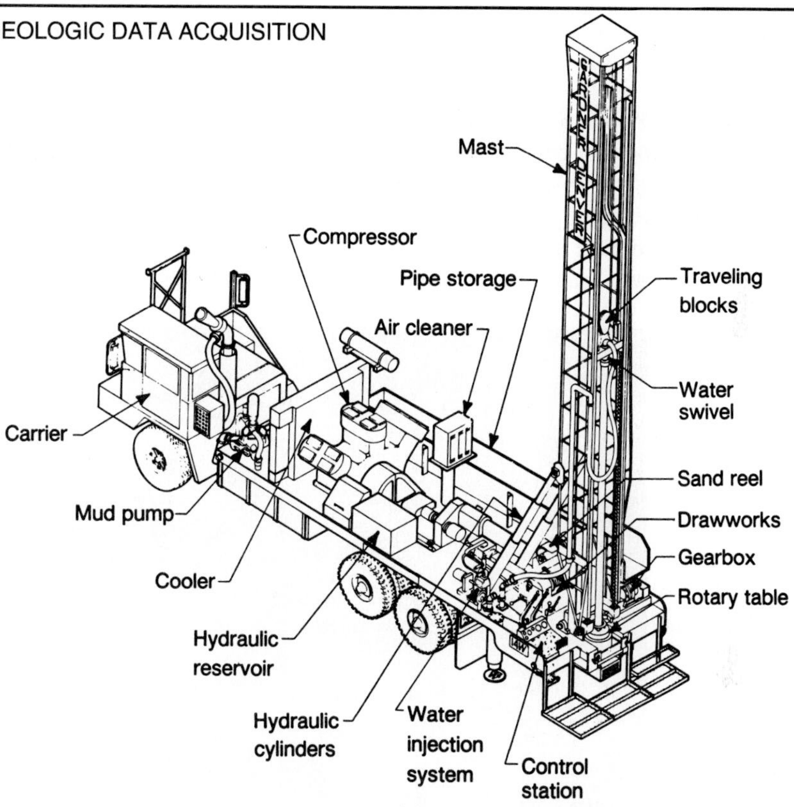

(a)

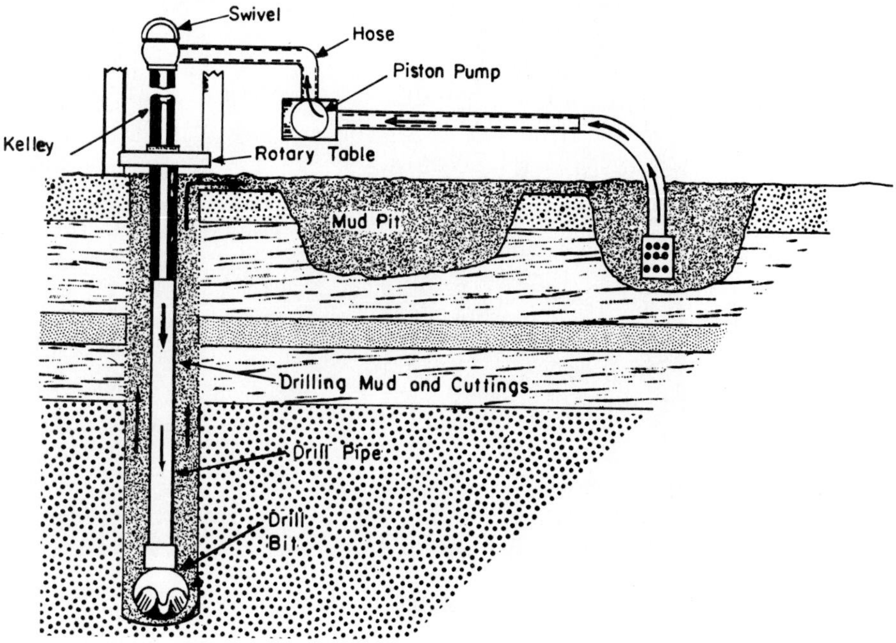

(b)

Figure 5.7 Wet rotary drilling equipment. Source: Scalf, et al., 1981.

Direct-Push Soil Probes. Direct-push soil probe systems are another relatively recent technology for collection of soil samples and installation of ground water monitoring points. Direct-push systems are generally smaller than conventional drilling equipment and may be mounted on a pick-up truck or small all-terrain vehicles, and, unlike conventional drill rigs, which have masts extending 30 ft or more vertically, direct push rigs can operate in locations where head space is limited by overhead power lines or piping (Figure 5.8). Di-

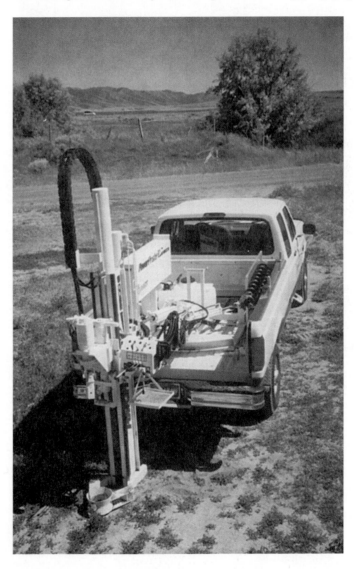

Figure 5.8 Direct-push soil probe.

rect-push rigs require much less set up time than conventional drill rigs and shallow sample collection is more rapid. On the other hand, because of their size, the practical working depth of direct-push rigs is limited, and a relatively small diameter sample (1–2 in) is obtained. While they have been used to obtain samples from as deep as 100 ft, their relative speed compared with other methods diminishes below 20–30 ft.

During direct-push sampling, the sampler is advanced into the subsurface by hydraulic push, augmented by a rapid percussion hammer to penetrate pavements and harder formations. The most common samplers in use are open acrylic-lined sampling tubes and closed piston samplers, described below. The sampler is most commonly lowered within the open borehole, which can result in collection of up-hole materials as the sampler scrapes along the borehole wall. Systems which advance a temporary casing to prevent hole collapse and minimize sample contact with the overlying formation are available, but the effective sampling depth, the sample diameter, and the speed of the operation are all reduced by such enhancements.

Small diameter shallow monitoring wells, constructed as either temporary or permanent installations, can be installed using direct-push rigs. In addition, a wide array of direct-sensing probes for identification of the water table or detection of contaminants have also been developed for use with direct-push rigs.

Unless they are to be converted to monitoring wells, soil core, soil probe, and CPT borings (described below) should be sealed upon completion to prevent migration of fluids from the surface down the borehole. This is especially critical when contamination is present above the water table and the soil boring has been advanced to ground water. The grout seal may consist of neat cement, a cement bentonite mixture, or specially developed sealing materials such as Volclay. Shallow and small diameter boreholes are often sealed with granular or pelletized bentonite. Some state regulatory agencies have specifications for grout composition and density. To ensure distribution of the grout over the full depth of the boring, grout should be placed using the tremie method. A length of pipe is lowered within a few feet of the base of the borehole, and the grout is pumped downhole under pressure.

5.6.3 Soil Sample Collection

A variety of tools and methods are available for soil or rock sampling, depending on subsurface conditions and the drilling equipment used. Some of the more common devices are described below.

Hand Auger. Hand augers are frequently used to collect soil samples from the shallowest portion of the subsurface, for example, depths less than 10 ft. Hand auger borings can be advanced to somewhat deeper depths (approximately 20 ft), but with depth the method becomes increasingly inefficient. Still, it may be the most practical method at locations where the presence of overhead or below-ground structures may prevent access by a truck-mounted drill rig. It can also be an effective means of collecting soil samples from soil trenches, since unshored excavations deeper than 3-4 ft with slopes steeper than one-to-one should not be entered due to the potential for collapse and possible presence of oxygen-deficient conditions.

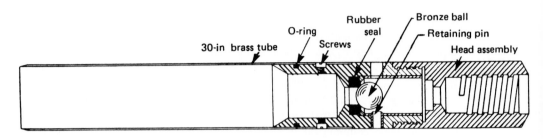

Figure 5.9 Shelby tube soil sampler. Source: Hunt, 1984.

Shelby Tube Sampler. In most conventional environmental drilling applications, subsurface soil samples are collected from cohesive clay soils using a 3-ft long by 3-in. diameter, thin-walled steel tube known as a Shelby tube sampler (Figure 5.9). The sample tube is pushed into and extracted from the soil using the hydraulic system on the drill rig. Once the sample is retrieved to the surface, it is extruded, also using the hydraulic system, and examined. Such soil samples are frequently referred to as "undisturbed" and are suitable for a variety of geotechnical, as well as environmental, analyses.

Following retrieval of the soil sample, the sample interval is drilled out to a diameter slightly larger than the diameter of the sampler prior to collection of the next sample. Drilling out the sample hole prevents the sampler from scraping the borehole en route to successive sample points and collecting soil from intervals already sampled.

Split-Spoon Sampler. In coarser grained, less cohesive soils, such as sands and clay-poor silts, a split-spoon sampler is used. Split-spoon samplers are constructed of two half-cylinders held together by threaded fittings at the top and base to form a 1.5-ft long by 1.5-in. diameter tube (Figure 5.10). The split-spoon sampler is driven into the soil by repeated blows from a rig-mounted hammer, then retrieved to the surface by the rig hydraulic system. The "blow count" or number of hammer blows of a standardized force required to drive the sampler 1 ft into the soil is frequently recorded as a measure of aquifer hardness. A core catcher inserted at the base of the sampler prevents unconsolidated materials from falling out of the sampler as it is removed from the borehole. Upon retrieval, the threaded ends are removed and the two half-cylinders separated to reveal the core for examination.

Due to the repeated impact as the sampler is driven to depth, split spoon samples are referred to as "disturbed" samples. Original sedimentary structures such as cross-bedding are not generally preserved, and any apparent bedding structures are probably artifacts of the sampling process. The upper portion of the sample may contain materials that had accumulated on the borehole floor and should be discarded. As with the Shelby tube sampler, following sample retrieval, the borehole should be drilled out to the next sample interval prior to resuming sample collection.

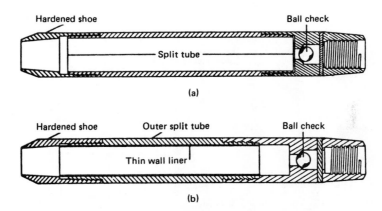

Figure 5.10 (a) Split-spoon soil sampler and (b) Split-spoon soil sampler with liner. Source: Hunt, 1984.

Split-Barrel Sampler. Some hollow-stem augers (see below) are equipped with a core barrel resembling a large split-spoon sampler which is placed inside the hollow-stem and collects a 5-foot continuous core sample during drilling. Under favorable conditions, good quality samples can be collected with a significant time savings over more conventional sampling methods. However, hard clays can pack the front end of the sampler and prevent further movement of soil into the core barrel giving disappointing core recovery. In very loose sand formations, the sample may not be retained. Therefore, these samplers should be used with caution, as significant sample loss may result in the need to re-drill the soil boring.

Direct-Push Samplers. Numerous variations on the basic principal of the pushed or driven sampling tube have been developed for use with direct-push soil probes and cone penetrometer rigs. The most common tools consist of steel tubes or split barrels fitted with acrylic or brass liners, which may be cut open or extruded in the field, or capped and sent directly to a laboratory for analysis. Also in common use are direct-push samplers with a plug at the opening held in place by a piston or other mechanism. These can be driven through an undisturbed soil column to a predetermined depth at which the piston is released and further driving of the sampler results on collection of a sample at the required depth (Figure 5.11).

A discrete soil sample is obtained using the Large Bore Soil Sampler by driving the assembled sampler to depth.

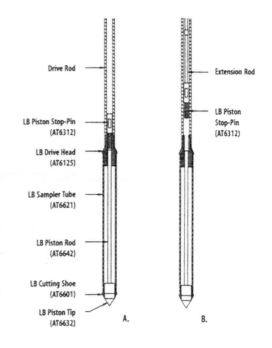

A. Driving the Sealed Sampler.
B. Removing the Piston Stop-Pin in Preparation for Sample Collection.

Figure 5.11 Direct-push sampler.

5.6.4 Rock Core Sample Collection

Samples are collected from formations of consolidated rock using rock coring barrels, which vary in size and design depending on the particular drilling conditions. Hunt (1984) provides a summary of the various designs and their applications.

Generally, the core barrel is fitted at its base with a ring-shaped carbide or diamond-tipped bit, which cuts the core during drilling. The coring device is rotated under pressure while drilling fluid is circulated down the drill string, through the bit, and up the annulus. The bit cuts a circular groove, leaving a column of intact rock standing within the core barrel. When the full length of the core barrel has been drilled, the core is broken from the formation and lodged in the barrel by the core lifter, and the core barrel is retrieved to the surface.

The time required to sample a borehole in a hard rock formation can be reduced by the use of a wire-line core barrel. In this application, a small-diameter core is diverted into a tube, which is brought to the surface by means of a retrieving "spear" lowered on a wire-line within the drill pipe, eliminating the need to trip the drill string out of the hole to retrieve the core barrel. Wire-line coring has also been adapted to rotary drilling in unconsolidated formations.

5.6.5 Core Logging

Logging of core samples for the purposes of hydrogeologic site investigations includes a description of both the geologic characteristics and the visual evidence of contamination, if present. Of primary importance from a hydrogeologic standpoint are those characteristics that influence the water-bearing capacity of the soil or rock, including grain size and secondary porosity features. Evidence of contamination may include chemical staining or odor. Core samples collected during drilling may be used for field screening or laboratory analysis. Special handling or preservation of samples is required for many analytical methods.

Soil Core Logging. Numerous soil classification schemes have been developed for various purposes. The system most commonly used in the environmental industry is the Unified Soil Classification System (USCS, Figure 5.12) and Hunt (1984). The USCS places most soils into one of two major divisions: coarse-grained soils including gravelly and sandy soils, and fine-grained soils including silts and clays. This binary scheme is appropriate to hydrogeologic site investigations where a primary objective is the differentiation of permeable water-bearing and low-permeability confining strata. In general, unconsolidated aquifers are composed of gravels, sands, and low plasticity silts, while clays and clay-rich or highly compacted silts form aquitards or aquicludes. Highly organic soils, such as peat and humus, form a third, smaller division.

In logging cores using the USCS, soils are classified on the basis of the major constituent: gravel, sand, silt, or clay. Modifiers referring to secondary constituents are used when that constituent accounts for 10% or more of the sample. Thus, a silty sand or clayey sand (SM or SC in USCS shorthand) contains greater than 50% sand and 10% or more silt or clay, respectively. If the silt or clay content is less than 10 per cent, the sand is either a well-graded or poorly-graded sand (SW or SP), with minor or trace silt or clay. Under the USCS, clay soils are divided into high and low-plasticity varieties based on the liquid and plastic limit values which are determined by laboratory testing (Hunt, 1984).

Although precise quantification of grain size distribution and liquid and plastic limits are determined by laboratory testing, field classification of soils with borderline compositions must be based on judgment. As a rule of thumb, high-plasticity clays can be rolled between the hands to form elongate strings, while low-plasticity clays will crumble when rolled. If a soil sample which appears to be either a silty clay or a clayey silt yields free ground water, it is more likely a clayey silt.

Secondary porosity features in fine-grained soils can transmit fluids at much higher rates than through the soil formation as a whole. Slickenside fractures, horizons of woody or

Major Divisions			Graph symbol	Letter symbol	Typical descriptions
Coarse-grained soils More than 50% of material is larger than no. 200 sieve size	Gravel and gravelly soil More than 50% of coarse fraction **retained** on a no. 4 sieve	Clean gravels (little or no fines)		GW	Well-graded gravel-sand mixtures, little or no fines
				GP	Poorly graded gravels, gravel-sand mixtures, little or no fines
		Gravels with fines (appreciable amount of fines)		GM	Silty gravels, gravel-sand-silt mixtures
				GC	Clayey gravels, gravel-sand-clay mixtures
	Sand and sandy soils More than 50% of coarse fraction **passing** a no. 4 sieve	Clean sand (little or no fines)		SW	Well-graded sands, gravelly sands, little or no fines
				SP	Poorly graded sands, gravelly sands, little or no fines
		Sands with fines (appreciable amount of fines)		SM	Silty sands, sand-silt mixtures
				SC	Clayey sands, sand-clay mixtures
Fine-grained soils More than 50% of material is smaller than no. 200 sieve size	Silts and clays	Liquid limit **less** than 50%		ML	Inorganic silts and very fine sands, rock flour silty or clayey fine sands or clayey silts with slight plasticity
				CL	Inorganic clays of low to medium plasticity, gravelly clays, sandy clays, silty clays, lean clays
				OL	Organic silts and organic silty clays or low plasticity
	Silts and clays	Liquid limit **greater** than 50%		MH	Inorganic silts, micaceous or diatomaceous fine sand or silty soils
				CH	Inorganic clays or high plasticity, fat clays
				OH	Organic clays of medium to high plasticity, organic silts
Highly organic soils				PT	Peat, humus, swamp soils with high organic contents

Figure 5.12 Unified soil classification system.

organic material, root zones, burrows, calcareous or other mineralized zones, and desiccation features frequently provide avenues of contaminant migration through low-permeability soils into underlying aquifers.

Other descriptive features such as color should be noted to the extent that they can be used to distinguish strata of similar composition from one another and may sometimes provide consistent stratigraphic markers, such as a gray clay overlying a red clay.

Rock Classification and Description. Rocks are broadly classified in terms of their origin as igneous (those having formed from a molten fluid, or magma), metamorphic (those having formed by recrystallization of a pre-existing rock subjected to heat and/or pressure), and sedimentary (those having formed from deposition and consolidation of soil or rock particles or as chemical precipitates from mineral saturated water. Core samples should be logged in terms of their mineralogic composition, as well as their water-bearing (Hunt, 1984).

Sedimentary rocks that have formed by accumulation and consolidation of soil or rock fragments, ranging in size from fine powders to house-sized boulders, are referred to as clastic or detrital rocks. The most commonly encountered water-bearing varieties include sandstones and conglomerates (rocks composed of grains of variable sizes, e.g., gravel and sand). The porosity in these rocks may be primary (intergranular porosity, as encountered in well sorted, poorly cemented sandstones) or secondary (fracture porosity, as may be encountered in well-cemented, jointed rocks), or both. Rocks which formed by chemical precipitation from a mineral-saturated water body include carbonate rocks (limestones and dolomites) and the less common evaporites (halites, gypsum, and anhydrites). Porosity in these rocks is usually secondary, occurring as fractures or solution cavities. The water-bearing capacity of sedimentary rocks can also be influenced by the degree of weathering.

In igneous and metamorphic rocks, significant water flow is generally limited to within fractures. A notable exception to this rule is vesicular basalt, which may have significant primary porosity due to entrapment of gas bubbles in the molten lava as it cooled and hardened.

5.6.6 Cone Penetrometer Testing

Subsurface formations can also be logged or inferred from a variety of what may be referred to as indirect methods; methods in which soil or rock is characterized by instrumental measurement of geophysical properties, rather than direct examination of pieces of the formation. Such methods can dramatically speed up the investigation, limit the potential for exposure to hazardous constituents, and minimize the need to manage investigation-derived wastes, all of which help control investigation costs. However, by their nature, such data must be interpreted, and interpretations are not necessarily unique, since more than one subsurface condition may produce an identical instrument response. Therefore, indirect methods should be used in conjunction with direct observation methods and instrument response calibrated to subsurface conditions whenever possible.

Originally developed for geotechnical investigation, the cone penetrometer test (or CPT) can be useful for defining stratigraphy to depths of up to 100 ft (rarely more) in fine-grained soils and unconsolidated sands. In cone penetrometer testing, electronic strain gauges mounted in a steel cone-shaped probe are pushed at a constant rate into the subsurface by a

Figure 5.13 Schematic of cone penetrometer testing.

truck-mounted hydraulic system (Figure 5.13). The gauges measure the resistance encountered at the tip of the cone tool, and the friction encountered along its side as the tool is advanced, producing a continuous, real-time log of these soil properties with depth (Figure 5.14). Empirical relationships for soils in various regions of the country have been developed to allow interpretation of soil type based on the resulting set of curves. High tip resistance and low friction indicate coarser grained soils; lower tip resistance and higher friction indicate finer grained soils. It is advisable to locate at least one CPT immediately adjacent to a continuously sampled soil boring, preferably one encountering a variety of soil types to allow correlation of the CPT response to local soil conditions.

In addition to the standard lithologic data, instrumentation has been developed to measure other physical properties for expanded interpretation of subsurface conditions. Electrical conductivity measurements can be used to identify the presence of ground water and hydrocarbon fluids; pore pressure measurements can be used to assess formation permeability; and laser-induced fluorescence can be used to identify the presence of specific free-phase hydrocarbon fluids in the subsurface.

Upon completion of cone testing, a small diameter monitoring well can be installed within the CPT hole. Limited soil sampling can also be performed with the cone penetrometer rig, though sample quality can be poor, and continuous sampling is not practical or cost-effective. Technologies under current development include high-resolution video cameras which can provide a "worm's eye view" of the subsurface geologic materials and free-phase contaminants.

A major advantage of the cone penetrometer is the speed and cost of data collection. At a rate of 2 cm/sec, a continuous log to a depth of 50 ft can be obtained in less than 15 min., while a continuously sampled soil boring to the same depth can take several hours. Footage rates for cone testing can be as little as half those of auger drilling. Investigation costs are further reduced by the absence of IDWs produced by this method. As an added benefit, delineation of nonaqueous phase liquids can in some instances be achieved by examining the grout returns during sealing of the CPT hole.

A second major advantage is that the lithologic data obtained, though subject to interpretation, are numerical measurements of soil properties, which can lend a degree of objectivity and consistency frequently missing on sites where soil cores have been described by numerous individual investigators. In addition, the data are continuous and can reveal subtle changes in soil properties on a much finer scale than can data changes in practice be recorded based on soil core description.

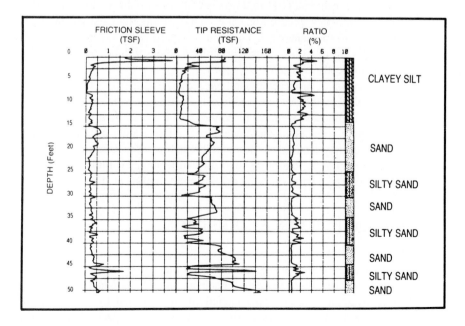

Figure 5.14 Log of cone penetrometer test. Source: Fugro Geosciences, Inc.

Apart from the inherent disadvantage of any indirect measurement (i.e., that the data are subject to interpretation), the major disadvantage of the cone rig is its size and weight, which can limit its mobility, particularly on unpaved sites.

5.6.7 Borehole and Surface Geophysical Methods

Subsurface geological conditions can also be evaluated indirectly using a variety of geophysical methods. Geologic strata or other buried features are differentiated by measuring the contrasting responses of differing geologic materials to physical forces such as electricity, magnetism, or seismic energy, or by measuring physical properties inherent in earth materials such as naturally occurring radioactivity. Geophysical methods are broadly divided into surface methods and borehole methods. Zohody et al. (1984) and Keys and MacCary (1971) provide guidelines for the applicability, acquisition, and interpretation of surface and borehole geophysical data, respectively.

In surface geophysical surveys, measurements are collected at regularly spaced intervals along a traverse or on a grid to produce a subsurface profile. Examples include conductivity surveys, most commonly used to identify salinity contrasts within an aquifer; magnetometer surveys, frequently used to identify buried drums, tanks, or ordnance, and ground penetrating radar (GPR), useful for identifying large scale buried geological or man-made features. The chief advantage of such methods is that broad regions of the subsurface can be surveyed rapidly in a noninvasive manner.

Borehole techniques utilize a variety of probes or sondes that measure physical properties of the soil or rock or contrasts between the drilling fluid and the fluids in the formation. Methods such as spontaneous potential and natural gamma ray logging are often used in lieu of core sampling to reduce costs, particularly when drilling conditions are difficult and required drilling depths are deep.

Application of surface and borehole geophysical methods to the environmental industry has been limited by the fact that a unique and definitive interpretation of the data is not generally possible. Because identical responses can be caused by a variety of conditions, the use of two or more types of measurements with interpretation by a highly knowledgeable specialist is frequently required to eliminate ambiguity. The need to run numerous tests, especially those employing the more sophisticated techniques, limits the ability of geophysical methods to compete cost-wise with drilling and sampling at shallow depths.

5.7 HYDROLOGIC DATA ACQUISITION

Assessment of the direction and rate of ground water flow beneath a site requires the following hydrologic data: lateral hydraulic gradient, hydraulic conductivity, and effective porosity. Of these, hydraulic gradient and conductivity are obtained by field measurements made in monitoring wells. Effective porosity (i.e., connected pore spaces through which ground water flows) is generally an estimated value (see Chapter 2). Because such determinations are most commonly made from measurements in piezometers and monitoring wells, we begin with a description of monitoring well construction.

5.7.1 Monitoring Well Construction

The monitoring well is the primary source of hydrologic and ground water quality data used in hydrogeologic site assessments. Most of the special requirements for monitoring well construction are due to their use in the collection of ground water quality data. For collection of hydrologic data, a piece of slotted pipe inserted into a borehole would be sufficient in most instances, but because of the dual purpose monitoring wells serve, careful attention must be paid to the materials used and the methods of construction. Many state environmental regulatory agencies have very particular construction specifications and require that well installation be performed by licensed drillers.

Hydrogeologic site investigations frequently require installation of a permanent monitoring well network to permit resampling and evaluation of changing site conditions. However, monitoring well installation is fairly expensive. To reduce the cost of a ground water plume delineation program, the use of temporary ground water sampling points is becoming increasingly common. A variety of configurations may be installed using a drill rig, direct-push soil probe rig, or cone penetrometer rig to provide samples for lateral and vertical plume delineation in a fraction of the time required to install a well. Following delineation, a relatively small number of permanent wells can be installed at strategic locations and depths to confirm plume boundaries and facilitate future monitoring.

The essential elements of a monitoring well are the well screen and riser, the filter pack, and the annular seal (Figure 5.15). The well screen, typically a section of slotted pipe, allows water to flow from the formation into the well while screening out coarse soil particles. The riser is a solid-walled or "blank" pipe that connects the well screen with the surface. The filter pack, also referred to as the sand or gravel pack, limits the influx of fine surface. The filter pack, also referred to as the sand or gravel pack, limits the influx of fine sediment from the formation. Above the gravel pack, a seal composed of low permeability material prevents fluids from above the screened interval (including percolating rainwater) from entering the well.

Well Design. Monitoring wells should be designed on the basis of the purpose of the well, the hydrogeologic setting, and the expected contaminants in the ground water, as well as cost. Monitoring objectives will determine such factors as the length and placement of the screen interval. Construction materials that are selected should minimize the potential for reaction with the formation fluids and the expected contaminants while providing adequate strength to withstand the pressures exerted by the formation.

For measuring the potentiometric surface, wells screens are positioned to intersect the top of the aquifer in confined flow systems, or to straddle the expected zone of water table fluctuation in unconfined aquifers. Placement of the screen across the top of the water-bearing zone permits detection of floating accumulations of light nonaqueous phase liquids (LNAPLs), while for investigation of dense nonaqueous phase liquids (DNAPLs), intersec-

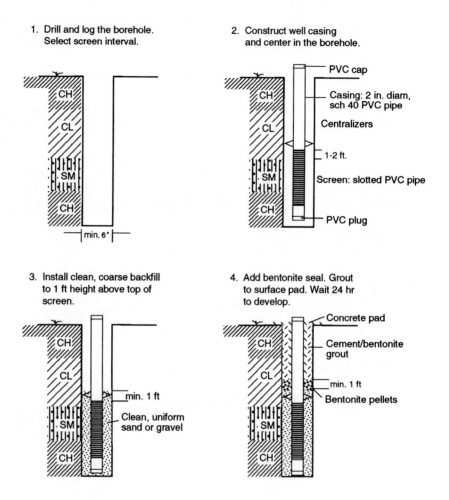

1. Drill and log the borehole. Select screen interval.

2. Construct well casing and center in the borehole.
   - PVC cap
   - Casing: 2 in. diam, sch 40 PVC pipe
   - Centralizers
   - 1-2 ft.
   - Screen: slotted PVC pipe
   - PVC plug

min. 6"

3. Install clean, coarse backfill to 1 ft height above top of screen.
   - min. 1 ft
   - Clean, uniform sand or gravel

4. Add bentonite seal. Grout to surface pad. Wait 24 hr to develop.
   - Concrete pad
   - Cement/bentonite grout
   - min. 1 ft
   - Bentonite pellets

Figure 5.15 Typical monitoring well installation.

tion of the screen with the base of the aquifer is more appropriate. Long screen sections yield water samples representing an average of conditions across their length; shorter screens (10 ft or less) yield more depth-specific data and are generally preferred, since low levels of contamination present over a limited depth interval may be overlooked due to dilution of the sample by uncontaminated water from elsewhere in the screen interval. In general screens in excess of 15 ft are avoided. Well diameters of 2 in. and 4 in., installed in 6 in. and 10 in. diameter boreholes, are most common.

To establish the vertical extent of ground water contamination, it may be necessary to drill monitoring wells through a contaminated upper zone into an uncontaminated lower zone. In such cases, it is necessary to first install isolation casing, consisting of a length of blank pipe sealed in place with cement or grout to prevent entrainment of contaminants from the upper zone to the lower zone during drilling. Once the casing is installed, drilling and well installation are resumed within the casing.

Materials of Construction. Well screens and risers are most commonly constructed of PVC. Threaded joints are generally specified, since the use of glues that contain organic solvents is discouraged. However, PVC reacts with some contaminants and is not always suitable. For example, high concentrations of chlorinated solvents can attack PVC, compromising ground water samples or damaging the well. In addition, the strength of PVC may not be adequate for very deep installations. Stainless steel is frequently used under such conditions, at significantly greater expense. Materials such as Teflon minimize reaction with contaminants, but their use is usually cost-prohibitive. Information on compatibility of various well materials with common contaminants can be found in Driscoll (1986).

Filter packs should be composed of graded silica sand. Blasting sand and other general-use sands may contain minerals that adsorb dissolved metals, potentially compromising the integrity of the ground water sample. The grain size interval of the filter pack material should be selected based on analysis of aquifer grain size distribution as described by Driscoll (1986).

Annular seals are most often composed of bentonite, frequently in combination with other materials. A 1 ft. to 2 ft. thick layer of bentonite pellets is usually placed atop the filter pack to protect the filter pack from invasion by the grout, which completes the seal to the ground surface. Grout may be composed of neat Portland cement, a mixture of cement and powdered bentonite, or other specialty materials such as Volclay.

Installation Procedures. In monitoring well installation, both the drilling and sampling equipment and the well construction materials must be free of contamination to prevent contamination of collection of ground water samples. Drilling equipment should be cleaned with pressurized hot water or steam and detergent, as needed, prior to drilling at each location. Well screen and riser should be packaged and handled to prevent fouling prior to well installation. Drilling and sampling personnel should handle the well pipe with clean gloves.

When wells are drilled using hollow-stem augers, the well screen and riser are lowered within the augers. For rotary drilled wells, the well is lowered within the open borehole. Drilling mud should be thinned by dilution with potable water to the extent practical prior to well installation to facilitate well development. A bottom cap or plug at the base of the well pipe prevents the flow of sediment into the bottom of the well. Silt traps or sumps, consisting of a short section of riser are frequently installed beneath the well screen to prevent fine sediment entering the well from accumulating in and clogging the screened interval. In deeper wells, "centralizers" may be placed above the screen section to maintain distance from borehole wall and ensure proper filter pack placement. Proper placement of the screen should be verified by careful measurement.

Once the screen and riser are in position, the filter pack is installed within the annulus around the well screen (Figure 5.15). The filter pack is generally placed from the base of the well to 1 ft to 2 ft above the top of the screen. In wells drilled by hollow-stem, the filter pack material is usually poured down the inside of the augers. The auger sections are pulled from the hole one at a time as the annulus is filled with sand. In deeper wells and wells drilled by wet rotary methods, it is frequently placed using the tremie method. Potable water is used to wash the filter material down a pipe lowered to the base of the well.

Following placement of the filter pack, the well is sealed to the ground surface to prevent migration of fluids from the surface or water-bearing zones above the screened interval down the borehole. Grout is frequently placed using the tremie method to ensure even placement up the borehole.

Monitoring wells are completed at the surface with a locking caps and/or casing to prevent tampering and a concrete surface pad to protect the annular seal. The elevations of the ground surface and top of well casings should be surveyed relative to a common datum such as mean sea level or an arbitrary datum established by a site benchmark. Top of casing elevations are required to convert depth to water measurements to static water level elevations and should be surveyed to the nearest 0.01 ft, and the point of measurement marked on the top of the well casing.

Well Development Procedures. Following installation, wells are developed to remove fine sediment and drilling mud from the filter pack and ensure collection of ground water samples that are representative of formation conditions, and prevent clogging of the well screen and pump damage. If the well has been installed in a low permeability aquifer using a dry drilling method, bailing out three to ten casing volumes may be sufficient to permit collection of representative ground water samples. If fluids have been introduced during drilling, larger volumes of water must be removed.

Development usually consists of a combination of pumping and surging. Surging the well, by running a close fitting cylinder up and down the inside of the well over the screened interval, causes a back-flushing action in the gravel pack, loosening fine sediment. Pumping from the well (preferably at a rate higher than the expected normal pumping rate) pulls fine sediment through the well screen into the well where it can be pumped to the surface.

5.7.2 Determination of Ground Water Flow Gradients

Ground water flow gradients are determined by measurement of water level elevations in site wells. In addition to the lateral gradient, determined by measurement of wells within the same water-bearing zone, the vertical gradient may be determined by measurement of closely spaced "nested pairs" of wells screened in different aquifers or within the upper and lower portions of the same aquifer. The presence of surface water features should be noted and surface water elevations determined to evaluate possible recharge/discharge relationships. The presence and discharge rate of any pumping wells on site should also be noted.

The water level in each well is measured to the nearest 0.01 ft using an appropriate instrument such as a water-sensitive probe on a graduated tape. The elevation of the potentiometric surface is obtained by subtracting the depth to water from the top of casing elevation. Ideally, water level surveys represent the potentiometric surface at one instant in time. Therefore, measurements should be made in as short a time frame as possible, since water levels within wells respond to such factors as barometric pressure or tidal influence. On sites with large numbers of wells, requiring several hours to survey, the first well measured should be remeasured at the end of the survey to detect possible changes in the potentiometric surface during the period of the survey. If more than one instrument is to be used in the survey, a common well should be measured simultaneously using each instrument to confirm that all instruments give the same reading.

On sites with LNAPLs, the water level survey should also include inspection of wells for the presence floating free-phase layers. If an LNAPL accumulation atop the water column is found, the water level must be corrected for its presence. The thickness of the LNAPL layer, measured with minimal disturbance using an electric interface probe, is multiplied by the specific gravity of the LNAPL (e.g., 0.75 for a typical gasoline). This value is added to the *measured* water level elevation to obtain the *corrected* water level elevation. (Note that the thickness of an LNAPL layer in a well is influenced by a number of factors and typically does not reflect an equivalent accumulation in the adjacent formation).

Upon completion of the survey, water level elevations are plotted on a scaled site map and potentiometric surface contours are drawn, and lateral and vertical flow gradients are determined as described in Section 5.8.

5.7.3 Determination of Hydraulic Conductivity

Slug Tests. Single-well slug tests are a common, cost-effective method for the estimation of hydraulic conductivity in hydrogeologic site assessments. Two major varieties, rising-head tests and falling-head tests can be used. Falling-head tests are more difficult to perform and analyze, and require addition of water to the well. Therefore, rising-head slug tests are more commonly performed.

During a rising-head test, the static water level in the well is first measured and then a "slug," typically a solid cylinder, of known volume is lowered within the well to just below the static level. Following re-equilibration of the water level in the well with that in the aquifer, the slug is removed from the well instantaneously, causing a sudden drop in the water level or head. The return of the water level to static conditions is then monitored. The rising head can be measured by hand in low permeability systems. Higher yield systems may recover too quickly to permit manual collection of the most critical early data, and require the use of pressure transducers placed in the well and monitored with an electronic data logger.

The resultant change in head over time is plotted on semi-log paper, and the curve analyzed according to one of several methods, depending on aquifer and well conditions. The method of analysis will depend on such factors as whether the aquifer is confined or unconfined, and what percentage of the saturated interval is screened in the well. Analytical methods for slug tests are described in Chapter 3.

Slug tests evaluate only the portion of the aquifer immediately surrounding the tested well. Therefore, tests should be performed at a selection of site wells, to best represent the variability in hydraulic conductivity for the aquifer.

Constant-Rate Pump Tests and Well Performance Tests. While slug tests provide reasonable estimates of hydraulic conductivity, they evaluate only the portion of the aquifer immediately adjacent to the well and are generally not adequate for the detailed design of a ground water pumping system. Constant-rate aquifer pumping tests are used to characterize conditions over a larger portion of the aquifer by measuring the response of the aquifer to pumping at observation wells located some distance from the pumping well, typically over a period of 24 hrs. or more. Analysis of constant rate tests is performed by plotting water level drawdown in individual observation wells versus elapsed pumping time, or drawdown in two or more observation wells versus distance from the pumping well at a specific time. The resulting curves are used to calculate aquifer transmissivity and storativity, well efficiency, and radius of influence, all of which are necessary for design of an efficient ground water pumping system. The more common methods of analysis are summarized in Chapter 3. Because constant rate tests are expensive to conduct, they are usually deferred until the detailed design phase of a ground water remediation program.

Stepped-rate well performance tests provide a measure of the specific capacity (discharge rate, Q, divided by drawdown, s) of a pumping well, from which transmissivity, T, [gpd/ft] can be estimated from the empirical relationship $Q/s = T/2000$ for a confined aquifer, or $Q/s = T/1500$ for unconfined units. Small scale well performance tests can be conducted during well development at relatively little extra cost. A stepped-rate pumping test, also referred to as a step-drawdown test, is generally conducted before a constant-rate aquifer pump test to determine the optimal pumping rate for the latter test. During a stepped rate test, the well is pumped at a constant rate until the water level in the well stabilizes. The specific capacity of the well is calculated, and the pumping rate can then be increased (stepped up) and the water level observed until it stabilizes again.

5.8 ACQUISITION OF SOIL AND GROUND WATER QUALITY DATA

Chemical analysis of soil and ground water samples is required to identify the contaminants, quantify their respective concentrations, and delineate their lateral and vertical extent. This section describes procedures for collection and handling of soil and ground water samples. The following discussion is intended only as a general guide. The project workplan should specify sampling and analysis protocol based on project goals and applicable regulations or guidelines.

5.8.1 General Sampling Procedures

To assure collection of data that accurately represent site conditions, proper protocol must be followed during sample collection and handling. In addition to providing design basis information for site clean-up, the data must also be of a quality acceptable to regulatory agencies. Data may also be admitted as evidence in legal proceedings and must withstand the scrutiny of opposing legal counsel.

Measures must be taken to ensure sample integrity, for example, to prevent the loss of contaminant mass from the sample as by volatilization or biodegradation. Equipment and tools that contact the samples should be composed of stainless steel, Teflon, or other materials, which will not react with the contaminants in the sample. Samples should be sealed in appropriate sample containers with preservatives specified by the analytical method (often an acid to inhibit microbial activity). Samples are retained on ice pending delivery to the laboratory and there refrigerated until tested to prevent loss of volatile constituents.

Equally important is preventing the introduction of contaminants into the sample from some other source (cross-contamination). The use of disposable or "dedicated" equipment minimizes the potential for cross-contamination. Alternatively, sampling equipment should be thoroughly cleansed between sample locations. Where possible, locations should be sampled in order of increasing contamination to minimize the possibility of cross-contamination between locations.

Most analyses have a specified maximum holding time between sample collection and analysis. Samples should be transported to the laboratory as expeditiously as possible, generally within 24 hrs. of collection. The shipment of samples must be accompanied by a chain-of-custody form, which includes the signatures and affiliations of the personnel collecting, relinquishing and receiving the samples, as well as the date and time of the transfer. Essential sample collection data (sample identification number, date, and time of collection) and the specifications of the laboratory program must also be included.

Soil Sample Collection and Handling Procedures. Soil samples should always be collected using clean sample tools composed of inert materials, such as stainless steel, Teflon, or nonreactive plastics. Tools should be thoroughly cleansed using hot water, steam, and/or detergents and rinsed, preferably with deionized water prior to use and between sampling locations.

Soil samples should be collected in clean glass jars (unless otherwise specified by laboratory procedure) with tight-fitting lids, and identified with an appropriate label bearing the unique identification number of the sample. The outer surface of soil cores should be trimmed using a clean knife prior to shipment to the laboratory to ensure that soils that have been in contact with formation fluids above the sample point or with the inside wall of the sampler are not tested.

Ground Water Sample Collection and Handling. Ground water sampling is usually preceded by measurement of water level in the well. The well should also be inspected for the presence of NAPLs using a hydrocarbon interface probe or transparent bailer, if there is reasonable potential for them to be present, and any accumulation or sheen is noted. Because ground water samples containing "free product" may not accurately represent dissolved phase concentrations, samples from wells containing NAPLs are frequently not analyzed.

To ensure collection of ground water samples that are representative of formation conditions to the maximum extent practical, monitoring wells are usually "purged" of water that has been standing in the well by pumping or bailing. Removal of three to five saturated casing volumes is a generally accepted minimum purge. Alternatively, wells are purged until measurements of water quality parameters such as temperature, specific conductance, and pH have stabilized. Samples are then collected in appropriate containers and preserved as specified by the analytical method.

As an alternative method, so-called low-flow purging and sampling has been gaining wider acceptance in recent years. The pump intake is set within the screen interval and water is pumped at a rate as low as 0.1 L/min. so that minimal drawdown occurs. Water quality parameters are measured continuously, and upon stabilization, the samples are collected. In addition to those mentioned above, dissolved oxygen and redox potential are frequently measured. No drawdown in the well indicates that the pump discharge is due primarily to flow into the well rather than exchange of water in casing storage.

Proponents of low-flow sampling claim less agitation and mixing of the water column results in collection of samples that are more representative of formation conditions. In addition, the volume of purge water requiring management as a waste is minimized. On the other hand, low-flow sampling can be more time consuming and require more highly trained sampling personnel than are required for conventional methods. In addition, dedicated low-flow pumps permanently installed in the wells are generally preferred, resulting in potentially significant capital costs. Use of peristaltic pumps can minimize the expense by requiring only dedicated tubing. However, use of peristaltic pumps is not universally accepted for collection of samples to be tested for volatile organic compounds and is limited to aquifers with water levels within the reach of suction lift.

Ground Water Field Measurements. Ground water sampling programs usually include field measurements of such general water quality parameters as temperature, specific conductivity, and pH, often to confirm adequate well purging. Redox potential (E_H) and dissolved oxygen content are also frequently measured at the time of sample collection to assess the potential for biodegradation and for design of treatment systems. Sample turbidity is frequently measured to assess the presence of suspended sediments on the results of metals analyses.

Sampling Quality Control Measures. Blank samples prepared from deionized water are frequently submitted for analysis as a quality control check on field and laboratory procedures. "Field blank" or "equipment blank" samples prepared in the field provide a quality control check on field sampling and equipment decontamination procedures. A sample of deionized water is decanted from the bailer or run through the sampling pump following the normal decontamination procedure, and submitted for laboratory analysis.

Workplans also often specify analysis of "trip blank" samples, usually for volatile organic compounds. This is a blank sample prepared in the laboratory and packed in the sample coolers, and which accompanies the other samples through the collection, transport, and analytical process.

Ground water samples collected for analysis of volatile organic constituents must be collected free of head space (air bubbles) to prevent volatile constituents from coming out of solution. Note, too, that excessive fine sediment content can interfere with some analyses, resulting in unacceptably high detection limits. Acids used in the preservation of samples collected for heavy metals analyses can leach naturally occurring metals from sediments in the sample, yielding false ground water sample results. Sample turbidity is frequently measured and filtered samples are sometimes collected to assess potential effects from suspended sediment.

5.8.2 Field Testing Methods

To aid in the preliminary assessment of the limits of the contaminated zone and to facilitate selection of samples for laboratory analysis, a variety of field testing methods are available for soil and ground water. Some service companies provide mobile laboratories that follow EPA-approved laboratory QA/QC procedures, and can provide results on-site within a few hours of collection. Also available are less expensive alternative methods, typically with relatively high detection limits (i.e., ppm vs. ppb) or merely semi-quantitative results, indicating the presence of the constituent. These can be used to establish the general limits of the contaminated zone, though confirmation of contaminant concentrations by an approved laboratory method is generally required.

Soil Gas Surveys. Soil gas surveys are a means of evaluating the presence of volatile organic constituents present in near-surface soils and ground water without actually collecting soil or ground water samples. A probe mounted on hollow pipe is pushed into the soil to the desired depth. Vapors are extracted from the probe by means of a vacuum pump and analyzed by a detection instrument, such as an organic vapor analyzer or portable gas chromatograph (GC) at the surface.

Because the results of vapor analyses are affected by a wide range of variables, and are frequently not acceptable to regulatory agencies as definitive of site conditions, soil gas surveys are most commonly used as a quantitative tool for assessing site conditions prior to a drilling and sampling program.

Soil Sample Headspace Vapor Analyses. An organic vapor analyzer or portable GC can also be used to measure the organic vapors in soil sample jar head space. Samples collected for this purpose must be sealed tightly in a partially filled jar and either agitated or allowed to sit for a period to permit constituents to volatilize. If laboratory analysis of volatile organics is also to be performed, the sample should be split and a portion properly stored for shipment to the laboratory.

The results of such head space analyses depend on variables such as soil type, the volatility of the constituents present, the temperature of the sample, residence time in the sample container, and the volume of soil versus head space in the container. Accordingly, they should be viewed as qualitative, providing a relative measure of the constituents present in the samples.

Colorimetric and Immunoassay Tests. Contaminant-specific test methods are also available for metals and organic compounds in soil and ground water. For soil samples, these methods typically require an extraction procedure followed by analysis of a liquid extract sample; ground water samples usually are tested directly. Most available field tests rely on either a chemical reaction or an immunoassay test to produce a coloration of the sample to detect the presence of particular contaminant or contaminant group. Immunoassay methods employ antibodies developed to exhibit a high sensitivity to a specific contaminant. The hue and intensity of the color developed in the sample is then usually compared to a chart that has been prepared using samples of known concentration to provide a semi-quantitative result.

Used in conjunction with a temporary ground water sampling installation, these methods can result in significant savings to the project budget by rapidly providing screening
level data preventing the installation of an unnecessary number of monitoring wells. However, the cost of the test kit and time required to perform the extraction and analytical procedures, and the limited quality of the data must be weighed against the cost of a more definitive laboratory analysis to ascertain whether such tests are worth conducting. Field screening
tests generally do not have detection limits sufficiently low to provide definitive ground water plume delineation. The quality control and repeatability of the data are also inadequate for
regulatory purposes in most instances. Therefore, results are generally confirmed by laboratory analysis of duplicate samples.

5.9 DATA EVALUATION PROCEDURES

Upon completion of the field and laboratory programs, site data must be integrated to construct a working model of contaminant plume migration within the ground water flow regime. As discussed earlier in this chapter, the key components of this hydrogeologic site
characterization are the geologic, hydrologic, and chemical data defining the occurrence and
movement of fluids in the subsurface and the entrainment of contaminants in this natural
flow system. Procedures for data organization and presentation are outlined below.

5.9.1 Geologic Data Evaluation

Available geologic data must be compiled to define the lateral and vertical configuration of
permeable and impermeable strata comprising the framework within which subsurface fluids
collect and flow. Conventional data presentation techniques include the following.
    Scaled geologic logs should be prepared for each soil boring, monitoring well, or geo-
physical profile completed on the site. As shown in Figure 5.16, in addition to a description
of the type and thickness of each stratum encountered, the log should indicate the drilling
location, ground surface elevation, drilling method, depth of ground water occurrence, driller
identification and date of completion (Hunt, 1984). For monitoring wells, as-built diagrams
should be prepared showing well construction and static water elevation with respect to
stratigraphy.
    Cross-section diagrams should illustrate the bedding and lateral continuity of the prin-
cipal stratigraphic units underlying the site. General guidelines for cross-section preparation
are provided in Hunt, 1984 and Tearpock and Bischke, 1991. Given the extreme variability of
shallow strata, care should be taken to avoid extrapolation of stratigraphic interpretations
beyond the area of available geologic logs. An example is provided on Figure 5.17.
    Structure maps and isopach drawings can be employed to characterize the physical con-
straints on ground water or contaminant flow through a water-bearing unit. Within a confined aquifer unit, a structure map (i.e., a topographic map of the upper surface of the water-
bearing unit) can be used to identify topographic highs or "traps" wherein floating

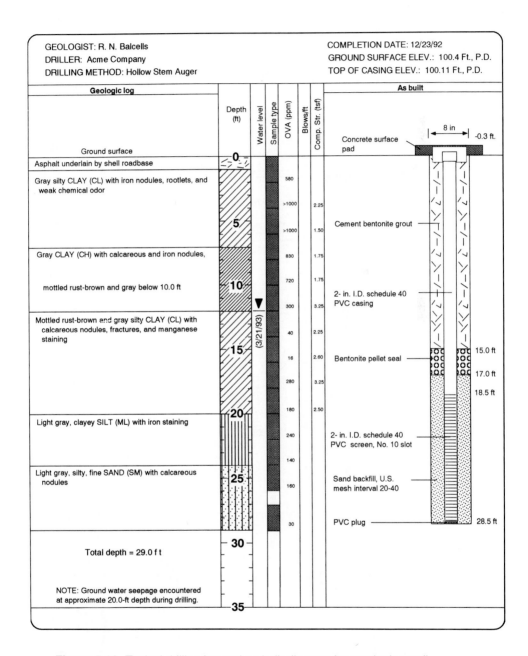

Figure 5.16 Typical drilling log and as-built diagram for monitoring well.

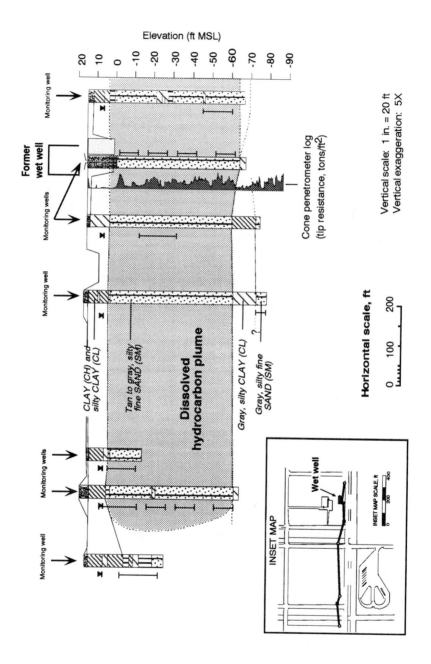

Figure 5.17 Geologic cross-section, west-east orientation, Case Study 1.

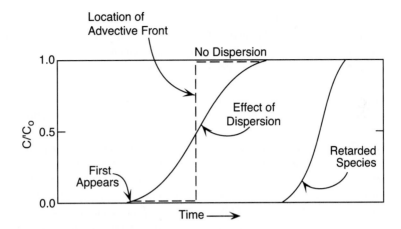

Figure 6.1 Breakthrough curves in 1-D showing effects of dispersion and retardation.

(Mackay et al., 1986; Roberts et al., 1986). LeBlanc et al. (1991) describe a natural gradient tracer experiment performed at Otis Air Base on Cape Cod, Massachusetts where more than 30,000 samples were analyzed over a two-year period. Detailed comparisons with the results from the Borden landfill were made (Section 6.10).

Borden and Bedient (1986), Rifai et al. (1988), and Barker et al. (1987) reported some success in measuring and modeling the biodegradation of contaminant plumes associated with naphthalene and BTEX in ground water. Several of these field projects are described in detail in later sections of the text.

The incorporation of the above transport mechanisms into ground water models for prediction and evaluation of waste sites has been described in many references over the past two decades. Some of the earliest efforts are presented in Bear (1972), Bredehoeft and Pinder (1973), Fried (1975), Anderson (1979), Bear (1979), and Freeze and Cherry (1979). More recently, Domenico and Schwartz (1998), Anderson and Woessner (1992), and Zheng and Bennett (1995) provide discussion of some of the more complex flow and transport issues facing the ground water modeler.

6.2 ADVECTION PROCESS

Advection represents the movement of a contaminant with the flowing ground water according to the seepage velocity in the pore space, which was defined in Eq. (2.5).

$$v_x = -\frac{K}{n}\frac{dh}{dL}$$

It is important to realize that seepage velocity equals the average linear velocity of a contaminant in porous media, and is the correct velocity for use in governing solute transport equations. As defined earlier, the average linear velocity, v_x, equals the Darcy velocity divided by effective porosity, n, associated with the pore space through which water can actually flow. The average linear velocity is less than the microscopic velocities of water molecules moving along individual flowpaths, due to tortuosity. The one dimensional (1-D) mass flux (F_x) due to advection equals the product of water flow and concentration (C) of solute, or $F_x = v_x n C$.

There are certain cases in the field where an advective model provides a useful estimate of contaminant transport. Some models include the concept of arrival time by integration along known streamlines (Nelson, 1977). Streamline models are used to solve for arrival times of particles that move along the streamlines at specified velocities, usually in a two dimensional (2-D) flow net. Others have set up an induced flow field through injection or pumping and evaluated breakthrough curves by numerical integration along flow lines. Dispersion is not directly considered in these models, but results from the variation of velocity and arrival times in the flow field (Charbeneau, 1981, 1982). In cases where pumping of ground water is dominating the flow field, it may be useful to neglect dispersion processes without loss of accuracy. In Chapter 10, it will be shown how advection is treated numerically by particle mover models, which represent the velocity of individual particles moving according to the local velocity field in the x or y direction.

6.3 DIFFUSION AND DISPERSION PROCESSES

Diffusion is a molecular-scale process, which causes spreading due to concentration gradients and random motion. Diffusion causes a solute in water to move from an area of higher concentration to an area of lower concentration. Diffusive transport can occur in the absence of velocity. Mass transport in the subsurface due to diffusion in 1-D can be described by Fick's first law of diffusion,

$$f_x = -D_d \frac{\partial C}{\partial x}$$

(6.1)

where

f_x = mass flux [M/L^2/T]
D_d = diffusion coefficient [L^2/T]
dC/d_x = concentration gradient [M/L^3/L]

Diffusion is usually only a factor in the case of very low velocities such as in a tight soil or clay liner, or in the case of mass transport involving very long time periods. Typical values of D_d are relatively constant and range from 1×10^{-9} to 2×10^{-9} m^2/sec at 25°C. Typical dispersion coefficients in ground water are several orders of magnitude larger and tend to dominate the spreading process when velocities are present.

A soil column similar to the one used by Darcy can be used to introduce the concept of advective-dispersive transport. The column is loaded continuously with tracer at relative concentration of $C/C_0 = 1$ across the entire cross section. Figure 6.1 shows the resulting concentration versus time response measured at $x = L$, called the breakthrough curve. The step function loading is begun at $t = 0$, and the breakthrough curve develops due to dispersion processes which create a zone of mixing between the displacing fluid and the fluid being displaced. The advective front (center of mass) moves at the average linear velocity (or seepage velocity) and $C/C_0 = 0.5$ at that point as shown in Figure 6.1. Velocity variations within the soil column cause some of the mass to leave the column in advance of the advective front and some lags behind, producing a dispersed breakthrough curve in the direction of flow. The size of the mixing zone increases as the advective front moves farther from the source, but at some distance behind the advective front, the source concentration C_0 is encountered, and it remains at steady state in this region. If there were no dispersion, the shape of the breakthrough curve would be identical to the step input function.

Dispersion is caused by heterogeneities in the medium that create variations in flow velocities and flow paths. These variations can occur due to friction within a single pore channel, due to velocity differences from one channel to another, or due to variable path lengths. Laboratory column studies indicate dispersion is a function of average linear velocity and a factor called dispersivity, α. Dispersivity in a soil column is on the order of centimeters, while values in field studies may be on the order of one to thousands of meters. Figure 6.2 shows the factors causing longitudinal dispersion (D_x) of a contaminant in the porous media.

Mass transport due to dispersion can also occur normal to the direction of flow. This transverse dispersion, D_y, is caused by diverging flowpaths in the porous media that cause mass to spread laterally from the main direction of flow. In most cases involving a two-dimensional plume of contamination, D_y is much less than D_x, and the shape of the plume tends to be elongated in the direction of flow.

Freeze and Cherry (1979) defined hydrodynamic dispersion as the process in which solutes spread out and are diluted compared to simple advection alone. It is defined as the sum of molecular diffusion and mechanical dispersion, where much dispersion is caused by local variations in velocity around some mean velocity of flow.

Dispersion in 2-D causes spreading in the longitudinal (x) and transverse (y) directions both ahead of and lateral to the advective front. Many typical contaminant plumes in ground water are represented by 2-D advective-dispersive mechanisms. Figure 6.3 depicts the normal shape of such a plume in 2-D compared to advection alone. Longitudinal dispersion causes spreading and decreases concentrations near the frontal portions of the

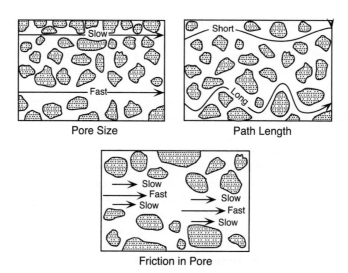

Figure 6.2 Factors causing longitudinal dispersion.

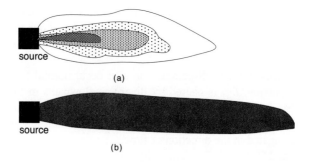

Figure 6.3 (a) Advection and dispersion. (b) Advection only.

plume. The main difference with the 1-D soil column results described above is that 2-D plumes have transverse spreading which reduces concentrations everywhere behind the advective front.

For the case of an instantaneous or pulse source (such as a sudden release or spill of contaminant into the subsurface), the variation in concentration with time and space is shown in Figure 6.4. The concentration distributions start out with sharp fronts and are smoothed out as the contaminant is diluted through dispersive mixing. The center of mass is advected at the average linear velocity. Concentrations can be described by

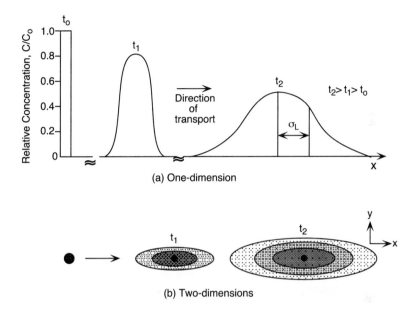

Figure 6.4 Instantaneous (Pulse) source. The shapes can be represented by Gaussian (Normal) distributions.

Gaussian or normal distributions in 1-D, 2-D, or 3-D geometries. Equations for prediction of pulse source concentrations as a function of space and time are presented in Sections 6.5 and 6.7. From the characteristics of the normal curves in Figure 6.4, one can show that dispersion coefficients can be related to the variance of the distributions, $D_x = \sigma_x^2/2t$ and $D_y = \sigma_y^2/2t$. Thus, by measuring the spread or variance in a plume, one can estimate a value for D_x and D_y at a field site. Dispersion is discussed in more detail in Sections 6.9 and 6.10.

6.4 MASS TRANSPORT EQUATIONS

Dispersive flux in a flow field with average linear velocity components v_x and v_y can be written in terms of the statistical fluctuations of velocity about the average, v_{x*} and v_{y*}. For the case of a uniform flow field where $v_x = \bar{v}_x$ a constant, and $v_y = 0$, dispersive flux is assumed proportional to the concentration gradient in the x direction:

$$f_{x*} = nCv_{x*} = -nD_x \frac{\partial C}{\partial x} \qquad (6.2)$$

where D_x is the longitudinal dispersion coefficient, n is effective porosity and C is concentration of contaminant tracer. Similarly, the dispersive flux f_{y*} is assumed proportional to the concentration gradient in the y direction:

$$f_{y*} = nCv_{y*} = -nD_y \frac{\partial C}{\partial y}$$
(6.3)

For a simple uniform flow field with average linear velocity $\bar{v}_x$

$$D_x = \alpha_x \bar{v}_x$$
(6.4)

$$D_y = \alpha_y \bar{v}_x$$
(6.5)

where α_x and α_y are the longitudinal and transverse dispersivities, respectively.

Dispersivity values have usually been set constant in transport models, but studies by Smith and Schwartz (1980) and Gelhar et al. (1979) indicate that dispersivity depends on the distribution of heterogeneities and the scale of the field problem. Many investigators during the decade of the eighties worked on the complex problem of estimating dispersivity from field tracer studies and pump tests, and both statistical and deterministic models have been postulated (Anderson, 1979; Freeze and Cherry, 1979; Mackay et al., 1986; Gelhar and Axness, 1983; Freyberg, 1986; Dagan, 1986, 1987, 1988; Neuman et al., 1987).

It should be noted that dispersion coefficients become more complex in a nonuniform flow field characterized by v_x and v_y. The dispersion coefficient relates the mass flux vector to the gradient of concentration and can be represented as a second rank tensor (Bear, 1979). Through careful definition of the coordinate system, relationships can be developed between D_x, D_y, and D_z and the components of the tensor [D] (Wang and Anderson, 1982).

6.4.1 Derivation of the Advection Dispersion Equation for Solute Transport

The equation governing transport in ground water is a statement of the law of conservation of mass. The derivation is based on those of Ogata (1970) and Bear (1972) and is presented in Freeze and Cherry (1979). It will be assumed that the porous medium is homogeneous and isotropic, and saturated; it is further assumed that the flow is steady-state and that Darcy's law applies. The flow is described by the average linear velocity or seepage velocity, which transports the dissolved substance by advection. If advection were the only transport mechanism operating, conservative solutes would move according to plug flow concepts. In reality, there is an additional mixing process, hydrodynamic dispersion, which is caused by velocity variations within each pore channel and from one channel to another. Hydrodynamic dispersion is used to account for the additional transport (spreading) caused by the fluctuations in the velocity field.

To establish the mathematical statement of the conservations of mass, the solute flux into and out of a representative elemental volume in the porous medium will be considered (Figure 6.5). In Cartesian coordinates the specific discharge v has components (v_x, v_y, v_z) and the average linear velocity $\bar{v} = v/n$ has components $(\bar{v}_x, \bar{v}_y, \bar{v}_z)$. The rate of advective trans port is equal to $\bar{v}$. The concentration of the solute C is defined as the mass of solute per unit volume of solution. The mass of solute per unit volume of porous media is therefore nC. For a homogeneous medium, the effective porosity n is a constant, and $\partial(nC)/\partial x = n\ \partial C/\partial x$. The mass of solute transported in the x-direction by the two mechanisms of solute transport can be represented as

$$\text{transport by advection} = \bar{v}_x nC\ dA \tag{6.6}$$

$$\text{transport by dispersion} = nD_x \frac{\partial C}{\partial x} dA$$

where D_x is the hydrodynamic dispersion coefficient in the x-direction and dA is the elemental cross-sectional area of the cubic element. The dispersion coefficient D_x is related to the dispersivity ax and the diffusion coefficient D_d by:

$$D_x = \alpha_x \bar{v}_x + D_d \tag{6.7}$$

The form of the dispersive component embodied in Eq. (6.6) is analogous to Fick's first law.

If F_x represents the total mass of solute per unit cross-sectional area transported in the x direction per unit time, then

$$F_x = \bar{v}_x nC - nD_x \frac{\partial C}{\partial x} \tag{6.8}$$

The negative sign before the dispersive term indicates that the contaminant moves toward the area of lower concentration. Similarly, expressions for flux in the other two directions can be written

$$F_y = \bar{v}_y nC - nD_y \frac{\partial C}{\partial y} \tag{6.9}$$

$$F_z = \bar{v}_z nC - nD_z \frac{\partial C}{\partial z} \tag{6.10}$$

The total amount of solute entering the fluid element (Figure 6.5) is

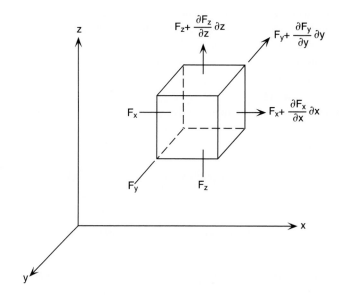

Figure 6.5 Mass balance in a cubic element in space.

$$F_x dzdy + F_y dzdx + F_z dxdy$$

The total amount leaving the representative fluid element is

$$\left(F_x + \frac{\partial F_x}{\partial x} dx \right) dzdy + \left(F_y + \frac{\partial F_y}{\partial y} dy \right) dzdx + \left(F_z + \frac{\partial F_z}{\partial z} dz \right) dxdy$$

The difference in the amount entering and leaving the fluid element is

$$\left(\frac{\partial F_x}{\partial x} + \frac{\partial F_y}{\partial y} + \frac{\partial F_z}{\partial z} \right) dxdydz$$

Because the dissolved tracer is assumed to be conservative (nonreactive), the difference between the flux into the element and the flux out of the element equals the amount of dissolved substance accumulated in the element. The rate of mass change in the element can be represented by

$$-n\frac{\partial C}{\partial t}dxdydz$$

The complete conservation of mass expression, therefore, becomes

$$\frac{\partial F_x}{\partial x}+\frac{\partial F_y}{\partial y}+\frac{\partial F_z}{\partial z}=-n\frac{\partial C}{\partial t} \tag{6.11}$$

Substitution of expressions for F_x, F_y, and F_z into (6.11) and cancellation of n from both sides of the equation yield:

$$\left[\frac{\partial}{\partial x}\left(D_x\frac{\partial C}{\partial x}\right)+\frac{\partial}{\partial y}\left(D_y\frac{\partial C}{\partial y}\right)+\frac{\partial}{\partial z}\left(D_z\frac{\partial C}{\partial z}\right)\right]$$

$$-\left[\frac{\partial}{\partial x}(\bar{v}_xC)+\frac{\partial}{\partial y}(\bar{v}_yC)+\frac{\partial}{\partial z}(\bar{v}_zC)\right]=\frac{\partial C}{\partial t} \tag{6.12}$$

In a homogeneous medium in which the velocity is steady and uniform (i.e., if it does not vary through time or space), and dispersion coefficients D_x, D_y, and D_z do not vary through space, (but $D_x \neq D_y \neq D_z$, in general), Eq. (6.12) becomes

$$\left[D_x\frac{\partial^2 C}{\partial x^2}+D_y\frac{\partial^2 C}{\partial y^2}+D_z\frac{\partial^2 C}{\partial z^2}\right]-\left[\bar{v}_x\frac{\partial C}{\partial x}+\bar{v}_y\frac{\partial C}{\partial y}+\bar{v}_z\frac{\partial C}{\partial z}\right]=\frac{\partial C}{\partial t} \tag{6.13}$$

In two dimensions, the governing equation for a one-dimensional velocity becomes

$$\left[D_x\frac{\partial^2 C}{\partial x^2}+D_y\frac{\partial^2 C}{\partial y^2}\right]-\left[\bar{v}_x\frac{\partial C}{\partial x}\right]=\frac{\partial C}{\partial t} \tag{6.14}$$

In one dimension, such as for a soil column, the governing equation reduces to the familiar advective-dispersion equation, which can be solved using Laplace transforms,

$$D_x\frac{\partial^2 C}{\partial x^2}-\bar{v}_x\frac{\partial C}{\partial x}=\frac{\partial C}{\partial t} \tag{6.15}$$

A number of analytical solutions exist for Eqs. (6.13), (6.14) and (6.15) under various simplifying assumptions and some of these are presented in Section 6.5.

6.5 ONE-DIMENSIONAL MODELS

The governing mass transport Eq. (6.13) is difficult to solve in field cases of practical interest due to boundary irregularities and variations in aquifer characteristics, so numerical methods must generally be employed. There are, however, a limited number of relatively simple,
1-D problems for which analytical solutions exist. Several of these cases are presented below
in order to gain insights into the effect of advection, dispersion, and adsorption on the overall
patterns produced.

The simplifying assumptions include the following: (1) the tracer is ideal, with constant density and viscosity; (2) the fluid is incompressible; (3) the medium is homogeneous
and isotropic; and (4) only saturated flow is considered. For the case of a nonreactive tracer in
1-D flow in the $+x$ direction, Eq. (6.15) applies.

$$D_x \frac{\partial^2 C}{\partial x^2} - v_x \frac{\partial C}{\partial x} = \frac{\partial C}{\partial t} \tag{6.16}$$

where D_x = coefficient of hydrodynamic dispersion and v_x = average seepage velocity. Note
that the bar over the velocity terms is dropped for convenience.

Several different solutions can be derived for Eq. (6.16) depending on initial and boundary conditions and whether the tracer input is a slug input or a continuous release (Figures
6.1 and 6.4a). Initial conditions ($t = 0$) in a soil column are usually set to zero ($C(x,0) = 0$)
or to some constant background concentration. Boundary conditions must be specified at the
two ends of the 1-D column. For a continuous source load at $x = 0$, the concentration is set
to $C(0,t) = C_0$ for $t > 0$. The concentration at the other boundary, $x = \infty$ is set to zero
$C(x, \infty) = 0$ for $t > 0$.

Case 6.1   Continuous Source in 1-D. For an infinite column with back-
ground concentration of zero and input tracer concentration C_0 at $-\infty \le x \le 0$ for $t \ge 0$, Bear
(1961) solves the problem using the Laplace transform at $x = L$, length of the column:

$$\frac{C(x,t)}{C_0} = \frac{1}{2}\left(\text{erfc}\left[\frac{L - v_x t}{2\sqrt{D_x t}} \right] + \exp\left(\frac{v_x L}{D_x} \right) \text{erfc}\left[\frac{L + v_x t}{2\sqrt{D_x t}} \right] \right) \tag{6.17}$$

where erfc is the complementary error function, $\text{erfc}(x) = 1 - \text{erf}(x) = 1 - \left(2/\sqrt{\pi} \right)\int_0^x e^{-u^2}\, du$

The center of mass ($C/C_0 = 0.5$) of the breakthrough curve travels with the average linear velocity v_x and corresponds to the point where $x = v_x t$. Note that the second term on the
right hand side of Eq. (6.17) can generally be neglected for most practical problems. The
error function erf (β) and erfc(β) are tabulated in Table 6.1.

TABLE 6.1 Values of erf (β) and erfc (β) for positive values of β

β	erf (β)	erfc (β)
0	0	1.0
0.05	0.056372	0.943628
0.1	0.112463	0.887537
0.15	0.167996	0.832004
0.2	0.222703	0.777297
0.25	0.276326	0.723674
0.3	0.328627	0.671373
0.35	0.379382	0.620618
0.4	0.428392	0.571608
0.45	0.475482	0.524518
0.5	0.520500	0.479500
0.55	0.563323	0.436677
0.6	0.603856	0.396144
0.65	0.642029	0.357971
0.7	0.677801	0.322199
0.75	0.711156	0.288844
0.8	0.742101	0.257899
0.85	0.770668	0.229332
0.9	0.796908	0.203092
0.95	0.820891	0.179109
1.0	0.842701	0.157299
1.1	0.880205	0.119795
1.2	0.910314	0.089686
1.3	0.934008	0.065992
1.4	0.952285	0.047715
1.5	0.966105	0.033895
1.6	0.976348	0.023652
1.7	0.983790	0.016210
1.8	0.989091	0.010909
1.9	0.992790	0.007210
2	0.995322	0.004678
2.1	0.997021	0.002979
2.2	0.998137	0.001863
2.3	0.998857	0.001143
2.4	0.999311	0.000689
2.5	0.999593	0.000407
2.6	0.999764	0.000236
2.7	0.999866	0.000134
2.8	0.999925	0.000075
2.9	0.999959	0.000041
3	0.999978	0.000022

Source: Domenico and Schwartz, 1990

Case 6.2   Instantaneous Source in 1-D. The corresponding solution can be derived for the injection of a tracer pulse (instantaneous input) at $x = 0$ with background concentration equal to zero in the column. As the slug moves downstream with v_x in the $+x$ direction, it spreads out according to

$$C(x,t) = \frac{M}{(4\pi D_x t)^{1/2}} \exp\left[-\frac{(x - v_x t)^2}{4D_x t}\right]$$ (6.18)

where M is the injected mass per unit cross-sectional area. Figure 6.4 shows the resulting Gaussian distribution of concentration for the instantaneous pulse source in one-dimension.

Plots comparing the shapes of Eqs. (6.17) and (6.18) are shown in Figures 6.1 and 6.4, respectively, at $x = L$ at the end of a soil column. The differences between instantaneous (spike) source and continuous source transport problems are obvious in 1-D. The continuous source produces a response or breakthrough curve, which starts at a low concentration and eventually levels off to the initial input concentration C_0 as a function of time. The spike source produces a normal or Gaussian distribution which continues to decrease in maximum concentration due to spreading out with time in the direction of flow. For the spike source, the amount of mass under each curve is identical if the tracer is conservative.

Case 6.3   Adsorption Effects. While there exist many reactions that can alter contaminant concentrations in ground water, adsorption onto the soil matrix appears to be one of the dominant mechanisms. Adsorption is covered in more detail in Chapter 7. The concept of the isotherm is used to relate the amount of contaminant adsorbed by the solids S to the concentration in solution, C. One of the most commonly used isotherms is the Freundlich isotherm,

$$S = K_d C^b$$ (6.19)

where S is the mass of solute adsorbed per unit bulk dry mass of porous media, K_d is the distribution coefficient, and b is an experimentally derived coefficient. If $b = 1$, Eq. (6.19) is known as the linear isotherm and is incorporated into the 1-D advective-dispersion equation in the following way:

$$D_x \frac{\partial^2 C}{\partial x^2} - v_x \frac{\partial C}{\partial x} - \frac{\rho_b}{n}\frac{\partial S}{\partial t} = \frac{\partial C}{\partial t}$$ (6.20)

where ρ_b is the bulk dry mass density, n is porosity, and

$$-\frac{\rho_b}{n}\frac{\partial S}{\partial t} = \frac{\rho_b}{n}\frac{dS}{dC}\frac{\partial C}{\partial t}$$

For the case of the linear isotherm, $(dS/dC) = K_d$, and

$$D_x \frac{\partial^2 C}{\partial x^2} - v_x \frac{\partial C}{\partial x} = \frac{\partial C}{\partial t}\left(1 + \frac{\rho_b}{n} K_d\right)$$

or finally,

$$\frac{D_x}{R}\frac{\partial^2 C}{\partial x^2} - \frac{v_x}{R}\frac{\partial C}{\partial x} = \frac{\partial C}{\partial t} \tag{6.21}$$

where $R = [1 + (\rho_b/n)\, K_d]$ = retardation factor, which has the effect of retarding the adsorbed species relative to the advective velocity of the ground water (Figure 6.1). The retardation factor is equivalent to the ratio of velocity of the sorbing contaminant and the ground water and ranges from one to several thousand.

The use of the distribution coefficient assumes that partitioning reactions between solute and soil are very fast relative to the rate of ground water flow. Thus, it is possible for nonequilibrium fronts to occur that appear to migrate faster than retarded fronts, which are at equilibrium. These complexities involve other rate-kinetic factors beyond the scope of simple models discussed in this chapter (see Chapter 7).

An interesting case study is that of a semi-infinite column where the column ($x > 0$) is initially at $C = 0$, and is connected to a contaminant source containing tracer at $C = C_0$ ($x = 0$). The tracer continuously moves down the column at seepage velocity v_x in the $+x$ direction. It is assumed that $C = 0$ at $x = \infty$. For the case of linear adsorption, Eq. (6.21) is used, where R = retardation factor ≥ 1 described earlier for adsorption. The solution in this case becomes (Bear, 1972)

$$C(x,t) = \frac{C_0}{2}\left[\text{erfc}\left(\frac{Rx - v_x t}{2\sqrt{RD_x t}}\right) + \exp\left(\frac{v_x x}{D_x}\right)\text{erfc}\left(\frac{Rx + v_x t}{2\sqrt{RD_x t}}\right)\right] \tag{6.22}$$

Ogata and Banks (1961) showed that the second term in Eq. (6.22) can be neglected where $D_x/v_x x < 0.002$; this condition produces an error of less than 3%. Equation (6.22) then reduces to a form similar to Eq. (6.17) with an adjustment for R.

Equation (6.17) or (6.22) can be used in laboratory studies to determine dispersion coefficients for nonreactive and adsorbing species. Retarded fronts can be derived from conservative fronts by adjusting v_x/R and D_x/R in 1-D. Typical values of R for organics often encountered in field sites range from 2 to 10 (Roberts et al. 1986). Larger values of D_x tend to spread out the fronts while large values of R tend to slow the velocity of the center of mass ($C/C_0 = 0.5$) and reduce D_x by a factor of $1/R$. Conceptually, in 1-D, these transport mechanisms are relatively well understood for laboratory scale experiments.

Case 6.4   Transport and 1-D with First Order Decay. One example of mass transport that includes a simple kinetic reaction is the first order decay of a solute. This could be caused by radioactive decay, biodegradation, or hydrolysis, and is generally represented in the transport equation by adding the term $-\lambda C$, where λ is the first order decay rate in units of t^{-1}. For example, Eq. (6.16) would become the following:

$$D_x \frac{\partial^2 C}{\partial x^2} - v_x \frac{\partial C}{\partial x} - \lambda C = \frac{\partial C}{\partial t} \qquad (6.23)$$

The resulting solution to the equation for a pulse source is given by Eq. (6.18) but multiplied by the factor $e^{-\lambda t}$. In general, the effect of the decay coefficient is to reduce mass and concentration as a function of time. This concept is described in more detail for hydrolysis and biodegradation in Chapters 7 and 8.

Example 6.1.   APPLICATION OF 1-D TRANSPORT EQUATION

a) An underground tank leaches an organic (benzene) continuously into a one-dimensional aquifer having a hydraulic conductivity of 2.15 m/day, an effective porosity of 0.1 and a hydraulic gradient of 0.04 m/m. Assuming an initial concentration of 1000 mg/L, and longitudinal dispersivity of 7.5 m, find the time taken for the contaminant concentration to reach 100 mg/L at $L = 750$ m. Neglect any other degradation processes.

Seepage velocity v_x is calculated from Darcy's Law:

$$v_x = \frac{K \Delta h / \Delta x}{n} = \frac{2.15 \times 0.04}{0.1} = 0.86 \text{ m/day}$$

$$D_X = \alpha_X v_X = 7.5 \times 0.86 = 6.45 \text{ m}^2/\text{day}$$

Using Eq. (6.17) and ignoring the second term,

$$C(L,t) = \frac{C_0}{2} \operatorname{erfc} \left(\frac{L - v_x t}{2\sqrt{D_x t}} \right)$$

$$100 = 500 \operatorname{erfc} \left(\frac{750 - 0.86t}{2\sqrt{6.45t}} \right)$$

$$\frac{750 - 0.86t}{2\sqrt{6.45t}} = 0.9064$$

By trial and error,

$$\boxed{t = 728 \text{ days} = 1.99 \text{ yr}}$$

b) One of the drums stored at the above site breaks and suddenly releases 1 kg of decaying Cs-137 (half life of 33 years) over the cross-section of flow, which is estimated to be 10 m². What is the concentration (in mg/m³) at $L = 100$ m, 90 days later?

Solution. The decay rate is calculated:

$$\lambda = \frac{\ln 2}{(33 \times 365)} = 5.755 \times 10^{-5} \text{ day}^{-1}$$

Using Eq. (6.18) and incorporating radioactive decay,

$$C(x,t) = \left\{ \frac{M}{\sqrt{4\pi D_x t}} \exp\left[-\frac{(x - v_x t)^2}{4 D_x t} \right] \right\} \exp(-\lambda t)$$

$$= \frac{10^6 \text{ mg} / 10\text{m}^2}{\sqrt{4\pi(6.45)(90)}} \exp\left\{ -\frac{[100 - (0.86)(90)]^2}{4 \times 6.45 \times 90} \right\} \exp\left(-5.755 \times 10^{-5} \times 90 \right)$$

$$\boxed{C(x,t) = 934.79\text{mg} / \text{m}^3 \text{ or } 0.935 \text{ mg/L}}$$

6.6 GOVERNING FLOW AND TRANSPORT EQUATIONS

The differential equation for simulating ground water flow in two dimensions is usually written (see Eq. (2.26) and (2.28))

$$\frac{\partial}{\partial x}\left(T_x \frac{\partial h}{\partial x} \right) + \frac{\partial}{\partial y}\left(T_y \frac{\partial h}{\partial y} \right) = S \frac{\partial h}{\partial t} + W \qquad (6.24)$$

where

$T_x = K_x b$ = transmissivity in the x direction [L²/T]
$T = K_x b$ = transmissivity in the y direction [L²/T]
b = aquifer thickness [L]
S = storage coefficient
W = source or sink term [L/T]
H = hydraulic head [L]

The governing flow equation in 2-D must be solved before the transport equation can be solved. Chapter 10 describes numerical methods that can be used to solve Eq. (6.24) for an actual field site. The resulting head distribution $h(x, y)$ can then be used to determine gradients and seepage velocities in two dimensions.

The governing transport equation in 2-D is usually written

$$\frac{\partial}{\partial x}\left(D_x \frac{\partial C}{\partial x}\right) + \frac{\partial}{\partial y}\left(D_y \frac{\partial C}{\partial y}\right) - \frac{\partial}{\partial x}\left(Cv_x\right) - \frac{\partial}{\partial y}\left(Cv_y\right) - \frac{C_0 W}{nb} + \Sigma R_k = \frac{\partial C}{\partial t} \qquad (6.25)$$

where

C = concentration of solute [M/L^3]

v_x, v_y = seepage velocity [L/T] averaged in the vertical direction

D_x, D_y = coefficient of dispersion [L^2/T] in x and y directions

C_0 = solute concentration in source or sink fluid [M/L^3]

R_k = rate of addition or removal of solute (±) [M/L^{3}T]

N = effective porosity

W = source or sink term

Equation (6.25) can only be solved analytically under the most simplifying conditions where velocities are constant, dispersion coefficients are constant, and source terms are simple functions. There are difficulties in attempting to use the mass transport equation to describe an actual field site, since dispersivities in the x and y directions are difficult to estimate from tracer tests due to the presence of spatial heterogeneities and other reactions in the porous media. Estimation of hydraulic conductivity, and associated velocities, can be quite difficult due to the presence of field heterogeneities that are often unknown. The source or sink concentrations that drive the model are usually assumed constant in time, but may actually have varied significantly. A particularly serious problem appears to be the reaction term, which may represent adsorption, ion exchange, or biodegradation. The assumption of equilibrium conditions and the selection of rate coefficients are both subject to some error and may create prediction problems at many field sites. In addition, fuels and solvents can create nonaqueous phase liquids (NAPLs) in the subsurface, which are difficult to measure and can provide sources of soluble contaminants for years to come (Chapter 11).

Despite all the above mentioned problems, mass transport models still offer the most reliable approach to organization of field data, prediction of plume migration, and ultimate management of waste-disposal problems. While a complete 3-D scenario with all rate coefficients included will probably never be achieved, presently existing 1-D and 2-D solute transport models have much to offer in simplifying and providing insight into complex ground water problems. Chapter 10 presents numerical methods for the solution of 2-D and 3-D flow and solute transport problems.

6.7 ANALYTICAL METHODS

Two-dimensional analytical modeling is one of the most useful tools for analyzing and predicting solute transport in a field situation. This type of model is considerably more versatile than the 1-D models previously discussed. Horizontal 2-D modeling can be used where (1) no vertical velocity components exist, or (2) observation wells or monitoring points are fully screened and provide averaged data in 2-D for a relatively uniformly thick aquifer. Nonuniformities in the flow field may be due to variations in topography and permeability, or to natural or artificial sinks such as wells and springs, or to recharge points such as injection wells or leakage from lagoons. Probably the most common reason for using a horizontal 2-D analysis is that the monitoring wells are typically distributed about the horizontal plane. Most wells are fully penetrating, and therefore any samples collected represent an approximate vertical average in that portion of the aquifer.

Sampling in the vertical direction may be warranted where there are significant differences between the contaminant density and water density or where detailed information is available on vertical variations in aquifer hydraulic conductivity or porosity. Profile 2-D models are available for such cases that represent a vertical slice of aquifer. A full 3-D picture is only rarely available for a field site, and requires the use of numerous wells in the x–y plane screened at vertical intervals for discrete sampling. The classic studies performed at the Borden Landfill in Canada provide excellent examples of a well-monitored field test in 3-D (Mackay et al., 1986).

To study the variation in contaminants in 2-D, it is first necessary to solve the governing equations (Eq. (6.24) and (6.25)) in the x and y directions. The techniques available for developing a solution include analytical, semi-analytical, and sophisticated numerical methods that have been developed over the past 25 years. Analytical methods basically provide a closed form solution for relatively simple boundary and initial conditions. Semi-analytical methods usually result in an integral type solution that must be evaluated by a simple numerical integration procedure. Numerical methods are discussed in Chapters 8 and 10.

Analytical models are developed by solving the transport equation for certain simplified boundary and initial conditions. Numerous analytical solutions are available in the literature (Bear, 1979; Hunt, 1978; Wilson and Miller, 1978; Cleary and Ungs, 1978; Shen, 1976; Galya, 1987; Javandel et al., 1984; Domenico and Robbins, 1985) for pulse and continuous contaminant sources with boundary conditions ranging from no flow to constant heads. Processes that may be included in these models are advection, dispersion, adsorption, and first order decay (biological or radioactive). Analytical solutions generally require constant parameters, simple geometries, and well-defined boundary conditions, but they do provide useful insights into many ground water contaminant sites where two-dimensional variation can be assumed.

One of the first 2-D analytical models was that developed by Wilson and Miller (1978). It is one of the simplest to use and can account for lateral and transverse dispersion, adsorption, and first order decay in a uniform flow field. Concentration C at any point in the x,y plane can be predicted by solving Eq. (6.14) for an instantaneous spike source or for continuous injection. First order decay is added to the equation by adding a term, $-\lambda C$ to the left-hand side of Eq. (6.14), where the first order decay rate is λ $[T^{-1}]$. Velocity in the y-direction is assumed to be zero, and the x-axis is oriented in the direction of flow. Contaminants are assumed to be injected uniformly throughout the vertical axis.

Bear (1972) provides a solution to Eq. (6.14) for the condition where steady state conditions have been reached and the plume has been stabilized. The solution requires use of K_0, defined as the modified Bessel function of second kind and zero order. Q equals the rate at which a tracer of concentration C_0 is being injected.

$$C(x,y) = \frac{C_0 Q}{2\pi(D_x D_y)^{1/2}} \exp\left(\frac{v_x x}{2D_x}\right) K_o \left\{ \frac{v_x^2}{4D_x} \left(\frac{x^2}{D_x} + \frac{y^2}{D_y} \right)^{1/2} \right\} \qquad (6.26)$$

Case 6.5 Pulse Source Models. If a pulse of contaminant is injected over the full thickness of a two-dimensional homogeneous aquifer it will move in the direction of flow and spread out with time. Figure 6.6 represents the theoretical pattern of contamination at various points in time. A line source model from De Josselin De Jong (1958) assumes that the spill occurs as a line source (well) loaded vertically into a two-dimensional flow field (x, y). If a tracer with concentration C_0 is injected over an area A at a point (x_0, y_0), the concentration at any point (x, y) at time t after the injection is given by the following equation. Average linear velocity v_x, longitudinal dispersion, D_x, and transverse dispersion, D_y, are all assumed to be constant in this equation.

$$C(x,y,t) = \frac{C_0 A}{4\pi t(D_x D_y)^{1/2}} \exp\left\{ -\frac{\left((x-x_0) - v_x t\right)^2}{4D_x t} - \frac{(y-y_0)^2}{4D_y t} \right\} \qquad (6.27)$$

The corollary equation in 3-D from a point source was derived by Baetsle (1969) and can sometimes be used to represent the sudden release from a single source or tank in the subsurface. Baetsle's model gives the following equation:

$$C(x,y,z,t) = \frac{C_0 V_0}{8(\pi t)^{3/2}\left(D_x D_y D_z\right)^{1/2}} \exp\left[-\frac{(x-vt)^2}{4D_x t} - \frac{y^2}{4D_y t} - \frac{z^2}{4D_z t} - \lambda t \right] \qquad (6.28)$$

where C_0 is the original concentration; V_0 is the original volume so that $C_0 V_0$ is the mass involved in the spill; D_x, D_y, D_z, are the coefficients of hydrodynamic dispersion; v is the velocity of the contaminant; λ is the first order decay constant for a radioactive substance. For a nonradioactive substance, the term λt is ignored.

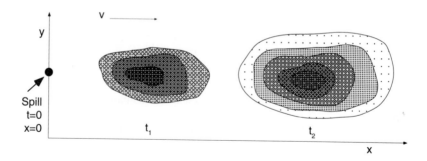

Figure 6.6 Plan view of instantaneous point source in time. Two dimensions.

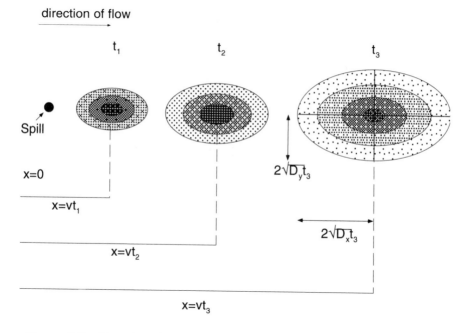

Figure 6.7 Plan view of plume developed from an instantaneous point source at three different times. Three dimensions.

With an idealized 3-D point source spill, spreading occurs in the direction of flow, and the peak or maximum concentration occurs at the center of the Gaussian plume where $y = z = 0$ and $x = vt$ (Figure 6.7).

$$C_{max} = \frac{C_0 V_0 e^{-\lambda t}}{8(\pi t)^{3/2}(D_x D_y D_z)^{1/2}} \tag{6.29}$$

The dimensions of the plume, assuming it actually started as a point source are

$$\sigma_x = (2D_x t)^{1/2}; \qquad \sigma_y = (2D_y t)^{1/2}; \qquad \sigma_z = (2D_z t)^{1/2} \tag{6.30}$$

where σ is the standard deviation, and $3\sigma_x$, $3\sigma_y$, and $3\sigma_z$ represent three standard deviations away from the mean within which 99.7% of the contaminant mass is contained.

EXAMPLE 6.2   TWO-DIMENSIONAL PULSE SOURCE.

A tank holding chloride at a concentration of 10,000 mg/L accidentally leaks over an area of 10 m^2 into an aquifer. Assuming that chloride is a completely conservative tracer, that $D_x = 1$ m^2/day and $D_y = 0.1$ m2/day, and that the seepage velocity is 1.0 m/day, calculate:

a) the time required for the center of mass of the plume to reach a point 75 m away;

b) the peak concentration at that point; and

c) the x and y dimensions of the plume at that point.

Solution.

a) Time required to reach 75 m:

$$t = \frac{R_t x}{V_w} = \frac{1\,(75\text{m})}{1\text{m}/\text{day}} = 75 \text{ days}$$

b) Peak concentration at 75 m:

$$C_{max} = \frac{C_0 A}{4\pi t (D_x D_y)^{1/2}}$$

$$= \frac{10^4 \,\text{mg}/\text{L} \times 10\text{m}^2}{4\pi \times 75 C_{max} \times (1\text{m}^2/\text{day} \times 0.1\text{m}^2/\text{day})^{1/2}}$$

$$= 335.7 \text{ mg/L}$$

c) Plume dimensions:

$$\sigma_x = (2D_x t)^{1/2} = (2 \cdot 1 \cdot 75)^{1/2} \text{ m} = 12.25 \text{ m}$$

$$x \text{ dimension} = 3\sigma_x = 36.7 \text{ m}$$

$$\sigma_y = (2D_y t)^{1/2} = (2 \cdot 0.1 \cdot 75)^{1/2} = 3.87 \text{ m}$$

$$y \text{ dimension} = 3\sigma_y = 11.6 \text{ m}$$

6.8 MULTIDIMENSIONAL METHODS

Multidimensional methods include consideration of longitudinal, transverse, and vertical dispersion along with advection in one dimension. The governing Eq. (6.12) is altered to include only velocity in the x direction, and a first-order decay term can be added. Domenico and Robbins (1985) solved the problem analytically for the various source geometries shown in Figure 6.8. In their solution, they assume that the 3-D solution is made up of the product of three 1-D solutions. The source dimensions and dispersivities largely control the concentrations $C(x,y,z,t)$ that are predicted in the plume. The model can be applied in two dimensions by neglecting the z terms and adjusting the constant from 1/8 to 1/4. The Domenico analytical model is quite useful for screening purposes and for comparison to more complex numerical results at actual field sites. It has recently been applied for the biodegradation of chlorinated solvents (Newell et al., 1999). But care should be exercised since the results are very sensitive to the selection of the average width of the source zone. The model was developed for the case of a continuously leaking source, but through linear superposition of solutions lagged in time, a finite source (in time and space) can be represented as shown in the example below.

For the source geometry shown in Figure 6.8c, the resulting equation for $C(x,y,z,t)$ becomes

$$\frac{C(x,y,z,t)}{C_0} = \left(\frac{1}{8}\right)\text{erfc}\left[\frac{(x-vt)}{2(\alpha_x vt)^{1/2}}\right]$$

$$\left\{\text{erf}\left[\frac{\left(y+\frac{Y}{2}\right)}{2(\alpha_y x)^{1/2}}\right] - \text{erf}\left[\frac{\left(y-\frac{Y}{2}\right)}{2(\alpha_y x)^{1/2}}\right]\right\}$$

$$\left\{\text{erf}\left[\frac{(z+Z)}{2(\alpha_z x)^{1/2}}\right] - \text{erf}\left[\frac{(z-Z)}{2(\alpha_z x)^{1/2}}\right]\right\} \tag{6.31}$$

For the plane of symmetry $y = z = 0$, the above equation becomes

$$\frac{C(x,0,0,t)}{C_o} = \left(\frac{1}{2}\right)\text{erfc}\left[\frac{(x-vt)}{2(\alpha_x vt)^{1/2}}\right]$$

$$\left\{\text{erf}\left[\frac{Y}{4(\alpha_y x)^{1/2}}\right]\text{erf}\left[\frac{Z}{4(\alpha_z x)^{1/2}}\right]\right\} \tag{6.32}$$

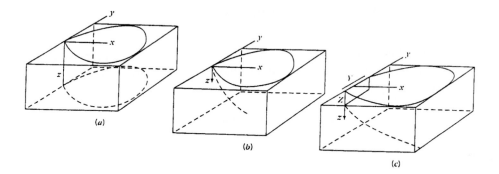

Figure 6.8 Geometrical considerations for a contaminant source. Shown in (a) is a vertical line source, in (b) a point source, and in (c) a finite plane source. Source: Domenico and Schwartz, 1998.

Note that when α_x and α_y approach zero, one obtains the original solution presented in Eq. (6.17) for the one-dimensional case.

Domenico (1987) presents the final form of the equation with first-order decay or degradation, which has the effect of a mass loss as the plume grows in space and time.

$$\frac{C(x,y,z,t)}{C_0} = \frac{1}{8}\exp\left\{\frac{x}{2\alpha_x}\left[1-\left(1+\frac{4\lambda\alpha_x}{v}\right)^{1/2}\right]\right\}\text{erfc}\left[\frac{x-vt\left(1+4\lambda\alpha_x/v\right)^{1/2}}{2\left(\alpha_x vt\right)^{1/2}}\right]$$

$$\left\{\text{erf}\left[\frac{\left(y+\dfrac{Y}{2}\right)}{2\left(\alpha_y x\right)^{1/2}}\right]-\text{erf}\left[\frac{\left(y-\dfrac{Y}{2}\right)}{2\left(\alpha_y x\right)^{1/2}}\right]\right\}\left\{\text{erf}\left[\frac{(z+Z)}{2\left(\alpha_z x\right)^{1/2}}\right]-\text{erf}\left[\frac{(z-Z)}{2\left(\alpha_z x\right)^{1/2}}\right]\right\} \tag{6.33}$$

EXAMPLE 6.3   APPLICATION OF THE MODEL TO A TRACER TEST.

There is a small dry cleaning facility with a PCE spill. A tracer test will be run at the site to enhance the understanding of hydraulic conditions. In order to design the test, develop a model using the Domenico and Robbins equations (Eqs. (6.31), (6.32), (6.33)) to simulate what should occur during the test. There are a total of six wells at the site; one injecting the tracer and five monitoring wells. Well diameter is 6 in. and the well screen fully extends into a 10 ft fine sand saturated zone. The tracer injected is 500 mg/L of bromide, injected at 3 gal/min. It is assumed that detection levels are down to the nearest 0.1 mg/L in the field.

Site characteristics:

- Aquifer is confined
- $K = 5 \times 10^{-3}$ cm/s
- The ground water gradient is 0.005

- Porosity is 0.3
- $\alpha_x = 0.5$ m, $\alpha_y = 0.1$ m
- 2-hr time step for testing

Solution. Taking into account the site and tracer characteristics and the placement of the five monitoring wells, model the breakthrough in the five wells. An Excel spreadsheet will greatly aid in the set-up and solving of this tracer problem. The model will be applied in 2-D by neglecting the z terms and adjusting the constant from 1/8 to 1/4 in Eq. (6.31). A one day pulse input can be modeled by superimposing a continuous input of C_0 and subtracting a negative input after one day. The resulting breakthrough curves can be plotted for each of the well locations. The results are clearly dependent on the selection of parameters in the model. Figure 6.9a shows the layout of the wells, Figure 6.9b shows the modeled concentrations of the tracer in the wells after a one day pulse, and Figure 6.9c shows the modeled concentrations for a continuous source. By observing concentrations from the tracer test and comparing to Figure 6.9b, one can determine or backout values for dispersivity in the x and y directions

Galya (1987) developed the horizontal plane source model (HPS). The model assumes 1-D velocity, but allows for 3-D dispersion in the x, y, and z directions. The governing equations are solved for a continuous release, although a finite source can be handled through linear superposition in time. The model's geometry is useful to analyze ponds or pits that leach contaminants from the surface down to the ground water table. The source term is treated in a unique way in order to maintain mass balances in the solution. This geometry is not as useful as the one used by Domenico above.

Another useful method, called the semi-analytical approach, has been developed by a number of researchers (Nelson, 1978; Bear, 1979). The method involves the computation of streamlines and equipotential lines over a flow domain via numerical integration. Javandel et al. (1984) showed how concentration versus time data for a single well can be mapped to other observation points to estimate spacial distribution in concentration. The computer program RESSQ calculates 2-D contaminant transport by advection and adsorption in a steady state flow field. Recharge wells and ponds act as sources and pumping wells act as sinks. RESSQ calculates streamline pattern in the aquifer, the location of contaminant fronts around sources at various times, and the variation of contaminant concentration with time at sinks. RESSQ was developed at the Lawrence Berkeley Laboratory based on a solution procedure by Gringarten and Sauty (1975). Javandel, et al. (1984) present a detailed discussion, listing, and users guide for the semi-analytical computer program RESSQ.

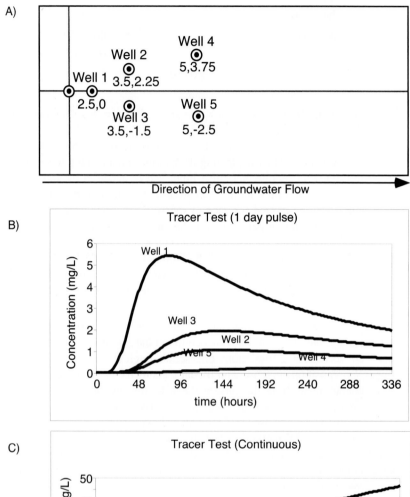

Figure 6.9 Site layout and tracer test plots (Example 6.3).

6.9 TESTS FOR DISPERSIVITY

To apply any 1-D or 2-D transport model properly to an actual site, it is first necessary to define the input parameters. For modeling a nonadsorbing solute such as chloride, the parameters of primary concern are water table elevation, hydraulic conductivity K, and dispersivity α. For small project sites, accurate delineation of the water table will depend on the number of wells that can be drilled. Porosity can easily be determined by laboratory testing of a few samples. While this limited sampling may result in errors in porosity of 10% to 20%, these errors will probably not be significant compared to the problems inherent in measuring hydraulic conductivity and dispersivity. Measurement of hydraulic conductivity was described in Chapters 3 and 5.

6.9.1 Laboratory Tests for Dispersivity

Soil column studies are often reported in terms of pore volumes where one pore volume represents the volume of water that completely will fill the voids along the column length. The total number of pore volumes U during a particular column test is the total discharge divided by a single pore volume.

$$U = \frac{v_x nAt}{ALn} = \frac{v_x t}{L} \tag{6.39}$$

where v_x = seepage velocity, A is the cross-sectional area, L is the length of the column, and n is porosity.

By rearranging Eq. (6.17) in terms of pore volumes and neglecting the second term on the right-hand side, one obtains a useful relation between C/C_0 and the pore volume function $(U-1)/U^{1/2}$. By plotting C/C_0 versus the pore volume function on normal probability paper, (Pickens and Grisak , 1981) demonstrated that data plot as a straight line, and the slope of the line is related to D_x, the longitudinal dispersion coefficient. The value of D_x can be found from

$$D_x = \frac{v_x L}{8} \left[J(0.84) - J(0.16) \right]^2 \tag{6.40}$$

where $J(0.84)$ = the value of the pore volume function when $C/C_0 = 0.84$
and $J(0.16)$ = the value of the pore volume function when $C/C_0 = 0.16$

because $D_x = \alpha_x v_x + D_d$

$$\alpha_x = \frac{D_x - D_d}{v_x} \tag{6.41}$$

Example 6.4   DISPERSION IN SAND COLUMNS

Pickens and Grisak (1981) studied dispersion in sand columns. They used sand with a mean grain size of 0.2 mm, porosity of 0.36 and uniformity coefficient of 2.3. The column had a length of 30 cm and diameter of 4.45 cm. Chloride (tracer) at a concentration of 200 mg/L was run through the column at a rate of 5.12×10^{-3} mL/s. Average linear velocity was 9.26×10^{-4} cm/s. The concentration of chloride in the effluent was measured as a function of U, and C/C_0 was plotted as a function of $[(U{-}1)/U^{1/2}]$ on probability paper as shown in Figure 6.10a.

At 25° C, the molecular diffusion coefficient for chloride in water is 2.03×10^{-5} cm²/s. From this, Pickens and Grisak estimated the effective diffusion coefficient to be 1.02×10^{-5} cm²/s. Hydrodynamic dispersion coefficients are based on the slope of the straight line. In the case of the above run, a hydrodynamic dispersivity of 4.05×10^{-5} cm²/s was obtained.

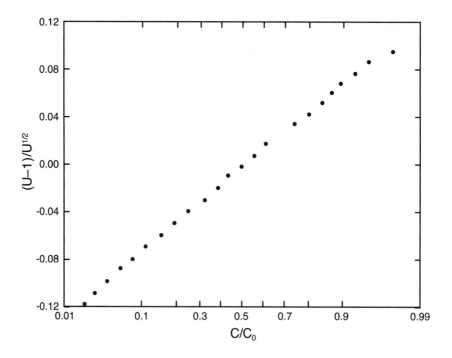

Figure 6.10a Plot of $(U{-}1)/U^{1/2}$ versus C/C_0 on probability paper for determination of dispersion in a laboratory sand column.

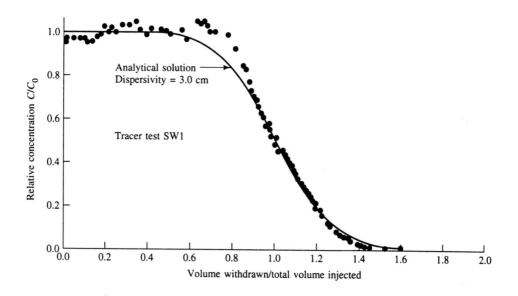

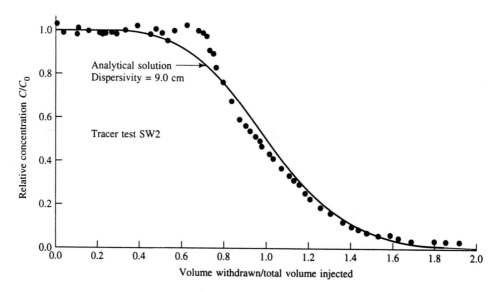

Figure 6.10b Comparison of measured C/C_0 values for a single well injection withdrawal test versus an analytical solution. Source: Pickens, 1981.

Finally, the dispersivity for the run was calculated using Eq. (6.41) as follows:

$$\alpha_x = \frac{D_x - D_d}{v_x}$$

$$= \frac{4.05 \times 10^{-5}\,cm^2/sec\ -\ 1.02 \times 10^{-5}\,cm^2/sec}{9.26 \times 10^{-4}\,cm/sec} = 0.033cm$$

6.9.2 Single Well Tracer Test

Pickens et al. (1981) report one of the very few field experiments for the *in situ* determination of dispersive and adsorptive properties of a well-defined sandy aquifer system. The aquifer was 8.2 m thick with $K = 1.4 \times 10^{-2}$ cm/s and porosity of 0.38. The technique involves the use of a radial injection dual-tracer test with ^{131}I as the nonreactive tracer and ^{85}Sr as the reactive tracer. Tracer migration was monitored at various radial distances and depths with multilevel point sampling devices. In the analysis of curves, nonequilibrium adsorption effects were incorporated into the dispersion terms of the solute transport equation rather than introducing a separate kinetic term.

Various curves were computed for different values of dispersivity and the curves were best fit to the field data collected at the well. Effective dispersivity values (α) obtained for ^{85}Sr ranged from 0.7 cm to 3.3 cm (mean of 1.9 cm), typically a factor of two to five times larger than those obtained for ^{131}I (range of 0.4 cm to 1.5 cm with a mean of 0.8 cm). The K_d values obtained by various analyses of the break-through curves ranged from 2.6 mL/g to 4.5 mL/g. These were within a factor of 4 of the mean values of K_d for ^{85}Sr based on a separate analysis of sediment cores in another part of the aquifer. The withdrawal phase for the well showed essentially full tracer recoveries for both compounds. The comparison of measured C/C_0 values for a single well tracer test versus an analytical solution is shown in Figure 6.10b. The two curves are based on longitudinal dispersivities of 3.0 cm and 9.0 cm, respectively. Thus, the usefulness of the dual-tracer injection tests has been demonstrated along with the existence of nonequilibrium conditions at a field site.

6.9.3 The Scale Effect of Dispersion

Dispersivity α is defined to be the characteristic mixing length and is a measure of the spreading of the contaminant. Unfortunately, this parameter has little physical significance and varies with the scale of the problem and sample method. Laboratory values range from 1 cm to 10 cm, while field studies often obtain values less than 1 m to over 1000 m.

Many investigators have recognized the scale effect of dispersion (Fried, 1975; Pickens and Grisak, 1981; Gelhar, 1986). A study by Gelhar et al. (1985) shows the scale dependency of longitudinal dispersivity at 55 actual field sites around the world (Figure 6.11). The data on the Gelhar graph from many sites around the world indicate a general increase in longitudinal dispersivity with scale, although the relation may not be linear. At the Borden landfill study described below (Mackay et al. 1986) determined that there was a small scale effect.

Since dispersion can be caused by slight differences in fluid velocity within a pore, or between pores, and because of different flow paths, the effect of different hydraulic conductivities in an aquifer can also cause spreading due to dispersion. The natural variation of hydraulic conductivity and porosity in a vertical and horizontal sense can play a key role in the scale effect of dispersion. As the flow path increases in length, ground water can encounter greater and greater variations in the aquifer. The deviations from the average increase along with the mechanical dispersion. It is logical to assume that dispersivity will approach some

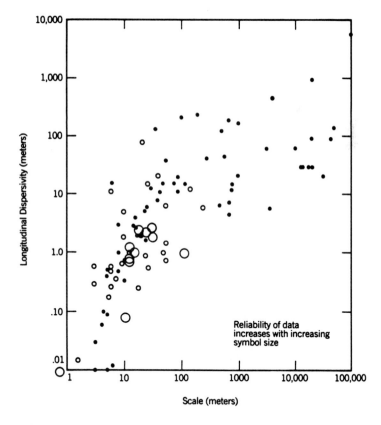

Figure 6.11 Scale of observation versus longitudinal dispersivity: reliability classification. Source: Gelhar, et al., 1985.

upper limit at long traveled distances and large travel times (Gelhar and Axness, 1983; Dagan, 1988). Due to a lack of field data, explanations of dispersion still represent an active research area.

6.10 NATURAL GRADIENT FIELD TESTS FOR DISPERSION

6.10.1 Borden Landfill Natural Gradient Test

One of the most extensively monitored field tracer tests in history was performed by Cherry's research group at the Canadian Forces Base Borden (Sudicky et al. 1983; Mackay et al., 1986; Freyberg, 1986). An area near the landfill shown in Figure 6.12a was monitored extensively with multilevel sampling devices. The aquifer is about 20 m thick and thins to about 10 m in the direction of ground water flow, with an average hydraulic conductivity of 1.16×10^{-2} cm/s. In August 1982 a natural gradient field experiment was begun by injecting 12 m^3 into the subsurface of the sand aquifer. The average linear ground water velocity was computed to be 29.6 m/yr. The ground water flow direction is indicated in Figure 6.12a.

The concept was simply to inject a known amount of two conservative tracers and five volatile organic compounds for one day into a shallow, sand aquifer. Monitoring was continued for about two years at over 5000 observation points in 3-D (each well had up to 18 vertical screened intervals for sampling). Figure 6.12b shows the vertically averaged Cl$^-$ distribution at four different times, and the various plumes were analyzed statistically by Freyberg (1986) in order to evaluate advection and dispersion in the natural gradient test. The mean ground water velocity was measured to be 0.091 m/day. It is clear from the gradual plume elongation depicted in Figure 6.12b that longitudinal dispersion was occurring and was much larger than transverse dispersion.

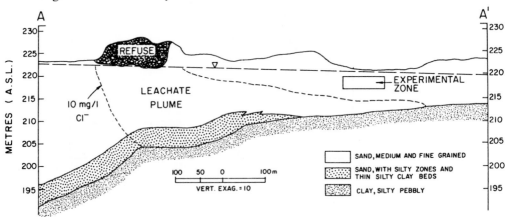

Figure 6.12a Approximate vertical geometry of aquifer along section AA'. Rectangle illustrates the vertical zone in which the experiment was conducted, which is above the landfill leachate plume (denoted by 10 mg/L chloride isopleth from 1979 data). Source: Mackay, et al., 1986.

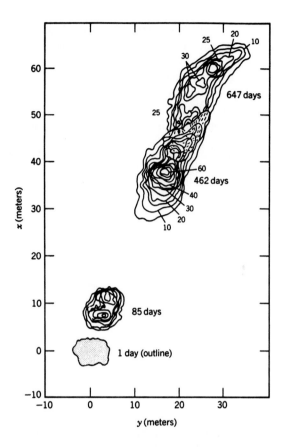

Figure 6.12b Vertically averaged concentration of distribution of Cl⁻ at various times after injection. Source: Mackay, et al., 1986.

Freyberg (1986) computed the center of mass of the chloride plume in 3-D as well as the variances in the longitudinal and transverse directions. The data was further analyzed by relating variance, time, and dispersivity. The dispersivities were first assumed to be constants with time, and then were shown to vary with time, indicating scale-dependent behavior. Freyberg (1986) calculated average linear values of α_x and α_y to be 0.36 m and 0.039 m, respectively, but indicated that α_x may be a function of time. Assuming scale-dependent behavior, a value of 0.43 m was computed, and was extrapolated to an asymptotic value of 0.49 m. Figure 6.12c shows the fit of the Borden data to a constant dispersivity model. The reader is referred to the complete set of six articles on the Borden natural gradient test in the December, 1986 issue of *Water Resources Research*.

Roberts et al. (1986) studied adsorption by analyzing arrival times of Cl⁻ compared to organics such as carbon tetrachloride at the wells at the Borden site. Chapter 7 describes the sorption results in more detail at the Borden site.

At an actual waste site, experimental determination of α_x and α_y is often impractical due to the very long flow times. In these cases, the most common approach is to run the transport model for a range of dispersivities and then adjust them until the predicted plume matches observed concentration data. Based on the Borden test data, a typical starting range for longitudinal dispersivity (α_x) in a sandy aquifer is 1 m to 10 m. Transverse dispersivity typically ranges from 10% to 30% of α_x. The procedure of fitting dispersivities to predict observed concentration patterns is admittedly crude but can lead to useful descriptions of contaminant transport.

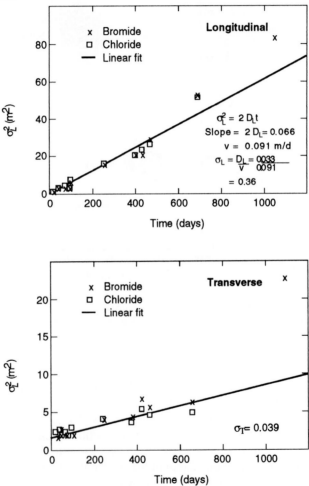

Figure 6.12c Fit of the Borden data to a constant dispersivity model. Source: Freyberg, 1986.

6.10.2 Natural Gradient Tracer Test, Cape Cod, Mass.

This natural gradient tracer experiment was designed to provide a well-defined set of initial conditions associated with contaminant release. An extensive and systematic monitoring program was undertaken so that a detailed description of the resulting contaminant plume could be established and maintained over an extended period of time as it moved and dispersed within the aquifer. The collected data was then used to evaluate the validity of currently accepted theories used to predict solute movement and behavior in the saturated zone. Results were compared to those that were found at the Borden Landfill Experiment.

Description of the Site and Experiment. The site of the experiment was a sand and gravel aquifer located on Cape Cod, Massachusetts (Figure 6.13) near Otis Air Base.

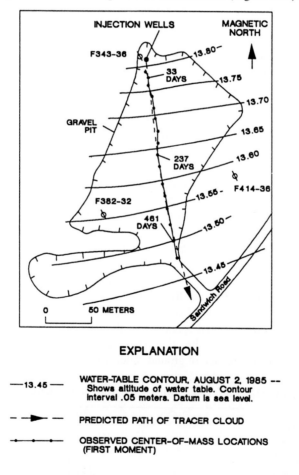

EXPLANATION

——13.45—— WATER-TABLE CONTOUR, AUGUST 2, 1985 --
Shows altitude of water table. Contour
interval .05 meters. Datum is sea level.

- — ► — — PREDICTED PATH OF TRACER CLOUD

•—•—•— OBSERVED CENTER-OF-MASS LOCATIONS
(FIRST MOMENT)

Figure 6.13 Horizontal trajectory of the center of mass of the bromide plume at the Cape Cod site. Source: Garabedian et al., 1991.

The nature of the site and the experiment was originally described by LeBlanc et al. (1991). The site was composed of approximately 100 m of unconsolidated sediments that overlay an impermeable bedrock stratum. The upper 30 m of the site consisted of horizontally stratified sand and gravel deposits. Beneath these deposits the sediments consisted of fine-grained sand and silt. These deposits formed an unconfined aquifer with a mean water table elevation located approximately 5 m beneath the ground surface. Several small-scale tracer tests that were conducted at the site revealed an overall effective porosity of 0.39. The magnitude of the horizontal hydraulic gradient was found to vary from 0.0014 to 0.0018 while a vertical gradient was nondetectable. The average hydraulic conductivity was estimated from an in situ flow test to be 110 m/d. More detailed analyses conducted with a borehole flow meter in conjunction with permeameter testing of core samples showed the hydraulic conductivity to vary by about one order of magnitude across the site due to the interbedded lens structure of the aquifer. Based on the values quoted above for effective porosity, hydraulic gradient, and hydraulic conductivity the mean ground water velocity at the site was calculated to be 0.4 m/d.

Solute injection at the Cape Cod site was accomplished by the placement of 7.6 m^3 of tracer solution into the saturated zone through three injection wells at the rate of 7.6 L/min (2.5 L/min/well). This slow injection rate was selected in order to minimize spreading of the plume during injection. Both nonreactive and reactive tracers were used. Bromide was selected as the nonreactive tracer due to the fact that chloride was present at relatively high natural concentrations in the aquifer. The reactive tracers used were lithium, molybdate, and fluoride. A summary of the solution composition is presented in Table 6.2.

The sampling array was composed of 656 multilevel samplers. All total there were 9,840 individual sampling points at the site. The focus of sample collection was on obtaining synoptic ("snapshot") data, thus sampling episodes took place on roughly monthly intervals over a three year period (1985-1988). The data collected at the site included approximately 30,000 bromide analyses, 33,000 lithium analyses, and 38,000 molybdate analyses. Fluoride was abandoned as a tracer early in the test due to the fact that it was so strongly sorbed that trace concentrations remaining in solution became indistinguishable from background levels. Figure 6.14 shows the sampling layout.

Overview of Plume Behavior. Significant features of the resulting contaminant cloud observed at the Cape Cod site include a predominant spreading in the direction of ground water flow, minimal spreading in the horizontal transverse direction, and essentially no spreading in the vertical direction. These features combined to create a narrow plume that was aligned in the direction of ground water flow. Figure 6.15 provides a comparison of the

TABLE 6.2 Injected Solutes at the Cape Cod Site

Solute	Injected Concentration (mg/L)	Injected Mass (g)	Background Concentration (mg/L)
Bromide	640	4900	<0.10
Lithium	78	590	<0.01
Molybdate	80	610	<0.02
Fluoride	50	380	<0.20

From LeBlanc et al., 1991.

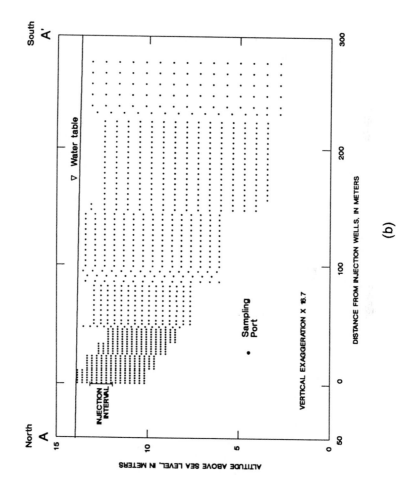

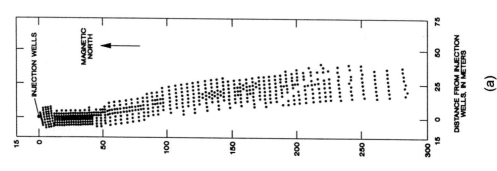

Figure 6.14 Locations of multilevel samplers and injection wells at the Cape Cod Site. (a) Plan view. (b) Vertical distribution of sampling points along representative section. Source: LeBlanc et al., 1991. © American Geophysical Union.

bromide, lithium, and molybdate plumes at various times following injection. Note that the movement of the reactive species, lithium and molybdate, is significantly retarded in comparison with the conservative bromide.

Inspection of the vertical concentration profiles for bromide recorded at the site reveals minimal vertical spreading. However, also of interest is the downward movement of the plume with horizontal travel distance (Figure 6.14b). This vertical movement was attributed to two effects: (1) vertical flow associated with areal recharge and (2) sinking of the plume due to density differences between the tracer solution and the natural ground water (LeBlanc et al., 1991).

Experimental Observations. As a conservative tracer, the total mass of bromide in solution should be constant with time and should be equal to the mass injected. Evaluation of the mass of bromide contained in each plume for each of 16 separate synoptic data sets yielded the plot of total mass versus time data. The trend of effectively constant mass over time may be inferred. The differences between the calculated mass and the injected mass may be attributed to measurement and estimation error (Garabedian et al., 1991).

A graphical representation of the horizontal trajectory of the center of mass of the tracer plume is given in Figure 6.13. The movement of the center of mass is quite linear and closely corresponds to the direction predicted by the water table gradient. While some vertical displacement of the center of mass was observed, as noted above, this movement was considered inconsequential by the researchers in comparison with the large horizontal displacement and so a strictly horizontal transport velocity could be assumed. The observed ground water flow velocity at the site as given by the slope of the line fitted through this data was computed as 0.42 m/d. This value is consistent with that calculated using the average measured porosity, hydraulic gradient, and hydraulic conductivity.

A theoretical approach to describing dispersivity in the ground water environment as a function of time has been developed by Dagan (1982, 1984). Dagan's theory suggests that limiting values of dispersivity will be reached for large values of time. Typically this large time value corresponds to a plume that has reached a scale of spreading that is significantly larger than the scale of hydraulic conductivity variability (Garabedian et al., 1991).

In order to study this idea of an asymptotic dispersivity the Cape Cod study was designed to incorporate a large (280 m) plume travel distance. Data from the experiment showed a constant value of longitudinal dispersivity, develop after a short period of nonlinear growth. The data also indicated a positive valued transverse dispersivity that was constant with time. The horizontal and transverse dispersivity values were determined to be 0.96 m and 0.018 m respectively. The vertical dispersivity was calculated to be 0.0015 m. While the asymptotic nature of the longitudinal dispersivity was clear, the nonzero value of transverse dispersivity was not in agreement with the theory of Dagan (1984). One may note from these results, however, that the typical assumption that the longitudinal dispersivity is an order of magnitude larger than the transverse dispersivity was supported by the data.

In order to study this idea of an asymptotic dispersivity the Cape Cod study was designed to incorporate a large (280 m) plume travel distance. Data from the experiment showed a constant value of longitudinal dispersivity develop after a short period of non-linear

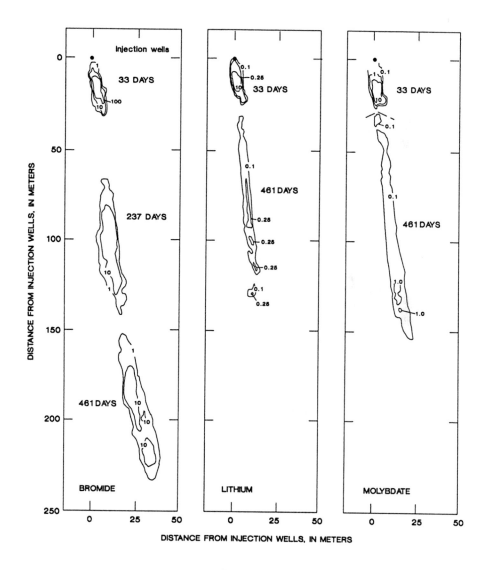

Figure 6.15 Vertical location of bromide plume at 33, 237, and 461 days after injection at the Cape Cod site. Source: LaBlanc, 1991.

growth. The data also indicated a positive valued transverse dispersivity that was constant with time. The horizontal and transverse dispersivity values were determined to be 0.96 m and 0.018 m respectively. The vertical dispersivity was calculated to be 0.0015 m. While the asymptotic nature of the longitudinal dispersivity was clear, the non-zero value of transverse dispersivity was not in agreement with the theory of Dagan (1984). One may note from these results, however, that the typical assumption that the longitudinal dispersivity is an order of magnitude larger than the transverse dispersivity was supported by the data.

Significant Findings and Comparisons. A large scale natural gradient tracer experiment was performed in a shallow, unconfined, sand and gravel aquifer. The purpose of this experiment was to assess the validity of the often-made simplifying assumptions used in the application of theoretical transport models to field situations where extensive data is not available. There were similarities between the results of the two tests at Borden and Cape Cod which include:

1. The advective velocity and trajectory of a solute can be adequately predicted using conventionally collected data (i.e., porosity, hydraulic gradient, and hydraulic conductivity estimated from any of several techniques).

2. The relative magnitudes of dispersion follow the trend of longitudinal dispersion > transverse dispersion > vertical dispersion and that transverse dispersion is an order of magnitude less than longitudinal dispersion.

3. A limiting value of dispersivity is reached at large values of time (travel distance) after an early period of nonlinear growth.

4. A retardation mechanism function to limit the movement of reactive solutes relative to nonreactive solutes.

Differences between the two tests indicate a much greater hydraulic conductivity and seepage velocity at Cape Cod (0.42 m/day) versus Borden (0.091 m/day). Longitudinal dispersivity was 0.96 m at Cape Cod versus 0.43 m at Borden, and the ratio of longitudinal to transverse dispersivity was much greater at Cape Cod (50 to 1) than at Borden (11 to 1). Garabedian et al. (1991) present more details on the comparison of the two tests.

SUMMARY

Basic concepts in ground water transport processes include problems in one, two, and three dimensions with advection, dispersion, adsorption, and biodegradation. The 1-D solutions to the advective dispersion equation allow simple predictions of breakthrough with adsorption or decay. Analytical expressions allow reasonable estimates for travel time and spreading of contaminant fronts in 1-D soil columns. Two-dimensional models can be solved analytically for simple boundary conditions, but numerical models are generally required for actual field problems. Multidimensional methods such as the Domenico model and the HPS model can provide useful estimates of concentrations from simple planar source areas. These models provide some idea of concentrations in time and space from continuously leaking source areas with a constant velocity flow field and simple boundary conditions. Other models such as RESSQ can be used to calculate steady-state streamline patterns and contaminant transport in the presence of recharge wells and ponds.

Tests for dispersivity in the laboratory and in the field are reviewed. There are many problems associated with parameter estimation at field sites, including estimation of hydraulic conductivity, dispersivity, and adsorption coefficients. Extrapolation of results from laboratory column experiments to field sites has proven to be quite difficult, and therefore methods that can be directly applied to the field are being developed by researchers. Results from the extensive natural gradient tracer studies performed at the Borden landfill in Canada and at the Cape Cod, Mass. are briefly described. These two sites represent the most comprehensive databases on advective-dispersive transport that are available in the general literature.

REFERENCES

Anderson, M. P., "Using Models To Simulate The Movement Of Contaminants Through Ground Water Flow Systems," *CRC Critical Rev. Environ. Control,* Chemical Rubber Co., 9, 96, 1979.

Anderson, M. P. and W. W. Woessner, *Applied Ground Water Modeling*, San Diego, CA, Academic Press, Inc, 1992.

Barker, J. F., G. C. Patrick, and D. Major, "Natural Attenuation of Aromatic Hydrocarbons in a Shallow Sand Aquifer," *Ground Water Mon. Rev.,* p. 64-71, 1987.

Bear, J. *Dynamics of Fluids in Porous Media.* New York: American Elsevier Publishing Company, 764 pp., 1972.

Bear, J., *Hydraulics of Ground Water*, New York, NY, McGraw-Hill, 1979.

Borden, R. C. and P. B. Bedient, "Transport Of Dissolved Hydrocarbons Influenced By Reaeration And Oxygen Limited Biodegradation: 1. Theoretical Development," *Water Resources Res.* 22:1973-1982, 1986.

Bredehoeft, J. D. and G. F. Pinder, "Mass Transport in Flowing Ground Water," *Water Resources Res.* 9, 192-210, 1973.

Charbeneau, R. J., "Ground Water Contaminant Transport With Adsorption And Ion Exchange Chemistry: Method Of Characteristics For The Case Without Dispersion, *Water Resources Res.,* 17:3:705-713, 1981.

Charbeneau, R. J., "Calculation Of Pollutant Removal During Ground Water Restoration With Adsorption And Ion Exchange, *Water Resources Res.,* 18:4:1117-1125, 1982.

Cleary, R. W. and M. J. Ungs, "Ground Water Pollution and Hydrology, Mathematical Models and Computer Programs," *Rep. 78-WR-15*, Water Resour. Program, Princeton, N.J., Princeton Univ., 1978.

Dagan, G., "Stochastic Modeling Of Ground Water Flow By Unconditional And Conditional Probabilities, 2, The Solute Transport," *Water Resources Res., 18(4)*, 835-848, 1982.

Dagan, G., "Solute Transport In Heterogeneous Porous Formations," *J. Fluid Mech., 145*, 151-177, 1984.

Dagan, G. "Statistical Theory of Ground Water Flow and Transport: Pore to Laboratory, Laboratory to Formation, and Formation to Regional Scale," *Water Resources Res.*, 22, no. 9:120S-134S, 1986.

Dagan, G., "Theory of Solute Transport in Water," *Annual Reviews of Fluid Mechanics*, 19:183-215, 1987.

Dagan, G. "Time-dependent Macrodispersion for Solute Transport in Anistropic Heterogeneous Aquifers," *Water Resources Res.*, 24, no. 9:1491-1500, 1988.

De Josselin De Jong, G., "Longitudinal and Transverse Diffusion in Granular Deposits. Transactions," American Geophysical Union 39, no. 1:67, 1958.

Domencio, P. A. and G. A. Robbins, "A New Method of Contaminant Plume Analysis," *Ground Water,* vol. 23, pp. 476-485, 1985.

Domenico, P. A. and F. W. Schwartz, *Physical and Chemical Hydrogeology*, New York, John S. Wiley and Sons, 1990.

Domenico, P. A. and F. W. Schwartz, *Physical and Chemical Hydrogeology*, 2nd Edition, New York, NY, John S. Wiley and Sons, 1998.

Freeze, R. A. and J. A. Cherry, *Ground Water,* Englewood Cliffs, NJ, Prentice-Hall, 1979.

Freyberg, D. L., "A Natural Gradient Experiment On Solute Transport In A Sand Squifer, (2) Spatial Moments And The Advection And Dispersion Of Nonreactive Tracers," *Water Resources Res.*, 22:13: 2031-2046, 1986.

Fried, J. J., *Ground Water Pollution*. Amsterdam, Elsevier, 1975.

Galya, D. P., "A Horizontal Plane Source Model for Ground-Water Transport," *Ground Water*, Vol. 25, No. 6, 1987.

Garabedian, S. P., D. R. LeBlanc, L. W. Gelhar, and M. A. Celia, "Large-Scale Natural Gradient Tracer Test In Sand And Gravel, Cape Cod, Massachusetts, 2, Analysis Of Spatial Moments For A Nonreactive Tracer," *Water Resources Res.*, 27(5), 911-924, 1991.

Gelhar, L. W. and C. L. Axness, "Three-dimensional Stochastic Analysis of Macrodispersion in Aquifers," *Water Resources Res.*, 19, no. 1:161-80, 1983.

Gelhar, L.W., A.L. Gutjahr, and R.L. Naff, "Stochastic Analysis Of Macrodispersion In A Stratified Aquifer," *Water Resources Res.*, 15:6:1387-1397, 1979.

Gelhar, L.W., A. Montoglou, C. Welty, and K.R. Rehfeldt, "A Review Of Field-Scale Physical Solute Transport Processes In Saturated And Unsaturated Porous Media," *Final Proj. Rep. EPRI EA-4190*, Palo Alto, CA,, Elec. Power Res. Inst., 1985.

Gelhar, L. W., "Stochastic Subsurface Hydrology from Theory to Applications," *Water Resources Res.*, 22, no. 9:135S-145S, 1986.

Gringarten, A. C. and J. P. Sauty, "A Theoretical Study of Heat Extraction from Aquifers with Uniform Regional Flow," *J. Geophys. Res.*, 80(35), 4956-4962, 1975.

Hunt, B., "Dispersive Sources in Uniform Ground-Water Flow," *J. Hydraulics Div.* ASCE 104:75-85, 1978.

Javandel, I., C. Doughty, and C.F. Tsang, *Ground Water Transport: Handbook of Mathematical Models,* American Geophysical Union, Water Resources Monograph 10, Washington, DC, 228 pp., 1984.

LeBlanc, D. R., S. P. Garabedian, K. M. Hess, L. W. Gelhar, R. D. Quadri, K. G. Stollenwerk, and W. W. Wood, "Large-Scale Natural Gradient Tracer Test In Sand And Gravel, Cape Cod, Massachusetts, 1, Experimental Design And Observed Tracer Movement," *Water Resources Res.*, 27(5), 895-910, 1991.

Mackay, D.M., D.L. Freyberg, P.V. Roberts, and J.A. Cherry, "A Natural Gradient Experiment On Solute Transport In A Sand Aquifer, (1) Approach And Overview Of Plume Movement," *Water Resources Res.*, 22:13:2017-2029, December 1986.

Mercer, J. W. and C. R. Faust, 1981, *Ground-Water Modeling*, NWWA, 2nd Ed., 1986.

Nelson, R. W., "Evaluating the Environmental Consequences of Groundwater Contamination. 1. An Overview of Contaminant Arrival Distributions as General Evaluation Requirements," *Water Resources Res.*, 14:409-515, 1977.

Neuman, S. P., C. L. Winter, and C. N. Newman, "Stochastic Theory Of Field-Scale Fickina Dispersion In Anisotropic Porous Media," *Water Resources Research* 23, no. 3:453-66, 1987.

Newell, C .J., Gonzales, J., and McLeod, R., *BIOSCREEN Natural Attenuation Decision Support System, Version 1.4* Revisions, U.S. Environmental Protection Agency, 1999.

Ogata, A., "Theory Of Dispersion In A Granular Medium," U.S. Geological Survey Professional Paper 411-I, 1970.

Pickens, J. F. and G. E. Grisak., "Scale-dependent Dispersion in a Stratified Granular Aquifer," *Water Resources Research* 17, no. 4:1191-1211, 1981.

Pickens, J. F., R. E. Jackson, K. J. Inch, and W. F. Merritt, "Measurement Of Distribution Coefficients Using A Radial Injection Duel-Tracer Test," *Water Resources Res.* 17, no. 3:529-44, 1981.

Rifai, H. S., P. B. Bedient, J. T. Wilson, K. M. Miller, and J. M. Armstrong, "Biodegradation Modeling At A Jet Fuel Spill Site," ASCE *J. Environmental Engr. Div.* 114:1007-1019, 1988.

Roberts, P.V., M.N. Goltz, and D.M. Mackay, "A Natural Gradient Experiment On Solute Transport In A Sand Aquifer, (4), Sorption Of Organic Solutes And Its Influence On Mobility," *Water Resources Res.*, 22:13:2047-2058, December 1986.

Shen, H.T., "Transient Dispersion in Uniform Porous Media Flow," *J. Hydrau. Div.* ASCE 102:707-716, 1976.

Smith, L., and F. W. Schwartz, "Mass Transport: 1. A Stochastic Analysis of Macroscopic Dispersion," *Water Resources Res.* 16:303-313, 1980.

Sudicky, E. A., J. A. Cherry, and E. O. Frind. "Migration of Contaminants in Ground Water at a Landfill: A Case Study, 4, A Natural Gradient Dispersion Test." *Journal of Hydrology* 63, no. 1/2:81-108, 1983.

Wang, H.F. and M.P. Anderson, *Introduction to Ground Water Modeling, Finite Difference and Finite Element Methods*, San Franciso, CA, W.H. Freeman and Company, 237 pp., 1982.

Wilson, J. L., Miller, P.J., "Two-Dimensional Plume in Uniform Ground Water Flow," *J. Hydrau. Div.* ASCE 104:503-514, 1978.

Zheng, C. and G. D. Bennett, *Applied Contaminant Transport Modeling: Theory and Practice,* New York, NY, Van Nostrand Reinhold, 1995.

CHAPTER 7

CONTAMINANT FATE PROCESSES

JOSEPH B. HUGHES

7.1 INTRODUCTION

The distribution and concentrations of contaminants in ground water systems is strongly influenced by interactions between the contaminant and the physical, chemical, and biological components of the subsurface. Collectively, these interactions are referred to as **fate processes**. In some cases, fate processes result in the alteration of the contaminants chemical structure ultimately resulting in the formation of nonhazardous compounds. Other fate processes result in a phase change, without altering the compounds chemical structure. In either case, fate processes must be considered during the evaluation of contaminant transport to accurately describe or predict the behavior of contaminants in ground water systems.

7.2 SORPTION AND DESORPTION

Sorption is defined as the association of a dissolved or gaseous contaminant with a solid material. In ground water systems, the solid materials of interest are aquifer materials or soil, and typically the contaminants are present in the dissolved phase. Common terminology used to describe participants in the sorption processes are **sorbent** and **sorbate**. The sorbent is the solid material (i.e., aquifer material) to which the dissolved or gaseous sorbate (i.e., the contaminant) associates. The term sorption encompasses two more specific processes referred to as **adsorption** and **absorption**. Adsorption is the association of a contaminant with the surface of a solid particle. Absorption is the association of a contaminant within a solid particle. Often it is difficult to distinguish between adsorption and absorption, since both may be occurring simultaneously; hence sorption is typically used to describe the overall phenomena.

Sorption is an important process effecting the transport of contaminants in the subsurface and can significantly influence the ability to remediate contaminated sites. Since aquifer material is static, a molecule that is associated with the solid phase is not moving. This **retardation** of contaminant transport is an essential component of accurately assessing migration rates or the ability to extract contaminants with pump and treat systems. Furthermore, sorption must be considered to determine the mass of contaminants present at a contaminated site and can also influence the rates of biodegradation processes.

The reverse of sorption is **desorption** — a term that describes the dissociation of a sorbed molecule and its return to the aqueous or gaseous phase. Interestingly, the observed behavior of desorption processes (i.e., rate and extent) may not be the reverse of the observed behavior of the sorption process (this will be discussed in more detail later in this section). It is important to recognize this distinction, as we will focus the discussion on a description of contaminant sorption and generally assume reversibility.

7.2.1 Factors That Influence Sorption

A simplistic way of describing sorption is the saying "like likes like." In more precise terminology, molecules tend to associate with other molecules that have similar properties. An analogy to this is solubility. Nonpolar molecules are more soluble in nonpolar solvents than in polar solvents, and ionic or polar molecules are more soluble in polar solvents than in nonpolar solvents. In the case of sorption, hydrophobic contaminants interact primarily with hydrophobic constituents of aquifer solids, while ionic or polar materials interact with charged mineral surfaces. In either case, the extent to which sorption may occur is influenced by the chemical properties of both the sorbent and the sorbate (see Figure 7.1).

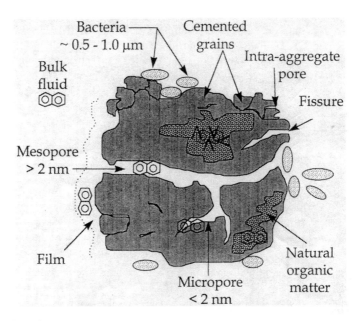

Figure 7.1 Schematic of soil grain sorption.

Unfortunately, soils and aquifer solids are complex materials that may support a range of sorption interactions (Schwartzenbach, et al., 1993; Weber and DiGiano, 1996). An individual soil grain is an extraordinarily heterogeneous composite containing minerals and natural organic matter. The mineral surfaces are dominated by polar or ionic functional groups capable of interacting with polar or ionic contaminants. The natural organic matter is generally **hydrophobic** material that tends to exclude water and other highly polar molecules (hydrophobic literally means water fearing). This fraction of soil or aquifer solids occurs typically where nonpolar/hydrophobic molecules associate.

If one considers the most common organic contaminants found in the subsurface, most are hydrophobic compounds. Examples of chemicals that exhibit this behavior include petroleum hydrocarbons (including benzene, toluene, ethylbenzene, and xylenes), chlorinated solvents (including TCE, PCE, CT, hexachlorobutadiene, and others), polychlorinated biphenyls (PCBs), and polynuclear aromatic hydrocarbons (PAHs) (see Chapter 4 for descriptions of these compounds). In all cases, the sorption of these compounds with soils or aquifer solids is primarily through the association with the natural organic matter fraction of the solid phase – simplifying the analysis of sorption in most cases (Chiou, et al., 1979).

The most accepted method of evaluating the propensity of an individual contaminant to associate with the organic fraction of aquifer solids is the **octanol-water partition test** (Briggs, 1973; Brown, et al., 1981). In this evaluation, octanol serves as a surrogate material for natural organic matter. Briefly, the test is conducted in a test tube containing equal volumes of octanol and water. Since octanol is immiscible in water, a two-phase system exists in the tube (similar to what occurs when olive oil is added to water). The contaminant is added to the tube and allowed to equilibrate between the two phases. After equilibration, the concentration of both phases is determined and the ratio of their concentrations is referred to as the **octanol-water partition coefficient** (k_{ow}). The mathematical definition of k_{ow} is presented in Eq. (7.1), where $[A]$ represents the concentration of the contaminant in either phase.

$$k_{ow} = \frac{[A]_{octanol}}{[A]_{water}} \qquad (7.1)$$

If the k_{ow} is less than 1, then the contaminant "prefers" the water phase, and would not associate extensively with natural organic matter. For most common ground water contaminants, the k_{ow} is greater than 1 and association with natural organic matter becomes an important process. In fact, many common contaminants have k_{ow} in excess of 100, some as high as 1×10^{6} indicating that common organic contaminants are highly attracted to a hydrophobic phase and will associate strongly with the natural organic fraction of soils or aquifer materials. The k_{ow} of common environmental contaminants are included in Table 7.1.

7.2.2 Equilibrium Evaluation Of Sorption — The Partition Coefficient

In order to calculate the migration rates of contaminants, or the total mass of contaminants present, the distribution of a contaminant between either the aqueous or solid phase must be established. This can become rather complicated if the kinetics of sorption must be considered. Fortunately, the association of hydrophobic contaminants with soil organic matter is usually fast when compared to the duration of contact between contaminants and aquifer solids at contaminated sites. Thus, local equilibrium conditions often exist.

The most common approach for evaluating a contaminant's distribution between the solid and aqueous phase is through the development of a **partition coefficient** (k_d), which is defined in Eq. (7.2) where $[A]$ is the concentration of a contaminant in either phase.

$$k_d = \frac{[A]_{solid}}{[A]_{aqueous}} \qquad (7.2)$$

This is a test analogous to the octanol-water partition test, where aquifer solids are used instead of octanol, and the test is conducted over a range of contaminant concentrations. The result of this test is an **isotherm**, as depicted in Figure 7.2, where concentrations of solid phase contaminant concentration are plotted against the equilibrium aqueous phase contaminant concentration. In the figure presented, the observed relationship is linear, and the k_d can be obtained through a simple linear regression of the data. There are more complicated cases where a linear result is not obtained. If however, the primary association is a hydrophobic

TABLE 7.1 Properties for Selected Organic Compounds

Compound/ Family	Formula	Specific Gravity	Solubility (mg/L)	K_{ow}	Vapor Pressure (mm Hg)	Henry's Law (unitless)
Fuels and derivatives						
Benzene	C_6H_6	0.879	1750	130	60	0.22
Ethylbenzene	C_8H_{10}	0.867	152	1400	7	0.32
Phenol	C_6H_6O	1.071	93,000	29	0.2	1.89×10^{-5}
Toluene	$C_6H_5CH_3$	0.866	535	130	22	0.26
o-Xylene	$C_6H_4(CH_3)_2$	0.880	175	890	5	0.22
PAHs						
Acenaphthene	$C_{12}H_{10}$	1.069	3.42	10,000	0.01	0.321
Benzopyrene	$C_{20}H_{12}$	1.35	0.0012	1.15×10^6	—	5.8×10^{-8}
Benzoperylene	$C_{22}H_{12}$	—	0.0007	3.24×10^6	—	5.8×10^{-6}
Naphthalene	$C_{10}H_8$	1.145	32	2800	0.23	4.9×10^{-2}
Methyl naphthalene	$C_{10}H_7CH_3$	1.025	25.4	13,000	—	0.0164
Ketones						
Acetone	CH_3COCH_3	0.791	inf	0.6	89	0.00104
Methyl ethyl ketone	$CH_3COCH_2CH_3$	0.805	2.68×10^5	1.8	77.5	0.00181
Halogenated aromatics						
Chlorobenzene	C_6H_5Cl	1.106	466	690	9	0.165
2-Chlorophenol	C_6H_4ClOH	1.241	29,000	15	1.42	7.4×10^{-4}
p-Dichlorobenzene (1,4)	$C_6H_4Cl_2$	1.458	79	3900	0.6	0.067
Hexachlorobenzene	C_6Cl_6	2.044	0.006	1.7×10^5	1×10^{-5}	0.062
Pentachlorophenol	C_6OHCl_5	1.978	14	1.0×10^5	1×10^{-4}	1.5×10^{-4}
1,2,4-Trichlorobenzene	$C_6H_3Cl_3$	1.446	30	20,000	0.42	0.059
2,4,6-Trichlorophenol	$C_6H_2Cl_3OH$	1.490	800	74	0.012	—

Specific gravity at various temperatures; refer to Nyer and others (1991) for details; inf is infinite solubility
Vapor pressure about 20 °C; 1 atm = 760 mm Hg.
Modified from Nyer and others (1991). Reprinted by permission of Ground Water Monitoring Review Copyright © 1991. All rights reserved.

TABLE 7.1 Properties for Selected Organic Compounds (continued)

Compound/ Family	Formula	Specific Gravity	Solubility (mg/L)	K_{ow}	Vapor Pressure (mm Hg)	Henry's Law Constant (unitless)
PCBs						
Aroclor 1254		1.5	0.012	1.07×10^6	7.7×10^{-5}	—
Halogenated aliphatics						
Bromodichloromethane	$CHBrCl_2$	2.006	4400	76	50	8.53
Bromoform	$CHBr_3$	2.903	3010	250	4	0.025
Carbon tetrachloride	CCl_4	1.594	757	440	90	1.25
Chloroform	$CHCl_3$	1.49	8200	93	160	1.41
Chloroethane	CH_3CH_2Cl	0.903	5740	35	1000	.212
1,1-Dichloroethane	$C_2H_4Cl_2$	1.176	5500	62	180	0.64
1,2-Dichloroethane	$C_2H_4Cl_2$	1.253	8520	30	61	0.05
1,1-Dichloroethene	$C_2H_2Cl_2$	1.250	2250	69	495	—
cis-1,2-Dichloroethene	$C_2H_2Cl_2$	1.27	3500	5	206	1.33
trans-1,2,-Dichloroethene	$C_2H_2Cl_2$	1.27	6300	3	265	0.221
Hexachloroethane	C_2Cl_6	2.09	50	39,800	0.4	—
Methylene chloride	CH_2Cl_2	1.366	20,000	19	362	0.13
1,1,2,2-Tetra-chloroethane	$CHCl_2CHCl_2$	1.600	2900	250	5	0.083
Tetrachloroethene	CCl_2CCl_2	1.631	150	390	14	1.21
1,1,1-Trichloroethane	CCl_3CH_3	1.346	1500	320	100	0.72
1,1,2-Trichloroethane	$CH_2ClCHCl_2$	1.441	4500	290	19	0.031
Trichloroethene	C_2HCl_3	1.466	1100	240	60	0.42
Vinyl chloride	CH_2CHCl	0.908	2670	24	266	3.58
Other						
2,6-Dinitrotoluene	$C_6H_3(NO_2)_2CH_3$	1.283	1320	100	—	—
1,4-Dioxane	$C_4H_8O_2$	1.034	4.31×10^5	1.02	30	—
Nitrobenzene	$C_6H_5NO_2$	1.203	1900	71	0.15	9.3×10^{-4}
Tetrahydrofuran	C_4H_8O	0.888	0.3	6.6	131	—

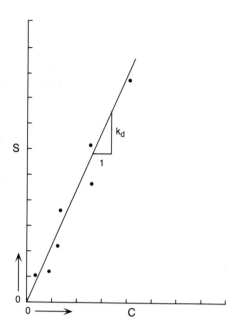

Figure 7.2 Linear sorption isotherm with distribution coefficient (k_d) determined by linear regression.

interaction and aqueous phase contaminant concentrations are less than approximately 50% of their aqueous solubility (typically the case in ground water systems), a linear isotherm is generally observed (Karickoff, 1981; Karickoff, 1984; Karickoff, et al., 1979). For the remainder of this section, only linear isotherm behavior will be considered.

If the k_d is known for a specific compound with a solid material of interest, the calculation of contaminant distribution is simple. For example, if the k_d value for benzene is 5 kg/L with a specific soil sample, and the ground water contains benzene at concentration is 1 mg/L, the sorbed benzene concentration would be 5 mg/kg. Beyond the evaluation of contaminant concentrations in both phases, the k_d allows for the determination of the fraction of the contaminant in the dissolved phase within a specific volume of an aquifer. This is an important consideration for calculating contaminant migration rates since only the dissolved fraction is subject to transport processes (Roberts, et al., 1986). The fraction of contaminant mass (f_w) present in the dissolved phase is defined mathematically in Eq. (7.3).

$$f_w = \frac{[A]_w V_w}{[A]_w V_w + [A]_s V_s} \tag{7.3}$$

$[A]_w$ and $[A]_s$ represent the concentration of contaminant in either the water or the solid, and V_w and V_s equal the volume of water and solid material being considered. If

$$[A]_s = k_d [A]_w \qquad (7.4)$$

then

$$f_w = \frac{[A]_w V_w}{[A]_w V_w + k_d [A]_w V_s} = \frac{V_w}{V_w + k_d V_s} \qquad (7.5)$$

Equation (7.5) can be simplified further if the porosity n, as defined in Eq. (7.6), of the aquifer is known.

$$n = \frac{Vw}{V_w + V_s} \qquad (7.6)$$

As is shown in Eq. (7.7), f_w can be described simply a function of k_d and n.

$$f_w = \frac{1}{1 + \left(\dfrac{1}{n} - 1\right)k_d} \qquad (7.7)$$

7.2.3 Predicting the Partition Coefficient, k_d

As stated previously, the sorption of nonionic organic molecules with aquifer materials is primarily due to an interaction with solid-phase natural organic matter. The extent to which this occurs is a function of two parameters : the amount of solid-phase natural organic matter present and the relative hydrophobicity of the contaminant itself. The amount of natural organic matter present is a site-specific parameter that cannot be estimated *a priori*. For example, some sands are almost devoid of organic material, while peat is almost exclusively organic in nature. Thus, the amount of solid-associated organic matter present in a given aquifer is determined in laboratory tests and is reported as the **fraction of organic carbon** (f_{oc}), a unitless term that describes the weight fraction of organic matter of the aquifer material. While the f_{oc} must be measured, it is possible to accurately estimate the relative hydrophobicity of a chemical using k_{ow} values. An increasing k_{ow} reflects an increasing degree of hydrophobicity and an increasing tendency to associate with natural organic matter. These properties that influence the partitioning of nonpolar organics can be incorporated in the mathematical description of k_d as is shown in Eq. (7.8) where k_{oc} is the partition coefficient between the contaminant and natural organic matter.

$$k_d = f_{oc} k_{oc} \qquad (7.8)$$

Studies have demonstrated that k_{oc} is a predictable value based upon correlations between observed behavior and k_{ow} values. Table 7.2 presents these correlations for a range of chemicals.

Example 7.1. CALCULATION OF k_{oc}

Given the following results from an isotherm test, and assuming a f_{oc} of 0.02, calculate the k_{oc} value of the contaminant.

Aqueous Phase Concentration (mg/L)	Solid Phase Concentration (mg/kg)
0.1	0.8
0.2	1.6
0.3	2.4
0.4	3.2
0.5	4

Solution. Linear regression of the data yields k_d of 8 kg/L.

$$k_{oc} = k_d/f_{oc} = 400 \text{ kg/L}$$

Example 7.2 CALCULATION OF SORPTION EXTENT

Given a k_d of 8 kg/L and $n = 0.25$, calculate the fraction of contamination associated with the aquifer solids.

Solution.

$$f_s = (1 - f_w) = 1 - \frac{1}{1 + \left(\frac{1}{n} - 1\right)k_d}$$

$$f_s = 1 - \frac{1}{25} = 0.96$$

7.2.4 Sorption And Migration Retardation

To this point, we have focused on contaminant sorption without consideration of contaminant desorption. In the next section, desorption processes will be discussed in some detail. For now, let us assume that the sorption-desorption process can be described through a rapid equilibrium. Under these conditions, a contaminant molecule will associate and dissociate

TABLE 7.2 Regression Equations for the Estimation of k_{OC}

Equation (a)	No. (b)	r^2 (c)	Chemical Class Represented	Ref.
$\log k_{oc} = -0.55 \log S + 3.64$ (S in mg/L)	106	0.71	Wide variety, mostly pesticides	Kenaga et al., (1978)
$\log k_{oc} = -0.54 \log S + 0.44$ (S in mole fraction)	10	0.94	Mostly aromatic or polynuclear aromatics; two chlorinated	Karickhoff et al., (1979)
$\log k_{oc} = -0.557 \log S + 4.277$ (S in μ moles/L)	15	0.99	Chlorinated hydrocarbons	Chiou et al., (1979)
$\log k_{oc} = 0.544 \log k_{ow} + 1.377$	45	0.74	Wide variety, mostly pesticides	Kenaga et al, (1978)
$\log k_{oc} = 0.937 \log k_{ow} - 0.006$	19	0.95	Aromatics, polynuclear aromatics, triazines and dinitroaniline herbicides	Brown et al. (1981)
$\log k_{oc} = 1.00 \log k_{ow} - 0.21$	10	1.00	Mostly aromatic or polynuclear aromatics; two chlorinated	Karickhoff et al., (1979)
$\log k_{oc} = 0.94 \log k_{ow} + 0.02$	9	(e)	s-Triazines and dinitroaniline herbicides	Brown et al. (1981)
$\log k_{oc} = 1.029 \log k_{ow} - 0.18$	13	0.91	Variety of insecticides, herbicides and fungicides	Rao et al., (1980)
$\log k_{oc} = 0.524 \log k_{ow} + 0.855$	30	0.84	Substituted phenylureas and alkyl-N-phenylcarbamates	Briggs (1973)
$\log k_{oc} = 0.0067 \, (P-45N) + 0.237$	29	0.69	Aromatic compounds: ureas, 1,3,5-triazines, carbamates and uracils	Hance (1969)
$\log k_{oc} = 0.681 \log BCF + 1.963$ (f)	13	0.76	Wide variety, mostly pesticides	Kenaga et al., (1978)
$\log k_{oc} = 0.681 \log BCF + 1.886$ (f)	22	0.83	Wide variety, mostly pesticides	Kenaga et al., (1978)

(a) k_{oc} = organic carbon sorption coefficient: S = water solubility; k_{ow} = octanol-water partition coefficient;
(b)   No. = number of chemicals used to obtain regression equation.
(c) r^2 = correlation coefficient for regression equation
(d)   Equation originally given in terms of k_{om}. The relationship $k_{om} = k_{oc}/1.724$ was used to rewrite the equation in terms of k_{oc}.
(e)   Not available.
(f)   Specific chemicals used to obtain regression equation not specified.

from the solid phase with the net distribution of molecules being described by k_d. At times when a contaminant molecule is in the aqueous phase, it will move with the bulk flow of ground water. When the molecule is sorbed, it will be stationary. The net effect of this behavior is the **retardation** of contaminant transport relative to the rate of nonsorbing species (Domenico and Schwartz, 1998; Fetter, 1999).

Equation (7.9) is the 1-D advection-dispersion equation including contaminant sorption presented previously in Chapter 6 (Eq. (6.20)).

$$D_x \frac{\partial^2 C}{\partial x^2} - v_x \frac{\partial C}{\partial x} - \frac{\rho_b}{n}\frac{dS}{dt} = \frac{\partial C}{\partial t} \qquad (7.9)$$

In this equation, C is the aqueous phase contaminant concentration, D_x is the dispersion coefficient, v_x is the ground water flow velocity, ρ_b is the bulk mass density (dry mass per volume soil), n is porosity, and S is the sorbed phase contaminant concentration (typically mg/kg). In cases where contaminant partitioning can be described with a linear isotherm, Eq. (7.9) can be rearranged to:

$$R\frac{\partial C}{\partial t} = D_x \frac{\partial^2 C}{\partial x^2} - v_x \frac{\partial C}{\partial x} \qquad (7.10)$$

where R is the retardation factor defined in Eq. (7.11).

$$R = \left(1 + \frac{\rho_b}{n}k_d\right) \qquad (7.11)$$

Conceptually, the retardation factor is the ratio of the ground water flow velocity to contaminant migration velocity. If $R = 10$, the ground water is moving, on average, ten times faster than the organic contaminant plume. An example of observed contaminant retardation is shown in Figure 7.3.

7.2.5 Desorption

The ability of chemicals to completely desorb from a solid is an area of current study (Fu, et al., 1994; Kan, et al., 1994; Kan, et al., 1997; Pignatello and Xing, 1995). The interest in this process stems from observations that cannot be reconciled with k_d values that describe the sorption process — in particular, the observation of solid phase contaminant concentrations exceeding the predicted concentration based on the aqueous phase contaminant concentration and k_d. Generally, this phenomena is observed in materials that have been contaminated for long time periods and contain low solid-phase contaminant concentrations (nominally less than 20 mg/kg). At high contaminant concentration, desorption patterns are generally predictable through equilibrium analysis. The importance of this observation is potentially enormous. Site remediation requirements include the removal of sorbed contamination.

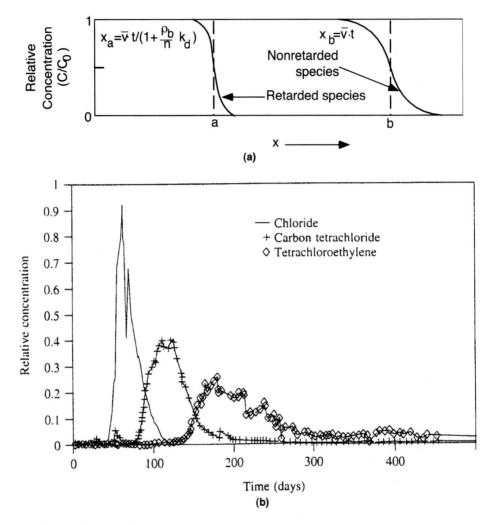

Figure 7.3 (a) Predicted advance of solutes in a one dimensional transport evaluation. (b) Observed field retardation data from the Borden landfill site, 5 meters downgradient from the injection well. Chloride is a non-sorbing tracer. Carbon tetrachloride and tetrachloroethylene are retarded by sorption.

If a contaminant does not desorb as readily as it sorbed, the ability to meet clean -up levels may be seriously threatened.

At this time, it is not possible to conclusively identify a physical mechanism that causes a resistance to desorption. One possible explanation is the rearrangement of the soil's natural organic matter as a result of contaminant sorption. After rearrangement, the contaminant can be physically sequestered within the organic matrix and not dissociate under conditions predicted by equilibrium partitioning. This theory is analogous to enzyme-substrate binding where a macromolecule changes its 3-D structure in response to the association with a smaller molecule. Other possible mechanisms can describe the observation of desorption resistance, but are outside the scope of this book.

7.3 ABIOTIC FATE PROCESSES

Several chemical reaction mechanisms have been identified that impact the fate of certain organic chemical in ground water systems. These reactions do not include the direct involvement of living organisms and are thus referred to as **abiotic processes**. Types of abiotic reactions include hydrolysis, oxidation-reduction reactions, and elimination reactions (Schwartzenbach, et al., 1993; Vogel and McCarty, 1987). The extent that any abiotic reactions may influence the fate of contaminates in the subsurface is highly compound-specific and can be strongly influenced by the conditions of the local environment. In this section, each process is discussed briefly.

7.3.1 Hydrolysis

Hydrolysis refers to a chemical reaction between a contaminant molecule and water. This process is important for certain contaminants, including alkyl halides, carboxylic acid esters, and carboxylic acid amides (Table 7.3). Common ground water contaminants such as aromatic hydrocarbons and chlorinated ethenes do not hydrolyze appreciably (Table 7.4). An example of a hydrolysis reaction is presented in Eq. (7.12) where 1-bromopropane reacts with water to form 1-propanol and bromide ion.

$$CH_3CH_2CH_2Br + H_2O \rightarrow CH_3CH_2CH_2OH + H^+ + Br^- \qquad (7.12)$$

TABLE 7.3 Organic Functional Groups Generally Resistant to Hydrolysis

Alkanes	Aromatic amines
Alkenes	Alcohols
Alkynes	Phenols
Benzenes/biphenyls	Glycols
Polycyclic aromatic hydrocarbons	Ethers
Heterocyclic polycyclic aromatic hydrocarbons	Aldehydes
Halogenated aromatics/PCBs	Ketones
Dieldrin/aldrin and related halogenated hydrocarbon pesticides	Carboxylic acids
Aromatic nitro compounds	Sulfonic acids

Source : Lyman et al., 1990

TABLE 7.4 Types of Organic Functional Groups That Are Potentially
Susceptible to Hydrolysis

Alkyl halides	Nitriles
Amides	Phosphonic acid esters
Amines	Phosphoric acid esters
Carbamates	Sulfonic acid esters
Carboxylic acid esters	Sulfuric acid esters
Epoxides	

Source : Lyman et al., 1990

The rate that a chemical undergoes hydrolysis is strongly influenced by the temperature and pH of the system (Schwartzenbach, et al., 1993). As temperature increases, hydrolysis rates increase. As pH become either acidic or alkaline (e.g., greater than or less than 7.0) rates of acid-catalyzed or base-catalyzed hydrolysis can increase. Typically, hydrolysis is described with a first-order rate expression as shown in Eq. (7.13)

$$\frac{dC}{dt} = -k_{hyd}C \tag{7.13}$$

where C is the concentration of the chemical species and k_{hyd} is a first order hydrolysis rate coefficient. Knowing factors such as pH and temperature is important in determining the appropriate rate coefficient for a particular contaminant.

Example 7.3   HYDROLYSIS RATE CALCULATION

Calculate the time required for 95% of a chemical to hydrolize in water assuming a hydrolysis rate coefficient of 0.001 day^{-1}.

Solution. To determine the time required, the rate expression must be integrated, yielding the following first-order rate expression

$$\ln \frac{C}{C_0} = -kt$$

so

$$\ln(0.05/1) = -0.001(t)$$

$$\boxed{t_{0.05} = 2{,}995 \text{ days} = 8.2 \text{ years}}$$

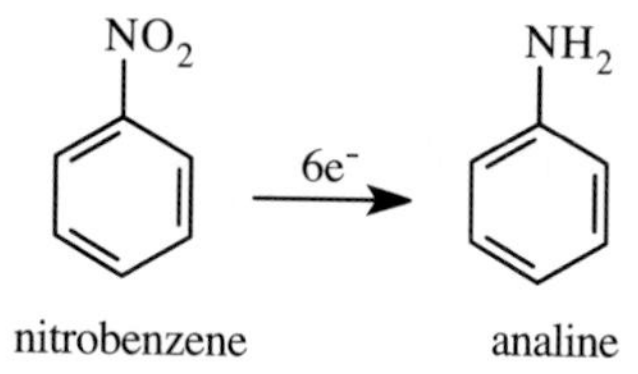

nitrobenzene   analine

$$CH_3CH_2Cl \xrightarrow{2e^-} CH_3CH_3 + Cl^-$$

chloroethane   ethane + chloride

Figure 7.4 Examples of abiotic nitro reduction and abiotic dehalogenation reactions.

7.3.2 Oxidation-Reduction

Oxidation-reduction reactions involve the transfer electrons between a contaminant molecule and another chemical species. If the contaminant loses an electron, or electrons, it has been oxidized. If the contaminant gains electrons, it has been reduced. Inorganic compounds, such as reduced metals and reduced sulfur, are possible mediators of oxidation-reduction reactions (Klecka and Gonsior, 1984; Macalaldy, et al., 1986; Schwartzenbach, et al., 1990). The presence or absence of inorganic species is often dependent on local conditions. For example, many anaerobic environments will contain elevated levels of Fe(II), H_2S/HS^-, and other reduced species that are capable of donating electrons and reducing certain contaminants. Examples of contaminants known to undergo abiotic oxidation-reduction reactions include halogenated hydrocarbons and nitroaromatics. Examples of each are presented in Figure 7.4. Biologically mediated oxidation-reduction reactions are often more rapid than abiotic reactions for many contaminants of interest in ground water systems, and thus abiotic oxidation-reduction are often neglected in transport calculations. In cases where they become important, oxidation-reduction processes are generally introduced as a first order reaction with respect to contaminant concentration — analogous to hydrolysis.

7.3.3 Elimination

Elimination reactions occur with a specific group of ground water contaminants, in particular, halogenated ethanes and propanes. For these chemicals, elimination reactions are characterized by the release of a halogen group and a proton from adjacent carbon atoms with the subsequent formation of a carbon-carbon double bond. An example of this is shown in Eq. (7.14), where the product of 1,1,1-trichloroethane elimination is 1,1-dichloroethene (Vogel and McCarty, 1987).

$$\text{Cl} - \overset{\overset{\displaystyle \text{Cl}}{|}}{\underset{\underset{\displaystyle \text{Cl}}{|}}{\text{C}}} - \overset{\overset{\displaystyle \text{H}}{|}}{\underset{\underset{\displaystyle \text{H}}{|}}{\text{C}}} - \text{H} \quad \longrightarrow \quad \overset{\text{Cl}}{\underset{\text{Cl}}{\diagdown}}\text{C} - \text{C}\overset{\text{H}}{\underset{\text{H}}{\diagup}} \qquad (7.14)$$

7.4 VOLATILIZATION

The transfer of a contaminant from the aqueous phase, nonaqueous phase liquid (NAPL), or sorbed phase directly to the gas phase is a process referred to as **volatilization**. The rate and extent to which volatilization occurs is strongly influenced by a number of parameters including the contaminant phase, the contaminant's vapor pressure, environmental factors (e.g., temperature, and others), proximity in respect to the vadose zone, and other site specific parameters (Mackay and Leinonen, 1975; Mackay and Wolkoff, 1973). Because of the range of factors that influence volatilization it becomes difficult to calculate the contribution of this process to the fate of chemicals in ground water.

In the simplest form, the process of volatilization can be illustrated in a manner analogous to the octanol-water partition test discussed previously. For the evaluation of volatilization however, consider a closed bottle that contains water and air instead of water and octanol. If a contaminant is introduced to the bottle (assuming that the resulting aqueous phase concentration does not exceed the aqueous solubility, thus avoiding the formation of a nonaqueous phase or a crystalline phase) and allowed to equilibrate, some fraction of the contaminant added will reside in the gas phase. The distribution of a chemical between the water and the gas at equilibrium is described by the **Henry's law coefficient** (Mackay, et al., 1979; Thibodeaux, 1996). Mathematically, Henry's law is presented in Eq. (7.15), where P_c is the partial pressure of the contaminant, $[C]_{aq}$ is the aqueous phase concentration of the contaminant, and H_c is the Henry's constant.

$$H_c = \frac{P_c}{[C]_{aq}} \qquad (7.15)$$

Despite the relative simplicity of H_c, a factor that complicates the use of reported values of H_c is the variety of units used in its expression. The units of Eq. (7.15) are [L-atm/mol]. Henry's law coefficients are also commonly expressed in dimensionless form where the gas phase concentration is expressed as mole/L instead of partial pressures. Also, H_c is strongly influenced by temperature and the ionic strength of the aqueous solution.

In ground water systems that are isolated from the vadose zone, Henry's law can be applied to estimate the distribution of contaminants between the aqueous phase and the gas phase. If direct exchange is possible with the vadose zone, equilibrium may not be achieved and the calculation of gas phase concentrations is more difficult. In the latter case, the atmosphere acts as an infinite sink for the contaminant and gas phase concentrations are always less than equilibrium. Despite the lower gas concentrations observed, the net flux of contaminants to the gas phase under these conditions can be very significant. Additionally, volatilization from NAPL's in the vadose zone or floating on the water table can yield high concentrations of contaminants in the gas phase. A discussion of volatilization from NAPL's is presented in Chapter 11.

Example 7.4   USING HENRY'S CONSTANT

An aquifer contaminated with vinyl chloride contains a residual gas saturation of 10% (i.e., the percent of porosity containing gas). If the aqueous phase vinyl chloride concentration is 0.70 mg/L, calculate the gas phase concentration (mg/L) and the percent of total vinyl chloride mass in the gas phase of this two-phase system ($T = 25$ °C, $P = 1$ atm).

$$H_c \text{ of vinyl chloride} = 22.4 \text{ L-atm/mol}$$

Step 1. Convert H_c to dimensionless form. At 25 °C and 1 atm pressure, the partial pressure of vinyl chloride [atm] equals the moles of VC per total moles of gas. Using the ideal gas law, the volume of 1 mol gas under these conditions = 24.45 L, so

$$22.4 \frac{L\text{-}atm}{mol} = 22.4 \frac{L_{H_2O} \cdot mol_{VC}}{mol_{gas} \cdot mol_{H_2O}} \times \frac{1 \, mol_{gas}}{24.45 \, L} = 0.916 \frac{L_{H_2O} \cdot mol_{VC}}{L_{gas} \cdot mol_{H_2O}}$$

Step 2. Calculate gas concentration

$$(0.7 \text{ mg/L}) (0.916) = 0.641 \text{ mg/L}$$

Step 3.

$$\text{Total mass} = (0.7 \text{ mg/L})(0.9 \text{ L/L}) + (0.64 \text{ mg/L})(0.1 \text{ L/L})$$
$$= 0.69 \text{ mg/L Aquifer}$$
$$\text{mass in gas} = 9\% \text{ of total}$$

7.5 BIODEGRADATION

The **biodegradation** of contaminants refers to the complete conversion of a contaminant to mineralized end products (i.e., CO_2, H_2O, and salts) through metabolism by living organisms. In ground water systems, the organisms that carry out this process are bacteria indigenous to the aquifer. In some cases, metabolic activity does change the chemical form of the contaminant but does not result in the mineralization. In these cases, the term **biotrans-formation** is typically used to describe the processes occurring.

The metabolism of ground water contaminants is an extremely important fate process since it has the potential to impact the fate of all organic ground water contaminants, and is a process that has the potential to yield nonhazardous products. It is a complicated fate process due to the diversity of bacteria that may be involved, and range of metabolic processes that can be expressed (Young and Cerniglia, 1995). Before discussing specific aspects of contaminant metabolism by bacteria, a short discussion of important concepts regarding microbiology is presented to provide a foundation for further discussion.

7.5.1 Energy Flow and Metabolism

All living organisms require energy to survive and the capture of usable energy through the process of **catabolism** is a significant part of an organism's overall metabolism. There are two forms of energy that can support life – light energy and chemical energy. Certain bacteria are capable of using light as their energy source and are classified as **phototrophs**. Since light energy does not penetrate the earth'S surface, the role of phototrophs in ground water systems in generally disregarded. Bacteria that obtain energy from chemical forms are classified as **chemotrophs**. Chemical energy sources are further differentiated as either inorganic or organic compounds. An organism that uses inorganic sources of energy is called a **lithotroph**. Examples of lithotrophic-substrates include ammonia (NH_3), hydrogen (H_2), ferrous iron (Fe^{2+}), and sulfide (HS^-). Organisms that use organic compounds as their energy source are called **organotrophs**. A comprehensive list of organotrophic-substrates would be enormous (just think of all the different foods you eat!). Examples of common ground water contaminants that serve as organotrophic-substrates include fuel components, PAH's, phenolics. Certain nitroaromatics and chlorinated solvents may also serve as a bacterium's energy source.

The extraction of energy from organic chemicals during catabolism occurs as a result of oxidation processes. As a chemical is oxidized, it loses electrons. For this reason, chemotrophic substrates are often referred to as **primary electron donors**. Electrons lost during oxidation are coupled with the reduction of electron acceptors. Eventually, the complex sequence of oxidation-reduction reactions that occur during catabolism results in the reduction of a **terminal electron acceptor**. Common terminal electron acceptors in ground water systems include oxygen (O_2), nitrate NO_3^-, ferric iron (Fe^{3+}), sulfate (SO_4^{2-}), and carbon dioxide (CO_2). When oxygen is the terminal electron acceptor, catabolism is classified **aerobic**. All other terminal electron acceptor conditions are classified as **anaerobic**. In most cases, an individual bacterial strain is capable of using only one terminal electron acceptor. The most common exceptions to this rule are **facultative aerobes** that can use nitrate as a terminal electron acceptor in the absence of oxygen. An important evaluation of contaminant biodegradation potential involves an analysis of the availability of primary electron donors and terminal electron acceptors, as their presence is required for organisms to obtain energy for survival and selects for the types of organisms that will be present.

The metabolism of organic contaminants can be broadly differentiated by the ability of organisms to use the contaminant for catabolic processes. If the compound is a primary electron donor and provides the bacterium with energy for cell growth, the contaminant is referred to as a **primary substrate**. In some cases, the oxidation of a contaminant will provide the cell with energy, but it is present at concentrations that are not sufficient to support the energy requirements of the organism. Contaminants of this type are referred to as **secondary substrates**. If a compound is metabolized fortuitously as the cell is obtaining energy from another primary electron donor, the transformation is referred to as **cometabolic**. The last category used to classify contaminant metabolism pertains to several very important contaminants and is referred to as **dehalorespiration**. In this case, certain chlorinated organics serve as an anaerobic terminal electron acceptor.

Bacterial Growth. Bacteria grow through the process of binary fission. In this process, a single cell divides into two cells that are identical to the original cell. The rate that bacteria grow is influenced by a number of parameters. For example, different strains have different minimum doubling times under ideal condition, and the observed rate of growth is controlled b substrate availability, temperature, and other environmental conditions. The classic demonstration of how a bacterial population responds to conditions that favor growth is shown in Figure 7.5. Initially, a lag phase is observed where growth does not occur. During this period, the organisms are adapting to the new medium conditions. Following the lag phase, microbial growth is exponential due to rapid binary fission of the microbes. Eventually, the culture enters stationary phase where bacterial numbers become constant. The cause of stationary phase is the depletion of an essential growth requirement in the medium. The availability of the **limiting substrate** then controls the ability of the culture to continue

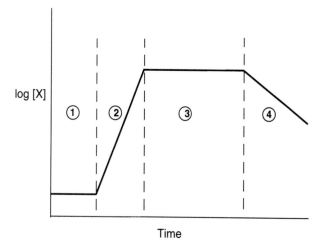

Figure 7.5 Microbial growth curve, where region 1 is the lag phase, region 2 is the exponential growth phase, region 3 is the stationary phase and region 4 is the decay phase.

to grow. Eventually, the medium becomes exhausted of constituents required to support viable organisms, and the culture enters the decay phase where cell death rates exceed any regrowth.

7.5.2 Stationary Phase Kinetics

A common interest in the evaluation of contaminant fate in the subsurface is the rate that contaminants are attenuated through biodegradation or biotransformation. Contaminant attenuation is typically evaluated with the assumption that organisms are in the stationary phase of growth, since lag phases and exponential growth occur rapidly relative to the time periods of interest in ground water systems. With this assumption, the rate of limiting substrate utilization can be predicted by the Monod expression (i.e., saturation kinetics) presented in Eq (7.16).

$$-\frac{dS}{dt} = \frac{kSX}{K_s + S} \tag{7.16}$$

In this equation, S is the limiting substrate concentration [mg/L], X is the biomass concentration [mass per volume or number per volume], k is the maximum substrate utilization rate [$S\cdot(X\cdot time)^{-1}$], and K_s is the half-saturation coefficient [mg/L]. The behavior of this function is illustrated in Figure 7.6 where at low concentration it displays first-order behavior (rate is linearly proportional to S) and at high concentrations it approaches zero-order behavior (rate is independent of S). In many cases, the concentrations of limiting substrates in ground water are low and first-order kinetics are observed. This is true when $S \ll K_s$, in Eq. (7.16), which then reduces to Eq. (7.17):

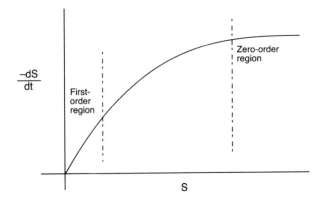

Figure 7.6 Observed rate of limiting substrate utilization (dS/dt) in a stationary phase bacterial culture. At low concentrations of S, –dS/dt is directly proportional to ΔS. At high concentrations of S, –dS/dt is unaffected by ΔS and the reaction rate is "saturated."

$$-\frac{dS}{dt} = \left(\frac{kX}{K_s}\right)S = k'S \qquad (7.17)$$

In this case, k' is an apparent first-order rate coefficient (time^{-1}).

Based upon the rate of limiting substrate utilization, it is possible to use reaction stoichiometry to determine the rate that microorganisms utilize other constituents of interest (Lee, et al., 1988). This is particularly important when the contaminant itself is not the limiting substrate — a condition that is often the case in ground water systems. For example, consider the oxidation of benzene by aerobic bacteria. The solubility of benzene in water is approximately 1,800 mg/L (at 25°C), while the solubility of O_2 in water in contact with the atmosphere is roughly 9.0 mg/L. Based on the reaction stoichiometry written in Eq. (7.18), the consumption of 1 mg/L of benzene (C_6H_6) requires 3.1 mg/L of O_2. Thus benzene concentrations of less than 3 mg/L can result in the complete utilization of dissolved oxygen in ground water. For this reason, it is common for the availability of O_2 to limit the extent of aerobic benzene oxidation (and the aerobic oxidation of other pollutants) and the rate of benzene attenuation will be predicted by the rate of O_2 utilization.

$$C_6H_6 + 7.5O_2 \Rightarrow 6CO_2 + 3H_2O \qquad (7.18)$$

7.5.3 Dissolved Oxygen Impacts

For several reasons, the presence or absence of dissolved oxygen from ground water is an important component in the evaluation of aquifer microbiology. The first reason is the impact that dissolved oxygen has on the types of viable organisms present. Similar to human beings and other organisms, certain bacteria require oxygen to survive. If oxygen is not present, these organisms will die or become inactive. Interestingly, the inverse is true for anaerobic bacteria (Brock and Madigan, 1991). For these organisms, oxygen is acutely toxic. Thus the presence or absence of oxygen is a strong selective pressure for the types of organisms that will be active within any contaminant plume.

An additional role of dissolved oxygen in contaminant fate is its direct participation in certain oxidation reactions catalyzed by aerobic bacteria. In particular, reactions catalyzed by oxygenase enzymes. An example of an oxygenase enzyme catalyzed reaction is illustrated in Figure 7.7 where benzene is oxidized to catechol through the direct incorporation of O_2 into the contaminant molecule. Without O_2, the reaction would not proceed. In addition to benzene, many other common contaminants are subject to oxygenase attack, including: fuel constituents, PAH's, certain chlorinated solvents, and others. This function of O_2 is physiologically distinct from its role as a terminal electron acceptor where oxygen is reduced forming water.

Example 7.5   STOICHIOMETRY OF CONTAMINANT METABOLISM

Assuming the following reaction, how much H_2 is required to reduce 1 mg/L PCE to ethene via reductive dechlorination?

$$C_2Cl_4 + 4H_2 \Rightarrow C_2H_4 + 4Cl^- + 4H^+$$

Based on the above stoichiometry, one mole of PCE (M.W. = 165.8) requires 4 moles of H_2 (M.W. = 2).

$$\frac{1\ mg_{PCE}}{L}\ \frac{1\ mmol_{PCE}}{165.8\ mg_{PCE}}\ \frac{4\ mmol_{H_2}}{1\ mmol_{PCE}}\ \frac{2\ mg_{H_2}}{1\ mmol_{H_2}} = \frac{0.0483\ mg_{H_2}}{L}$$

Therefore, 0.0483 mg/L of H_2 would be sufficient for the complete dechlorination of 1 mg/L PCE.

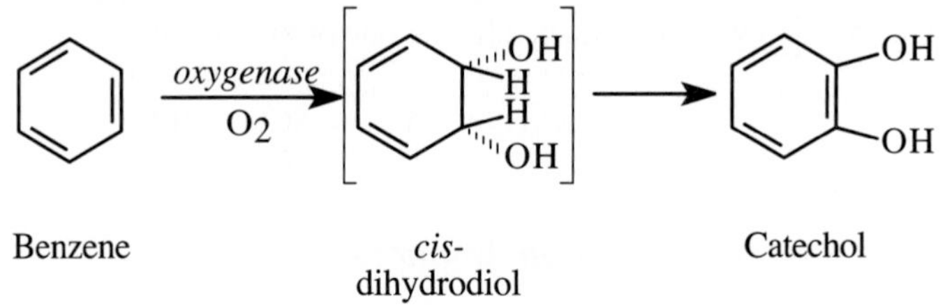

Benzene   cis-   Catechol
                      dihydrodiol

Figure 7.7 Enzymatic oxidation of benzene to catechol. The first step of benzene metabolism under aerobic conditions.

7.5.4 Metabolic Pathways Of Common Contaminants

An overview of how bacteria are capable of metabolizing various contaminants is presented in the following sections. It is important to note that this continues to be an area of intense research. Paradigms continue to change and it is difficult to assert definitive analysis regarding the totality of metabolic processes that may impact an individual contaminant's fate. To this end, the following sections focus on established concepts but also illustrate current uncertainties.

Monoaromatic Hydrocarbons. As constituents of gasoline, diesel, and jet fuels, monoaromatic hydrocarbons are common ground water contaminants due to accidental spills and leaking underground storage tanks. Of particular concern are benzene, toluene, ethylbenzene and xylene isomers – collectively abbreviated as BTEX. Under aerobic conditions, all BTEX compounds are rapidly biodegraded as primary substrates (Alvarez and Vogel, 1991). Unfortunately, the oxygen demand resulting from the aerobic oxidation of these compounds can exceed the solubility of oxygen in water. Dissolved oxygen concentrations are rapidly depleted due or the biodegradation of these and other fuel constituents, yielding anaerobic conditions in contaminated aquifers (Lee, et al., 1988).

The biodegradation of BTEX compounds under anaerobic conditions is not as well characterized as it is under aerobic conditions. Only recently has the biodegradation of all BTEX compounds been confirmed under all anaerobic electron acceptor conditions in laboratory studies. From these studies it appears that toluene is the most degradable under all electron acceptor conditions and benzene is the least degradable. In many laboratory studies conducted under anaerobic conditions, benzene degradation is not observed. Certain modeling studies of certain well-characterized contaminated field sites infer that anaerobic benzene degradation may occur *in situ*. Several recent laboratory studies conducted under anaerobic conditions have demonstrated that benzene may degrade in the absence of oxygen (Lovely, et al. 1995). Certainly the anaerobic biodegradation of BTEX is possible, and the anaerobic degradation of TEX most likely occurs in many contaminated sites. The factors controlling the rate or extent of anaerobic benzene biodegradation have not been elucidated, making an *a priori* evaluation of this potentially important fate pathway difficult at this time. In any case, the anaerobic degradation of BTEX compounds is generally slower than observed through aerobic processes.

Polynuclear Aromatic Hydrocarbons. The class of contaminants referred to as polynuclear aromatic hydrocarbons (PAHs) represent a number of compounds with physiochemical characteristics that vary dramatically. In particular, the aqueous phase solubility (i.e., hydrophobicity) varies from approximately 30 mg/L for naphthalene to less than 1 μg/L for benzo-(a)-pyrene. PAHs sorb extensively due to their high hydrophobicity, resulting in low observed aqueous phase concentrations of these contaminants. PAH biodegradation is generally limited to aerobic metabolism that is initiated by oxygenase attack (similar to that depicted in Figure 7.7). PAHs of three or fewer rings, including naphthalene, fluorene, and phenanthrene are known to be primary substrates for bacterial growth. Larger and more hydrophobic PAHs (i.e., four rings and higher) tend to behave as secondary substrates in the presence of the smaller, more water soluble PAHs (Hughes, et al., 1997). The observation of anaerobic PAH metabolism is rare, and is limited to naphthalene.

Phenolic Compounds. Phenol and chlorinated phenols are biodegraded as primary substrates under aerobic and anaerobic conditions. These compounds are often recalcitrant in the environment due to their toxicity and the low water solubility of certain chlorinated forms (i.e., pentachlorophenol (PCP)). When present at concentrations below toxic thresholds, phenols can be rapidly mineralized by a wide range of microorganisms. As the number of chlorine substituents increases, the rate of degradation often decreases.

MTBE. Fuel additives (also called oxygenates) have been is use in the United States for approximately two decades. These compounds have been added to gasoline to increase octane ratings and to decrease exhaust emissions of certain air pollutants. Since the late 1980's, the most common additive used for either purpose has been **methyl *tert*-butyl ether (MTBE)**. The percent of gasoline comprised by MTBE is as high as 10% in regions of the country where urban air pollution exceeds federal standards, and MTBE is now a common contaminant of ground water as a result of gasoline spills. Since MTBE is currently listed as a probable human carcinogen, its presence in ground water is of concern. Furthermore, MTBE is more soluble, less volatile, and less hydrophobic than other fuel constituents (i.e., BTEX compounds). Thus, it is prone to dissolve to higher aqueous phase concentrations than other fuel-derived contaminants and migrate more rapidly (Squillace et al., 1997.).

Since MTBE has only recently become a ground water concern, less is known regarding its biodegradability than many other pollutants. Based on its chemical structure, MTBE is not a compound that would be expected to be readily biodegradable. MTBE contains two structural features that generally reduce biodegradability. The first is the highly stable ether linkage between the methyl- and *tert*-butyl group. Second is the degree of branching associated with the *tert*-butyl group itself. There are several studies that suggest that MTBE can be biodegraded under conditions representative of the subsurface; however, degradation is not always observed in controlled laboratory tests and observations from contaminated sites often indicate limited, if any, biodegradation (Borden et al., 1997; Schirmer and Barker, 1998).

Based on current information, MTBE biodegradation is more likely to occur under aerobic conditions than anaerobic conditions. Aerobic oxidation of MTBE may occur via cometabolic degradation (Steffan et al., 1997) and as a growth substrate (Mo et al., 1997; Salanitro et al., 1994.). In aerobic conditions, oxidation of MTBE is initiated at the ether link and *tert*-butyl alcohol is often observed as an intermediate (depicted in Eq. 7.19). Further oxidation can result in CO_2 formation (Bradley et al., 1999). Under anaerobic conditions, degradation has rarely been observed (Mormile et al., 1994; Yeh and Novak, 1994; Squillace et al. 1997). In cases where anaerobic degradation has been documented, pathways similar to those observed under aerobic conditions are believed to occur.

$$
\begin{array}{ccc}
\underset{\displaystyle\overset{\displaystyle CH_3}{|}}{H_3C-C-O-CH_3} & \longrightarrow & \underset{\displaystyle\overset{\displaystyle CH_3}{|}}{H_3C-C-OH} \\
\end{array}
\qquad (7.19)
$$

methyl *tert*-butyl ether   *tert*-butyl alcohol

The extent to which anaerobic or aerobic biodegradation processes will influence the fate of MTBE in contaminated aquifers is the basis for current research and experimentation. Certainly, our understanding of its biodegradation is far behind what is known regarding other common contaminants. Based on the information available, MTBE appears to be a highly mobile and highly recalcitrant ground water pollutant.

Chlorinated Solvents. Chlorinated methanes, ethanes, and ethenes comprise a group of compounds commonly referred to as chlorinated solvents. These compounds have been used extensively as degreasers, dry cleaning agents, and paint removers, and their presence and persistence in the environment is widespread (Pankow and Cherry, 1996). Chlorinated solvents used extensively in the United States (also see Chapter 4) include: perchloroethene (PCE), trichloroethylene (TCE), 1,1,1-trichloroethene (TCA), carbon tetrachloride, and dichloromethane (e.g., methylene chloride).

The metabolism of chlorinated solvents is perhaps more diverse than any other group of environmental contaminants. Depending on the compound of interest, the electron acceptor condition, and the presence of inducing substrates, the metabolism of chlorinated solvents may occur through primary metabolism, secondary metabolism, cometabolism, or through terminal electron acceptor processes. Additionally, the metabolism of these compounds often does not result in the formation of benign products. This is particularly true for metabolism through cometabolic processes or through terminal electron accepting processes.

Only a few chlorinated solvents are known to be primary substrates for growth. Dichloromethane is a primary substrate under both aerobic and anaerobic conditions and is perhaps the most biodegradable of all the chlorinated solvents (Brunner, et al., 1980; Freedman and Gossett, 1991). Vinyl chloride, a compound used to produce PVC materials and a biotransformation product of PCE and TCE, can be used as an electron donor under aerobic conditions. Isomers of DCE may also be oxidized under aerobic conditions as growth substrates. This process is not well understood, however, and often is not observed at contaminated sites. The secondary metabolism of chlorinated solvents may occur when contaminants are present at low concentration, but is limited to those compounds that can serve as primary substrates.

A common anaerobic biotransformation process for chlorinated solvents is **reductive dechlorination**. A half-reaction that describes this process is shown in Eq. (7.20).

$$R–Cl + 2e^- + H^+ \Rightarrow R – H + Cl^- \qquad (7.20)$$

In this example, R (a generic notation for any organic compound) is being reduced with the evolution of chloride ion. The reducing equivalents (e^-) for this process originate from the oxidation of a primary electron donor. The process of reductive dechlorination results in the formation a number of chlorinated and non-chlorinated compounds (Bouwer and McCarty, formation a number of chlorinated and non-chlorinated compounds (Bouwer and McCarty, 1983). This is illustrated in Figures 7.8 through 7.10 for common chlorinated methanes, ethanes and ethenes.

The process of reductive dechlorination may result from either cometabolic processes or dehalorespiration. At this time, dehalorespiration has been confirmed for the chlorinated ethene series only (cometabolism of chlorinated ethenes is also possible). In general, cometabolic transformations are slow and the reducing equivalents consumed account for only asmall percent of the electron donor consumed. Various anaerobes are capable of cometabolic reductive dechlorination, including methanogens. This is due to the nonspecific nature of the reaction. Reduced cofactors that are present in many anaerobes, including vitamin B-12, are responsible for catalyzing cometabolic reductive dehalogenation (Egli, et al., 1990, Gantzer and Wackett, 1991, Wood, et al., 1968).

Dehalorespiration is a rapid reaction in comparison to cometabolic transformation, and it is possible for a high percent of the reducing equivalents generated through the oxidation

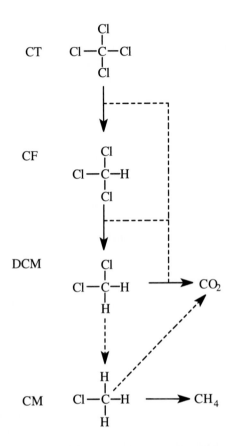

Figure 7.8 Pathway for the anaerobic metabolism of chlorinated methanes. Initial metabolism of carbon tetrachloride (CT) and chloroform (CF) metabolism are reduction to the level of dichloromethane (DCM). Subsequent metabolism results eventually in CO_2 production, although traces of chloromethane (CM) may accumulate as an intermediate. Source: Egli, et al., 1988; Freedman and Gossett, 1991; Galli and McCarty, 1989.

of electron donors to be used in this form of metabolism. To date, a handful of organisms capable of dehalorespiration have been isolated. Most are capable of dechlorinating PCE and TCE to the level of *cis*-DCE only. One isolate, *Dehalococcoides ethenogenes* strain 195, isknown to carry out PCE dehalorespiration to the level of ethene (Maymó-Gatell, et al., 1997). At contaminated sites, high levels of vinyl chloride and ethene are often observed – indicating that this form of metabolism beyond DCE may be common. One important aspect of dehalogenation processes is the interaction of these organisms with other anaerobes, in particular, fermentative bacteria that produce hydrogen as a bi-product of organotrophic catabolism. Hydrogen is a preferred primary substrate for dechlorinators and thus these organ-

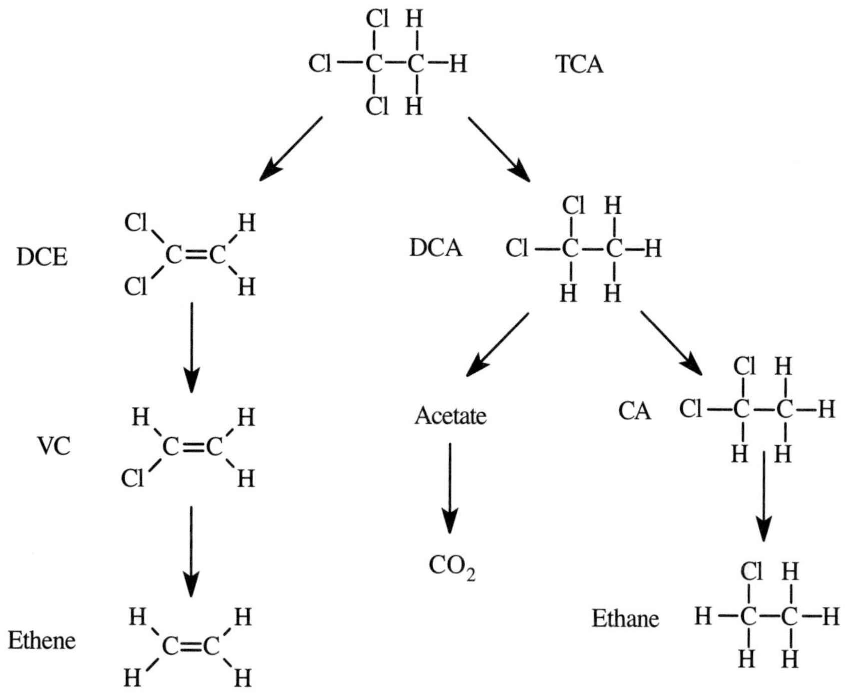

Figure 7.9 Pathway for the anaerobic transformation of a common chlorinated ethane 1,1,1-trichloroethane (TCA) through reductive dechlorination and dehydrodehalogenation. Reductive dechlorination yields dichloroethane (DCA) which can be oxidized to acetate or reduced to chloroethane (CA). Dehydrodehalogenation yields 1,1-dichloroethene (DCE), which can then be reduced to vinyl chloride (VC), and eventually ethene. Source: Galli and McCarty, 1989; Vogel, et al., 1987.

isms rely on the activity of the fermentors. Also, hydrogen production via fermentation is strongly influenced by the types of organic substrates present. It is important to note that lithotrophic organisms utilize hydrogen as well and compete with dehalorespiring bacteria for the "hydrogen pool" in anaerobic environments (Carr and Hughes, 1998; DiStefano, et al., 1991).

A distinct form of chlorinated solvent metabolism is oxidation through cometabolic processes. These reactions are the result of oxygenase activity expressed by organisms utilizing certain primary substrates – not chlorinated solvents – for catabolic purposes. Examples of substrates that induce oxygenase enzymes capable of chlorinated solvent cometabolism include monoaromatic hydrocarbons, methane (and other alkanes), and ammonia. This process has been studied in detail due to the potential for nonhazardous end-product formation (including CO_2) (Young and Cerniglia, 1995). Several interesting aspects of this metabolism

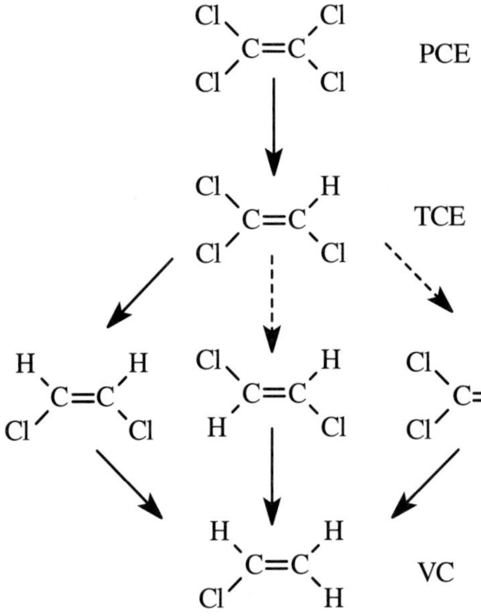

Figure 7.10 Reductive dechlorination of chlorinated ethenes including per-chloroethene (PCE), trichloroethene (TCE), the three isomers of dichloroethene (DCE's), vinyl chloride (VC). Dechlorination of VC would yield a non-chlorinated product – ethene. Source: Belay and Daniels, 1987; Freedman and Gossett, 1989; Vogel and McCarty, 1985.

influence the rate and extent to which this process will occur. First, is the oxygenase enzyme itself. Oxygenases, induced by various substances, differ in their intrinsic rates of chlorinated solvent oxidation. Second, the inducing substance acts as a competitive inhibitor for chlorinated solvent binding, reducing reaction rates. Third, the reaction catalyzed by the oxygenase results in the formation of compounds that are toxic to the microorganism. For example, the product of TCE oxidation is TCE-epoxide, a highly reactive molecule that reacts rapidly with cell components. After cometabolizing a certain mass of chlorinated solvent, the cell loses viability due to product toxicity (Alvarez-Cohen and McCarty, 1991).

Not all chlorinated solvents are oxidized through cometabolism. PCE and carbon tetrachloride are resistant to this process, and TCA is poorly metabolized in this manner. TCE, DCE's, and vinyl chloride can be cometabolized. Chloroform (the dehalogenation product of carbon tetrachloride) is oxidized by oxygenase enzymes. This reaction is rarely sustained, however, as the product of oxidation is phosgene – a short-lived but highly toxic compound. Cometabolic degadation of chlorinated solvents has been studied primarily as an engineered bioremediation system, although it may be an important component of chlorinated solvent natural attenuation, in particular, at sites where chlorinated solvents are found in the presence of inducing substances (e.g., fuel constituents or dissolved methane gas) and dissolved oxygen.

Nitroaromatic Compounds. Nitroaromatics are common pollutants of water and soils as a result of their use in plastics, dyes, and explosives. The nitro group is a strong electron withdrawing functionality that reduces the efficacy of oxygenase attack of the aromatic ring. Recent studies have demonstrated that certain organisms are capable of oxidizing certain nitroaromatic compounds and to obtain energy for growth (i.e., primary metabolism). This activity is generally limited to nitroaromatics containing two or fewer nitro groups (Reiger and Knackmuss, 1995).

Under anaerobic conditions, nitroaromatic transformation generally yields reduced aromatic products. For example, the product of the complete reduction of nitrobenzene is analine (aminobenzene). The formation of an aryl amine from an aryl nitro group requires that two intermediate forms be produced. First is the aryl nitroso intermediate followed by an aryl hydroxylamine. Recent work has demonstrated the importance of the aryl hydroxylamine intermediate in the ultimate fate of nitroaromatics under anaerobic conditions. The hydroxylamine can be reduced to the amine, or undergo more complex reactions that can result in the binding with natural organic matter or the formation of an aminophenol through rearrangement reactions (Hughes, et al., 1998; Hughes, et al., 1999).

7.6 EVALUATION OF FATE PROCESSES

Translating molecular level fate process to field-scale evaluations is a difficult but important task. The heterogeneous nature of the subsurface is a significant complicating factor. For example, the organic carbon content of aquifer solids can vary enormously with depth as different geologic units are encountered. This variation must be considered in the prediction of contaminant retardation. Electron acceptor condition is another spatial variable that is extremely important to characterize for the accurate evaluation of contaminant fate as the rate biodegradation processes are strongly controlled by this factor. Several tools are available to assist in these evaluations and are briefly discussed in the remainder of this chapter.

7.6.1 Site Characterization

Specific measurements and other site information used to characterize contaminated aquifers discussed in Chapter 5 are used extensively in the assessment of fate processes at individual sites. For example, the distribution of contaminants and the existing ground water chemistry are typically obtained during site characterization. With this data, it is possible to identify areas where different forms of metabolism may be occurring (i.e., aerobic or anaerobic). Also, site characterization facilitates the evaluation of sorption and retardation, as f_{oc} distributions will typically be evaluated in contaminated areas. In some cases, additional information may be required beyond standard site characterization. This may include additional work at the contaminated site. Frequently, studies are conducted in the laboratory or through modeling studies to support the evaluation of fate processes. Each is discussed in the following two paragraphs.

7.6.2 Microcosm Studies

Microcosm studies are laboratory evaluations of fate processes specific to a contaminated area, where materials are obtained from contaminated areas and experiments can be conducted in a controlled setting. An example of a common microcosm study is the evaluation of contaminant biodegradation rates under site conditions. In these tests, samples of aquifer solids and ground water are obtained from contaminated areas of interest. The materials are taken to the lab and transferred into bottles, which can be sealed and incubated. Care is taken in the construction of microcosms not to change conditions and perturb the results. For example, if a site is anaerobic, the construction of the microcosm will be conducted in a manner to avoid the introduction of oxygen. Samples are taken periodically. and the rate of contaminant degradation can be calculated directly. The results of microcosm studies can be very beneficial in cases where unusual field conditions are encountered, or where additional confidence is required. They are not, however, a common component of site characterization.

7.6.3 Modeling

Contaminant transport models are very valuable tools that can be used to approximate the rate of extent of fate processes occurring at contaminated sites. Details regarding the use of fate and transport models are presented in Chapters 8, 10, and 12. Basically, modeling studies are used to incorporate the characteristics of a site's hydrogeology, contaminants, and ongoing fate processes to predict the observed distribution of contaminants and their concentrations. The calibration of models requires an understanding of the processes that are occurring, their rates, and the extent to which they are exerted spatially. Often, this process of model calibration will yield approximate transformation rates (abiotic and biotic), volatilization rates, or the retardation coefficient. Site modeling is particularly valuable because the calibration of these models to what has occurred to date allows for prediction of contaminant fate into the future.

SUMMARY

Sorption, abiotic transformation, volatilization, and biodegradation processes have a significant impact on the transport and fate of organic chemicals in ground water. Sorption retards transport through the accumulation of contaminants on the stationary solid phase and strongly influences the time required to remediate contaminated sites. Abiotic transformation processes are important for certain contaminant classes and may represent a significant removal process for those contaminants. Volatilization is a mechanism where contaminants may be lost from the water to the vadose zone. This is further discussed in Chapter 11. Biodegradation is a very important fate process since it can impact any organic chemical in ground water. The rate and extent of biodegradation is dependent on site-specific conditions. In some cases, biodegradation is not complete, yielding hazardous end products. Site characterization efforts or remediation plans must account for these processes in order to obtain accurate predictions of contaminant behavior in ground water systems.

REFERENCES

Alvarez, P. J. J. and T. Vogel, "Substrate Interactions of Benzene, Toluene, and para-Xylene During Degradation by Pure Cultures and Mixed Culture Aquifer Slurries," *Appl. Environ. Microbiol.*, 57:2981-2985, 1991.

Alvarez-Cohen, L. and P. L. McCarty, "Product Toxicity and Cometabolic Competitive Inhibition Modeling of Chloroform and Trichloroethylene Transformation by Methanogenic Resting Cells," *Appl. Environ. Microbiol.*, 57:1031-1037, 1991.

Belay, N. and L. Daniels, "Production of Ethane, Ethylene, and Acetylene from Halogenated Hydrocarbons by Methanogenic Bacteria," *Appl. Environ. Microbiol.*, 53:1604-1610, 1987.

Borden, Robert C., R. A. Daniel, L. E. LeBrun IV, and C. W. Davis, "Intrinsic Biodegradation of MTBE and BTEX in a Gasoline-Contaminated Aquifer," *Water Resources Res.*, vol. 33, No. 5, pp. 1105-1115, 1997.

Bouwer, E. J. and P. L. McCarty, "Transformation of 1- and 2-Carbon Halogenated Aliphatic Organic Compounds Under Methanogenic Conditions," *Appl. Environ. Microbiol.*, 45:1286-1294, 1983.

Bradley, Paul M., J. E. Landmeyer, and F. H. Chapelle, "Aerobic Mineralization of MTBE and *tert*-Butyl Alcohol by Stream-Bed Sediment Microorganisms," *Environ. Sci. Technol.*, 33, pp. 1877-1879, 1999.

Briggs, G. G., "A Simple Relationship between Soil Adsorption of Organic Chemicals and Their Octanol/Water Partition Coefficients," *Proc. 7th British Insecticide and Fungicide Conf.*, Boots Company Ltd., G. B. Nottingham, Vol. 1, 1973.

Brock, T. D. and M. T. Madigan, *Biology of Microorganisms*, Englewood Cliffs, NJ, Prentice Hall, 1991.

Brunner, W., D. Staub, and T. Leisinger, "Bacterial Degradation of Dichloromethane," *Appl. Environ. Microbiol.*, 40:950-958, 1980.

Brown, D. S., S. W. Karickhoff and E. W. Flagg, "Empirical Prediction of Organic Pollutant Sorption in Natural Sediments," *J. Environ. Qual.* (103):382-386, 1981.

Carr, C. S. and J. B. Hughes, "Enrichment of High Rate PCE Dechlorination and Comparative Study of Lactate, Methanol, and Hydrogen as Electron Donors to Sustain Activity," *Environ. Sci. and Technol.*, 32:1817-1824, 1998.

Chiou, C. T., L. J. Peters, and V. H. Freed, "A Physical Concept of Soil-water Equilibria for Nonionic Organic Compounds," *Science,* 206:831-832, 1979.

DiStefano, T. D., J. M. Gossett, and S. H. Zinder, "Reductive Dechlorination of High Concentrations of Tetrachloroethene to Ethene by an Anaerobic Enrichment Culture in the Absence of Methanogenis," *Appl. Environ. Microbiol.*, 57:2287-2292, 1991.

Domenico, P.A., and F. W. Schwartz, *Physical and Chemical Hydrogeology,* 2nd edition, New York, John S. Wiley and Sons, 1998.

Egli, C., Stromeyer, S., Cook, A. M. and Leisinger, T., "Transformation of Tetra- and Trichloro-methane to CO_2 by Anaerobic Bacteria is a Non-Enzymatic Process," *FEMS Microbiol. Let.*, 68:207-212, 1990.

Egli, C., T. Tschan, R. Scholtz, A. M. Cook, and T. Leisinger, "Transformation of Tetrachloro-methane to Dichloromethane and Carbon Dioxide by *Acetobacterium Woodii*," *Appl. Environ. Microbiol.*, 54:2819-2842, 1988.

Fetter, C.W., *Contaminant Hydrogeology*, 2nd edition, New York, Prentice Hall, 1999.

Freedman, D. L. and J. M. Gossett, "Biological Reductive Dechlorination of Tetrachloroethylene and Trichloroethylene to Ethylene Under Methanogenic Conditons," *Appl. Environ. Microbiol.*, 55:2144-2151, 1989.

Freedman, D. L. and J. M. Gossett, "Biodegradation of Dichloromethane and its Utilization as a Growth Substrate Under Methanogenic Conditions," *Appl. Environ. Microbiol.*, 57:2847-2857, 1991.

Fu, G., Kan, A.T., and M. B. Tomson, "Adsorption and Desorption irreversibility of Polycyclic Aromatic Hydrocarbons in Surface Sediment. I. Characterization of Desorption Hysteresis," *Environ. Toxicol. Chem.*, 13(10):1559-1567, 1994.

Galli, R. and P. L. McCarty, "Biotransformation of 1,1,1-Trichloroethane, Trichloromethane, and Tetrachloromethane by a *Clostridium* sp.," *Appl. Environ. Microbiol.*, 55:837-844, 1989.

Gantzer, C. J. and L. P. Wackett, "Reductive Dechlorination Catalyzed by Bacterial Transition-Metal Coenzymes," *Environ. Sci. Technol.*, 25:715-722, 1991.

Hance, R.J., "An Empirical Relationship between Chemical Structure and the Sorption of Some Herbicides by Soils," *J. Agric. Food Chem.* 17:667-668, 1969.

Hughes, J. B., C. Wang, and C. Zhang, "Anaerobic Transformation of 2,4- and 2,6-Dinitrotoluenes by *Clostridium acetobutylicum*: A Pathway Through Dihydroxylamino-Intermediates," *Environ. Sci. Technol.*, 1999.

Hughes, J. B., C. Wang, K. Yesland, A. Richardson, R. Bhadra, G. Bennett, and F. Rudolph, "Bamberger Rearrangement During TNT-Metabolism by *Clostridium acetobutylicum*," *Environ. Sci. Technol.*, 32:494-500, 1998.

Hughes, J. B., D. M. Beckles, S. D. Chandra, and C. H. Ward, "Utilization of Bioremediation Processes for the Treatment of PAH-Contaminated Sediments," *J. Indust. Microbiol. and Biotech.*, 18:152-160, 1997.

Kan, A. T., G. Fu, and M. B. Tomson, "Adsorption/Desorption Hysteresis in Organic Pollutant and Soil/Sediment Interaction," *Environ. Sci. Technol.*, 28:859-867, 1994.

Kan, A. T., G. Fu, M. A. Hunter, and M. B. Tomson, "Irreversible Adsorption of Naphthalene and Tetrachlorobiphenyl to Lula and Surrogate Sediments," *Environ. Sci. Technol.*, 31:2176-2185, 1997.

Karickhoff, S.W., "Estimation of Sorption of Hydrophobic Semi Empirical Pollutants on Natural Sediments and Soils," *Chemosphere,* 108:833-846, 1981.

Karickhoff, S.W., "Organic Pollutant Sorption in Aquatic Systems," *J. Hydraulic Engineering,* 1106):707-735, 1984.

Karickhoff, S. W., D. S. Brown, T. A. and Scott, "Sorption of Hydrophobic Pollutants on Natural Sediments," *Water Res.*, 13:241-248, 1979.

Kenaga, E. E., and C. A. I. Goring, "Relationship Between Water Solubility, Soil-Sorption, Octanol-Water Partitioning, and Bioconcentration of Chemicals in Biota," prepublication copy of paper dated October 13, 1978, given at the American Society for Testing and Materials, Third Aquatic Toxicology Symposium, October 17-18, New Orleans, LA, 1978.

Klecka, G. M. and S. L. Gonsior "Reductive Dechlorination of Chlorinated Methanes and Ethanes by Reduced Iron II) Porphyrins," *Chemosphere*, 13:391-402, 1978.

Lee, M. D., J. M. Thomas, R. C. Borden, P. B. Bedient, C. H. Ward, and J. T. Wilson, "Biorestoration of Aquifers Contaminated with Organic Compounds," *CRC Cri. Rev. Environ. Control*, 18:29-89, 1988.

Lovely D. R., J. D. Coates, J. C. Woodward and E. J. P. Phillips, "Benzene oxidation coupled to sulfate reduction," *Appl. Environ. Microbiol.*, 61:953-958, 1995.

Lyman, W. J., W. F. Reehl, and D. H. Rosenblatt, *Handbook of Chemical Property Estimation Methods,* Washington, D.C, American Chemical Society, 1990.

Macalaldy, D. L., P. G. Tratnyek, and T. J. Grundl, "Abiotic Reduction Reactions of Anthropogenic Organic Chemicals in Anaerobic Systems: A Critical Review," *J. Cont. Hydrol.*, 1:1-28, 1986.

Mackay, D., and P. J. Leinonen, "Rate of Evaporation of Low Solubility Contaminants from Water Bodies to Atmosphere," *Environ. Sci. Technol.* 9:1178-1180, 1975.

Mackay, D., and A. W. Wolkoff, "Rate of Evaporation of Low Solubility Contaminants from Water Bodies to Atmosphere," *Environ. Sci. Technol.* 7:611-614, 1973.

Mackay, D., W. Y. Shiu, and R. P. Sutherland, "Determination of Air-Water Henry's Law Constants for Hydrophobic Pollutants," *Environ. Sci. Technol.* 13:333-337, 1979.

Maymó-Gatell, X., Y. Chien, J. M. Gossett, and S. H. Zinder, "Isolation of a Bacterium that Reductively Dechlorinates Tetrachloroethene to Ethene," *Science*, 276:1568-1571, 1997.

Mo, K., C. O. Lora, A. E. Wanken, M. Javanmardian, X. Yang, C. F. Kulpa, "Biodegradation of Methyl *t-butyl* Ether by Purce Bacterial Cultures," *Applied Microbiol. Biotechnol.*, 47:69-72, 1997.

Mormile, M. R., S. Liu, and J. M. Suflita, "Anaerobic Biodegradation of Gasoline Oxygenates: Extrapolation of Information to Multiple Sites and Redox Conditions," *Environ. Sci. Technol.*, 28, pp., 1727-1732, 1994.

Pankow, J. F., and J. A. Cherry, *Dense Chlorinated Solvents and Other DNAPLs in Groundwater,* Portland, Waterloo Press, 1996.

Pignatello, J. P., and B. Xing, "Mechanisms of Slow Sorption of Organic Chemicals to Natural Particles," *Environ. Sci. Technol.*, 10:1-11, 1995.

Rao, P. S. C., and J. M. Davidson, "Estimation of Pesticide Retention and Transformation Parameters Required in Nonpoint Source Pollution Models," *Environmental Impact of Nonpoint Source Pollution,* M. R. Overcash and J. M. Davidson, Eds., Ann Arbor, MI, Ann Arbor Science Publishers, 1980.

Reiger, P. G. and H. J. Knackmuss, *Biodegradation of Nitroaromatic Compounds;* Spain, J.C. Ed., 49:1-18, New York, Plenum Press, 1995.

Roberts, P. V., M. N. Goltz, and D. M. Mackay, "A Natural Gradient Experiment on Solute Transport in a Sand Aquifer. 3. Retardation Estimates and Mass Balances for Organic Solutes," *Water Resources Res.*, (2213):2047-2058, 1986.

Salanitro, J. P., L. A. Diaz, M. P. Williams, and H. L. Wisniewski, "Isolation of a Bacterial Culture That Degrades Methyl *t*-Butyl Ether," *Applied and Environmental Microbiology*, vol. 60, No. 7, pp. 2593-2596, 1994.

Schirmer, Mario, and James F. Barker, "A Study of Long-Term MTBE Attenuation in the Border," Aquifer, Ontario, Canada, *Ground Water Monitoring and Review*, pp. 113-122, 1998.

Schwartzenbach, R. P., P. M. Gschwend, and D. M. Imboden, *Environmental Organic Chemistry,* New York, John S. Wiley and Sons, 1993.

Squillace, Paul J., J. F. Pankow, N. E. Kortes, and J. S. Zogorski, "Review of The Environmental Behavior and Fate of Methyl *tert*-Butyl Ether," *Environmental Toxicology and Chemistry*, Vol. 16(9), pp. 1836-1844, 1997.

Steffan, Robert J., K. McClay, S. Vainberg, C. W. Condee, and D. Zhang, "Biodegradation of the Gasoline Oxygenates Methyl *tert*-Butyl Ether, Ethyl *tert*-Butyl Ether, and *tert*-Amyl Methyl Ether by Propane-Oxidizing Bacteria," *Applied and Environmental Microbiology*, Vol. 63, No. 11, pp. 4216-4222, 1997.

Swartzenbach, R. P., R. Stierli, and J. Zeyer, "Quinone and Iron Porphryrin Mediated Reduction of Nitroaromatic Compounds in Homogeneous Aqueous Solutions," *Environ. Sci. Technol.*, 24:1566-1574, 1990.

Thibodeaux, L. T., *Environmental Chemodynamics: Movement of Chemicals in Air, Water, and Soil,* New York, John S. Wiley and Sons, 1996.

Vogel, T. M., C. Criddle, and P. L. McCarty,, "Transformation of Halogenated Aliphatic Compounds," *Environ. Sci. Technol.*, 21:722-736, 1987.

Vogel, T.M. and P. L. McCarty, "Biotransformation of Tetrachloroethylene to Trichloroethylene, Dichloroethylene, Vinyl Chloride, and Carbon Dioxide Under Methanogenic Conditions," *Appl. Environ. Microbiol.*, 49:1080-1083, 1985.

Vogel, T. M. and P. L. McCarty, "Abiotic and Biotic Transformation of 1,1,1-Trichloroethane under Methanogenic Conditions," *Environ. Sci. Technol.*, 21:1208-1213, 1987.

Weber, W. J. and F. A. DiGiano, *Process Dynamics in Environmental Systems*, New York, John S. Wiley and Sons. 1996.

Wood, J. M., F. S. Kennedy, and R. S. Wolfe, "The Reaction of Mutli Halogenated Hydrocarbons with Free and Bound Reduced Vitamin B12," *Biochemistry*, 7:1707-1713, 1968.

Yeh, Carol K. and John T. Novak, "Anaerobic Biodegradation of Gasoline Oxygenates in Soils," *Water Environment Research,* Vol. 66, No. 5, pp., 744-752, 1994.

Young, L. Y., C. E. Cerniglia, *Microbial Transformation and Degradation of Toxic Organic Chemicals*, New York, John S. Wiley and Sons, 1995.

C H A P T E R   8

MODELING BIODEGRADATION AND NATURAL ATTENUATION

8.1 KINETICS AND RATES OF BIODEGRADATION

Chapter 7 focused on contaminant fate processes including sorption, volatilization, abiotic and biotic transformations. A detailed discussion of microbiologically mediated transformations was presented along with the most common pathways for biodegradation of fuel hydrocarbons and chlorinated solvents and other contaminants. These fate processes greatly affect contaminant transport and remediation; however, they are somewhat difficult to quantify at the field scale, especially biodegradation processes. A better understanding of fate processes at the field scale can be achieved using fate and transport models that simulate these processes and their impacts on contaminant concentrations in the subsurface. This chapter, in particular, focuses on integrating the biodegradation mechanisms into the transport equations discussed in Chapter 6. Since biodegradation has been demonstrated to be a key mechanism for reducing contaminant concentrations and contaminant mass in aquifers, it is beneficial to develop models that allow an assessment of the efficacy of these processes at the field scale.

Modeling biodegradation involves selecting an applicable kinetic model as well as determining the appropriate biodegradation rates for use in the selected model. This chapter will focus on the various kinetic expressions that have been used to date for fuel hydrocarbons and chlorinated solvents and will present biodegradation rate data for these compounds. The chapter will also focus on current biodegradation models and will present a set of new tools that have recently emerged for simulating natural attenuation processes (described in more detail in Chapter 12).

8.1.1 Biodegradation Kinetics

The main expressions that have been utilized for modeling biodegradation include:

1. Monod kinetics
2. First-order decay kinetics
3. Instantaneous reaction kinetics

Monod kinetics have been described in Chapter 7. It is important to note that the main difficulty with using Monod kinetics is the lack of data for the various chemicals under different electron acceptor conditions. Suarez and Rifai (1999) reported Monod kinetic data from 18 studies for BTEX (mostly aerobic). Their research presented a range between $0.01 - 20.3$ mg/L for the half-saturation constant for BTEX and a range between 4×10^{-5} and 19.0 day^{-1} for μ_{max}. They found virtually no Monod kinetic data for chlorinated solvents.

The first-order decay model, one of the most commonly used expressions for representing the biodegradation of an organic compound, involves the use of an exponential decay relationship:

$$C = C_0 \cdot e^{-kt} \tag{8.1}$$

where C is the biodegraded concentration of the chemical, C_0 is the starting concentration, and k is the rate of decrease of the chemical in units of time^{-1}. First-order rate constants are often expressed in terms of a half-life for the chemical:

$$t_{1/2} = \frac{0.693}{k} \tag{8.2}$$

The first-order decay model shown in Eq. (8.1) assumes that the solute degradation rate is proportional to the solute concentration. The higher the concentration, the higher the degradation rate. This method is usually used to simulate biodegradation in dissolved hydrocarbon plumes. Modelers using the first-order decay model typically use the first-order decay coefficient as a calibration parameter, and adjust the decay coefficient until the model results match field data. With this approach, uncertainties in a number of parameters (e.g., dispersion, sorption, biodegradation) are lumped together in a single calibration parameter.

The electron-acceptor limited model, commonly referred to as the instantaneous reaction model, was first proposed by Borden and Bedient (1986) for simulating the aerobic biodegradation of fuel hydrocarbons. Borden and Bedient (1998) observed that microbial biodegradation kinetics are fast in comparison with the transport of oxygen, and that the growth of microorganisms and utilization of oxygen and organics in the subsurface can be simulated as an instantaneous reaction between the organic contaminant and oxygen.

From a practical standpoint, the instantaneous reaction model assumes that the rate of utilization of the contaminant and oxygen by the microorganisms is very high, and that the time required to biodegrade the contaminant is very small, or almost instantaneous. Using oxygen as an electron acceptor, for example, biodegradation is calculated using the expression:

$$\Delta C_R = -\frac{O}{F} \tag{8.3}$$

where ΔC_R is the change in contaminant concentration due to biodegradation, O is the concentration of oxygen, and F is the utilization factor, or the ratio of oxygen to contaminant consumed. The variable, F, is obtained from the redox reaction involving the organic and the electron acceptor (see Chapter 12). The instantaneous reaction model has the advantage of not requiring kinetic data. The model, however, is limited to situations where the microbial biodegradation kinetics are fast relative to the rate of ground water flow.

Example 8.1 BIODEGRADATION EXPRESSIONS

The purpose of this example is to illustrate the differences between the three expressions that can be used to simulate biodegradation: first-order decay, Monod kinetics and an instantaneous reaction. Assume that the dissolved benzene concentration at a downgradient location in a given aquifer is 12.0 mg/L. Also assume that aerobic biodegradation is occurring in the aquifer and that 8.0 mg/L of oxygen are available for utilization by the microorganisms over a period of 10 days. A simple calculation can be made using each of the three biodegradation expressions to estimate the anticipated reduction in benzene concentrations due to the presence of the 8.0 mg/L of oxygen:

Instantaneous reaction expression. Assuming that 3.0 mg/L of oxygen are required to biodegrade 1.0 mg/L of contaminant:

Benzene reduction $= 8.0/3.0 = 2.67$ mg/L

Resulting benzene concentration $= 12.0 - 2.67 = 9.33$ mg/L

Monod kinetic expression. Assuming an oxygen half saturation constant of 0.1 mg/L (Borden et al., 1986), a benzene half-saturation constant of 22.16 mg/L, a maximum utilization rate of 9.3 days[-1] (Tabak et al., 1990) and a microorganisms population of 0.05 mg/L:

$$\text{Benzene reduction} = 9.3 \times \frac{12}{12 + 22.16} \times \frac{8}{8 + 0.1} \times 10 \times 0.05 = 1.59 \text{ mg/L}$$

Resulting benzene concentration $= 12 - 1.59$ mg/L $= 10.4$ mg/L

First-order decay expression. Assuming a half-life of benzene of 5 days (Howard et al., 1991):

$$\text{First-order decay rate (from 8.2)} = \frac{0.693}{t_{1/2}} = 0.1386 \text{ day}^{-1}$$

Resulting benzene concentration $= 12 \times e^{-.1386 \times 10} = 3.0$ mg/L

The above calculations show that the Monod kinetic model is the most conservative model in predicting the amount of biodegradation that occurs. Only 1.59 mg/L of benzene concentration reduction is attributed to biodegradation. The BIOPLUME II model assumes total utilization of the oxygen available during the 10-day period thus resulting in a predicted reduction in benzene concentration of 2.67 mg/L. Finally, the first-order decay expression predicts an unrealistic resulting concentration of benzene of 3.0 mg/L after 10 days. The 3.0 mg/L concentration is unrealistic because there is not enough oxygen in the aquifer to reduce the benzene concentration to the predicted level. Therefore, it is important to recognize that the first-order expression does not incorporate the electron acceptor limitation and thus care should be taken when using this expression.

8.1.1 Rates of Biodegradation

Much research has been undertaken to determine biodegradation rates for organics in the subsurface. Field biodegradation rates generally refer to the rate of mass loss or concentration declines of contaminants as a function of time. Laboratory biodegradation rates similarly refer to the rate of removal of contaminants during the controlled experiment. Overall, laboratory rates are easily determined; however, their usefulness may be limited because of the limitations of microcosm studies. Additionally, laboratory degradation rates are very dependent on the soil and ground water used in the experiment, and may vary from one location to another in the same site. A methodology has not yet been established that would allow the transfer of laboratory determined biodegradation rates to field situations with any degree of confidence.

The main difficulty in determining field rates of biodegradation is due to the complicating transport processes such as advection, dispersion, and sorption. Additionally, biodegradation under many field situations is limited by the transport of the required nutrients into the plume. Outside of conducting controlled field experiments where the total initial mass of contaminants is known and extensive monitoring allows calculating contaminant mass at any time during the experiment, it is somewhat difficult to accurately determine the field rates of biodegradation. Often, as will be seen in the next section, researchers and practitioners indirectly verify the occurrence of biodegradation at the field scale and calculate an "apparent" rate of biodegradation based on the changes in total mass or concentration in the plume as a function of time. Such a rate may incorporate the effects of the other physical and chemical processes occurring at the site.

In recent years, there has been more interest in estimating biodegradation rates from field data using a first-order degradation rate. A number of researchers have developed methods for estimating decay rates using simplified approaches. Wiedemeier et al. (1996), for example, described the use of a normalized field data set to compute a decay rate. To determine approximate biodegradation rate constants with this method, measured concentrations of dissolved BTEX are corrected for the effects of dispersion, dilution from recharge, volatilization, and sorption using a tracer.

One tracer that has proved useful in some, but not all, ground water environments is trimethylbenzene (TMB). The three isomers of this compound (1,2,3-TMB, 1,2,4-TMB, and 1,3,5-TMB) have Henry's Law constants and soil sorption coefficients similar to (although somewhat higher than) those of the BTEX compounds. Also, the TMB isomers are generally present in sufficient quantities in fuel mixtures to be readily detectable in ground water in contact with a fuel spill. Finally, they often are recalcitrant to biodegradation in the anaerobic portion of a plume. Other compounds of potential use as conservative tracers are the tetramethylbenzene isomers, provided they are detectable throughout most of the plume.

Buscheck and Alcantar (1995) derive a relationship that allows calculation of approximate biodegradation rate constants assuming a steady-state plume. This method involves coupling the regression of contaminant concentration (plotted on a logarithmic scale) versus distance downgradient (plotted on a linear scale) to an analytical solution for one-dimensional, steady-state, contaminant transport that includes advection, dispersion, sorption, and biodegradation. The effects of volatilization are assumed to be negligible. For a steady-state plume, the first-order decay rate is approximated by (Buscheck and Alcantar, 1995):

$$\lambda = \frac{v_c}{4\alpha_x}\left(\left[1 + 2\alpha_x\left(\frac{k}{v_x}\right)\right]^2 - 1\right) \tag{8.4}$$

where

λ =   first-order biological decay rate

v_c =   retarded contaminant velocity in the x-direction

α_x =   dispersivity

k/v_x =   slope of line formed by making a log-linear plot of contaminant concentration versus distance downgradient along flow path

When used with accurate estimates of dispersivity and ground-water flow and solute transport velocity, this method gives reasonable first-order biodegradation rates. Examples of how to apply this method are given in Buscheck and Alcantar (1995) and Wiedemeier et al. (1996). This method can also be used to estimate biodegradation rates for chlorinated solvents dissolved in ground water.

For sites where sufficient historical data have been collected (a minimum of three sampling events), a biodegradation rate constant can be calculated by estimating the change in dissolved mass within the plume as a function of time. One of the methods for calculating the dissolved mass (DM) at time t includes the use of an average plume concentration $C_{avg,t}$.

$$DM_t = C_{avg,t} \times b \times n \times L \times W \qquad (8.5)$$

where

b =   aquifer thickness

n =   porosity

L =   plume length

W =   plume width

This method was used by Rifai et al. (1988) and Chiang et al. (1989) at two sites in Michigan. Their studies estimated a rate constant of approximately 0.01 day^{-1} for BTEX at these sites.

Another method (graphically based) was presented by the RTDF (1997). The method is based on having good isoconcentration maps for the site in question. The RTDF (1997) method draws several lines perpendicular to the flow and at various distances away from the source on the site isoconcentration map, and use the thickness of the aquifer and the ground water velocity to estimate the mass of ground water per year that passes through each line.

8.1.2 First-Order Biodegradation Rates for Fuel Hydrocarbons

Suarez and Rifai (1999) have compiled a database for first-order degradation rates for fuel hydrocarbons. Their data indicate a range from 0 to 6 day^{-1} for aerobic and anaerobic biodegradation rates for BTEX (using both field and laboratory data). Table 8.1 lists the minimum, maximum, mean, and median rates for BTEX sorted by electron acceptor. Suarez and Rifai (1999) developed a number of conclusions from this database:

TABLE 8.1 Summary of BTEX first-order decay rates (day^{-1}) sorted by electron acceptor

	All Studies	Redox Process					
		Aerobic Respiration	Nitrate Reduction	Iron Reduction	Sulfate Reduction	Methano-genesis	Mixed
BENZENE							
Number of rates	149	26	41	20	16	15	25
Minimum	0.0000	0.0000	0.0000	0.0000	0.0000	0.0000	0.0000
Mean	0.0654	0.3350	0.0083	0.0085	0.0077	0.0100	0.0092
Median	0.003	0.198	0	0.00495	0.0026	0	0.004
Maximum	2.5	2.5	0.089	0.034	0.049	0.077	0.087
TOLUENE							
Number of rates	135	16	49	13	14	24	17
Minimum	0.0000	0.0160	0.0000	0.0000	0.0001	0.0000	0.0000
Mean	0.2498	0.2618	0.4589	0.0116	0.0621	0.0371	0.3018
Median	0.04	0.1665	0.09	0.0099	0.035	0.02065	0.004
Maximum	4.8	1.63	4.32	0.045	0.21	0.186	4.8
ETHYLBENZENE							
Number of rates	82		37	7	8	12	17
Minimum	0.0000		0.0000	0.0000	0.0000	0.0000	0.0000
Mean	0.1258		0.2699	0.0034	0.0021	0.0103	0.0096
Median	0.00257		0.0158	0.0015	0.00055	0.00105	0.002
Maximum	6.048		6.048	0.017	0.0072	0.054	0.078
m-XYLENE							
Number of rates	90	4	41	8	7	12	16
Minimum	0.0000	0.0080	0.0000	0.0012	0.0040	0.0000	0.0000
Mean	0.0582	0.1630	0.0887	0.0100	0.0808	0.0194	0.0042
Median	0.0045	0.107	0.017	0.002452055	0.056	0.001	0.002
Maximum	0.49	0.43	0.49	0.037	0.32	0.104	0.025
o-XYLENE							
Number of rates	92	10	38	8	6	12	16
Minimum	0.0000	0.0080	0.0000	0.0000	0.0000	0.0000	0.0000
Mean	0.0212	0.0860	0.0117	0.0031	0.0268	0.0262	0.0087
Median	0.004	0.035	0.0045	0.001803425	0.0105	0.00105	0.003
Maximum	0.38	0.38	0.068	0.016	0.084	0.214	0.057
p-XYLENE							
Number of rates	65	3	21	8	4	10	18
Minimum	0.0000	0.0080	0.0000	0.0008	0.0023	0.0000	0.0000
Mean	0.0378	0.2070	0.0678	0.0098	0.0108	0.0180	0.0063
Median	0.00353		0.008	0.001835616	0.009	0.0025	0.002
Maximum	0.44	0.43	0.44	0.037	0.022	0.081	0.031

Source: Suarez and Rifai (1999)

- Maximum first-order biodegradation rates reported in literature for BTEX compounds were 4.8 day^{-1} and 6.05 day^{-1} under aerobic and anaerobic conditions, respectively.

- Anaerobic rates for BTEX were approximately one order of magnitude smaller than aerobic rates (average median value for aerobic BTEX biodegradation was 0.08 day^{-1} while average median value for anaerobic BTEX biodegradation was 0.009 day^{-1}).

- Among BTEX compounds, the most readily biodegradable substrate under aerobic conditions was benzene, whereas for anaerobic biodegradation, it was toluene.
- The median reported degradation rates for benzene, ethylbenzene and xylene were very similar with an average median value of 0.0035 or 0.35% per day for the three compounds. Toluene, the only exception, significantly exceeded this value (0.9% per day).

8.1.3 First-Order Biodegradation Rates for Chlorinated Solvents

Suarez and Rifai (1999) also compiled a similar database for chlorinated organics. Their study indicates a biodegradation rate ranging from 0 to 8 day^{-1} for these compounds (Table 8.2). Their conclusions from the database indicate that:

- Maximum first-order biodegradation rates reported in literature for chlorinated solvents were 1.96 day^{-1} and 3.13 day^{-1} under aerobic and anaerobic conditions, respectively.
- The higher-chlorinated solvents biodegrade anaerobically with an average median rate of 0.033 day^{-1} while the less-chlorinated solvents biodegrade aerobically with an average median rate of 0.16 day^{-1}.

8.2 MODELING BIODEGRADATION

The problem of quantifying biodegradation in the subsurface can be addressed by using models that combine physical, chemical and biological processes. Developing such models is not simple, however, due to the complex nature of microbial kinetics, the limitations of computer resources, the lack of field data on biodegradation, and the need for robust numerical schemes that can simulate the physical, chemical, and biological processes accurately.

The reduction of contaminant concentrations using Monod kinetics, for example, can be expressed as

$$\Delta C = M_t \mu_{max} \left(\frac{C}{K_c + C} \right) \Delta t \tag{8.6}$$

where C is contaminant concentration, M_t is the total microbial concentration, μ_{max} is maximum contaminant utilization rate per unit mass microorganisms, K_c is contaminant half saturation constant, and Δt is the time interval being considered.

Incorporating Eq. (8.6) into the 1-D transport equation, for example, results in:

TABLE 8.2 Summary of chlorinated solvent first-order decay rates sorted by redox conditions. Source: Suarez and Rifai, 1999

	All Studies	Aerobic Oxidation	Cometabolism	Reductive dechlorination					Anaerobic Oxidation
				Nitrate reducing	Iron reducing	Sulfate reducing	Methanogenesis	Mixed	Iron reducing
CARBON TETRACHLORIDE									
Number of rates	13	1	1	6	2			2	
Minimum	0.0037			0.0207					
Mean	0.1077			0.0776	0.1169			0.32	
Median	0.049			0.0645					
Maximum	0.49			0.16					
DCA (all isomers)									
Number of rates	25	2	5				13	3	
Minimum	0		0.014				0.00006		
Mean	0.0172	0.000	0.0668				0.0026	0.0061	
Median	0.0007		0.047				0.0004		
Maximum	0.131		0.131				0.028		
DCE (all isomers)									
Number of rates	61		13		8	3	8	2	
Minimum	0		0		0.000082		0.0023		
Mean	0.1406		0.5908		0.0020	0.0453	0.0470	0.0007	
Median	0.004		0.434		0.0015		0.016		
Maximum	1.96		1.96		0.0052		0.2		
PCE									
Number of rates	50	10	3	3	2	1	22	1	
Minimum	0	0		0.000			0		
Mean	0.0506	0.001	0.0247	0.000	0.0040		0.1003		
Median	0.0087	0.000					0.0795		
Maximum	0.41	0.004					0.41		
TCA									
Number of rates	47	11	5	4	1	2	17	1	
Minimum	0	0	0	0			0.0026		
Mean	0.2610	0.0021	0.2467	0.0000		0.0099	0.4976		
Median	0.0102	0	0.013	0.000			0.125		
Maximum	2.33	0.022	1.18	0.000			2.33		
TCE									
Number of rates	85	11	17	1	11	7	10	2	
Minimum	0	0	0.024		0	0.0017	0		
Mean	0.1746	0.0055	0.5862		0.0034	0.0111	0.0145	0.0014	
Median	0.0046	0	0.26		0.0016	0.0078	0.0038		
Maximum	3.13	0.0278	1.65		0.011	0.023	0.109		
VINYL CHLORIDE									
Number of rates	27	4	5		2		3		7
Minimum	0.000034	0.043	0.055						0.0013
Mean	0.5180	0.0873	2.4222		0.2604		0.2300		0.0421
Median	0.051	0.091	1.5						0.012
Maximum	8.02	0.125	8.02						0.12

$$\frac{\partial C}{\partial t} = D_x \frac{\partial^2 C}{\partial x^2} - v \frac{\partial C}{\partial x} - M_t \mu_{\max} \left(\frac{C}{K_c + C} \right) \tag{8.7}$$

where v is the seepage velocity, and D_x is the dispersion coefficient.

For aerobic biodegradation, and assuming that oxygen and the contaminant are the only substrates required for growth, the change in contaminant and oxygen concentrations due to biodegradation is given by:

$$\Delta C = M_t \mu_{\max} \left(\frac{C}{K_c + C} \right) \left(\frac{O}{K_o + O} \right) \Delta t \tag{8.8}$$

$$\Delta O = M_t \mu_{\max} F \left(\frac{C}{K_c + C} \right) \left(\frac{O}{K_o + O} \right) \Delta t \tag{8.9}$$

where O is oxygen concentration, K_o is oxygen half saturation constant, and F is ratio of oxygen to contaminant consumed.

Incorporating Eqs. (8.8) and (8.9) into the transport equation results in a system of partial differential equations as follows (Borden and Bedient, 1986):

$$\frac{\partial C}{\partial t} = \frac{1}{R_c} \nabla \cdot (D \nabla C - vC) - M_t \frac{\mu_{\max}}{R_c} \left(\frac{C}{K_c + C} \right) \left(\frac{O}{K_o + O} \right) \tag{8.10}$$

$$\frac{\partial O}{\partial t} = \nabla \cdot (D \nabla O - vO) - M_t \mu_{\max} F \left(\frac{C}{K_c + C} \right) \left(\frac{O}{K_o + O} \right) \tag{8.11}$$

$$\frac{\partial M_s}{\partial t} = \frac{1}{R_m} \nabla \cdot (D \nabla M_s - vM_s) + M_s \mu_{\max} Y \left(\frac{C}{K_c + C} \right) \left(\frac{O}{K_o + O} \right) + \frac{k_c Y(OC)}{R_m} - bM_s \tag{8.12}$$

where C is the contaminant concentration, O is the oxygen concentration, D is a dispersion tensor, v is the ground water velocity, R_c is the retardation coefficient for the contaminant, M_s and M_t are the concentration of microbes in solution and the total microbial concentration, respectively ($M_t = R_m \cdot M_s$ where R_m is the microbial retardation factor), μ_{max} is the maximum contaminant utilization rate per unit mass of microorganisms, Y is the microbial yield coefficient, K_c is the half saturation constant for the contaminant, K_o is the half saturation constant for oxygen, OC is the natural organic carbon concentration, F is the ratio of oxygen to hydrocarbon consumed, and b is the microbial decay rate.

8.3 BIODEGRADATION MODELS

8.3.1 Developed Biodegradation Models

Many biodegradation models have been developed in recent years, most of which utilize some form of the three expressions presented earlier. Table 8.3 lists many of the biodegradation models. This section will focus on some of the more popular models and on their application to field biodegradation and bioremediation analyses.

TABLE 8.3   Biodegradation models.

Name	Dimension	Description	Author
X	1	aerobic. microcolonv.	Molz. et al. (1986)
BIOPLUME	1	aerobic. Monod	Borden. et al. (1986)
X	1	analvtical first-order	Domenico (1987)
BIO1D	1	aerobic and anaerobic,	Srinivasan and Mercer
X	1	cometabolic, Monod	Semprini and McCarty (1991)
X	1	aerobic. anaerobic. nutrient limitations. microcolony. Monod	Widdowson, et al.
X	1	aerobic. cometabolic. multiple substrates. fermentative. Monod	Celia, et al. (1989)
BIOSCREEN	1	analvtical first-order. instantaneous	Newell. et al.
BIOCHLOR	1	analvtical	Aziz, et al. (1999)
BIOPLUME II	2	aerobic. instantaneous	Rifai. et al. (1988)
X	2	Monod	MacQuarrie. et al.
X	2	denitrification	Kinzelbach. et al. (1991)
X	2	Monod. biofilm	Odencrantz. et al. (1990)
BIOPLUME III	2	aerobic and	Rifai. et al. (1997)
RT3D	3	aerobic and	Clement. et al. (1998)

8.3.2 The Biofilm Model

McCarty et al. (1984) believe that the nature of the ground water environment (low substrate concentration and high specific surface area) dictates that the predominant type of bacterial activity will be bacteria attached to solid surfaces in the form of biofilm. The attached bacteria remain generally fixed in one place and obtain energy and nutrients from the ground water that flow.

Figure 8.1 is an illustration of an idealized biofilm having a uniform cell density of X_f [ML^{-3}] and a locally uniform thickness of L_f. An idealized biofilm is a homogeneous matrix of bacteria and their extracellular polymers that bind them together and to the inert surface (McCarty et al., 1981). Ground water flows past the biofilm in the x direction, while substrates are transported from the water to the biofilm in the z direction. The distance L represents the thickness of a mass-transport diffusion layer through which substrate must pass in order to go from the bulk liquid into the biofilm, where utilization occurs.

Within the biofilm, two processes occur simultaneously: namely, utilization of the substrate by the bacteria, assumed to follow a Monod-type relation, and diffusion of the substrate through the biofilm according to Fick's Law. Figure 8.2 shows the interaction of these processes—substrate utilization, molecular diffusion within the biofilm and mass transport across the diffusion layer. For a thick biofilm (Case A), the substrate concentration approaches zero and the biofilm is called deep. If the biofilm is very thin (Case C), almost no

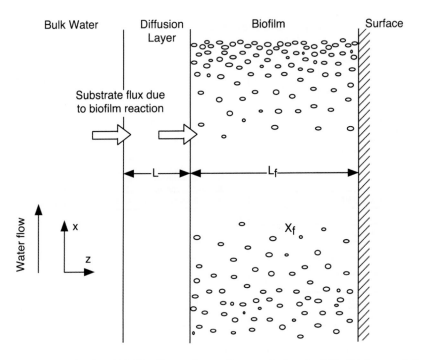

Figure 8.1 Idealized biofilm illustrating uniform cell density (Xf), thickness (Lf), water flow, and substrate flux into biofilm. Source: McCarty et al., 1984.

substrate utilization occurs and the biofilm is essentially fully penetrated at the surface concentration S_s. The remaining cases are termed shallow (Case B).

8.3.3 Microcolony Models

Molz et al. (1986) and Widdowson et al. (1987) developed 1-D and 2-D models for aerobic biodegradation of organic contaminants in ground water coupled with advective and dispersive transport. A microcolony approach was utilized in the modeling, microcolonies of bacteria were represented as disks of uniform radius and thickness attached to aquifer sediments. A boundary layer of a given thickness was associated with each colony across which substrate and oxygen are transported by diffusion to the colonies.

Their results indicate that biodegradation would be expected to have a major effect on contaminant transport when proper conditions for growth exist. Simulations of 2-D transport suggested that under aerobic conditions microbial degradation reduces the substrate concentration profile along longitudinal sections of the plume and retards the lateral spread of the plume. Anaerobic conditions developed in the plume center due to microbial consumption and limited oxygen diffusion into the plume interior.

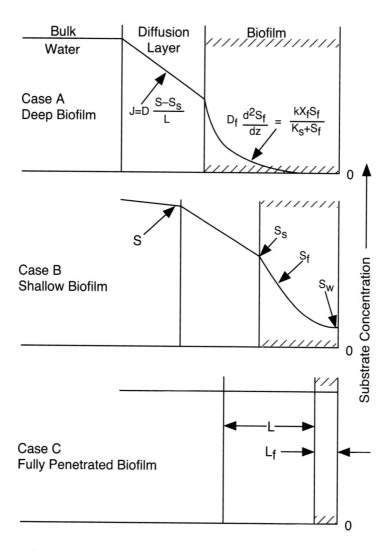

Figure 8.2 Interactions of substrate utilization, molecular diffusion within biofilm and mass transport across diffusion layer. Source: McCarty et al., 1984.

Widdowson et al. (1988) extended their 1986 and 1987 studies to simulate oxygen- and/or nitrate based respiration. Basic assumptions incorporated into the model included a simulated particle-bound microbial population comprised of heterotrophic, facultative bacteria in which metabolism is controlled by lack of either an organic carbon-electron donor source (substrate), electron acceptor (O_2 and/or NO_3), or mineral nutrient (NH_4^+), or all three simultaneously. Transport of substrate and oxygen in the porous medium is assumed to be governed by advection-dispersion equations with surface adsorption. Microbial degradation

enters the two basic transport equations as sink terms. Based on the assumptions, five coupled, nonlinear equations govern microbial growth dynamics in porous media.

8.3.4 BIO1D Model

Srinivasan and Mercer (1988) presented a 1-D, finite difference model for simulating biodegradation and sorption processes in saturated porous media. The model formulation allowed for
accommodating a variety of boundary conditions and process theories. Aerobic biodegradation
was modeled using a modified Monod function; anaerobic biodegradation was modeled using
Michaelis-Menten kinetics. In addition, first-order degradation is allowed for both substances.
Sorption can be incorporated using linear, Freundlich, or Langmuir equilibrium isotherms
for either substance.

The Srinivasan and Mercer (1988) model is an extension of that presented by Borden
and Bedient (1986). The governing equations are:

$$f = D\frac{\partial^2 S}{\partial x^2} - V\frac{\partial S}{\partial x} - B\,(S,\,O) - [1 + A(S)]\frac{\partial S}{\partial t} = 0 \tag{8.13}$$

$$g = D\frac{\partial^2 O}{\partial x^2} - V\frac{\partial O}{\partial x} - F \cdot B\,(S,\,O) - [1 + A(O)]\frac{\partial O}{\partial t} = 0 \tag{8.14}$$

For Aerobic Conditions:

$$B(S,O) = Mk\,\frac{S}{k_s + S}\cdot\frac{O}{k_o + O}\cdot\frac{S - S_{min}}{S} \tag{8.15}$$

for

$$S \geq S_{min}$$

and

$$O \geq O_{min}.$$

otherwise

$$B(S,\,O) = 0$$

For Anaerobic Conditions: $B\,(S,\,O)$ reduces to $B\,(S)$ and only one equation is solved for S.

$$B(S) = M_n k_n\,\frac{S}{k_{sn} + S} \tag{8.16}$$

where S is the substrate concentration in the pore fluid $[ML^{-3}]$, O is the oxygen concentration in the pore fluid $[ML^{-3}]$, D is the longitudinal hydrodynamic dispersion coefficient
$[L^2T^{-1}]$, x is the distance, V is the interstitial fluid velocity $[LT^{-1}]$, $B(S,\,O)$ is a biodegradation term expressed as a function of the dependent variables S and O $[ML^{-3}T^{-1}]$, $A(S)$ is the

adsorption term expressed as a function of S (the term $[1 + A(S)]$ is the retardation factor), t is the time, M is the microbial mass, k is the maximum substrate utilization rate per unit mass of microorganisms, k_s is the substrate half-saturation constant, k_o is the oxygen half-saturation constant, S_{min} is the minimum substrate concentration that permits growth and decay, O_{min} is the minimum oxygen concentration that permits growth and decay, and F is the ratio of oxygen to substrate consumed. Note that M_n, k_n, and k_{sn} are counterparts of M, k, and k_s under anaerobic conditions.

8.3.5 The BIOPLUME II Model

The BIOPLUME II model was developed by modifying an existing 2-D transport model developed by the USGS and known as the Method of Characteristics (MOC) model (Konikow and Bredehoeft, 1978; see Chapter 10). Two governing equations are solved in MOC: the ground water flow equation and the transport equation. The numerical approximation to the flow equation is a finite difference expression that is solved using an alternating-direction implicit procedure. The method of characteristics is utilized to solve the transport equation (Rifai et al., 1988).

The basic concept applied to modify the USGS MOC model and to develop the BIOPLUME II model includes the use of a dual-particle mover procedure to simulate the transport of oxygen and contaminants in the subsurface. The transport equation is solved twice at every time step to calculate the oxygen and contaminant distributions:

$$\frac{\partial(Cb)}{\partial t} = \frac{1}{R_c}\left(\frac{\partial}{\partial x_i}\left(bD_{ij}\frac{\partial C}{\partial x_j}\right) - \frac{\partial}{\partial x_i}\left(bCV_i\right)\right) - \frac{C'W}{n} \tag{8.17}$$

$$\frac{\partial(Ob)}{\partial t} = \left(\frac{\partial}{\partial x_i}\left(bD_{ij}\frac{\partial O}{\partial x_j}\right) - \frac{\partial}{\partial x_i}\left(bOV_i\right)\right) - \frac{O'W}{n} \tag{8.18}$$

where C and O are concentrations of contaminant and oxygen respectively, C' and O' are concentrations of contaminant and oxygen in a source or sink fluid, n is effective porosity, b is saturated thickness, t is time, x_i and x_j are cartesian coordinates, W is volume flux per unit area, V_i is seepage velocity in the direction of x_i, and D_{ij} is coefficient of hydrodynamic dispersion.

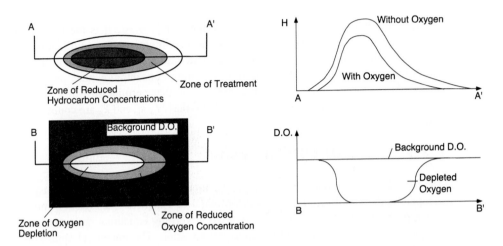

Figure 8.3 Principle of superposition for organics and oxygen in BIOPLUME II model. Source: Rifai et al., 1988.

The two plumes are combined using the principle of superposition to simulate the instantaneous reaction between oxygen and the contaminants, and the decrease in contaminant and oxygen concentrations is calculated from:

$$\Delta C_{RC} = O/F \; ; \; O = 0 \quad \text{where } C > O/F \tag{8.19}$$

$$\Delta C_{RO} = C \cdot F \; ; \; C = 0 \quad \text{where } O > C \cdot F \tag{8.20}$$

where ΔC_{RC}, ΔC_{RO} are the calculated changes in concentrations of contaminant and oxygen, respectively, due to biodegradation.

Figure 8.3 is a conceptual schematic of the BIOPLUME II model. On the left of the figure, a plan view of the contaminant and oxygen plumes with and without biodegradation are shown. After the two plumes are superimposed, the contaminant plume is reduced in size and concentrations. The dissolved oxygen is depleted in zones of high contaminant concentrations and reduced in zones of relatively moderate contaminant concentrations. The right schematics in Figure 8.3 present transects down the plume centerline and help to illustrate the distributions of contaminant and oxygen concentration with and without biodegradation. It is noted that field data have verified the correlation between oxygen and contaminant concentrations at sites.

There are two methods that can be used to simulate biodegradation in the BIOPLUME II model: first-order decay and instantaneous reaction. For the first-order decay model, the reaction rate, k, is required as input. The model input parameters required for the instantaneous reaction include the amount of dissolved oxygen in the aquifer prior to contamination, and the oxygen demand of the contaminant determined from a stoichiometric relationship. Modeling the biodegradation of several components such as benzene, toluene, and xylenes (BTX) at a site requires that an average stoichiometric coefficient for the three components be calculated.

Two additional sources of oxygen can be specified in BIOPLUME II. Injection of oxygen in a bioremediation project can be simulated by using injection wells or infiltration galleries. Reaeration from the unsaturated zone can be simulated in an indirect way by specifying a first-order decay rate for the contaminants at the site. Holder et al. (1999) address reaeration using advanced methods and models.

The output from the MOC/BIOPLUME II model consists generally of a head map and a chemical concentration map for each node in the grid. Immediately following the head and concentration maps is a listing of the hydraulic and transport errors. If observation wells had been specified, a concentration history for those wells would be included in the output.

The sensitivity of aerobic biodegradation to some of the model parameters has been analyzed in detail by Rifai et al. (1988). Their analyses indicate that biodegradation is mostly sensitive to the hydraulic conductivity (Figure 8.4). This result verifies some field observations about the applicability of bioremediation for systems with relatively large hydraulic conductivities. Biodegradation was not sensitive to the retardation factor or disper-

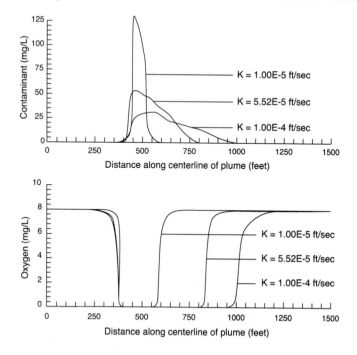

Figure 8.4 Variation of contaminant and oxygen concentrations with hydraulic conductivity. Source: Rifai et al., 1988.

sion. BIOPLUME II is one of the most widely used models for the simulation of aerobic biodegradation at field sites. A new version of the model, BIOPLUME III, is described in Section 8.5.

Example 8.2. MODELING BIOREMEDIATION USING BIOPLUME II

A modeling analysis using BIOPLUME II is presented to demonstrate how the model might be used for designing bioremediation systems. Bioremediation involves the injection of oxygen and other limiting nutrients to enhance biodegradation and accelerate the remediation of contaminated sites (see Chapter 13).

TABLE 8.4 Model parameters used in example 8.2.

Grid Size	20 x 20
Cell Size	50 ft x 50 ft
Transmissivity	0.002 sq. ft/s
Aquifer thickness	10 ft
Hydraulic Gradient	0.001 ft/ft
Longitudinal Dispersivity	10 ft
Transverse Dispersivity	3 ft
Effective Porosity	30%

A hypothetical aquifer with the parameters shown in Table 8.4 is being bioremediated for two years using three injection wells and three pumping wells. Each of the wells is pumping/injecting at rate of 1 gpm. The initial plume and well locations are shown in Figure 8.5. Three different scenarios were modeled: first, no oxygen was injected and biodegradation was due only to a background oxygen concentration of 3 mg/L. Then, 20 mg/L of oxygen were injected throughout the pumping period. Finally, in a different simulation, 40 mg/L were injected into the wells. The latter two concentrations were selected because they are values that can be obtained by the injection of liquid oxygen.

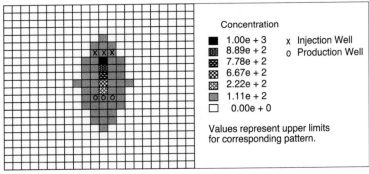

Figure 8.5 Initial contaminant plume for Example 8.2.

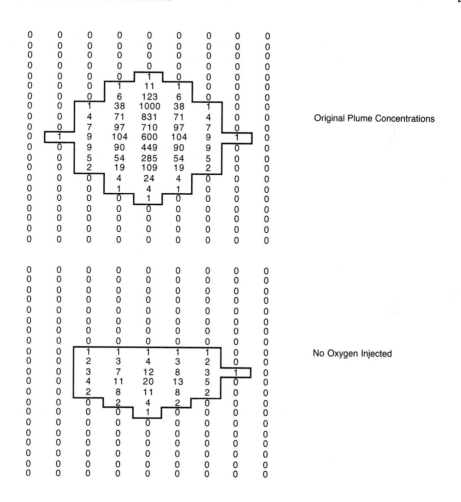

Original Plume Concentrations

No Oxygen Injected

Figure 8.6 Plume concentrations with no oxygen amendment for Example 8.2.

Figure 8.6 shows the extent of the contaminant plume when pumping has occurred without enhanced biodegradation. The highest contaminant concentration after two years of pumping is 20 mg/L, down from the original maximum of 1000 mg/L. Figure 8.7 is the output for the plume after 20 mg/L of oxygen were injected. The maximum concentration in this case is 15 mg/L. Fewer cells have concentrations greater than 5 mg/L, and the resulting plume is smaller in size.

When 40 mg/L of oxygen are injected, the resulting plume shown in Figure 8.8 is not much different than that in Figure 8.7. The maximum concentration, however, is now 9 mg/L instead of 15 mg/L. This indicates marginal benefits from doubling the oxygen concentration. The main reason for this observation is the fact that oxygen is not getting transported to the contamination areas, where it can be most useful. One way around this is to move the injection wells closer to the contaminated zones. The other alternative is to inject oxygen concentrations in gradual increments (This would save on costs because less oxygen is required).

In conclusion, there is an optimal level of oxygen that will be of benefit in cleanup operations. The overall extent of biodegradation for this hypothetical scenario can be summed up in Figure 8.9, which shows contaminant concentrations across the center-

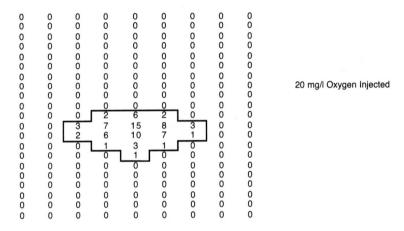

Figure 8.7 Plume concentrations with 20 mg/L oxygen injected in Example 8.2.

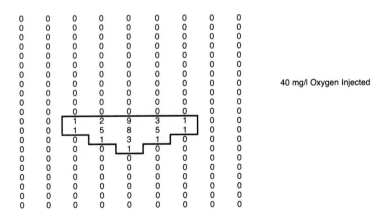

Figure 8.8 Plume concentrations with 40 mg/L oxygen injected in Example 8.2.

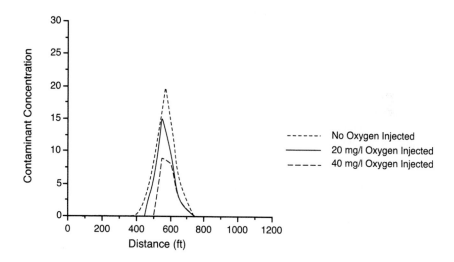

Figure 8.9 Contaminant concentration along plume centerline for Example 8.2.

line (from top to bottom) of the resultant plumes. It is obvious that biodegradation can be of immense benefit when conditions for its use prevail. Several homework problems for Chapter 8 lead the student through the above example in more detail.

8.3.6 Other Models

Other models have been presented by Kissel et al. (1984), Baek et al. (1989), McQuarrie et al. (1990) and MacQuarrie and Sudicky (1990). Kissel et al. (1984) developed differential equations describing mass balances on solutes and mass fractions in a mixed culture biological film within a completely mixed reactor. The models incorporated external mass transport effects, Monod kinetics with internal determination of limiting electron donor or acceptor, competitive and sequential reactions, and multiple active and inert biological fractions which vary spatially.

The model presented by Baek et al. (1989) simulates the mitigation of contaminants by microbial activity in unsaturated soil systems. Their model, BIOSOIL, incorporated the influence of microorganisms on soil water flow and chemical removal rates. From the modeling study, the authors concluded that the depth of the unsaturated zone seems to be less crucial in bioremediation scenarios than it would be in land disposal scenarios.

MacQuarrie et al. (1990) and MacQuarrie and Sudicky (1990) used a similar approach to those of Borden et al. (1986) and Rifai et al. (1988) to develop their model. The advection-dispersion equation was coupled with a dual-Monod relationship. The system of equations was solved using an iterative principal direction finite element technique. The authors applied their model to laboratory columns as well as plume behavior in uniform and random flow fields.

More recently and since the early 1990s, researchers have focused their efforts on developing models in support of natural attenuation of fuel hydrocarbons and chlorinated solvents. A number of analytical and numerical models have been developed to simulate aerobic and anaerobic biodegradation of these compounds along with the other natural attenuation processes of advection, dispersion, and sorption. The following section will focus on presenting a number of these models, including BIOSCREEN, BIOCHLOR, BIOPLUME III, and the RT3D model (See Table 8.3).

8.4 ANALYTICAL NATURAL ATTENUATION MODELS

8.4.1 The BIOSCREEN Decision Support System

The BIOSCREEN Natural Attenuation Decision Support System is a public domain, spreadsheet-based, screening tool for simulating the natural attenuation of dissolved hydrocarbons at petroleum fuel release sites (Newell et al., 1996; Newell et al., 1997). The model is based on the Domenico (1987) analytical solute transport model (Figure 8.10) that simulates ground water flow and a fully-penetrating vertical plane source oriented perpendicular to ground water flow. The model incorporates a linear isotherm sorption and 3-D dispersion. The model extends the Domenico solution by incorporating a decaying source concentration and a simple electron-acceptor limited "instantaneous" reaction assumption. BIOSCREEN was developed by the Air Force Center for Environmental Excellence (AFCEE) and is currently being distributed by the EPA through their website at (http://www.epa.gov/ada/bioscreen.html).

BIOSCREEN attempts to answer both fundamental natural attenuation questions: (1) how far will the plume migrate, and (2) how long will the plume persist? The conceptual model assumes that ground water upgradient of the source contains electron acceptor and that as the upgradient water moves through the source zone, non-aqueous phase liquids (NAPLs) and contaminated soil release dissolvable BTEX into ground water. Biological reactions occur until the available electron acceptors in ground water (biodegradation capacity, see Chapter 12) are consumed.

BIOSCREEN has the limitation that as an analytical model, it assumes simple ground water flow conditions and should not be applied where pumping systems create a complicated flow field. In addition, the model should not be applied where vertical flow gradients affect contaminant transport. Also, the model only approximates more complicated processes that occur in the field and should not be applied where extremely detailed, accurate results that closely match site conditions are required. More comprehensive numerical models such as BIOPLUME III or RT3D (described in the following section) should be applied in these cases.

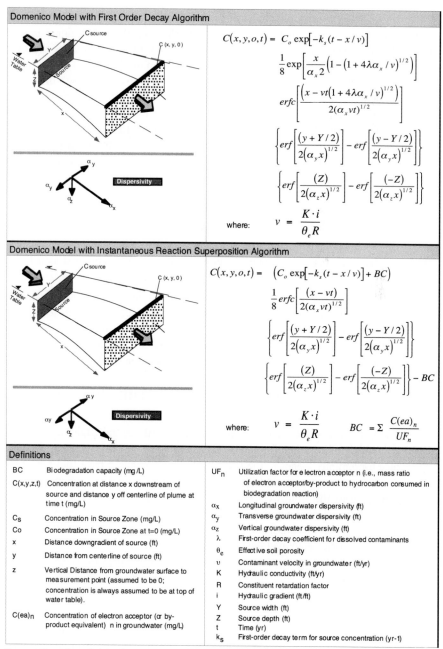

Domenico Model with First Order Decay Algorithm

$$C(x,y,o,t) = C_o \exp\left[-k_s(t - x/v)\right]$$

$$\frac{1}{8}\exp\left[\frac{x}{\alpha_x 2}\left(1 - (1 + 4\lambda\alpha_x/v)^{1/2}\right)\right]$$

$$erfc\left[\frac{\left(x - vt(1 + 4\lambda\alpha_x/v)^{1/2}\right)}{2(\alpha_x vt)^{1/2}}\right]$$

$$\left\{erf\left[\frac{(y + Y/2)}{2(\alpha_y x)^{1/2}}\right] - erf\left[\frac{(y - Y/2)}{2(\alpha_y x)^{1/2}}\right]\right\}$$

$$\left\{erf\left[\frac{(Z)}{2(\alpha_z x)^{1/2}}\right] - erf\left[\frac{(-Z)}{2(\alpha_z x)^{1/2}}\right]\right\}$$

where: $\quad v = \dfrac{K \cdot i}{\theta_e R}$

Domenico Model with Instantaneous Reaction Superposition Algorithm

$$C(x,y,o,t) = \left(C_o \exp\left[-k_s(t - x/v)\right] + BC\right)$$

$$\frac{1}{8}erfc\left[\frac{(x - vt)}{2(\alpha_x vt)^{1/2}}\right]$$

$$\left\{erf\left[\frac{(y + Y/2)}{2(\alpha_y x)^{1/2}}\right] - erf\left[\frac{(y - Y/2)}{2(\alpha_y x)^{1/2}}\right]\right\}$$

$$\left\{erf\left[\frac{(Z)}{2(\alpha_z x)^{1/2}}\right] - erf\left[\frac{(-Z)}{2(\alpha_z x)^{1/2}}\right]\right\} - BC$$

where: $\quad v = \dfrac{K \cdot i}{\theta_e R} \qquad BC = \Sigma\,\dfrac{C(ea)_n}{UF_n}$

Definitions

BC	Biodegradation capacity (mg/L)
C(x,y,z,t)	Concentration at distance x downstream of source and distance y off centerline of plume at time t (mg/L)
C_s	Concentration in Source Zone (mg/L)
Co	Concentration in Source Zone at t=0 (mg/L)
x	Distance downgradient of source (ft)
y	Distance from centerline of source (ft)
z	Vertical Distance from groundwater surface to measurement point (assumed to be 0; concentration is always assumed to be at top of water table).
C(ea)n	Concentration of electron acceptor (or by-product equivalent) n in groundwater (mg/L)

UF_n	Utilization factor for electron acceptor n (i.e., mass ratio of electron acceptor/by-product to hydrocarbon consumed in biodegradation reaction)
α_x	Longitudinal groundwater dispersivity (ft)
α_y	Transverse groundwater dispersivity (ft)
α_z	Vertical groundwater dispersivity (ft)
λ	First-order decay coefficient for dissolved contaminants
θ_e	Effective soil porosity
υ	Contaminant velocity in groundwater (ft/yr)
K	Hydraulic conductivity (ft/yr)
R	Constituent retardation factor
i	Hydraulic gradient (ft/ft)
Y	Source width (ft)
Z	Source depth (ft)
t	Time (yr)
k_s	First-order decay term for source concentration (yr-1)

Source: Newell et al. (1996)

Figure 8.10 The Domenico Analytical Model Used in BIOSCREEN.

BIOSCREEN output includes: (1) plume centerline graphs, (2) 3-D color plots of plume concentrations, and (3) mass balance data showing the contaminant mass removal by each electron acceptor (instantaneous reaction option). Other features of the original model (v. 1.3) included a concentration versus time animation module and a water balance showing the volume of water in the plume and the flux of water moving through the plume. In a later release (BIOSCREEN v. 1.4), a mass flux calculator was added, which shows the mass flux of contaminants at any point in the plume. With the mass flux calculator, dilution calculations can be performed for plumes that are discharging to streams.

The original Domenico (1987) model assumes the source is infinite (i.e., the source concentrations are constant). In BIOSCREEN, however, an approximation for a declining source concentration was added, and is based on the following assumptions:

- There is a finite mass of organics in the source zone present as a free-phase or residual NAPL. The NAPL in the source zone dissolves slowly as fresh ground water passes through.

- The change in source zone concentration can be approximated as a first-order decay process.

- The mass flux of contaminant leaving the source can be approximated by multiplying the source times a representative source concentration for the first order decay model (thereby assuming no biodegradation in the source zone) or by multiplying the source times the sum of the source concentration and biodegradation capacity (thereby assuming there is biodegradation in the source zone).

Example 8.3   BIOSCREEN MODELING OF THE HILL AFB UST SITE 870

The Hill Air Force Base (AFB) is located in north central Utah. Site 870 at the base is on a plateau-like bench formed by sediment deposits of the ancient Weber River. Surface topography slopes to the southwest. The site has a base fuel tank farm including the former location of a 1,000-gallon tank and a plume of contaminated ground water extending to the southwest of the tank site (Figure 8.11). The shallow aquifer at the site, composed of medium to coarse grained sands, ranges from 3ft to 22 ft in thickness at a depth varying from 4 to 15 ft Slug tests performed in five monitoring wells at the site indicate an average hydraulic conductivity of 8.05×10^{-3} cm/sec. Ground water flow is to the southwest with an approximate gradient of 0.048 ft/ft with almost no seasonal variation (Montgomery Watson, 1994). More details about this site are provided in example 8.5.

The BIOSCREEN model was used to reproduce plume movement at Site 870. The site characteristics are listed in Table 8.5. An infinite source in the high concentration zone of the plume area (near MW-1, Figure 8.11) was assumed for the site because no esti-

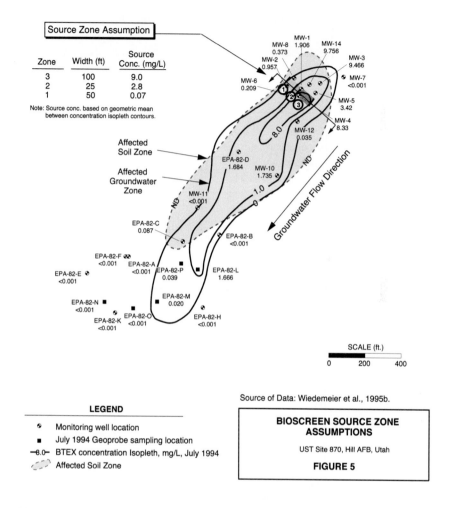

Figure 8.11 Bioscreen Source Zone assumptions, UST Site 870, Hill AFB, Utah. Source: Newell et al., 1996

mates for source mass were available from soil sampling data. Instantaneous reaction kinetics were assumed. Model results indicate a reasonable match between the modeled plume and the measured concentrations, as can be seen in Figure 8.12. Using the BIOSCREEN model without biodegradation, in comparison, generated a plume over 8,000 ft long in contrast with the 1,450 ft plume that was delineated at the site. Plume mass calculations using the "no biodegradation" scenario and the calibration scenario indicated a greater than 99% reduction in dissolved mass during the five-year simulation run.

TABLE 8.5   Example 8.3, Hill Air Force Base, UST Site 870, Utah

DATA	PARAMETE	VALUE				SOURCE
Hydrogeology	Hydraulic Hydraulic Porosity:	8.05 x 10³ (cm/sec) 0.048 (ft/ft) 0.25				Slug-tests results Static water level Estimated
Dispersion	Original Longitudinal Transverse Vertical Dispersivity:	28.5 ft 2.85 ft 0 ft				Based on estimated plum of 1450 ft. Note: No calibration was to match observed plume
Adsorption	Retardation Soil Bulk Density ρ_b: foc: Koc:	1.3 1.7 (kg/L) 0.08% B: 38 T: 135 E: 95 X: 240				Calculated Estimated Lab Analysis Literature -- use Koc
Biodegradation	Electron Acceptor: Background Conc. Minimum Conc. Change in Conc. Electron Acceptor: Max. Conc. Avg. Conc.	O_2 6 -0.22 5.78 Fe 50.5 11.3	NO_3 17 0 17 CH_4 2.04 0.414	SO_4 100 0 100		Based on July 1994 grou sampling program condu Parsons Engineering Sci
General	Modeled Area Modeled Area Simulation	1450 (ft) 320 (ft) 5 (yrs)				Based on area of affecte water Steady-state flow
Source Data	Source Thickness Source	10 (ft) see Figure				Based on geologic logs a BTEX monitoring
Actual Data	Distance from Source BTEX Concentration	340 8.0	1080 1.0	1350 0.02	1420 0.005	Based on observed contour at site (see Figur
OUTPU	Centerline	see Figure				

Source: Newell et al. 1996

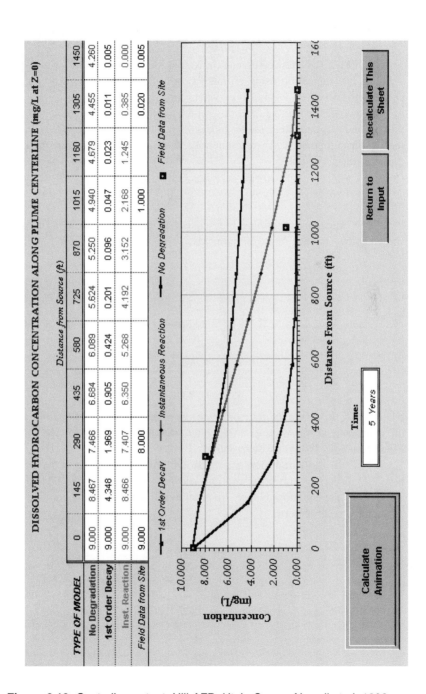

Figure 8.12 Centerline output. Hill AFB, Utah. Source Newell et al. 1996

8.4.2 The BIOCHLOR Decision Support System

The BIOCHLOR Natural Attenuation Model (Aziz et al., 1999) simulates chlorinated solvent natural attenuation using an interface similar to BIOSCREEN. BIOCHLOR simulates chlorinated solvent biodegradation, where the reaction kinetics may be much slower. This process involves sequential reactions, where the parent compound biodegrades into a daughter product and that daughter product biodegrades into another daughter product, and so on. For the chlorinated ethenes, the reaction sequence is shown below for the degradation of PCE through ethene (ETH):

$$\text{PCE} \rightarrow \text{TCE} \rightarrow \text{DCE} \rightarrow \text{VC} \rightarrow \text{ETH}$$

$$k_1 \quad\quad k_2 \quad\quad k_3 \quad\quad k_4 \tag{8.21}$$

The equations describing the sequential first order biodegradation reaction rates are shown below for each of the components:

$$r_{PCE} \;=\; -k_1 C_{PCE} \tag{8.22}$$

$$r_{TCE} \;=\; k_1 C_{PCE} - k_2 C_{TCE} \tag{8.23}$$

$$r_{DCE} \;=\; k_2 C_{TCE} - k_3 C_{DCE} \tag{8.24}$$

$$r_{VC} \;=\; k_3 C_{DCE} - k_4 C_{VC} \tag{8.25}$$

$$r_{ET} \;=\; k_4 C_{VC} \tag{8.26}$$

where k_1, k_2, k_3, k_4 are the first order rate constants and C_{PCE}, C_{TCE}, C_{DCE}, C_{VC} and C_{ETH} are the aqueous concentrations of PCE, TCE, DCE, vinyl chloride, and ethene, respectively. These equations assume no degradation of ethene.

To describe the transport and reaction of these compounds in the subsurface, 1-D advection, 3-D dispersion, linear adsorption, and sequential first order biodegradation are assumed as shown in the equations below. All equations, but the first, are coupled to another equation through the reaction term.

$$R_{PCE}\frac{dC_{PCE}}{dt} = -v\frac{dC_{PCE}}{dx} + D_x\frac{d^2C_{PCE}}{dx^2} + D_y\frac{d^2C_{PCE}}{dy^2} + D_z\frac{d^2C_{PCE}}{dz^2} - k_1 C_{PCE} \tag{8.27}$$

$$R_{TCE}\frac{dC_{TCE}}{dt} = -v\frac{dC_{TCE}}{dx} + D_x\frac{d^2C_{TCE}}{dx^2} + D_y\frac{d^2C_{TCE}}{dy^2} + D_z\frac{d^2C_{TCE}}{dz^2} + k_1 C_{PCE} - k_2 C_{TCE} \tag{8.28}$$

$$R_{DCE} \frac{dC_{DCE}}{dt} = -v \frac{dC_{DCE}}{dx} + D_x \frac{d^2 C_{DCE}}{dx^2} + D_y \frac{d^2 C_{DCE}}{dy^2} + D_z \frac{d^2 C_{DCE}}{dz^2} + k_2 C_{TCE} - k_3 C_{DCE} \quad (8.29)$$

$$R_{VC} \frac{dC_{VC}}{dt} = -v \frac{dC_{VC}}{dx} + D_x \frac{d^2 C_{VC}}{dx^2} + D_y \frac{d^2 C_{VC}}{dy^2} + D_z \frac{d^2 C_{VC}}{dz^2} + k_3 C_{DCE} - k_4 C_{VC} \quad (8.30)$$

$$R_{ETH} \frac{dC_{ETH}}{dt} = -v \frac{dC_{ETH}}{dx} + D_x \frac{d^2 C_{ETH}}{dx^2} + D_y \frac{d^2 C_{ETH}}{dy^2} + D_z \frac{d^2 C_{ETH}}{dz^2} + k_4 C_{ETH} \quad (8.31)$$

where R_{PCE}, R_{TCE}, R_{DCE}, R_{VC}, and R_{ETH} are the retardation factors, v is the seepage velocity, and D_x, D_y, and D_z are the dispersivities in the x, y, and z directions.

BIOCHLOR uses a novel analytical solution to solve these coupled transport and reaction equations in an Excel spreadsheet. To uncouple these equations, BIOCHLOR employs transformation equations developed by Clement et al., (1998). The uncoupled equations were solved using the Domenico model, and inverse transformations were used to generate concentration profiles. Details of the transformation are presented in Clement et al., 1998. Example concentration profiles for biodegradation of PCE through ethene are shown in Figure 8.13. Typically, source zone concentrations of *cis*-1,2-dichloroethythene (DCE) are high because biodegradation of PCE and TCE has been occurring since the solvent release.

BIOCHLOR also simulates different first-order decay rates in two different zones at a chlorinated solvent site. For example, BIOCHLOR is able to simulate a site with high dechlorination rates in a high-carbon area near the source that becomes a zone with low dechlorination rates downgradient when fermentation substrates have been depleted.

Example 8.4   BIOCHLOR MODELING AT CAPE CANAVERAL

The BIOCHLOR model was used to reproduce the movement of the Cape Canaveral plume from 1965 to 1998. The Cape Canaveral site (Figure 8.14) in Florida exhibits a TCE plume approximately 1,200 ft long and 450 ft wide. TCE concentrations as high as 15.8 mg/L have been measured recently at the site. The site characteristics used in the BIOCHLOR model are listed in Table 8.6. The hydraulic conductivity assumed in the model was 1.8×10^{-2} cm/sec, and the hydraulic gradient was 0.0012. A porosity of 0.2 was assumed as well as the Xu and Eckstein model for longitudinal dispersivity. The lateral dispersivity was assumed to be 10% of the longitudinal dispersivity, and vertical dispersion was neglected.

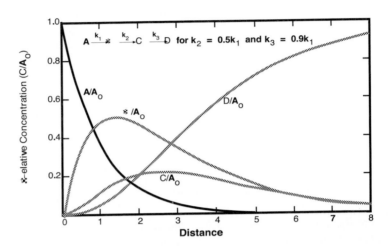

Figure 8.13   Concentration profiles simulated in BIOCHLOR. Source: Wiedemeier et al. 1999.

A median value for the retardation factor was used (R = 5.3) since BIOCHLOR accepts only one value for this parameter. The site was modeled using one anaerobic zone with one set of rate coefficients, shown in Table 8.6. This is justified because the dissolved oxygen readings at the site were less than 0.7 mg/L at all monitoring points. The rate coefficients were calculated by calibrating the model to the 1997 field data. The source zone was simulated as a spatially variable source and the source concentrations ranged from 0.001 to 98.5 mg/L for the various compounds, shown in Table 8.6. The source thickness was estimated by using the deepest point in the aquifer where chlorinated solvents were detected.

Centerline concentrations for all five species (PCE, TCE, c-DCE, VC, and ETH) predicted by the model are shown in Figures 8.15 and 8.16. Figure 8.15 shows the centerline predictions for each chlorinated solvent and a no-degradation curve for all of the chlorinated solvents as well as field data. Figure 8.16 shows the centerline concentrations for TCE, with and without biodegradation. The data in Figure 8.16 indicate that TCE concentrations discharging into the ocean will be less than 0.001 mg/L.

8.5 NUMERICAL NATURAL ATTENUATION MODELS

Numerical models provide approximate (relative to analytical methods) and, in some cases, non unique solutions to the governing advection-dispersion equation. As with analytical

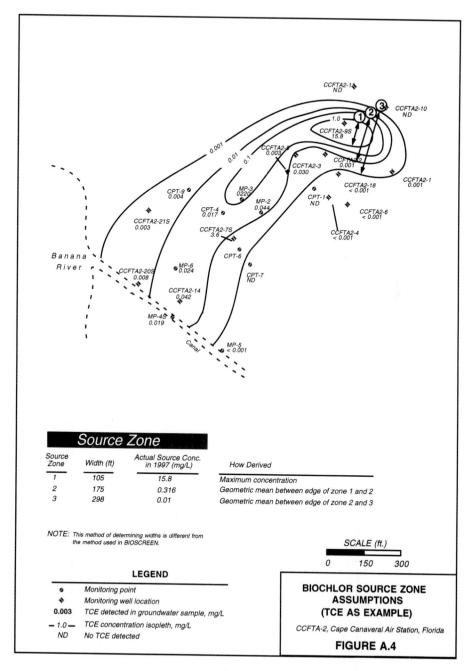

Figure 8.14 BIOCHLOR source zone assumptions (TCE as example), CCFTA-2, Cape Canaveral Air Station, Florida. Source: Aziz et al. 1999.

TABLE 8.6 BIOCHLOR Example, Cape Canaveral Air Station, Florida

DATA TYPE	PARAMETER	VALUE				SOURCE
Hydrogeology	Hydraulic Conductivity: Hydraulic Gradient: Porosity:	1.8×10^{-2} (cm/sec) 0.0012 (ft/ft) 0.2				Slug-tests results Static water level measurements Estimated
Dispersion	Original Longitudinal Dispersivity: Transverse Dispersivity: Vertical Dispersivity:	varies with x varies with x 0 ft				Based on estimated plume length of 1450 ft. Note: No calibration was necessary to match observed plume length
Adsorption	Individual Retardation Factors:	PCE: 6.7 c-DCE: 2.8 ETH: 5.3	TCE: 2.8 VC: 5.6			Calculated
	Common Retardation Factor:	5.3				Median Value
	Soil Bulk Density ρb:	1.6 (kg/L)				Estimated
	foc:	0.184%				Lab Analysis
	Koc: (L/kg)	PCE: 398 c-DCE: 126 ETH: 302	TCE: 126 VC: 316			Literature correlation using solubilities at 20 °C
Biodegradation	Biodegradation Rate Coefficients (1/year) PCE ---->TCE TCE ----> c-DCE c-DCE ----> VC VC ----> ETH	 2.0 0.9 0.6 0.4				Based on calibration to field data using a simulation time of 32 years. Started with literature values and then adjusted model to fit field data.
General	Modeled Area Length Modeled Area Width Simulation Time	1085 (ft) 700 (ft) 33 (yrs)				Based on area of affected ground water plume from 1965 (first release) to 1998 (present)
Source Data	Source Thickness Source Widths (ft)	56 (ft) Zone 1 105	 Zone 2 175	 Zone 3 298		Based on geologic logs and monitoring data (see Figure 8.14)
	Source Concentrations (mg/L) PCE TCE c-DCE VC ETH	 Zone 1 0.056 15.8 98.5 3.080 0.030	 Zone 2 0.007 0.316 1.0 0.089 0.013	 Zone 3 0.001 0.01 0.01 0.009 0.003		 Source concentrations are aqueous concentrations
Actual Data	Distance from Source (ft) PCE Concentration (mg/L) TCE (mg/L) c-DCE (mg/L) VC (mg/L) ETH (mg/L)	560 <0.001 0.22 3.48 3.080 0.188	650 ND 0.0165 0.776 0.797 ND	930 <0.001 0.0243 1.200 2.520 0.107	1085 <0.001 0.019 0.556 5.024 0.150	Based on observed concentrations at site near centerline of plume
OUTPUT	Centerline Concentration	see Figures 8.15, 8.16				

Source: BIOCHLOR Manual

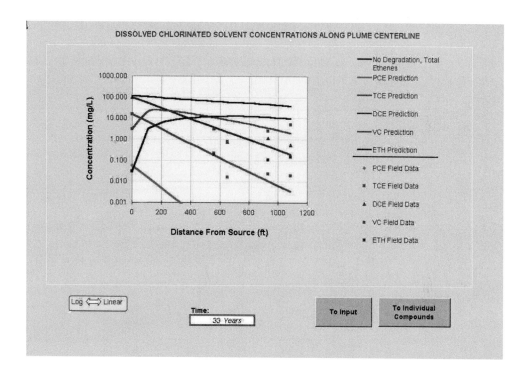

Figure 8.15 Centerline output. Cape Canaveral Air Force Base, Florida. Source: Aziz et al. 1999.

models, the use of numerical models requires the user to make some simplifying assumptions about the solute transport system. However, numerical models can simulate more complex systems. Numerical models can be used to simulate contaminant transport affected by multiple reactions for which rates or properties may vary spatially. More details on numerical modeling are provided in Chapter 10.

8.5.1 The BIOPLUME III Model

The BIOPLUME III model (Rifai et al., 1997) is a recent and major upgrade to the BIOPLUME II model presented by Rifai et al. in 1988. The main enhancement to the model was the incorporation of anaerobic biodegradation processes explicitly rather than lumping them together using a first-order decay model as was the case in BIOPLUME II. The model simulates biodegradation using a number of aerobic and anaerobic electron acceptors: oxygen, nitrate, iron (III), sulfate, and carbon dioxide. BIOPLUME III is still based on the U. S. Geologic Survey (USGS) Method of Characteristics model dated July 1989 (Konikow and Bredehoeft, 1978). The model can be downloaded from EPA's website (http://www.epa.gov/ada/csmos).

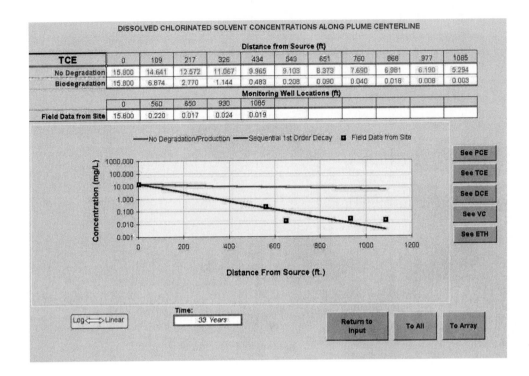

Figure 8.16 Individual centerline output for TCE, Cape Canaveral Air Station, Florida. Source: Aziz et al. 1999.

The BIOPLUME III code was developed primarily to model the natural attenuation of organic contaminants in ground water. The model solves the transport equation six times to determine the fate and transport of the hydrocarbons and the electron acceptors/reaction by-products. For the case where iron (III) is used as an electron acceptor, the model simulates the production and transport of iron (II) or ferrous iron. Three different kinetic expressions can be used to simulate the aerobic and anaerobic biodegradation reactions. These include: first-order decay, instantaneous reaction, and Monod kinetics. The principle of superposition is used to combine the hydrocarbon plume with the electron acceptor plume(s).

Major differences between BIOPLUME II and BIOPLUME III include:

- BIOPLUME III runs in a Windows95 environment, whereas BIOPLUME II was mainly developed in a DOS environment.

- BIOPLUME III model was integrated with a sophisticated ground water modeling platform known as Environmental Impact System from ZEi/MicroEngineering, Inc., of Annandale, Virginia.

The conceptual model used in BIOPLUME III to simulate these biodegradation processes tracks six plumes simultaneously: hydrocarbon, oxygen, nitrate, iron (II), sulfate, and carbon dioxide. Iron (III) is input as a concentration matrix of ferric iron in the formation. Once ferric iron is used for biodegradation, BIOPLUME III simulates the production and transport of ferrous iron.

Biodegradation occurs sequentially in the following order:

$$Oxygen \rightarrow Nitrate \rightarrow Iron (III) \rightarrow Sulfate \rightarrow Carbon Dioxide$$

The biodegradation of hydrocarbon in a given location using nitrate, for example, can occur only if oxygen has been depleted to its threshold concentration at that location.

BIOPLUME III is generally used to answer a number of questions regarding natural attenuation:

1. How long will the plume extend if no engineered/source controls are implemented?

2. How long will the plume persist until natural attenuation processes completely dissipate the contaminants?

3. How long will the plume extend or persist if some engineered controls or source reduction measures are undertaken (for example, free phase removal or residual soil contamination removal)?

The model can also be used to simulate bioremediation of hydrocarbons in ground water by injecting electron acceptors (except for iron(III)) and can also be used to simulate air sparging for low injection air flow rates. Finally, the model can be used to simulate advection, dispersion, and sorption without including biodegradation.

As with any model, there are limitations to the use of BIOPLUME III. The assumptions used in the USGS MOC code include:

1. Darcy's law is valid and hydraulic-head gradients are the only driving mechanism for flow.

2. The porosity and hydraulic conductivity of the aquifer are constant with time, and porosity is uniform in space.

3. Gradients of fluid density, viscosity, and temperature do not affect the velocity distribution.

4. No chemical reactions occur which affect the fluid properties or the aquifer properties.

5. Ionic and molecular diffusion are negligible contributors to the total dispersive flux.

6. Vertical variations in head and concentration are negligible.

7. The aquifer is homogeneous and isotropic with respect to the coefficients of longitudinal and transverse dispersivity.

The limitations imposed by the biodegradation expressions incorporated in BIOPLUME III include:

1. The model does not account for selective or competitive biodegradation of the hydrocarbons. This means that hydrocarbons are generally simulated as a lumped organic, which represents the sum of benzene, toluene, ethyl benzene or xylene. If a single component is to be simulated, the user would have to determine how much electron acceptor would be available for the component in question.
2. The conceptual model for biodegradation used in BIOPLUME III is a simplification of the complex biologically mediated redox reactions that occur in the subsurface.

Much like the approach used in developing BIOPLUME II, the 1989 version of the MOC model was modified to become a six-component particle mover model to simulate the transport of hydrocarbon, oxygen, nitrate, iron(II), sulfate, and carbon dioxide. Since the biodegradation of hydrocarbon uses iron (III) as an electron acceptor, iron (III) concentrations are simulated as an initial concentration of ferric iron that is available in each cell. Once the iron (III) is consumed, hydrocarbon concentrations are reduced and ferrous iron is produced. The resulting ferrous iron is then transported in the aquifer. The BIOPLUME III equations are very similar to those presented earlier for BIOPLUME II. Three additional equations similar to Eqs. 8.17 and 8.18 are written for nitrate, sulfate, and carbon dioxide.

The biodegradation of hydrocarbon using the aerobic and anaerobic electron acceptors is simulated using the principle of superposition and the following equations:

$$H(t+1) \quad = \quad H(t) - R_{HO} - R_{HN} - R_{HFe} - R_{HS} - R_{HC} \tag{8.32}$$

$$O(t+1) \quad = \quad O(t) - R_{OH} \tag{8.33}$$

$$N(t+1) \quad = \quad N(t) - R_{NH} \tag{8.34}$$

$$Fe(t+1) \quad = \quad Fe(t) - R_{FeH} \tag{8.35}$$

$$F(t+1) \quad = \quad R_{FeH} \tag{8.36}$$

$$S(t+1) \quad = \quad S(t) - R_{SH} \tag{8.37}$$

$$C(t+1) \quad = \quad C(t) - R_{CH} \tag{8.38}$$

where R_{HO}, R_{HN}, R_{HFe}, R_{HS}, R_{HC} are the hydrocarbon concentration losses due to biodegradation using oxygen, nitrate, ferric iron, sulfate and carbon dioxide as electron acceptors, respectively. The terms R_{OH}, R_{NH}, R_{FeH}, R_{SH}, R_{CH} are the corresponding concentration losses in the electron acceptors. These reaction terms are computed using one of the three biodegradation expressions: first-order, instantaneous, or Monod, which were discussed previously in the chapter. The reader is referred to Rifai et al. (1997) for additional information on equation formulation, and solution methods. A detailed example is described in Example 8.5.

8.5.2 The RT3D Model — Chlorinated Organics

Very few models exist (analytical or numerical) that are specifically designed for simulating the natural attenuation of chlorinated solvents in ground water. Ideally, a model for simulating natural attenuation of chlorinated solvents would be able to track the degradation of a parent compound through its daughter products and allow the user to specify differing decay rates for each step of the process. This may be referred to as a reactive transport model, in which transport of a solute may be tracked while it reacts, its properties change due to those reactions, and the rates of the reactions change as the solute properties change. Moreover, the model would also be able to track the reaction of those other compounds that react with or are consumed by the processes affecting the solute of interest (e.g., electron donors and acceptors).

Researchers at Battelle Pacific Northwest Laboratories have developed a numerical model referred to as RT3D. RT3D (Reactive Transport in 3 Dimensions, Sun et al., 1996) is a FORTRAN 90-based model for simulating multi-species, reactive transport in ground water. This model is based on the 1997 version of MT3D (DOD Version 1.5), but has several extended reaction capabilities. The model requires the USGS ground water flow code MODFLOW for computing ground water head distributions.

RT3D can accommodate multiple sorbed and aqueous phase species with any reaction framework that the user needs to define. RT3D can simulate different scenarios, since seven preprogrammed reaction packages are already provided and users have the ability to specify their own reaction kinetic expressions. This allows, for example, natural attenuation processes or an active remediation to be evaluated. Simulations can be applied to modeling contaminants such as heavy metals, explosives, petroleum hydrocarbons, and/or chlorinated solvents.

RT3D's pre-programmed reaction packages include:

1. Instantaneous Aerobic Decay of BTEX

2. Instantaneous Degradation of BTEX using Multiple Electron Acceptors (O_2, NO_3^-, Fe^{2+}, SO_4^{2-}, CH_4)

3. Kinetically limited hydrocarbon biodegradation using multiple electron acceptors (O_2, NO_3^-, Fe_2^+, SO_4^{2-}, CH_4)

4. Rate-Limited Sorption Reactions

5. Double Monod Model

   6. Sequential Decay Reactions

   7. Aerobic/Anaerobic Model for PCE/TCE Degradation

A more detailed example of RT3D is shown in Section 10.8.

8.6 FIELD SITE APPLICATIONS

8.6.1 Gas Plant Facility in Michigan

Soluble hydrocarbon and dissolved oxygen (DO) were characterized in a shallow aquifer beneath a gas plant facility in Michigan by Chiang et al. (1989). The distributions of benzene,
toluene, and xylene (BTX) in the aquifer had been monitored in 42 wells for a period of three
years. A general site plan including the locations of the wells is shown in Figure 8.17.

   Results from the three-year sampling period showed a significant reduction in total
benzene mass with time in ground water (Figure 8.18). The plume sampled in 1984 contained an approximate total mass of 9.83 kg, while the plume sampled in 1985 and 1986
contained 5.66 kg and 2.27 kg, respectively.

   Chiang et al. (1989) determined the attenuation rates of the soluble benzene, and determined the effects of DO on the biodegradation of BTX through a combination of material
balance, statistical analyses, soluble transport modeling, and laboratory microcosm experiments.

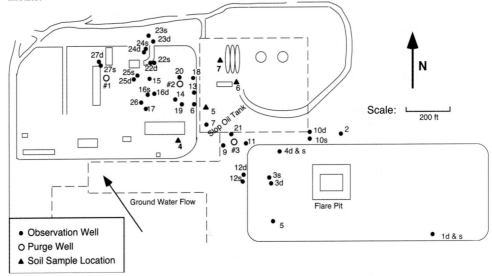

Figure 8.17 General plan of gas plant facility. Source: Chiang et al., 1989.

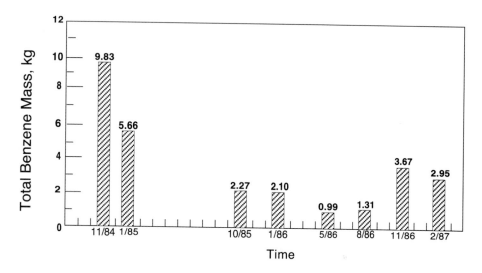

Figure 8.18 Calculated total soluble benzene mass in aquifer vs. time, November 1984 to February 1987. Source: Chiang et al., 1989

The site geology is characterized as a medium to coarse sand with interbeds of small gravel and cobbles. The general direction of ground water flow is northwesterly. The depth to water table ranges from 10 ft to 25 ft below land surface, and the slope of the water table was estimated as 0.006. Based on ground water and soil sampling data, Chiang et al. (1989) concluded that the flare pit was the major source of the hydrocarbons found in the aquifer; while the slope oil tank was a secondary source.

Dissolved oxygen concentrations in the ground water were measured by the Winkler titration method and with a field DO probe on two occasions (February and July 1987). Figure 8.19 shows the total BTX and DO concentration distributions of the February and July analyses, respectively. It can be seen from Figure 8.19 that the DO concentrations are high at low BTX concentrations and vice versa. The DO concentrations increase from their low values of < 1.0 ppm inside the 1,000 ppb BTX contour to higher concentrations of > 1.0 ppm outside the 100 ppb BTX contour line.

Chiang et al. (1989) also studied the decay rates of BTX in soil microcosms at an initial DO concentration of 0 to 6 ppm and concluded that a minimum DO (threshold) level may exist in ground water, which could sustain the natural biodegradation of BTX by microorganisms. Chiang et al. (1989) also conducted a detailed modeling analysis of their field data using the BIOPLUME II model as will be seen in Section 8.6.

Chiang et al. (1989) evaluated a first-order decay biodegradation approach and the BIOPLUME II model for simulating biodegration at the gas plant facility. Using the model and assuming first-order decay, they performed several simulations to match the observed benzene concentration distribution of 1/22/85 by setting the observed concentration distribution of 11/1/84 as the initial condition. The variables involved included the distribution of

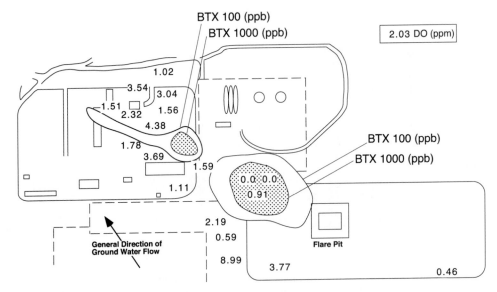

Measurements taken in February 1987

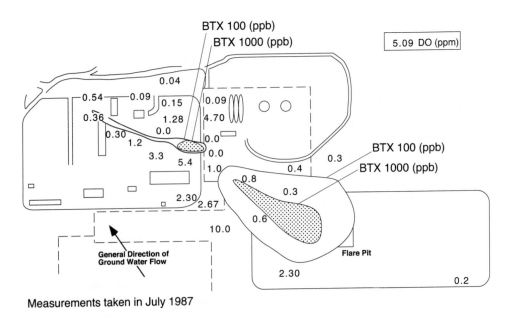

Measurements taken in July 1987

Figure 8.19 Total BTEX and dissolved oxygen concentration distributions in ground water. Source: Chiang et al., 1989

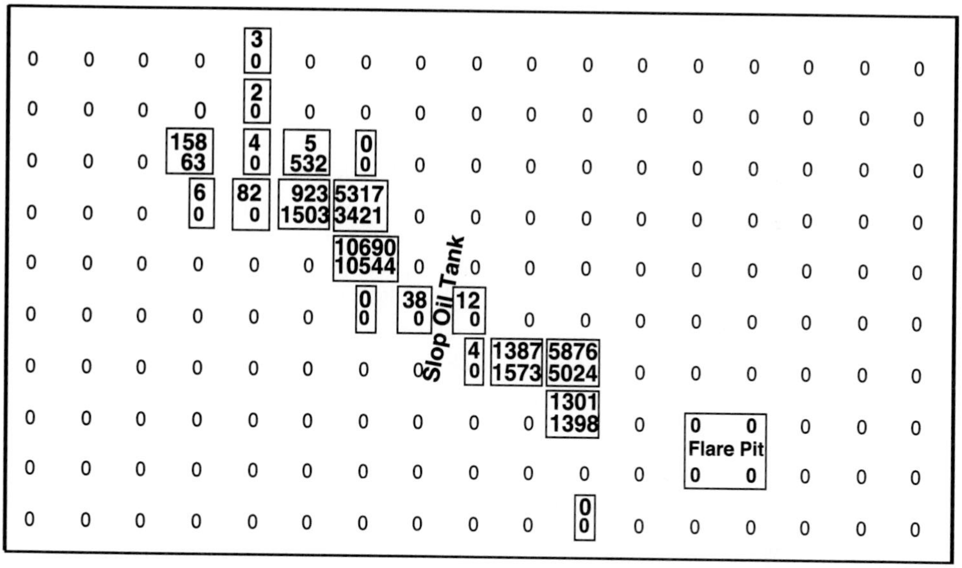

```
0   0   0   0  |3|  0   0   0   0   0   0   0   0   0   0   0   0
                |0|

0   0   0   0  |2|  0   0   0   0   0   0   0   0   0   0   0
                |0|

0   0   0 |158||4||5||0|  0   0   0   0   0   0   0   0   0   0
          |63 ||0||532||0|

0   0   0 |6 ||82 ||923 |5317|  0   0   0   0   0   0   0   0   0   0
          |0 ||0  ||1503|3421|

0   0   0   0   0   0 |10690|  0  Slop Oil Tank  0   0   0   0   0   0   0   0
                     |10544|

0   0   0   0   0   0 |0|  |38| |12|  0   0   0   0   0   0   0   0
                     |0|  |0 | |0 |

0   0   0   0   0   0   0   0 |4 |1387|5876|  0   0   0   0   0   0
                              |0 |1573|5024|

0   0   0   0   0   0   0   0   0   0 |1301|  0  |0    0|  0   0   0
                                     |1398|     |Flare Pit|

0   0   0   0   0   0   0   0   0   0   0   0  |0    0|  0   0   0

0   0   0   0   0   0   0   0   0   0 |0|  0   0   0   0   0   0
                                     |0|
```

Figure 8.20 Predicted (bottom number) and observed (top number) BTX by BIOPLUME II (ppb). Source: Chiang et al., 1989.

the leakage/spill rates between the flare pit and the slop oil tanks and macrodispersivities of the aquifer.

The BIOPLUME II model was used to simulate the July 1987 data by setting the observed concentration distribution of February 1987 as an initial condition. Figure 8.20 shows correlations between the measured and the simulated soluble BTX concentrations of July 1987. As can be seen from Figure 8.20, the correlations for BTX were reasonable. The correlations, however, for oxygen were not as similar. The authors attributed the differences to the fact that the BIOPLUME II model assumes a requirement of 3 ppm of oxygen for 1 ppm of benzene, whereas the actual requirement is in the range of 1 - 3 ppm.

Example 8.5 MODELING THE HILL AFB UST 870 SITE WITH BIOPLUME III

The 870 site at Hill AFB was modeled previously with BIOSCREEN in order to simulate the movement of the dissolved BTEX plume and estimate the mass loss due to biodegradation (see Example 8.3). This site was further analyzed with the BIOPLUME III model in an effort to evaluate the effectiveness of natural attenuation as a remedy for the contaminated ground water. The source and mass of contamination at UST Site 870 is uncertain as was seen in the BIOSCREEN example. The former UST may have contributed to contamination, but it is also possible that former underground pipelines contributed to the spill. Soil BTEX contamination is widespread; extending approximately 1,600 ft downgradient from the source area and exhibiting a width of 500 ft at its thickest extent (see Figure 8.21). The highest observed soil concentration is 554 mg/kg in the heart of the contamination at soil boring EPA-82-I.

Mobile LNAPL is present at several monitoring wells, as shown in Figure 8.22. The LNAPL plume extends 750 ft downgradient from the source area with an areal extent of approximately 225,000 sq. ft. Ground water sampling during 1991-1994 provided BTEX concentrations in the shallow aquifer (Figure 8.23). BTEX was detected in 79 of the 125 samples collected with the highest dissolved BTEX measured at 26.85 mg/L in well MW-03 in August 1992. Comparison between the plume extent in 1993 and that of 1994 suggests a significant reduction in contaminant concentrations and aerial extent. Ground water samples analyzed for geochemical characteristics yielded information on the electron acceptor capacity in the shallow aquifer (Figures 8.24a through 8.24e).

A 20 × 30 model grid (85 ft wide by 110 ft long) was used in BIOPLUME III, (Figure 8.25). Tables 8.7 and 8.8 list the model parameters used for the site. Constant head boundaries were established along the northeast and southwest (top and bottom) grid perimeter to simulate the northeast to southwest ground water flow direction. A 12-yr source release scenario was used to simulate the existing plume delineated in 1994. A total of 20 injection wells were used to simulate release from the LNAPL plume into the ground water.

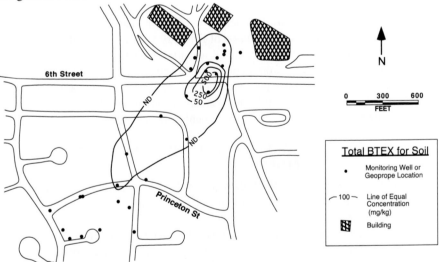

Figure 8.21 Soil Contamination contour map: Hill AFB. Source: Parsons Engineering Science, 1994.

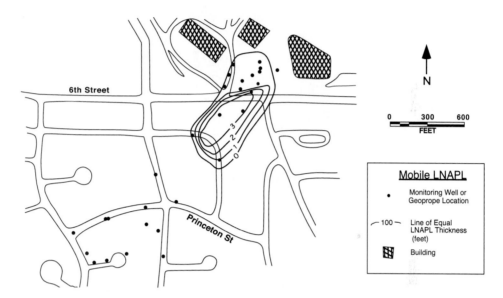

Figure 8.22 Total BTEX contour map for groundwater: Hill AFB. Source: Parsons Engineering Science, 1994.

The extent of the calibrated plume is in good agreement with the measured BTEX plume, as can be seen from Figure 8.23. The maximum modeled concentration of 13.6 mg/L is comparable to the observed 9.8 mg/L.

The calibrated model was used to analyze plume conditions 12 years into the future without source control. Plume predictions indicate that the plume reaches a quasi-steady state with the plume extent remaining approximately the same as the calibrated plume. Concentrations within the plume, however, attenuate from 13.6 mg/L to 5.4 mg/L with the heart of the plume having migrated nearer the area of greatest mobile LNAPL thickness, approximately 450 ft downgradient. The BIOPLUME III modeling results suggest that further reductions in plume size and concentrations can be achieved through source reduction.

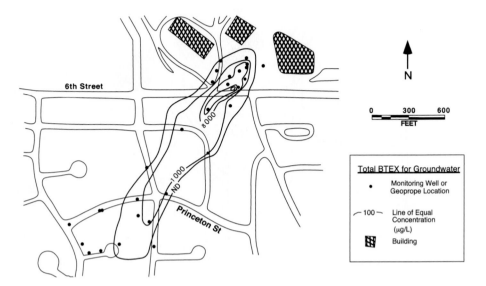

Figure 8.23 Total BTEX contour map for groundwater: Hill AFB. Source: Parsons Engineering Science, 1994.

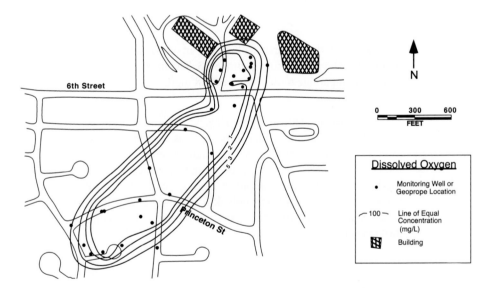

Figure 8.24a Dissolved oxygen contour map, Hill AFB; Source: Parsons Engineering Science, 1994.

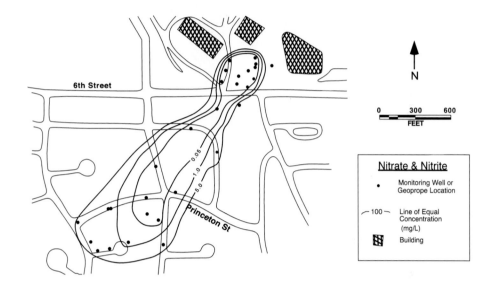

Figure 8.24b Nitrate and nitrite contour map, Hill AFB; Source: Parsons Engineering Science, 1994.

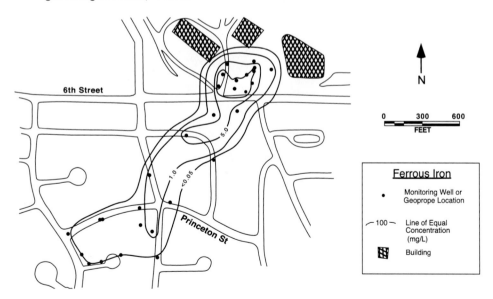

Figure 8.24c Ferrous iron contour map, Hill AFB; Source: Parsons Engineering Science, 1994.

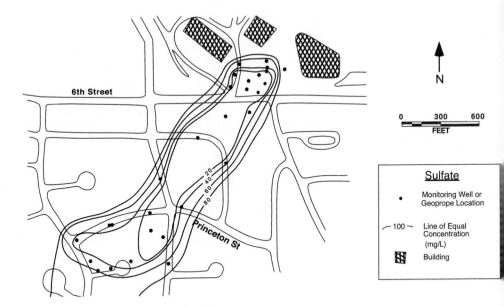

Figure 8.24d Sulfate contour map, Hill AFB; Source: Parsons Engineering Science, 1994.

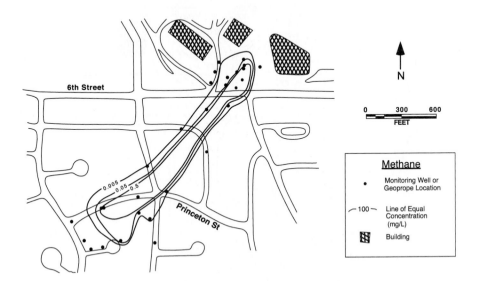

Figure 8.24e Methane contour map, Hill AFB. Source: Parsons Engineering Science, 1994.

TABLE 8.7 **BIOPLUME II Model Parameters for Hill AFB**

Description	Calibrated Model Setup
Time step interval for printing data	1
Number of iteration parameters	7
Max. allowable number of iterations in ADIP	200
Initial number of particles per node	9
Particle movement interval (IMOV)	0
Option for printing computed velocities	2
Option to print computed dispersion equation coefficients	2
Option to print computed changes in concentration	1
Option to punch velocity data	0
Option for biodegradation, retardation and decay	1
Convergence criteria in ADIP	0.001
Storage coefficient	0 (Steady-state)
Time increment multiplier for transient flow	
Ratio of transverse to longitudinal dispersivity	0.1
Max. cell distance per particle move	0.5
Ratio of Tyy to Txx	1 (Isotropic)
Stoichiometric ratio of hydrocarbon to oxygen	3.1

TABLE 8.8 **Electron Acceptor Input Data for Hill AFB**

Description	Value
Background concentration for oxygen (mg/L)	6.0
Biodegradation kinetics specifier for oxygen	2
Stoichiometric ratio of oxygen to contaminant	3.14
Threshold concentration of oxygen (mg/L)	0
Background concentration for nitrate (mg/L)	5.0
Biodegradation kinetics specifier for nitrate	2
Stoichiometric ratio of nitrate to contaminant	4.8
Threshold concentration of nitrate (mg/L)	0
Background concentration for iron (mg/L)	5.0
Biodegradation kinetics specifier for iron	2
Stoichiometric ratio of iron to contaminant	21.5
Threshold concentration of iron (mg/L)	0
Background concentration for sulfate (mg/L)	54.0
Biodegradation kinetics specifier for sulfate	2
Stoichiometric ratio of sulfate to contaminant	4.6
Threshold concentration of sulfate (mg/L)	0
Background concentration for carbon dioxide (mg/L)	1.0
Biodegradation kinetics specifier for carbon dioxide	2
Stoichiometric ratio of carbon dioxide to contaminant	2.14
Threshold concentration of carbon dioxide (mg/L)	0

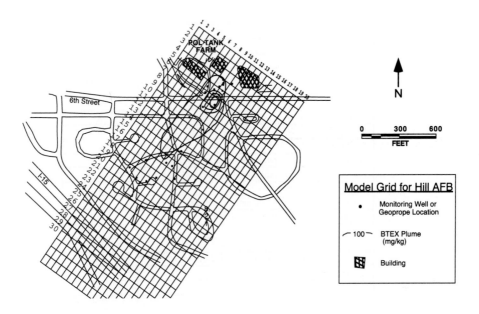

Figure 8.25 Bioplume III Model Grid, Hill AFB. Source: Parsons Engineering Science, 1994.

SUMMARY

Biodegradation processes attenuate contaminant concentrations in ground water. A variety of laboratory and field procedures are necessary to verify and quantify the contribution of these processes to contaminant transport in ground water aquifers. Biodegradation models can then be used to predict contaminant behavior for different conditions and scenarios. Both analytical and numerical models are available for the analysis of biodegradation processes. A number of these are reviewed in this chapter (Table 8.3). In particular BIOPLUME III and RT3D are used in a number of applications.

REFERENCES

Aziz, C. E., C. J. Newell, A. R. Gonzales, P. Haas, T. P. Clement, and Y. Sun, "BIOCHLOR Natural Attenuation Decision Support System User's Manual," prepared for the Air Force Center for Ennvironmental Excellence, Brooks AFB, San Antonio, TX, 1999. (see also www.gsi-net.com)

Baek, N. H., L. S. Clesceri, and N. L. Clesceri, "Modeling of Enhanced Biodegradation in Unsaturated Soil Zone," *Journal of Environmental Engineering*, 115, (1), 150-172, 1989.

Borden, R. C. and P. B. Bedient, "Transport of Dissolved Hydrocarbons Influenced by Oxygen-Limited Biodegradation: 1. Theoretical Development," *Water Resources Res.*, 13:1973-1982, 1986.

Borden, R. C., P. B. Bedient, M. D. Lee, C. H. Ward, and J. T. Wilson, "Transport of Dissolved Hydrocarbons Influenced by Oxygen-Limited Biodegradation: 2. Field Application," *Water Resources Res.*, 13:1983-1990, 1986.

Buscheck, T.E., and C. M. Alcantar, "Regression Techniques and Analytical Solutions to Demonstrate Intrinsic Bioremediation, *Proceedings,* 1995 Battelle International Conference on In Situ and On Site Bioreclamation, Columbus, OH, Battelle Press, April 1995.

Celia, M. A., J. S. Kindred, and I. Herrera, "Contaminant Transport and Biodegradation: 1. A Numerical Model for Reactive Transport inn Porous Media," *Water Resources Res.* 25(6):1141-1148, 1989.

Chiang, C. Y., J. P. Salanitro, E. Y. Chai, J. D. Colthart, and C. L. Klein, "Aerobic Biodegradation of Benzene, Toluene, and Xylene in a Sandy Aquifer - Data Analysis and Computer Modeling," *Ground Water*, 6:823-834, 1989.

Clement, T. P., Y. Sun, B. S. Hooker, and J. N. Petersen, "Modeling Multispecies Reactive Transport in Ground Water," *Ground Water Monitoring & Remediation,* 18(2):79-92, 1998.

Domenico, P. A., "An Analytical Model for Multidimensional Transport of a Decaying Contaminant Species, *J. Hydrol.,* vol. 91, No. 2, pp 49-58, 1987.

Holder, Anthony W., P. B. Bedient, and J. B. Hughes, "Modeling the Impact of Oxygen Reaeration on Natural Attenuation," *Bioremediation Journal*, accepted March 1, 1999.

Howard, P. H., R. S. Boethling, W. F. Jarvis, W. M. Meylan, and E. M. Michalenko, *Handbook of Environmental Degradation Rates,* Chelsea, MI, Lewis Publishers, 1991.

Kinzelbach, W., W. Schafer, and J. Herzer, "Numerical Modeling of Natural and Enhanced Denitrification Processes in Aquifers," *Water Resources Res.* 27(6):1123-1135, 1991.

Kissel, J. C., P. L. McCarty, and R. L. Street, Numerical Simulation of Mixed Culture Biofilm, *J. Environ. Engineering,* Division ASCE, 110, 393, 1984.

Konikow, L. F. and J. D. Bredehoeft, "Computer Model of Two-Dimensional Solute Transport and Dispersion in Ground Water, Automated Data Processing and Computations," Techniques of Water Resources Investigations of the U.S.G.S., Washington, D.C., 100 pp., 1978.

MacQuarrie, K. T. B., E. A. Sudicky, and E. O. Frind, "Simulation of Biodegradable Organic Contaminants in Ground Water: 1. Numerical Formulation in Principal Directions," *Water Resources Res.*, 26(2):207-222, 1990.

MacQuarrie, K. T. B., and E. A. Sudicky, "Simulation of Biodegradable Organic Contaminants in Groundwater: 2. Plume behavior in uniform and random flow field," *Water Resources Res.*, 26(2):223-240, 1990.

McCarty, P. L., M. Reinhard, and B. E. Rittman, "Trace Organics in Ground Water," *Environ. Sci. Technol.*, 15(1): 40-51, 1981.

McCarty, P. L., B. E. Rittman, and E. J. Bouwer, "Microbiological Processes Affecting Chemical Transformations in Ground Water." *Ground Water Pollution Microbiology*, eds. G. Bitton and C. P. Gerba: New York, John Wiley and Sons, p. 89-115, 1984.

Molz, F. J., M. A. Widdowson, and L. D. Benefield, "Simulation of Microbial Growth Dynamics Coupled to Nutrient and Oxygen Transport in Porous Media," *Water Resources Res.*, 22(8):1207-1216, 1986.

Montgomery Watson, "Hill Air Force Base site 870 UST," 1994.

Newell, C. J., J. W. Winters, H. S. Rifai, R. N. Miller, J. Gonzales and T. H. Wiedemeier, "Modeling Intrinsic Remediation with Multiple Electron Acceptors: Results from Seven Sites," *Proceedings,* NGWA Conference, pp. 33-48, Houston, TX, November 1995.

Newell, C. J., R. K. McLeod, and J. R. Gonzales, *BIOSCREEN Natural Attenuation Decision Support System User's Manual*, Version 1.3, EPA/600/R-96/087, August 1996. Ada, OK, Robert S. Kerr Environmental Research Center, 1996.

Newell, C. J., R. K. McLeod, and J. R. Gonzales, BIOSCREEN, Natural Attenuation Decision Support System, Version 1.4 Revisions, 1997.

Odencrantz, J. E., A. J. Valocchi, and B. E. Rittman, "Modeling Two-dimensional Solute Transport with Difference Biodegradation Kinetics," *Proceedings,* Petroleum Hydrocarbons Conference, NWWA, Houston, TX, October 31-Novermber, 1990.

Parsons Engineering-Science, Inc., 1994d, Intrinsic Remediation Engineering Evaluation/Cost Analysis for UST Site 870, Ogden, Utah, Hill Air Force Base, Parsons Engineering Science, Inc., Denver, Colorado, Sept. 1994.

Rifai, H. S., C. J. Newell, J. R. Gonzales, S. Dendrou, L. Kennedy, and J. Wilson, *BIOPLUME III Natural Attenuation Decision Support System Version 1.0 User's Manual,* prepared for the U.S. Air Force Center for Environmental Excellence, San Antonio, TX, Brooks Air Force Base, 1997.

Rifai, H. S., P. B. Bedient, J. T. Wilson, K. M. Miller, and J. M. Armstrong, "Biodegradation Modeling at Aviation Fuel Spill Site," *Journal of Environmental Engineering*, 5:1007-1029, 1988.

RTDF, Natural Attenuation of Chlorinated Solvents Seminar, Presented on September 17 - 18, 1997 at the University of Texas at Austin, J. J. Pickle Research Campus, 1997.

Semprini, L., and P. L. McCarty, "Comparison between Model Simulations and Field Results for In Situ Biorestoration of Chlorinated Aliphatics: Part 1. Biostimulation of Methanotrophic Bacteria," *Ground Water,* 29(3):365-374, 1991.

Srinivasan, P. and J. W. Mercer, "Simulation of Biodegradation and Sorption Processes in Ground Water," *Ground Water*, 4: 475-487, 1988.

Suarez, M. P. and H. S. Rifai, Biodegradation Rates for Fuel Hydrocarbons and Chlorinated Solvents in Groundwater, *Bioremediation Journal*, (accepted), 1999.

Sun, Y., J. N. Peterson, T. P. Clement, and B. S. Hooker, "A Modular Computer Model for Simulating Natural Attenuation of Chlorinated Organics in Saturated Ground-Water Aquifers,," *Proceedings,* Symposium on Natural Attenuation of Chlorinated Organics in Ground Water, Dallas, TX, Sept. 11-13, EPA/540/R-96/509, U.S. EPA, Washington, DC, 1996.

Tabak, H. H., S. Desai, and R. Govind, "Determination of Biodegradability Kinetics of RCRA Compounds Using Respirometry for Structure-Activity Relationships," EPA/600/D-90/136, 1990.

Widdowson, M A., F. J. Molz, and L. D. Benfield, "Development and Application of a Model for Simulating Microbial Growth Dynamics Coupled to Nutrient and Oxygen Transport in Porous

Media," in *Proc.* AGWSE/IGWMCH Conference on Solving Ground Water Problems with Models, Denver, CO, Dublin, OH, NWWA, 28-51, 1987.

Widdowson, M. A., F. J. Molz, and L. D. Benefield, "A Numerical Transport Model for Oxygen- and Nitrate-Based Respiration Linked to Substrate and Nutrient Availability in Porous Media," *Water Resources Research*, 9:1553-1565, 1988.

Wiedemeier, T. H., J. T. Wilson, D. H. Kampbell, R. N. Miller, and J. E. Hansen, "Technical Protocol for Implementing Intrinsic Remediation With Long-Term Monitoring for Natural Attenuation of Fuel Contamination Dissolved in Groundwater ", Vol. 1, Air Force Center for Environmental Excellence, Technology Transfer Division, Brooks AFB, San Antonio, TX, 1995.

Wiedemeier, T. H., H. S. Rifai, C. J. Newell, and J. T. Wilson, *Natural Attenuation of Fuel Hydrocarbons and Chlorinated Solvents*, New York, John Wiley and Sons, 1999.

Wiedemeier, T. H., et al., *Technical Protocol for Evaluating Natural Attenuation of Chlorinated Solvents in Groundwater,* U.S. Air Force Center for Environmental Excellence, Technology Transfer Division, Brooks Air Force Base, San Antonio, TX, 1996.

C H A P T E R 9

FLOW AND TRANSPORT IN THE UNSATURATED ZONE

Manar El-Beshry

9.1 CAPILLARY ACTION

Flow and transport mechanisms in the unsaturated zone are much more complex than in the saturated zone due to the effect of capillary forces and nonlinear soil characteristics. In an unsaturated porous medium, part of the pore space is filled with water and part is filled with air, and the total porosity is defined as the sum of the two moisture contents:

$$n = \theta_w + \theta_a \tag{9.1}$$

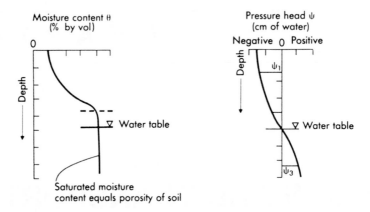

Figure 9.1 Typical θ and ψ relationships with depth in the unsaturated zone.

The moisture content θ_w is defined as the ratio of the volume of water to the total volume of porous media sample, and θ_a is the ratio of the volume of air to the total volume of porous media. The unsaturated or vadose zone constitutes that part of the soil profile where water content is less than the soil porosity, and where the soil water pressure is negative. The water-saturated capillary fringe just above the water table is also considered part of the unsaturated zone.

Figure 9.1 shows the variation of moisture content and pressure head ψ with depth. Near the water table a capillary fringe can occur where ψ is a small negative pressure corresponding to the air entry pressure. In this zone, the pores are saturated but the pressure is slightly less than atmospheric. This capillary zone is small for sandy soils but can be up to two meters for fine grained soils. By definition, pressure head is negative (under tension) at all points above the water table and is positive for points below the water table. The value of ψ is greater than zero in the saturated zone below the water table and equals zero at the water table. Soil physicists refer to ψ < 0 as the tension head or capillary suction head, which can be measured by an instrument called a tensiometer (Section 9.5).

The water that is in the unsaturated zone is adsorbed as a film on the surface of the grains, held strongly by suction pressure. As more water is added to the porous structure, water movement is restricted due to the strong sorption and capillary forces. Eventually, a continuous wetting phase will form, and the air can become trapped in the larger pores, thus restricting the air phase. Full water saturation is generally not achieved in the unsaturated zone because of the trapped residual air.

One can consider actual porous media to be similar to a bundle of thin glass tubes of radius r. A curved surface will tend to develop at the interface between water and air and the difference in pressure across the interface is called **capillary pressure**, and is directly proportional to the interfacial tension and inversely proportional to the radius of curvature. The capillary pressure P in a thin tube can be determined from a balance between the weight of the water column in the tube and capillary forces pulling upward, or

$$P = \frac{2\sigma \cos \gamma}{r} \tag{9.2}$$

where σ is the interfacial tension, r is the radius of the tube, and γ is the interface angle between the two liquids. Capillary forces and wettability of a fluid, the tendency of the fluid to preferentially spread over a solid surface, is described in detail in Section 11.3.

9.2 SOIL-WATER CHARACTERISTIC CURVES

Hydraulic conductivity $K(\theta)$ relates velocity and hydraulic gradient in Darcy's law. Moisture content θ is defined as the ratio of the volume of water to the total volume of a unit of porous media. To complicate the analysis of unsaturated flow, both θ and K are functions of the capillary suction ψ. Also, it has been observed experimentally that the θ–ψ relationships differ significantly for different types of soil. Figure 9.2a shows the characteristic drying and wetting curves that occur in soils that are draining water or receiving infiltration of water. The nonlinear nature of these curves for several selected soils are shown in Figure 9.2b. The curves reflect the fact that the hydraulic conductivity and moisture content of an unsaturated soil increase with decreasing capillary suction. The sandier soils show a very different response compared to the tighter loam and clay soils.

At atmospheric pressure, the soil is saturated with water content equal to θ_s. The soil will initially remain saturated as the capillary pressure (matric potential) is gradually decreased. Eventually, water will begin to drain from the soil as the pressure is lowered, and the moisture content will continue to decline until it reaches some minimum water content θ_r. Further reductions in the capillary pressure will not result in any additional moisture, as shown in Figure 9.2a. Thus the sandier soils are drained (or lose moisture) more quickly than the tighter soils. This is due to the fact that the sands have larger pores.

Some simple empirical expressions used to relate water content of a soil to the capillary pressure head include the one from Brooks and Corey (1964)

$$\theta = \theta_r + \left(\theta_s - \theta_r\right)\left(\psi / \psi_b\right)^{-\lambda} \tag{9.3}$$

where

θ	=	volumetric water content
θ	=	volumetric water content at saturation
θ_r	=	irreducible minimum water content
ψ	=	matric potential or capillary suction
ψ_b	=	bubbling pressure
λ	=	experimentally derived parameter

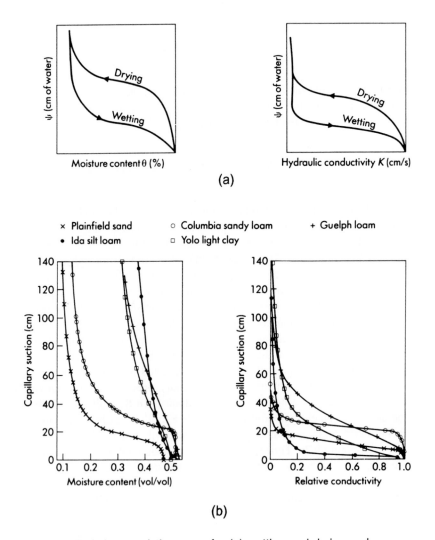

Figure 9.2 Soil characteristic curves for (a) wetting and drying and (b) different soil types

Brooks and Corey (1964) also defined an effective saturation, S_e, as

$$S_e = \frac{S_w - \theta_r}{1 - \theta_r} \qquad (9.4)$$

where $S_w = \theta / \theta_s$, the saturation ratio.

Van Genuchten (1980) also derived an empirical relationship between capillary pressure head and volumetric water content, defined by

$$\theta = \theta_r + \frac{\theta_s - \theta_r}{\left[1 + (\alpha \psi)^n \right]^m} \tag{9.5}$$

where α, m, and n are constants. Generally, these equations work well for medium- and coarse-textured soils with predictions for fine-textured materials usually being less accurate. These equations are often used in computer models to represent soil characteristics for flow in the unsaturated zone. For large capillary heads, the Brooks and Corey and Van Genuchten models become identical if $\lambda = mn$ and $\psi_b = 1/\alpha$.

A drying curve occurs when one allows an initially saturated sample to desorb water by applying suction. If the sample is then resaturated with water, thus decreasing the suction, it will follow a wetting curve. The fact that the drying curve and the wetting curve will generally not be the same produces the hysteretic behavior of the soil water retention curve as illustrated in Figure 9.3. The soil water content is not a unique function of capillary pressure, but depends on the previous history of the soil. The hysteretic nature of θ is due to the presence of different contact angles during wetting and drying cycles, and to geometric restrictions of single pores (Nielsen et al., 1986). For example, the contact angle between the water and the soil surface is greater during the advance of a water front than during its retreat.

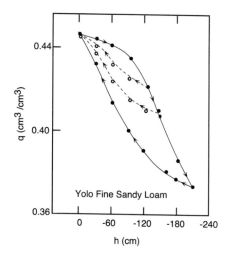

Figure 9.3 Water retention curves for a sample of Yolo fine, sandy loam. The solid curves are eye-fitted through measured data along the two main boundary curves. Dashed curves represent primary wetting scanning curves. Arrows indicate the direction at which the pressure head changes are imposed. Source: Nielson et al., 1986. © American Geophysical Union.

Air trapped in pores during a wetting cycle will reduce the water content of a soil during wetting, but eventually that trapped air will dissolve. Hysteresis effects are usually augmented by the presence of trapped air, and soil shrinking and swelling (Davidson et al., 1966). Hysteresis creates a significant problem for the prediction of flow rates and transport phenomena in the unsaturated zone.

9.3 UNSATURATED HYDRAULIC CONDUCTIVITY

Evidence suggests that Darcy's law is still valid for unsaturated flow except that hydraulic conductivity is now a function of moisture content. Darcy's law is then used with the unsaturated value for K and can be written

$$v = -K(\theta)\, \partial h / \partial z \tag{9.6}$$

where v is darcy velocity, z is depth below surface [L], ψ is tension or suction [L], $K(\theta)$ is unsaturated hydraulic conductivity [L/T], h is potential or head ($h = z + \psi$) [L/T], and θ is volumetric moisture content.

Unsaturated hydraulic conductivity can be determined by both field methods and laboratory techniques, both of which are time-consuming and tedious. Estimates are often made from soil parameters obtained from soil-water retention relationships such as those from Brooks and Corey (1964) and Van Genuchten (1980). Figure 9.4 shows observed values and calculated curves for relative hydraulic conductivity as a function of capillary pressure.

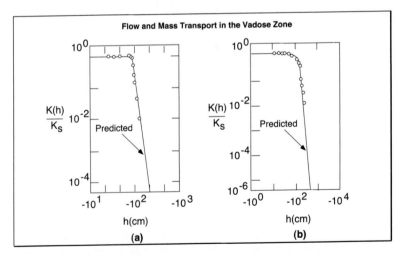

Figure 9.4 Observed values (open circles) and calculated curves (solid lines) for relative hydraulic conductivity of (a) Hygiene sandstone and (b) Touchet silt loam. Source: Van Genuchten, 1980.

9.4 GOVERNING EQUATION FOR UNSATURATED FLOW

The water table defines the boundary between the unsaturated and saturated zones and is defined by the surface at which the fluid pressure P is exactly atmospheric, or $P = 0$. Hence, the total hydraulic head $h = \psi + z$, where $\psi = P/\rho g$, the capillary pressure head.

Considerations of unsaturated flow include the solution of the governing equation of continuity and Darcy's law in an unsaturated porous media. The governing equation, originally derived by Richard in 1931, is based on substituting Darcy's law Eq. (9.6) into the unsaturated continuity equation,

$$- \left[\frac{\partial(\rho v_x)}{\partial x} + \frac{\partial(\rho v_y)}{\partial y} + \frac{\partial(\rho v_z)}{\partial z} \right] = \frac{\partial}{\partial t} \rho \theta \tag{9.7}$$

The resulting equation is

$$\frac{\partial \theta}{\partial t} = -\frac{\partial}{\partial z} \left[K(\theta) \frac{\partial \psi(\theta)}{\partial z} \right] - \frac{\partial K(\theta)}{\partial z} \tag{9.8}$$

where

θ = volumetric moisture content
z = distance below the surface [L]
θ = capillary suction (pressure) [L of water]
$K(\theta)$ = unsaturated hydraulic conductivity [L/T]

Equation (9.8) is called Richards (1931) equation and is a nonlinear partial differential equation that is quite difficult to solve. The Richards equation assumes that the presence of air can be ignored, that water is incompressible, and that the soil matrix is nondeformable. Both numerical and analytical solutions exist for certain special cases. The most difficult part of the procedure is determining the characteristic curves for a soil (Figure 9.2). The characteristic curves reduce to the fundamental hydraulic parameters K and n in the saturated zone and remain as functional relationships in the unsaturated zone.

A number of analytical and numerical solution techniques have been developed over the last 35 years for Eq. (9.8). Analytical approaches require greatly simplified conditions for boundaries, and are generally restricted to 1-D vertical systems. Early work by Philip and de Vries (1957) provided much of the physical and mathematical ground work for subsequent analyses. The analytical approaches are useful for deriving physically based expressions for infiltration rates in unsaturated soils. A more recent approach based on the method of characteristics has been applied to gravity-dominated flow in the unsaturated zone (Smith 1983; Charbeneau, 1984).

Charbeneau (1984) considers the kinematic theory of soil moisture and solute transport in the vertical direction for unsaturated ground water recharge. It is assumed that the soil starts at and eventually drains to field capacity. Analytical expressions are developed for water content and moisture flux as a function of depth and time, and the approach is extended for an arbitrary sequence of surface boundary conditions. In this approach, dissipative terms are neglected in the governing equations, thus allowing the powerful method of characteristics to be used in the solution. Numerical methods are more suited to handling actual laboratory and field situations. Finite difference methods were proposed by Rubin and Steinhardt (1963) and Freeze (1969, 1971). Finite difference numerical techniques are presented in detail in this chapter for flow and transport in the unsaturated zone.

There are two extreme cases which should be considered. For large values of moisture content, $\partial\psi/\partial\theta$ is approximately zero and the continuity equation becomes

$$\frac{\partial\theta}{\partial t} = -\frac{\partial K(\theta)}{\partial z} \tag{9.9}$$

Equation (9.9) leads to the kinematic theory of modeling the unsaturated flow, where capillary pressure gradients are neglected. The theory is also applicable if ψ = CONSTANT within the profile. Thus, Darcy's law predicts that flow is downward under a unit gradient. The second extreme case occurs when capillary forces completely dominate gravitational forces, resulting in a nonlinear diffusion equation. This latter form is useful for modeling evaporation processes.

To summarize the properties of the unsaturated zone as compared to the saturated zone, Freeze and Cherry (1979) state that:

For the unsaturated zone (vadose zone):

1. It occurs above the water table and above the capillary fringe.
0. The soil pores are only partially filled with water; the moisture content θ is less than the porosity n.
3. The fluid pressure P is less than atmospheric; the pressure head ψ is less than zero.
4. The hydraulic head h must be measured with a tensiometer.
5. The hydraulic conductivity K and the moisture content θ are both functions of the pressure head ψ.

For the saturated zone:
1. It occurs below the water table.
2. The soil pores are filled with water; and the moisture content θ equals the porosity n.

3. The fluid pressure P is greater than atmospheric, so the pressure head ψ (measured as gauge pressure) is greater than zero.

4. The hydraulic head h must be measured with a piezometer.

5. The hydraulic conductivity K is not a function of the pressure head ψ.

Finally, more details on the unsaturated zone can be found in Fetter (1999), Rawls et al. (1993), Charbeneau and Daniel (1993) and Guyman (1994).

9.5 MEASUREMENT OF SOIL PROPERTIES

Moisture characteristic curves for a particular soil can be determined by any of three approaches (Charbeneau and Daniel, 1993). The first technique is to estimate the curve (water content versus capillary pressure head) from published data for similar soils. For example, Rawls et al. (1983) collected and analyzed data from over 500 soils. Gupta and Larson (1979) describe the use of grain-size distribution data, organic content, and bulk density to estimate moisture characteristic curves. The second technique is to assume an analytic function such as that of Brooks and Corey (1964) or Van Genuchten (1980). These equations were presented in Section 9.2. The empirical coefficients in these functions are usually estimated based on correlations of various soil characteristics.

The third approach is to actually measure the soil moisture characteristic curve directly. Incremental equilibrium methods allow the soil to come to equilibrium at some moisture content θ, and then capillary pressure ψ is measured. Next θ is changed and time is allowed for equilibrium to reestablish and ψ is remeasured. The process is repeated until a sufficient number of ψ–θ points have been measured to define the entire curve (Figure 9.2). One can also allow ψ to come to equilibrium and measure θ for changes in ψ. The pressure plate is the most commonly used method of measurement and involves placing a chamber around soil samples that have been soaked with water. Positive air pressure is used to force water out of the soil samples and the outflow is monitored to confirm equilibrium. After equilibrium is established, the chamber is disassembled, and the soil samples are oven dried to determine θ.

Hydraulic conductivity in unsaturated soils is determined from Ks, the value at saturation and the relative permeability kr, which is a function of capillary pressure head, volumetric water content or degree of water saturation. The relative permeability kr can be estimated from other soil properties or can be directly measured in the laboratory. Klute and Dirksen (1986) summarize several methods of unsaturated hydraulic conductivity in the laboratory. They report on steady state methods for a steady flow through a soil column with controlled pressure at both ends of the column. This technique is not practical for soils with low K because the flow rate cannot be measured accurately. Olson and Daniel (1986) report on transient tests where soil is placed in a pressure plate device, a step increase in air pressure is imposed, the rate of water flow out of the soil is measured versus time, and K is computed from the resulting data.

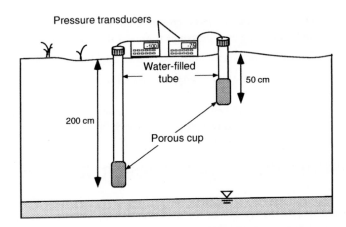

Figure 9.5   Two tensiometers used to determine the gradient of the soil-water potential.

Hydraulic conductivity at saturation K_s is measured in the laboratory using rigid-wall permeameters and flexible-wall permeameters. Hydraulic conductivity tests may be performed with a constant head, falling head or constant flux (Olson and Daniel, 1986; Klute and Dirksen, 1986). Differences have been noted between laboratory determined values and those estimated from field tests. Olson and Daniel compared laboratory and field measured K_s values for 72 data sets involving clayey soils and found significant differences, since hydraulic conductivity tends to increase with increasing scale of measurement relating to structural features of the soil.

Capillary pressure head can be measured in an undisturbed soil sample in the laboratory or the measurement can be obtained in the field. In both cases, a tensiometer, consisting of a porous element inserted into the soil and a pressure sensing device at the surface, is often used. The tensiometer is initially saturated with a liquid and when brought into contact with the soil, and the soil will pull water out of the tensiometer creating a negative pressure, that can be measured (Charbeneau and Daniel, 1993). A tensiometer generally cannot read more negative than 0.9 bar due to problems of cavitation of water. Figure 9.5 depicts a tensiometer for field use.

9.6 INFILTRATION MODELS

Infiltration is the process of vertical movement of water into a soil from rainfall, snowmelt, or irrigation. Infiltration of water plays a key role in surface runoff, ground water recharge, evapotranspiration, and transport of chemicals into the subsurface. Models to characterize infiltration for field applications usually employ simplified concepts that predict the infiltration rate assuming surface ponding begins when the surface application rate exceeds the soil infiltration rate. Empirical, physically based, and physical models have all been developed for the infiltration process. A more detailed review of infiltration can be found in Rawls et al. (1993).

Richards Equation, Eq. (9.8), is the physically based infiltration equation used for describing water flows in soils. Philip (1957) solved the equation analytically for the condition of excess water at the surface and given characteristic curves. Their coefficients can be predicted in advance from soil properties and do not have to be fitted to field data. However, the more difficult case where the rainfall rate is less than the infiltration capacity cannot be handled by Philip's equation. Another limitation is that it does not hold valid for extended time periods. Swartzendruber (1987) presented a solution to Richards equation that holds for both small, intermediate and large times.

A number of operational infiltration models have been developed over the years and are covered in detail in hydrology textbooks such as Chow, et al. (1988), Bedient and Huber (1992), and Rawls et al. (1993). These include the SCS runoff curve number method, the Horton method, and the Holtan method (SCS, 1986; Horton, 1940; Holtan, 1961).

One of the most interesting and useful approaches to solving the governing equation for infiltration was originally advanced by Green and Ampt (1911). In this method, water is assumed to move into dry soil as a sharp wetting front that separates the wetted and unwetted zones. At the location of the front, the average capillary suction head $\psi = \psi_f$, is used to represent the characteristic curve. The moisture content profile at the moment of surface saturation is shown in Figure 9.6a. The area above the moisture profile is the amount of infiltration up to surface saturation F and is represented by the shaded area of depth L in Figure 9.6a. Thus, $F = (\theta_s - \theta_i)L = M_d L$, where θ_i is the initial moisture content, θ_s is the saturated moisture content, and $M_d = \theta_s - \theta_i$ the initial moisture deficit.

Darcy's law is then applied as an approximation to the saturated conditions between the soil surface and the wetting front, as indicated in Figure 9.6b (Bedient and Huber, 1992).

The volume of infiltration down to the depth L is given by

$$F = L(\theta_s - \theta_i) = LM_d \tag{9.10}$$

Neglecting the depth of ponding at the surface, the original form of the Green-Ampt equation

$$f = K_s[1 - (\theta_s - \theta_i)\psi_f/F]$$
$$= K_s[1 - M_d\psi_f/F] \tag{9.11}$$

Because ψ_f is negative, Eq. (9.11) indicates that the infiltration rate is a value greater than the saturated hydraulic conductivity, as long as there is sufficient water at the surface for infiltration, as sketched in curves C and D of Figure 9.6c. Functionally, the infiltration rate decreases as the cumulative infiltration increases.

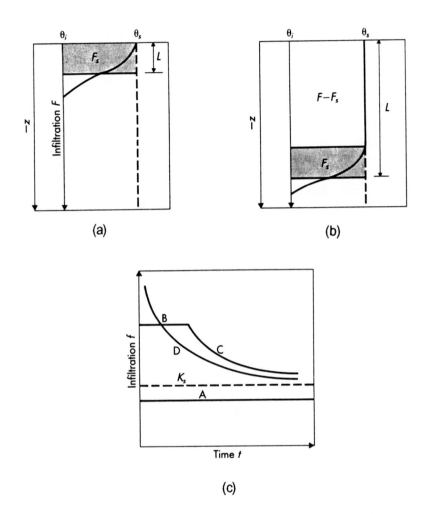

Figure 9.6 Moisture and infiltration relations. (a) Moisture profile at moment of surface saturation. (b) Moisture profile at later time. (c) Infiltration behavior under rainfall. Source: Mein and Larson, 1973.

The rainfall intensity, i, is often less than the potential infiltration rate given by Eq. (9.11), in which case $f = i$. Let the corresponding volume of infiltration be F_s. With $f = i$, Eq. (9.11) can then be solved for F_s, the volume of infiltration at the time of surface saturation (t_s, the time at which Eq. (9.11) becomes valid),

$$F_s = [(\theta_s - \theta_i)\psi_f]/[1 - i/K_s] = M_d\psi_f/(1 - i/K_s) \qquad (9.12)$$

We require $i > K_s$ in Eq. (9.12) and remember that ψ_f is negative. The Green-Ampt infiltration prediction is thus the following:

If $i \ K_s$, then $f = i$ (curve A in Figure 9.6c)

If $i > K_s$, then $f = i$ until $F = it_s = F_s$ (Eq. (9.12)

After the surface is saturated, the following is used, $f = K_s[1 - M_d\psi_f/F]$ (Eq. (9.11)) for $i > K_s$ and $f = i$ for $i \ K_s$.

The combined process is sketched in curves B and C of Figure 9.6c. As long as the rainfall intensity is greater than the saturated hydraulic conductivity, the infiltration rate asymptotically approaches K_s, as a limiting lower value. Mein and Larson (1973) found excellent agreement when using the Green-Ampt method, numerical solutions of Richard's equation, and experimental soils data. If the rainfall rate starts above K_s, drops below it, and then rises back above it during the infiltration computation, the use of Green-Ampt becomes more complicated, making it necessary to redistribute the moisture in the soil column rather than maintaining the assumption of saturation from the surface down to the wetting front shown in Figure 9.6b. The use of the Green-Ampt procedures for unsteady rainfall sequences is illustrated by Skaggs and Khaleel (1982).

Equation (9.11) predicts infiltration rate, f, as a function of cumulative infiltration, F, not time. Because $f = F/t$, the equation can be converted into a differential equation, the solution of which can be solved iteratively for $F(t)$ (Chow et al., 1988). Then Eq. (9.11) can be used to determine $f(t)$.

A major advantage of the Green-Ampt model is that, in principle, the necessary parameters, K_s, ψ_f, and $M_d = \theta_s - \theta_i$, can be determined from physical measurements in the soil, rather than empirically as for the Horton parameters. For example, saturated hydraulic conductivity (often loosely called permeability) is tabulated by the U.S. Soil Conservation Service (SCS) for a large number of soils as part of that agency's Soil Properties and Interpretation sheets (available from local SCS offices). An increasing quantity of tension versus moisture content data (of the type shown in Figure 9.2) are also available, from which a value of ψ_f can be obtained by integration over the moisture content of interest. For example, several volumes of such information have been assembled for Florida soils (e.g., Carlisle et al., 1981). In practice, the Green-Ampt parameters are often calibrated, especially when used in continuous simulation models.

A useful source of information on Green-Ampt parameters is provided by Rawls et al. (1983), who present data for a large selection of soils from across the United States. These data are shown in Table 9.1. Two porosity values are given: total and effective. Effective porosity accounts for trapped air and is the more reasonable value to use in computations. It can be seen in Table 9.1 that as the soil particles get finer, from sands to clays, the saturated hydraulic conductivity, K_s, decreases, the average wetting front suction, ψ_f, increases (negatively), and porosity, θ_s, is variable. Table 9.1 provides valuable estimates for Green-Ampt parameters, but local data (e.g., Carlisle et al., 1981) are preferable if available. Missing is the initial moisture content, θ_i, since it depends on antecedent rainfall and moisture condi-

TABLE 9.1 Green-Ampt infiltration parameters for various soil texture classes

Soil Class	Porosity η	Effective Porosity θ_E	Wetting Front Soil Suction Head ψ (cm)	Hydraulic Conductivity K(cm/hr)	Sample Size
Sand	0.437 (0.374-0.500)	0.417 (0.354-0.480)	4.95 (0.97-25.36)	11.78	762
Loamy sand	0.437 (0.363-0.506)	0.401 (0.329-0.473)	6.13 (1.35-27.94)	2.99	338
Sandy loam	0.453 (0.351-0.555)	0.412 (0.283-0.541)	11.01 (2.67-45.47)	1.09	666
Loam	0.463 (0.375-0.551)	0.434 (0.334-0.534)	8.89 (1.33-59.38)	0.34	383
Silt loam	0.501 (0.420-0.582)	0.486 (0.394-0.578)	16.68 (2.92-95.39)	0.65	1206
Sandy clay loam	0.398 (0.332-0.464)	0.330 (0.235-0.425)	21.85 (4.42-108.0)	0.15	498
Clay loam	0.464 (0.409-0.519)	0.309 (0.279-0.501)	20.88 (4.79-91.10)	0.10	366
Silty clay loam	0.471 (0.418-0.524)	0.432 (0.347-0.517)	27.30 (5.67-131.50)	0.10	689
Sandy clay	0.430 (0.370-0.490)	0.321 (0.207-0.435)	23.90 (4.08-140.2)	0.06	45
Silty clay	0.479 (0.425-0.533)	0.423 (0.334-0.512)	29.22 (6.13-139.4)	0.05	127
Clay	0.475 (0.427-0.523)	0.385 (0.269-0.501)	31.63 (6.39-156.5)	0.03	291

The numbers in parentheses below each parameter are one standard deviation around the parameter value given.
Source: Rawls, Brakensiek, and Miller, 1983.

tions. Typical values for $M_d = \theta_s - \theta_i$, are given in the SCS Soil Properties and Interpretation sheets and are usually termed "available water (or moisture) capacity, in./in." Values usually range from 0.03 to 0.30. The value to use for a particular soil in question must be determined from a soil test. Otherwise, a conservative (low) M_d value could be used for design purposes (e.g., 0.10).

Example 9.1   GREEN-AMPT TIME TO SURFACE SATURATION

Guelph Loam has the following soil properties (Mein and Larson, 1973) for use in the Green-Ampt equation:

$$K_s = 3.67 \times 10^{-4} \text{ cm/sec}$$
$$\theta_s = 0.523$$
$$\psi = -31.4 \text{ cm water}$$

For an initial moisture content of $\theta_i = 0.3$, compute the time to surface saturation for the following storm rainfall:

$$i = 6K_s \text{ for 10 min}$$
$$i = 3K_s \text{ thereafter}$$

Solution.   The initial moisture deficit, $M_d = 0.523 - 0.300 = 0.223$. For the first rainfall segment, we compute the volume of infiltration required to produce saturation from Eq. (9.12):

$$Fs = \psi_f M_d / (1 - i/K_s) = (-31.4 \text{ cm})(0.223) / (1 - 6K_s/K_s) = 1.40 \text{ cm}$$

The rainfall volume during the first 10 minutes is

$$10i = (10 \text{ min}) (6 \cdot 3.67 \times 10^{-4} \text{ cm/sec})(60 \text{ sec/min}) = 1.31 \text{ cm}$$

since $1.31 < 1.40$, all rainfall infiltrates and surface saturation is not reached, and $F(10\text{min}) = 1.31$ cm.

The volume required for surface saturation during the lower rainfall rate of $i = 3Ks$ is

$$F_s = (-31.4 \text{ cm})(0.223) / (1 - 3K_s/K_s) = 3.50 \text{ cm}$$

Thus, an incremental volume of $F = F_s - F(10 \text{ min}) = 3.50 - 1.31 = 2.19$ cm must be supplied before surface saturation occurs. This requires an incremental time of

$$t = F/i = (2.19 \text{ cm}) / (3 \cdot 3.67 \times 10^{-4} \text{ cm/sec}) = 1989 \text{ sec}$$
$$= 33.15 \text{ min}$$

Thus, the total time to surface saturation is $10 + 33.15 = 43.15$ min.

9.7 TRANSPORT PROCESSES IN THE UNSATURATED ZONE

The movement of contaminants in the vadose zone is an important hydrologic problem. The unsaturated zone, the region bounded at its top by the soil surface and below by the ground water table, represents the conduit through which liquid and gaseous constituents can be attenuated and transformed. Surface and ground waters are linked by the unsaturated zone, which is recognized as a key factor in the improvement and protection of the quality of ground water supplies.

The three major environmental health and safety problems that result from gasoline spills to the subsurface are: soil contamination, ground water contamination, and fire and explosion hazards (Hoag and Marley, 1986). In reality, transport in the unsaturated zone is much more complex than in the saturated zone mainly because there are numerous phases of interest: soil, water, air, and contaminant. Chemicals exist in the unsaturated zone in four phases: dissolved in soil moisture, sorbed to the soil particles, as nonaqueous phase liquids (NAPL), and as an envelope of organic vapors. As time goes by, the immiscible liquid migrates downwards leaving behind blobs of material trapped by capillary forces in the pores, often referred to as the residual phase. If the spilled product is less dense than water, it accumulates on top of the water table forming a light nonaqueous phase liquid (LNAPL) pool. Figure 9.7 shows NAPL migration in the subsurface. The free product can be recovered by bailing or skimming. Unfortunately, after the source has been removed, the threat posed from the residual phase still persists as the sorbed and the retained materials serve as a constant reservoir of contamination to the underlying aquifers and overlying ground surface. Ground water contamination from the residual phase that exists in the vadose zone has been an issue of major concern. The parameters of interest in this case are: the travel time from the ground surface to the water table, the amount of contaminant that actually reaches the water table, and the rate at which it enters the ground water aquifer.

Organic vapors have been identified as one of the more ubiquitous groups of hazardous chemicals present in contaminated soils and ground water. They can migrate much faster than the liquid phase. Moreover, the vapor flow velocities and direction are not controlled by ground water gradients. Volatilization from residual NAPL or from NAPL dissolved in water results in the formation of a vapor plume, which can spread by vapor diffusion, and by density induced advection of the soil gas mixture. As it spreads, the vapor plume also contaminates the soil moisture and soil matrix as a result of phase partitioning. Vapors less dense than air may rise to the ground surface where they become a potential for inhalation or explosion if they get into the basement of structures (Sleep and Sykes, 1989). On the other hand, ground water contamination can occur due to vapor migration downwards towards the capillary fringe, due to a rise in the water table, and due to recharge by infiltration.

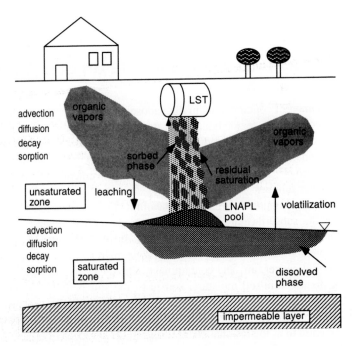

Figure 9.7 Contamination migration pathways in the unsaturated zone.

9.7.1 Volatile Emissions from Soil

Investigations of fate and transport of chemicals in the unsaturated zone must inherently deal with multiphase issues. Contaminants exist in four phases: aqueous, soil, vapor, and immiscible oil phases. The pore space is filled by the sum of the fluids present so that porosity equals the sum of the volumetric fluid contents. The concentrations of a constituent in the aqueous, vapor, and oil phases are designated C_a, C_v, and C_o, all on a mass per unit volume basis. The chemical soil phase concentration is designated as mass of chemical sorbed per unit mass of soil, C_s. The total concentration is specified by C_T.

The modeling of emissions to the atmosphere from soil processes has been dealt with by Jury et al. (1983) and Enfield et al. (1985). Jury et al. (1983) assume that: (1) the chemical of total concentration C_{Ti} is incorporated uniformly to a specified depth, L; (2) volatilization of the chemical takes place through a stagnant air layer just above the soil surface; (3) there is a steady flux of water through the soil; and (4) there is an infinite depth of uniform soil below the zone of incorporation. The boundary conditions considered by Jury et al. (1983) are as follows:

$$C_T = C_{T_i}, \qquad 0 < X < L \quad \text{for} \quad t = 0 \tag{9.13}$$

$$C_T = 0, \qquad X > L \qquad \text{for} \quad t = 0 \tag{9.14}$$

The transport of the chemical through the stagnant boundary is equal to the flux at the soil surface such that:

$$-D_E \frac{\partial C_T}{\partial X} + V_E C_T = -H_E C_T \quad \text{for} \quad X = 0 \ \text{at all} \ t \tag{9.15}$$

where D_E, V_E are the effective dispersion coefficient, effective velocity, and H_E is the effective mass transfer coefficient defined by:

$$H_E = \frac{h}{B_v} \tag{9.16}$$

where h is the mass transfer coefficient across the stagnant air film, and B_v is defined by:

$$B_v = \left[\frac{\theta}{H} + \theta_o \frac{K^{o-w}}{H} + \theta_a + \rho \frac{K_d}{H} \right] \tag{9.17}$$

where θ is the volumetric water content, ρ is the density of the soil phase, θ_o is the volumetric oil content, θ_a is the volumetric vapor content, K_d is the soil water partitioning coefficient, H is the Henry's Law constant, and K^{o-w} is the oil-water partitioning coefficient.

The vapor flux at the surface of the soil is estimated using:

$$J(0,t) = -H_E C_T \qquad (9.18)$$

Jury et al. (1983) solved the appropriate equations analytically and obtained an expression for the vapor flux of organics from soils.

Thibodeaux and Hwang (1982) have also presented solutions for estimating volatile emissions from land treatment. Their approach (illustrated in Figure 9.8) assumes that there is no movement of liquids in the soil, and that no adsorption or biodegradation takes place. It is assumed that the soil is contaminated between depths h_s and h_p. As the contaminant evaporates and the vapor diffuses upward to the surface, a "dried-out" zone develops. The flux through the surface (ignoring mass transfer through the stagnant boundary layer above the soil) is given by:

$$J(0,t) = -\frac{D_V C_{WZ}}{h_p - y} \qquad (9.19)$$

where D_V is the effective diffusivity in the air-filled pores and C_{WZ} is the vapor phase concentration of the contaminant in the wet zone.

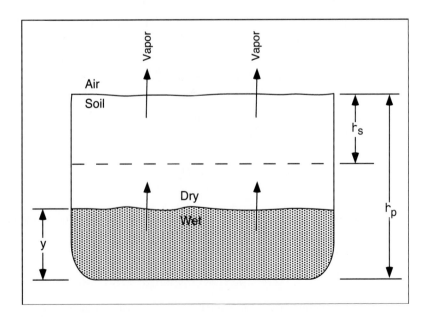

Figure 9.8 Thibodeaux-Hwang land treatment volatilization model. Source: Short, 1986.

A mass balance on the system using the appropriate boundary conditions yields an expression for the flux through the wet-dry interface:

$$J(0,t) = D_V C_{WZ} \sqrt{h_s^2 + 2(h_p - h_s) D_V C_{WZ} At M_A} \qquad (9.20)$$

where M_A is the mass of contaminant applied, and A is the soil surface area over which the contaminant is applied.

9.7.2 Soil Gas Investigation

Recently sampling and analysis of soil gas for delineation of subsurface volatile organic compounds (VOCs) has become very popular. The presence of VOCs in soil gas indicates that volatile organics may be present either in the vadose zone or in the saturated zone. Therefore, soil gas surveys are often applied to define the areal extent of contamination from a source in the vadose zone or to identify ground water contamination problems. The data obtained from these surveys are used for locating soil borings and monitoring wells, which are required to delineate the distribution of subsurface contamination (Pankow and Cherry, 1996).

Good detection of vapors is common in shallow ground water settings and fairly permeable soils. Compounds that are more suitable for detection are those that have a boiling point less than 150 °C, low aqueous solubility, and vapor pressure higher than 10 mm Hg at 20 °C.

Soil gas samples may be collected by pumping a sample from the vadose zone, which can be analyzed in the field and actual concentrations are measured (Figure 9.9). This method may disturb the vapor distribution due to sample withdrawal. Another method of sampling is by burying an absorbent material within the vadose zone and capturing the VOCs by sorption. The disadvantage of this method is that it measures relative concentrations and not absolute concentrations at the different locations. Several methods currently being used for the analysis of soil gas samples are listed in Table 9.2.

TABLE 9.2 Methods of Sampling for VOCs

Method	Usage
Electron capture detector (ECD)	Sensitive to halocarbon compounds such as TCE, PCE, TCA
Flame ionization detector (FID)	Sensitive to hydrocarbon compounds
Photoionization detector (PID)	Sensitive to vinyl chloride
Hall electrolytic conductivity detector	Sensitive to most halogenated compounds

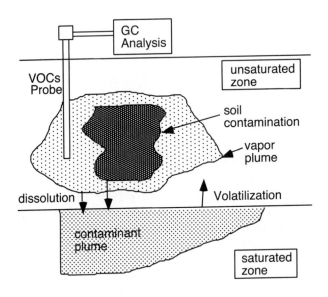

Figure 9.9 Soil gas sampling.

9.8 GOVERNING EQUATIONS FOR VAPOR TRANSPORT

Vapor flow and transport in porous media may occur in response to pressure and concentration gradients (Massmann, 1989). Pressure gradients may arise from: barometric pressure fluctuations (Massmann and Farrier, 1992); vaporization of a liquid (Baehr and Bruell, 1990; Mendoza and Frind, 1990a); water table fluctuations (McCarthy and Johnson, 1993); or density gradients (Falta et al., 1989; Sleep and Sykes, 1989). Volatile compounds with high molecular weights result in higher vapor densities that drive advective flows. Transport may also arise from induced advective flows created by applying vacuum as in soil vapor extraction (SVE) systems. In case of negligible pressure gradients, transport is dominated by concentration gradients (diffusion). Pressure gradients due to barometric fluctuations can be neglected at small pressure variations (up to 10 mbar) (Conant et al., 1996). Sensitivity analyses conducted by Mendoza and Frind (1990), have demonstrated that advective fluxes caused by vaporization of organic compounds are of minor importance compared to density-driven advection. Mechanical dispersion and molecular diffusion play a big role in spreading contaminants in the gas phase. Air diffusion coefficients for organic compounds are several orders of magnitude larger than aqueous diffusion coefficients; therefore, molecular diffusion is usually more dominant than mechanical dispersion in vapor movement, except for areas close to venting wells in SVE systems where vapor velocities are very high (Benson et al., 1993).

9.8.1 Flow Equation

The similarity between air and water flow has resulted in modifying ground water flow equations to represent gas flows. The major differences that exist between water and gas flow are as follows (Brusseau, 1991):

1. Water is incompressible whereas gas is compressible, that is, gas density is dependent on pressure, which results in a nonlinear flow equation. Gas compressibility can be neglected where the pressure difference inducing gas flow is less than 20%. Almost all soil venting systems operate under these conditions, and the incompressibility assumption is valid.

2. Slip flow for water is negligible, whereas nonzero gas fluxes at pore walls are not negligible. Slip flows are not observed when the pressure difference is less than 20%, and can be excluded from the modeling process for gas transport in venting systems.

3. Water flow in porous media is laminar and Darcy's law is applicable. Darcy's law does not describe gas flow since small pressure gradients usually generate significant gas flows. Laminar flow may not be valid under these conditions. However, conditions under which gas compressibility and slip flows are negligible would be appropriate for using Darcy's law.

Equations of fluid flow in porous media are obtained by combining the mass continuity equation with Darcy's Law which yields the following 3-D air flow equation (Bear, 1979):

$$\frac{\partial}{\partial x}\left(k_{gxx}\frac{\partial \phi}{\partial x}\right) + \frac{\partial}{\partial y}\left(k_{gyy}\frac{\partial \phi}{\partial y}\right) + \frac{\partial}{\partial z}\left(k_{gzz}\frac{\partial \phi}{\partial z}\right) = S_g\frac{\partial \phi}{\partial t} \tag{9.21}$$

$$\phi = P_g^2 \tag{9.22}$$

where x,y,z are Cartesian coordinates aligned along the major axes of the effective air permeability tensor with diagonal components k_{gxx}, k_{gyy}, k_{gzz}. S_g is the pneumatic equivalent of specific storage [L^{-1}], and P_g is the gas/vapor pressure [M/LT^2]. P_g^2 is substituted by ϕ for linearization of the equation.

The differential equation governing air flow is nonlinear because air density increases with air pressure. However, if the difference in air pressure within flow fields does not exceed 0.2 atm, which is common to natural and soil vapor extraction systems, the linear ground water flow equation may be used to simulate air flow (Massman, 1989).

The flow equation may be solved numerically by finite difference or finite element techniques (Anderson and Woesner, 1992). Alternatively, the flow equation may be simplified and solved analytically as described by Johnson (1991).

9.8.2 Organic Vapor Transport

The vapor phase transport of mass has much in common with the transport of dissolved contaminants in ground water. The processes of advection and dispersion operate to physically transport the mass, while the chemical processes are involved with the generation of the contaminants through volatilization and subsequent interactions with the water and solid phases in the system.

Removal of mass from a spill depends upon the process of volatilization, which is a phase partitioning between a liquid and a gas. For solvents, the process is described in terms of equilibrium theory by a form of Raoult's law,

$$P_i = x_i \gamma_i P_i^0 \qquad (9.23)$$

where P_i is the vapor pressure of component i (atm) in the soil gas, x_i is the mole fraction of the component in the solvent, and P_i^0 is the vapor pressure of the pure solvent at the temperature of interest; these are tabulated constants (e.g., Verschueren, 1983). An activity coefficient γ_i for the ith component in the mixture is added to account for nonidealities (Hinchee et al., 1986). By applying the ideal gas equation, the partial pressures calculated in Eq. (9.23) can be expressed in terms of concentration:

$$C_{s,i} = \frac{P_i MW_i}{RT} \qquad (9.24)$$

where $C_{s,i}$ is the saturation concentration of compound i [mg/cm^3], T is temperature [K], R is the universal gas constant [82.04 atm·cm^3·mole^{-1}·K^{-1}], MW_i is the molecular weight of compound i [mg/mole], and P_i is the partial pressure of the compound i [atm].

The equilibrium approach applies in cases where the rate of volatilization is large relative to the rate of physical transport through the medium. Where the flow of air contacts residual product in every pore, phase equilibrium is achieved quite rapidly at least for the more volatile compounds at the start of venting. One important reason for less than equilibrium concentrations of vapor is geologic heterogeneities that cause some of the air flow to avoid most of the contaminated zones.

With spills of complex solvent mixtures like gasoline, soil venting removes the components with higher vapor pressure first. The residual contamination, thus, becomes progressively enriched in the less volatile compounds. Because of this compositional change, the overall rate of mass removal decreases with time. This process has been described mathematically by Marley and Hoag (1984) and Johnson (1991) using forms of Eq. (9.24) and information on the most volatile components of gasoline.

Vapor pressures for organic compounds increase significantly as a function of increasing temperature. For example, the vapor pressure for a volatile compound like benzene increases from 0.037 atm at 32 °F to 0.137 atm at 80 °F (Johnson et al., 1988; Johnson, 1991). Over the same temperature range, the vapor pressure for n-dodecane increases from

2.8×10^{-5} atm to 2.3×10^{-4} atm. The main implication of this result is that the overall time required for cleanup will change depending upon temperature.

The physical transport process, advection and dispersion, play an important role with respect to vapor transport. The simplest and most extensively analyzed model of physical transport assumes that advection transports contaminants from the point of generation to the vapor extraction well (Figure 9.10a), that the distribution of contaminants would be reasonably homogeneous, and that much of the air flow would have the opportunity to move through the bulk of the spill. Ideally, the vapor concentration in the fraction of air moving through the spill is the equilibrium concentration determined by Raoult's law. In Figure 9.10a, about 25% of the air passes through the spill giving a vapor concentration in the well

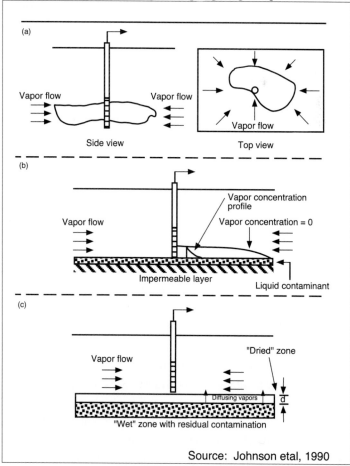

Source: Johnson etal, 1990

Figure 9.10 Different ways in which the circulating air interacts with a volatile contaminant source.

that is 25% of equilibrium value and a removal rate of $0.25QC_s$, where Q is the airflow, C_s is the equilibrium concentration.

However, in heterogeneous media or when pure product is present, the air flow may not pass directly through the spill. Specific examples cited by Johnson et al. (1988, 1990) include: (1) air flow across the surface of a free-liquid floating on the water table or low permeability layer (Figure 9.10b), or (2) product trapped in a lower permeability lens (Figure 9.10c). In both of these cases, the mass loss rate of contaminants is controlled by the rate at which mass can diffuse into the moving vapor stream. Thus, when flowing air bypasses the spill, the rate of mass removal may be much lower than for the homogeneous case. The result may be a vapor extraction system that circulates considerable quantities of air without removing much of the contaminant. Mathematical approaches for estimating the contaminant removal rates under these more complex conditions are presented by Johnson et al. (1990).

9.8.3 Transport Equations

The primary mechanisms involved in contaminant transport in porous media are: advection, diffusion, dispersion, and reactions as previously described in chapter 6. The general mass balance equation for each chemical component i in each fluid phase α is: (Rathfelder et al., 1991):

$$\frac{\partial}{\partial t}\left(nS_\alpha C_{\alpha i}\right) = -\nabla \cdot nS_\alpha\left(C_{\alpha i}V_{m\alpha} + J^d_{\alpha i} + J^m_{\alpha i}\right) + nS_\alpha C_\alpha \Gamma_{\alpha i} - I^i_{\alpha\beta} \qquad (9.25)$$

subject to

$$\sum_{i=1}^{N_\alpha} C_{\alpha i} = C_\alpha \qquad (9.26)$$

where S_α is the fluid saturation [dimensionless], $C_{\alpha i}$ is the component concentration in each phase [M/L^3], $C_{\alpha i}V_{m\alpha}$, $J^d_{\alpha i}$, and $J^m_{\alpha i}$ are the component mass flux in each phase by advection, dispersion and diffusion [M/L^{2}T] respectively, $\Gamma_{\alpha i}$ is the rate of component mass production/removal by pumping/injection or reactions per unit mass of each phase [1/T], $I^i_{\alpha\beta}$ is the interphase mass transfer [M/L^{3}T] between adjacent phases, α and β. A similar equation is expressed for the solid phase by replacing the concentration terms with $\rho_b C_{si}$, where ρ_b is the soil bulk density [M/L^3], and C_{si} is the component concentration in the solid phase [M/M]. Equation (9.26) states that the sum of component concentrations in each phase is equal to the density of the phase. N_α represents the number of components.

Advective fluxes follow Darcy's law

$$nS_\alpha V_{m\alpha} = \frac{kk_{r\alpha}}{\mu_\alpha} \nabla P_\alpha = \vec{V}_\alpha \tag{9.27}$$

where k is the intrinsic permeability tensor [L^2], and $k_{r\alpha}$ is the fluid relative permeability [dimensionless], μ_α is the fluid viscosity [M/LT], P_α is the fluid pressure [M/LT^2], and $\vec{V}_\alpha$ is the fluid specific discharge vector [L/T].

Dispersive fluxes follow Fick's law

$$J_{\alpha i}^d + J_{\alpha i}^m = -D_{\alpha i} \cdot \nabla C_{\alpha i} \tag{9.28}$$

where $D_{\alpha i}$ is the dispersion tensor for each component in each phase [L^2/T], which is evaluated by the following expression (Bear, 1979):

$$(D_{\alpha i})_{ij} = \alpha_T \bar{V} \delta_{ij} + (\alpha_L - \alpha_T) \bar{V}_i \bar{V}_j / \bar{V} + D_{\alpha i}^* \delta_{ij} \tag{9.29}$$

where $i,j = x,y,z$, α_L and α_T, are the longitudinal and transverse dispersivity of the porous media respectively [L], $\bar{V}$ is the average velocity, δ_{ij} is the Kronecker Delta [dimensionless], and $D_{\alpha i}^*$ is the effective molecular diffusion coefficient for each component in each phase [L^2/T]. If advective flows are high, then the first two terms in Eq. (9.29) will be more dominant than the diffusion term. More often, if advective fluxes are negligible, the dispersion coefficient will be a function of the air diffusion coefficient, and the transport equation reduces to Fick's Law.

As moisture contents vary in the vadose zone, the pore space available for vapor and water diffusion is reduced, and the transport pathways become more convoluted. Thus, the molecular diffusion coefficient is calculated using the Millington and Quirk (1961) relationship to account for tortuosity (Mendoza and Frind, 1990a):

$$D_{\alpha i}^* = \frac{\theta_\alpha^{10/3}}{n^2} D_{\alpha i} \tag{9.30}$$

where $D_{\alpha i}^*$ is the effective molecular diffusion coefficient for each component in each phase [L^2/T], θ_α is the porosity filled by each phase [L^3/L^3], $D_{\alpha i}$ is the component diffusion coefficient at each phase [L^2/T]. Air diffusion coefficients for organic compounds are much larger than aqueous diffusion coefficients. Therefore, diffusion is generally more significant in gas transport than in ground water systems. The free air diffusion coefficient is temperature dependent. However, this phenomenon is usually neglected since it was observed that a 10 °C increase in the temperature of the unsaturated zone results in a 6% increase of the diffusion coefficient (Conant et al., 1996).

Many investigators have considered vapor transport in the gas phase and water phases, since the NAPL phase is immobile in the unsaturated zone (Sleep and Sykes, 1989). The interphase mass transfer terms in the water transport equation represent vapor-water partitioning, desorption from the solid phase, and dissolution from the NAPL phase. The interphase mass transfer terms in the gas/vapor transport equation represent vapor-water partitioning and volatilization from the NAPL phase. The transport equations for the vapor and water phases are linked by the vapor-water partitioning terms. In many instances, the reaction term is neglected in order to assume the worst case condition, that is, no biodegradation or transformation is assumed to occur. Some investigators have considered transport in the gas phase only assuming that soil moisture is usually below or at residual saturation, and may not be affected by the mobile vapor phase in the unsaturated zone.

9.8.4 Equilibrium Partitioning

Equilibrium partitioning between phases is in many cases a valid assumption. The equilibrium form is valid in diffusion-dominated or weakly advective environments. In these cases, it is assumed that chemical equilibrium exists between the contaminant concentrations in the different phases, and that interphase mass transfer is not rate-limited, that is phase transfer is instantaneous. The linear relationships between contaminant concentrations in different phases allow for expressing the advection-dispersion equation in terms of an individual phase concentration (Rathfelder et al., 1991). Although linear isotherm equations are usually satisfactory for describing water-soil equilibrium, nonlinear isotherms can better represent many organic and inorganic chemicals (Brusseau, 1994). The transport equations are summed over all phases, eliminating all interphase terms and a retardation coefficient determines the delay in vapor movement due to phase partitioning or sorption processes.

9.8.5 Non-Equilibrium Partitioning

Under strongly advective conditions, such as in SVE systems, equilibrium partitioning is not always suitable since it does not reproduce the tailing phenomenon that is observed in experimental studies (Armstrong et al., 1994). Tailing occurs when venting systems are restarted after shutdown, and has been attributed to the rate-limited interphase mass transfer processes. Moreover, equilibrium partitioning may dominate while contaminants are present in a NAPL form, but not for dilute solutions. Following removal of NAPL, VOC transfer to the gas phase occurs by desorption from the solid phase into the pore water, then through volatilization from pore water into the gas phase. Rate limited mass transfer controls these stages (Rathfelder et al., 1995). Rate limiting processes may be generated by: (1) rate limited mass transport between phases including film transfer limitations and intraaggregate diffusional processes (Brusseau, 1991; Gierke et al., 1990); (2) physical by passing of the contaminated region due to low permeability; (3) aquifer heterogeneity (Ho and Udell, 1992); (4) non-equilibrium adsorption/desorption (Brusseau, 1991).

Mass transfer processes at the interface of two adjacent phases may be visualized as a series of steps: (1) advection/diffusion in the bulk phase of one fluid towards the interface,

(2) accumulation, advection/diffusion, reaction, and sorption/desorption at the interface, (3) advection/diffusion away from the interface in the bulk phase of the other fluid (Powers et al., 1991). Mass transfer limited processes are modeled by incorporating first-order kinetic expressions into the interphase terms of the transport equation, whereby the mass transfer driving force is proportional to the difference between equilibrium and actual concentrations.

9.9 VADOSE ZONE FLOW AND TRANSPORT MODELS

Mathematical models have become an important tool in predicting vapor excursion distances and directions which help in evaluating vapor control alternatives. A vapor transport model can greatly assist in the correlation of vapor phase to ground water aqueous phase concentrations, in designing and evaluating the performance of SVE systems, and in evaluating the long term hazards associated with the problem and the system response to alternative remedial measures (Metcalfe and Farquhar, 1987, Benson et al., 1993, Jordan et al., 1995, Rathfelder et al., 1995). A number of mathematical models have been presented in the literature for the description of multiphase flow and transport in the vadose zone. These vary greatly in level of complexity and in the processes they describe (Rathfelder et al., 1995).

9.9.1 Types of Models

Screening models are rather simple and require limited site data; thus, they can be used to make preliminary determinations of the extent of contamination and the feasibility of SVE systems as a method of remediation at contaminated sites. Screening models such as Hypervent (Johnson, 1991) can aid in determining site permeability, extraction well radius of influence and flow rate and mass removals using analytical, semi-analytical or numerical solutions that may be subject to fairly limiting assumptions such as a homogeneous subsurface and a single extraction well. The initial determination of whether SVE is potentially feasible for a site should be with a screening tool.

Numerical air flow models can accomodate complex geologic and boundary conditions. They can allow representation of two and three dimensions in space rather than the 1-D axisymmetric domain represented by most screening tools. For more detailed analysis of contaminant migration and design of SVE systems, models such as AIRFLOW/ SVE (see Table 9.3) may provide quantitative flow analysis of soil gas pressure, flow rates, extraction well placement, extraction rates and air flow patterns.

A more accurate description of vapor movement may also be provided by vapor flow and transport models (compositional models) such as VENT3D (Benson et al., 1993; Benson, 1994), which can simulate the physical and chemical processes that govern vapor movement in the subsurface. The advantage of using these models is that they can estimate the air flow regime and the movement or removal of contaminants by SVE. They may also be used to design and evaluate the effectiveness of SVE systems, and to estimate contaminant removals and the effect of mass transfer limitations and soil heterogeneities on system

TABLE 9.3   Selected Models for Unsaturated Zone Analysis

Model Name	Model Description	Model Processes
SCREENING MODELS		
HyperVentilate (1991) Paul C. Johnson. Available from EPA	A screening model that can be used to determine the potential feasibility of SVE for remediation at contaminated sites. The flow equation is solved analytically. The transient one-dimensional multicomponent contaminant transport equation is solved by finite difference.	Steady-state, radial, confined air flow to a vapor extraction well. Transient, mass balance approach, volatilization based on Raoult's Law.
BioSVE (1998) Scientific Software Group. Washington, D. C.	A screening model based on Johnson's model Hypervent (1991) that evaluates different remediation schemes such as SVE, Vacuum Enhanced Recovery and Bioventing. Models recovery versus time of up to 250 components partitioned between water, vapor, NAPL and soil.	Equilibrium partitioning between phases is assumed. Nonequilibrium partitioning may be incorporated using an efficiency factor. Oxygen limited biodegradation based on instantaneous reaction. Kinetics effects handled using a bio-efficiency factor. Can simulate recovery of the free floating product along with bioventing the unsaturated zone.
AIR FLOW MODELS		
MODAIR (1996) P3DAIR (1989) Guo Zheng Scientific Software Group, Washington , D. C.	MODAIR simulates airflow based on MODFLOW, the groundwater code. P3DAIR simulates the advective movement of vapors in the unsaturated zone. It is a particle tracking program for calculating air flow paths and travel times. The two models are used together for SVE system design.	Air flow and pressure calculations are computed by MODAIR. Vapor extraction wells can be specified as pressure controlled or volumetric rate controlled. P3DAIR calculates the travel times and pathlines for each particle along the x,y, and z coordinates and initial and final positions of particles captured by sources/sinks. It can be used in 2-D or 3-D, steady-state or transient.
MULTIPHASE MODELS		
T2VOC (1995) R. W. Falta Karsten Pruess Stefan Finsterle Alfredo Battistelli	Three-dimensional, finite difference model for simulating flow and transport of organic contaminants in non-isothermal, heterogeneous, multi-phase systems.	Flow and transport of air, water and a VOC are simulated. Interphase mass transfer include evaporation and boiling of NAPL, dissolution of NAPL into the aqueous phase, condensation of VOC into the NAPL, equilibrium partitioning between the gas, aqueous, and NAPL phases, evaporation and boiling of the aqueous phase, and condensation of water vapor from the gas phase. Accounts for heat transfer due to conduction, multiphase convection, and gaseous diffusion.
Bioventing (1997) Environmental Systems and Technologies, Inc. Blacksburg, VA.	Finite difference, one dimensional, multiphase, multicomponent model for evaluation of design options for air-based in situ remedial technologies.	Air flow rates are calculated. Contaminant composition and recovery versus time is calculated. The model considers leakage from the ground surface, equilibrium partitioning, oxygen-limited biodecay, air turnover rates and their effect on recovery. The model computes costs for design options.

TABLE 9.3 Selected Models for Unsaturated Zone Analysis (Continued)

Model Name	Model Description	Model Processes
FLOW AND TRANSPORT MODELS IN UNSATURATED/SATURATED ZONE		
FEMWATER/ FECWATER (1987) Yeh, G. T. Ward, D. S.	Two-dimensional finite element model to simulate transient cross-sectional flow in saturated / un-saturated, anisotropic, heterogeneous porous media	Capillary action, infiltration, ponding
VAM3D (1988) Huyakorn, P. S.	Three-dimensional finite element model that simulates flow and transport in variably saturated porous media	Advection, dispersion, adsorption and degradation
Chemflo (1989) Nofziger, D. L. Scientific Software Group, Washington, D. C.	One-dimensional, finite difference model that simulates the movement of water and chemicals in unsaturated soils.	Water movement is modeled using Richard's equation, and contaminant transport using the convection-dispersion equation. Partitioning is instantaneous and reversible.
AIRFLOW/SVE (1993) Waterloo Hydrogeologic Software, Ontario, Canada.	Three-phase, finite difference model for simulating vapor flow and transport of multicomponent mixtures in heterogeneous, anisotropic soils.	Steady-state, radial, symmetric vapor flow and transport towards an extraction well Accounts for depletion of NAPL residuals, lenses or pools. Allows for equilibrium and non-equilibrium partitioning. Different types of sorption isotherms are considered.
VENT3D (1994) David Benson	Three-dimensional, finite difference model of vapor transport and phase distribution of multiple compounds.	Flow and transport of multicomponent mixtures in the vapor phase are simulated. Equilibrium partitioning between phases is assumed.
3DFEMFAT (1998) Scientific Software Group, Washington, D. C.	Three-dimensional, finite element model for flow and transport through saturated/unsaturated, heterogeneous, anisotropic media.	Can simulate infiltration, wellhead protection, agricultural pesticides, sanitary landfills, radionuclide and hazardous waste disposal sites, density induced flow and transport
BIOF&T 3-D (1998) Scientific Software Group, Washington, D. C.	Models flow and transport and biodegradation in the saturated/unsaturated zone in 2-D or 3-D, in heterogeneous, anisotropic media.	Models convection, dispersion, diffusion, desorption, and microbial processes based on oxygen-limited, anaerobic, first-order, or Monod biodegradation kinetics as well as anaerobic or first order sequential degradation involving multiple daughter species.
SESOIL (1998) M. Bonazountas Scientific Software Group, Washington, D. C.	Seasonal compartment model which simulates long-term pollutant fate and migration in the unsaturated soil zone.	Computes pollutant masses in water, soil and air phases. Pollutant migration to ground water, and volatilization to ground surface. Pollutant migration due to surface runoff and erosion.

performance. They can also predict post remedial soil concentrations to determine if cleanup goals were met. Some of the compositional models simulate multicomponent mixtures (such as gasoline), which is useful in predicting which components remain in the system after SVE has been applied to the site. Some models assume equilibrium partitioning between the different phases, while others accommodate mass transfer limitations that can hinder SVE performance.

Vapor migration can also be characterized by multiphase flow and transport models such as T2VOC (Falta et al., 1995; McRay and Falta, 1997), which describe the simultaneous flow and transport of contaminants in the different phases (vapor, water, NAPL, and sorbed phases)). These models demand a high degree of computing power and data input. Gathering the data required by these models is usually difficult, but, these models can be useful in describing the migration of different chemical species in complex settings.

Model selection is usually influenced by site data availability. For small leaking underground storage tanks where little data is available, a screening or an air flow model may prove useful. For a larger site with extensive data available from site characterization, a more complex, compositional or multiphase model may be used. Table 9.3 provides a listing of some of the available flow and transport models for the unsaturated/saturated zones.

9.9.2 Description of a Screening Model: Hypervent

Johnson et al. (1988, 1990) have exploited the analogy to ground water flow in developing simple screening models to describe the distribution in pressure around venting wells. Based on the assumption that vapor behaves as an ideal gas, the governing equation for vapor flow for conditions of radial flow, the governing equation can be written as follows:

$$\frac{1}{r}\frac{\partial}{\partial r}\left(r\frac{\partial P'}{\partial r}\right) = \left(\frac{\theta_a \mu}{k P_{atm}}\right)\frac{\partial P'}{\partial t} \qquad (9.31)$$

where P' is the deviation of pressure from the reference pressure P_{atm}, k is soil permeability, μ is the vapor viscosity, θ_a is vapor filled porosity, and t is time. When Eq. (9.31) is solved with appropriate boundary conditions, with b as the thickness of the unconfined zone and r as the radial distance from the well to the point of interest,

$$P' = \frac{Q}{4\pi b(k/\mu)} W(u) \text{ where } u = r^2 \theta_a \mu / 4k P_{atm} t \qquad (9.32)$$

and $W(u)$ is the well function of u, which is a commonly tabulated function.

Calculations with Eq. (9.32) show that for sandy soils ($10 < k < 100$ darcys), the pressure distribution approximates a steady state in one to seven days. Thus, it is appropriate to model pressure distributions using a steady state solution to the governing flow equation. For the following set of boundary conditions: $P = P_w$ at $r = R_w$ and $P = P_{atm}$ at $r = R_I$, where

P_w is the pressure at the well with radius R_w and P_{atm} is the ambient pressure at the radius of influence R_I.

Johnson et al. (1988) provide the following solution to the steady-state equation for radial flow

$$P^2(r) - P_w^2 = \left(P_{atm}^2 - P_w^2\right) \frac{\ln(r/R_w)}{\ln(R_I/R_w)}$$ (9.33)

As Johnson et al. (1988) point out, while not explicitly represented in Eq. (9.33), the properties of the soil do influence the steady-state pressure distribution because the radius of influence (R_I) does vary as a function of permeability and layering. Johnson et al. (1988) develop corresponding solutions for radial darcy velocity and volumetric flow rate for this steady-state case. The latter of these solutions provides a useful way to determine what the theoretical maximum air flow is to a vapor extraction well and is written

$$Q = H\pi \frac{k}{\mu} P_w \frac{[1 - (P_{atm}/P_w)^2]}{\ln(R_w/R_I)}$$ (9.34)

where H is the total length of the screen. Just as is the case with well hydraulics, these kinds of analytical equations form the basis not only for predictive analysis, but also for well testing methods for permeability estimations.

Analytical solutions are most useful for screening purposes and for exploring the relationships among variables; however, their practical applicability is limited to simple problems. An alternative way of solving differential equations like Eq. (9.31) is with powerful numerical models. Numerical models are effective in modeling complicated problems of the type commonly encountered in practice.

By analogy with problems involving ground water flow to wells, the general pattern of air circulation will be influenced by features of the fluid being circulated, the geologic system and the well system used to withdraw and inject air. The permeability is the most important of all the parameters that influence flow. Ultimately, it is the permeability that determines the efficacy of vapor extraction because flow rates at steady state for a well under a specified vacuum are a direct function of permeability. Vapor extraction, to be practically useful, requires some minimal rate of air circulation, which may not be feasible in some low permeability units.

From an analytical model, Johnson et al. (1990) developed a series of relationships between permeability and flow rate (Figure 9.11). For a given vacuum in the extraction well, the steady-state rate of air flow is a linear function of permeability (log scales). An increase in the vacuum (smaller P_w) at a given permeability will increase the air flow. However, the maximum change that might be expected is about an order of magnitude in flow rate. It is well known from ground water flow theory that variability in permeability plays an important role in controlling the pattern of flow. This is also the case for patterns of air circula-

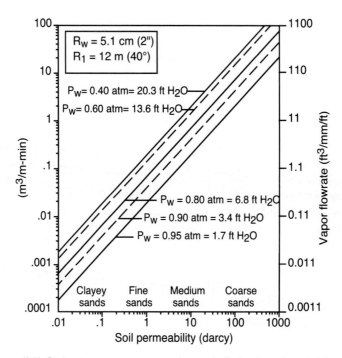

(ft H2O) denote vacuums expressed as equivalent water column heights

Figure 9.11 Predicted steady-state rates of air flow per unit length of well screen from a vapor extraction well for a range of permeabilities and applied vacuums (Pw). Source: Johnson et al., 1990.

tion. Most circulation will occur through the most permeable zones for a layered system, and this can have a profound effect on the rate and efficiency of cleanup schemes.

Features of the design of the system as a whole also control air circulation. The most important factors in this respect include: (1) the flow rates in the injection/extraction wells,(2) the types and locations of wells in a multiwell system, and (3) the presence of a surface seal. For a single vacuum well, Figure 9.11 illustrates how reducing P_w increases the air withdrawal rate. Similarly, adding more wells to the system will also do the same. Furthermore, the pattern of air circulation can be controlled by the types and locations of the wells. Hypervent (Johnson, 1991) is a screening tool used to determine the potential feasibility of SVE as a remedial option at contaminated sites. It is available free of charge from USEPA and can run on PCs and Apple Macintosh. The model runs in hypertext framework, which consists of several screens that are linked to other screens that provide information, text, files, pictures or calculation sheets. Some of the screens contain tips and diagrams on SVE operation and design, while others prompt the user for input and analytical calculations. The model is based on the Johnson et al. (1990), article.

Vapor Concentrations and Removal Rates. A simplistic equilibrium-based model is used to assess how effective soil venting may be used for remediating a site with a spill of given composition. The total mole balance on each component i is given by:

$$M_i = \frac{z_i P \theta_a V}{RT} + x_i M_{HC} + y_i M_{H_2O} + k_i y_i \frac{M_{soil}}{M_{w,H_2O}} \tag{9.35}$$

where x_i is the mole fraction of component i in free liquid phase, z_i is the mole fraction of component i, in the vapor phase, P is the total vapor pressure [atm], V is the volume of contaminated soil (cm^3), R is the universal gas constant [82.1 cm^3/mole-K], T is the absolute temperature in soil [K], M_{HC} is the total moles in free liquid phase, M_{H_2O} is the total moles in soil moisture phase, y_i is the mole fraction of i dissolved in soil moisture, k_i is the sorption coefficient for i, M_{soil} is the total mass of contaminated soil [g], and M_{w,H_2O} is the molecular weight of H$_2$O.

The vapor concentrations are calculated using Raoult's Law, or linear partitioning depending on the phases present:

$$\text{Raoult's Law: } C_i^a = \frac{x_i P_i^v MW_i}{RT} \tag{9.36}$$

$$\text{Linear Partitioning: } C_i^a = \frac{HC_{i,soil}}{\left[\left(\dfrac{H\theta_a}{\rho_{soil}} + \theta + k_i\right)\right]} \tag{9.37}$$

where C_i^a is the concentration in the vapor phase [g/cm^3], P_i^v is the component vapor pressure [g/cm-s^2], MW_i is the component molecular weight [g/mole], H is Henry's Law constant (dimensionless), $C_{i,soil}$ is the component concentration in soil [g/g], θ is the moisture content [cm^3/g], and ρ_{soil} is the soil density [cm^3/g].

Removal rates are calculated by QC_i^a, and the volume of vapor required to achieve desired cleanup is calculated by $QT/$(Spill mass). The minimum number of extraction wells required is calculated by:

$$\frac{\{\text{Volume of required vapor}\} \bullet \{\text{Spill mass}\}}{\{\text{Desired cleanup time}\} \bullet Q}$$

Hypervent will not completely design an SVE system, give the length of required operation, or predict the behavior of the system. Hypervent data requirements include soil permeability, extraction well radius, screened interval, well radius, radius of influence, contaminant composition other than gasoline, contaminant mass, contaminant concentration, components' vapor pressure, components' molecular weights, desired cleanup time, air pumping test data, and radius of contaminated zone. Hypervent output provides extraction well flowrates, contaminant removal rates, soil permeability from pumping tests, if desired, and an optimum number of extraction wells.

Example 9.3   VAPOR EXTRACTION COMPUTATIONS

Johnson et al. (1988) examined mass removals (Figure 9.12) for a hypothetical case in which 400 gal (approximately 1500 L) of gasoline were spilled into 1412 ft³ of soil at a 10% moisture content. This spill provides a residual saturation of 2% gasoline by dry weight or 20,000 ppm total petroleum content. Other conditions specified include: a soil bulk density of 1.5 gm/cm³, a porosity of 0.40, an organic carbon fraction (f_{oc}) of 0.01, an air flow rate of 20 ft³/min, a soil temperature of 60 °F, and a relative humidity for the incoming air of 100%. The problem assumes that 25% of the circulating air passes through the spill. Thus, component concentrations in the vapor extraction well will be at equilibrium for an air flow of 5 ft³/m, which is the value used in subsequent calculations. Also required for the calculation is information about the compounds found in gasoline, their molecular weights and mass fractions, and their physical properties (see Johnson et al., 1988).

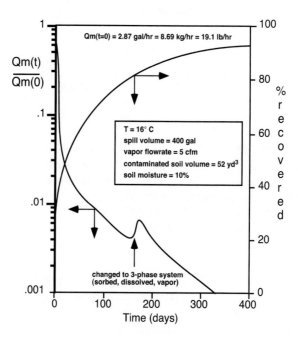

Figure 9.12 Predicted mass loss rates for a hypothetical venting operation. Source: Johnson et al., 1990.

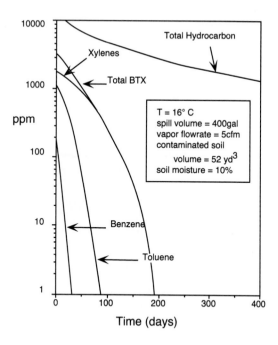

Figure 9.13 Predicted soil concentrations of hydrocarbons for a hypothetical venting operation. Source: Johnson et al., 1990.

The total rate of mass loss from vapor extraction for the entire gasoline mixtures is the sum of the mass loss rates C_iQ for the compounds. The total mass loss rate as a ratio of the initial mass loss rate is plotted versus time in Figure 9.12. Also depicted in the figure is the cumulative percentage of the initial spill recovered as a function of time. The example clearly shows how the rate of mass loss decreases with time as the most volatile components are removed from the mixture. Figure 9.13 displays the time variation in the soil concentrations of a number of the most volatile compounds in gasoline. The pattern of removal rates (i.e., benzene > toluene > xylenes) is explained by the respective vapor pressures (i.e., 0.10 > 0.029 > 0.0066 to 0.0088 atm). At the end of 400 days, the residual product consists mainly of the larger molecular weight compounds in gasoline having vapor pressures in general less than 0.005 atm. Thus, about 25 days are required to recover half of the original spill mass, but about 400 days are required to collect 90%.

9.9.3 Description of a Flow and Transport Model: VENT3D

VENT3D, is a 3-D, finite-difference code for vapor flow and transport (Benson, 1994; Benson et al., 1993). VENT3D solves the 3-D vapor flow and transport equation for a multicomponent mixture, and describes the movement of compounds in the vapor phase and the

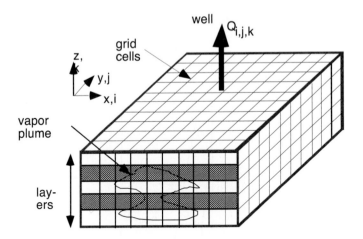

Figure 9.14 Schematic of VENT3D structure.

phase distribution of each compound in the other three phases (NAPL phase, dissolved phase, and sorbed phase). The equilibrium four-phase distribution of each compound in the mixture is solved between vapor phase moving periods. The model domain is divided into an orthogonal grid in the x and y plane, and into several layers in the z direction. Thus, the domain is divided into blocks, each block may be given unique properties such as permeability or contaminant concentrations. Extraction and injection wells can be simulated. Figure 9.14 shows a schematic diagram of the code structure. The code was compiled for a Sun Sparc Workstation.

The gas phase is the only moving phase, and gas transport occurs due to diffusion in the gas phase and advection in case of forced venting, where molecular diffusion is calculated as a function of the air diffusion coefficient and air saturation. The model does not account for interphase mass transfer. Vapor pressure is entered at 20 °C and is calculated by the model at higher and lower temperature. The model assumptions are as follows:

- equilibrium partitioning between the gas phase and all other phases (dissolved, sorbed, and NAPL)
- the system is isothermal
- constant gas viscosity
- linear sorption
- air is incompressible
- elevation head is ignored compared to pressure head

A detailed example of vapor extraction modeling using VENT 3D is presented in Chapter 13.

Flow Algorithm. Elevation head is ignored compared to pressure head in the formulation of soil gas head. Hence, the 3-D steady-state gas flow equation based on the principle of mass conservation is as follows:

$$\frac{\partial}{\partial x}\left(k_x \frac{\partial P^2}{\partial x}\right) + \frac{\partial}{\partial y}\left(k_y \frac{\partial P^2}{\partial y}\right) + \frac{\partial}{\partial z}\left(k_z \frac{\partial P^2}{\partial z}\right) = \frac{2\mu WRT}{dx \cdot dy \cdot dz \cdot MW} \tag{9.38}$$

where k is the soil vapor permeability tensor [L^2], P is the soil-gas pressure [$ML^{-1}T^{-2}$], μ is the soil-gas viscosity [$ML^{-1}T^{-1}$], W is the vapor mass flux source/sink [MT^{-1}], R is the universal gas constant [$ML^2T^{-2}mole^{-1}K^{-1}$], T is the temperature [K], and MW is the molecular weight of soil-gas [$M \cdot mole^{-1}$].

To solve the flow equation, an orthogonal grid is used to discretize the model domain and boundary conditions should be specified. The bottom layer is always assumed as a no-flow boundary, the top layer is specified by the user as a no-flow boundary (sealed surface) or an open to the atmosphere boundary. The lateral boundary can also be open or closed to the surrounding.

The flow equation is solved by finite differences for pressures in between gridlines. The effective permeability,which is the permeability of the porous medium to each fluid, is calculated as a function of the relative saturation of this fluid using the Brooks and Corey (1964) relationship. Because the volumes of liquid contaminant and soil moisture in the pores are changing all the time during a simulation, the effective permeability should be recalculated.

$$k = k^* \left(\frac{\theta_a}{n}\right)^3 \tag{9.39}$$

where k^* is the intrinsic permeability of the porous media [L^2], θ_a is the air filled porosity [dimensionless], and n is the porosity [dimensionless]. With the Brooks and Corey expression the permeability field can be re-calculated at each time step to reflect the ongoing depletion of pore fluids. The time step is computed internally by the model. Hence, the gas pressure is calculated in between blocks, and the interblock gas flow v is also determined by Darcy's law in the x,y,z directions as follows:

$$v_x = \frac{k_x}{\mu\theta_a}\frac{\partial P_x}{\partial x}, v_y = \frac{k_y}{\mu\theta_a}\frac{\partial P_y}{\partial y}, v_z = \frac{k_z}{\mu\theta_a}\frac{\partial P_z}{\partial z} \tag{9.40}$$

Transport Algorithm. The model describes the movement of compounds in the vapor phase and their phase distribution. The flux of each chemical compound in the vapor phase is composed of the advective motion of soil gas and the dispersive flux of that compound. The change in molar concentration within the differential element with respect to time is the difference between the sum of directional fluxes and a chemical source/sink as represented by Eq. (9.41) (Benson, 1994). The dispersive flux consists of the diffusive flux due to molecular diffusion and the velocity dependent hydrodynamic dispersion as shown in Eq. (9.42).

$$\frac{\partial M_i}{\partial t} + F_i = \nabla \cdot \left[D_i \nabla(C_i) - \nabla(qC_i) \right] \tag{9.41}$$

where M_i is the total molar concentration of each compound in mixture [mole/L^3], C_i is the molar concentration of each compound [mole/L^3], q is the vapor discharge vector [L/T], F_i is the volumetric molar loss/addition rate of compound [mole·L^{-3}T^{-1}], and D_i is the dispersion tensor [L^2/T], as follows:

$$D_i = D_m I + \alpha_{xyz} \frac{q_x q_y}{\theta_a \overline{q}} \tag{9.42}$$

where D_m is the molecular diffusion coefficient [L^2/T], I is the identity vector, α_{xyz} is the vapor dispersivity [L], q_x, q_y are the vapor flows in x and y directions [L/T], and $\overline{q}$ is the magnitude of the discharge vector [L/T]. The molecular diffusion is a function of air diffusion coefficients and is determined by the Millington and Quirk expression represented by Eq. (9.43). The molecular diffusion is a function of air filled porosity, which changes with movement of compounds and fluid saturation, as follows:

$$D_m = D_0 \frac{\theta_a^{10/3}}{n^2} \tag{9.43}$$

where D_0 is the free air diffusion coefficient [L^2/T], θ_a is the air-filled porosity, and n is the total porosity.

Knowing the flows between the blocks, the 3-D advection-dispersion equation is solved by finite-difference for each chemical compound. The advective transport term is solved by three different algorithms: central weighted scheme if diffusive flux is larger than advective flux; single-point upwind if advective flux is larger than diffusive flux; third order, with variable weighting of gradients, if dispersive flux is high. The last algorithm alleviates oscillation and numerical dispersion with sharp fronts. After the chemical compounds have been moved by the appropriate advective algorithm, each node carries a new concentration of each compound. The dispersive term in Eq. (9.42) is evaluated using standard explicit finite-differences.

In case of a soil contaminated with a number of chemical compounds, the contaminants are present in the gas phase, dissolved in the soil moisture, sorbed to the soil, and forming a separate nonaqueous phase. Equilibrium partitioning is assumed between the different phases for each compound. As vapors migrate between time steps, the vapor composition and concentrations will change and nonequilibrium will occur between the existing phases. The total molar concentration of each compound is expressed as a function of the vapor concentration and the sum of the molar concentrations in the four phases as shown in Eq. (9.44). The four terms on the right-hand side of Eq. (9.44) represent the contribution to the total soil contamination of the vapor phase, the NAPL phase, the dissolved phase and the sorbed phase respectively. When a separate phase is present, the sum of the mole fractions of the non-aqueous phase liquid has to be equal to 1.0 as represented by Eq. (9.45). Between time steps, moles of each compound are moved into and out of each finite-difference cell. By solving Eq. (9.44) and Eq. (9.45) iteratively, equilibrium is re-calculated at the end of each time step.

$$M_i = C_i \left[\theta_a + \frac{M_{HC}RT}{P_i^v} + \frac{M_{H_2O}RT}{\alpha_i P_i^v} + \frac{K_d^i \rho RT \delta_{H_2O}}{\alpha_i P_i^v MW_{H_2O}} \right] \tag{9.44}$$

subject to

$$\sum_{i=1}^{\#compounds} \frac{C_i RT}{P_i^v} = 1 \tag{9.45}$$

where M_{HC} is the molar concentration of NAPL phase in soil [mole/L^3], P_i^V is the compound vapor pressure [atm], M_{H_2O} is the molar concentration of dissolved phase [mole/L^3], γ_i is the activity coefficient of compound in water [dimensionless], K_d^i is the distribution coefficient of compound [dimensionless], ρ is the soil density [M/L^3], MW_{H_2O} is the molecular weight of water [18 gm/mole], and δ_{H_2O} is the soil moisture flag = 1 if present, 0 if not present.

To solve the equilibrium Eq. (9.44), it is necessary to estimate activity coefficients and component vapor pressures at the temperature of interest. Activity coefficients are obtained using Eq. (9.46):

$$\gamma_i = \frac{MC_{H_2O} \times MW_i}{S_i} \tag{9.46}$$

where MC_{H_2O} is the molar concentration of water (55.5 mole/L^3), MW_i is the molecular weight of compound i (M/mole), and S_i is the pure component solubility of compound i (M/L^3). For gases the activity is calculated by multiplying Eq. (9.46) by [1 atm / P^v].

Vapor pressures at temperatures of interest are calculated using the Claussius-Clapyron equation.

$$P^v = P^v_{20\hat{I}C} \exp\left[\frac{T_b \cdot 20\hat{I}C}{(T_b - 20\hat{I}C)}\left(\frac{1}{T} - \frac{1}{20\hat{I}C}\right)\ln\left(\frac{P^v_{20\hat{I}C}}{1\ atm}\right)\right] \qquad (9.47)$$

where $P^v_{20°C}$ is the vapor pressure of compound at 20 °C [atm], T_b is the boiling point of compound [°C], and T is the temperature of interest [°C].

VENT3D assumes a linear sorption isotherm between the dissolved and sorbed phases.

$$K_d^i = 0.63 K_{ow}^i f_{oc} \qquad (9.48)$$

where K_{ow}^i is the octanol/water partition coefficient of compound [M/M], and f_{oc} is the fraction of organic carbon [M/M].

Mass Balance Calculations. The mass of each contaminant compound remaining within the model has the potential of changing with every time step. The mass balance within the program is a measure of the accuracy of the simulation. The model computes an internal time step size to ensure stability and low mass balance errors. Three different methods are used to calculate the time step size: the dispersion rate, the pumping rates, and the soil gas velocity. The model selects the smallest time step size of the three at each time step. Mass balance errors are computed at the end of each time step by comparing the mass removed, the mass remaining, and the initial mass. The mass balance equations are taken from Konikow and Bredehoeft (1978). A detailed application of VENT3D to a field site at Hill AFB in Utah is shown in Section 13.9.3.

Data Requirement. Parameters common to domain: contaminant composition, fraction of organic carbon, bulk density, and grid dimensions. Parameters common to each grid block: permeability, contaminant concentration, extraction/injection rate, and injected air humidity. Parameters common to each layer: permeability anisotropy, layer depth, porosity, and moisture content. Boundary conditions: ground surface open or closed to atmosphere; lateral boundaries at atmospheric pressure, no flux or known flux; bottom surface represents water table, i.e., no flux.

Model Output. Parameters common to domain: initial moles, pumped moles, domain loss moles, remaining moles for each compound, initial total mass, total pumped mass, mass lost from domain, remaining mass, and mass balance errors. Parameters common to each grid block: pressure, vacuum, horizontal and vertical air permeability, discharge, remaining total contaminant mass in soil, remaining mass for each compound in soil, remaining soil gas concentrations, and off-gas concentrations for each compound at extraction wells.

Example 9.4.   VAPOR EXTRACTION APPLICATION

An example of a VENT3D application to a contaminated site in California is presented by Jordan et al. (1995). The site is formed of different layers, a coarse sand layer at 10 to 30 ft below ground surface (BGS), a silt and clay rich layer at 30 to 40 ft BGS and a well sorted sand below the silty/clayey layer where a water table exists. The highest contamination was found just above the water table. During the field study, vapor was withdrawn from one well for 275 days, followed by withdrawal from other wells at different locations for 950 days. The site was modeled in two dimensions using VENT 3D. A plot of the measured soil vapor total petroleum hydrocarbon (TPH) concentrations and simulated concentrations are shown in Figure 9.15, and demonstrate the usefulness of the model.

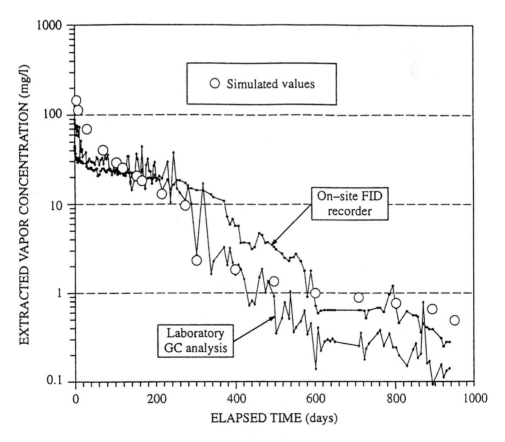

Figure 9.15 Simulated and measured decline of TPH concentrations in vapor extracted from the Costa Mesa sites. Measured values are represented by connected points. Simulated values are represented by large open circles.

SUMMARY

Flow and transport processes in the unsaturated zone are much more complex than in the saturated zone due to the effect of capillary forces, nonlinear soil characteristics, and the presence of four phases of interest: soil, water, air, and NAPL. Being bound at its top by the ground surface and below by ground water, the unsaturated zone serves as a conduit through which liquid and gaseous contaminants can reach the underlying aquifers and overlying ground surface. Contaminants in the residual phase can reach the water table by dissolution, infiltration, vapor migration, or water table fluctuation. Vapor flow to ground surface or basements of structures may occur by pressure and concentration gradients. Vapor transport is governed by diffusion, advection, dispersion, and reactions. A number of screening, compositional, and multiphase transport models have been developed to simulate processes in the unsaturated zone. Hypervent is an example of a screening model, and VENT3D is an example of a compositional model.

REFERENCES

Anderson, M. P., and W. W. Woesner, "Applied Ground Water Modeling: Simulation of Flow and Advective Transport." New York, Academic Press, 1992.

Armstrong, J. E., Frind, E. O., and R. D. McClellan, "Nonequilibrium Mass Transfer between the Vapor, Aqueous, and Solid Phases in the Unsaturated Soils during Vapor Extraction." *Water Resources Res.*, 30(2), 355-368, 1994.

Baehr, A. L., and C. J. Bruell, "Application of the Stefan-Maxwell Equations to Determine Limitations of Fick's Law when Modeling Organic Vapor Transport in Sand Columns" *Water Resources Res.*, 26(6), 1155-1163, 1990.

Bear, J., *Hydraulics of Ground water*, New York, McGraw Hill, 1979.

Bedient, P. B., and W. C. Huber, *Hydrology and Floodplain Analysis*, Reading, MA, Addison-Wesley, 1992.

Benson, D. A., Huntley, D., and P. C. Johnson, "Modeling Vapor Extraction and General Transport in the Presence of NAPL Mixtures and Nonideal Conditions" *Ground Water*, 31(3), 437-445, 1993.

Benson, D., "User's Manual to VENT3D: A Three-Dimensional Multi-Compound, Multi-Phase Partitioning Vapor Transport Model," 1994.

Brooks, R. H. and A. T. Corey, "Hydraulic Properties of Porous Media," *Hydrol. Pap. 3*, Colo. State Univ., Fort Collins, pp. 27, 1964.

Brusseau, M. L., "Transport of Organic Chemicals by Gas Advection in Structured or Heterogeneous Porous Media: Development of a Model and Application to Column Experiments," *Water Resources Res.*, 27(12), 3189-3199, 1991.

Brusseau, M. L., "Transport of Reactive Contaminants in Heterogeneous Porous Media," *Reviews of Geophysics*, 32(3), 285-313, 1994.

Carlisle, V. W., C. T. Hallmark, F. Sodek III, R. E. Caldwell, L. C. Hammond and V. E. Berkheiser, "Characterization Data For Selected Florida Soils," Soil Characterization Laboratory, Soil Science Department, Gainesville, University of Florida, 1981.

Clapp, R. B. and G. M. Hornberger, "Empirical Equations For Some Soil Hydraulic Properties," *Water Resources Res.*, Vol. 14, pp. 601-604, 1978.

Charbeneau, R. J., "Kinematic Models for Moisture and Solute Transport," *Water Resources Res.*, Vol. 20(6), pp. 699, 706, 1984.

Charbeneau, R. J., "Groundwater Hydraulics and Pollutant Transport," Course Notes, University of Texas, Austin, Texas, 1990.

Charbeneau, R. J., and D. E. Daniel, "Contaminant Transport in Unsaturated Flow," *Hand Book of Hydrology*, Chapter 15, D. R. Maidment, ed., New York, McGraw-Hill, 1993.

Chow, V. T., D. R. Maidment and L. W. Mays, *Applied Hydrology*, New York, McGraw-Hill, 1988.

Conant, B. H., Gillham, R. W., and C. A. Mendoza, "Vapor Transport of TCE in the Unsaturated Zone: Field and Numerical Modeling Investigations." *Water Resources Res.*, 32(1), 9-22, 1996.

Davidson, J. M., D. R. Nielsen and J. Biggar, "The Dependency of Soil Water Uptake and Release Upon the Applied Press Increment," *Soil Sci. Soc. Am. Proc.*, Vol. 30(3), pp. 298-304, 1966.

Enfield, C. G., D. M. Walters, J. T. Wilson and M. Piwoni, "Behavior of Organic Pollutants During Rapid Infiltration of Wastewater Into Soil: II. Mathematical Description of Transport and Transformation," submitted for publication, *Journal of Environmental Quality,* 1985.

Falta, R. W., K. Pruess, S. Finsterle, and A. Battistelli, "T2VOC User's Guide," Earth Sciences Dept., Clemson University; Earth Sciences Dept., University of California, Berkeley, 1995.

Falta, R. W., Javandel, I., Pruess, K., and P. A. Witherspoon, "Density-Driven Flow of Gas in the Unsaturated Zone due to the Evaporation of Volatile Organic Compounds." *Water Resources Res.*, 25(10), 2159-2169, 1989.

Fetter, C. W., *Contaminant Hydrogeology*, Upper Saddle River, NJ, Prentice Hall, 1999.

Freeze, R. A., "The Mechanism of Natural Groundwater recharge and Discharge: 1. One-dimensional, Vertical, Unsteady, Unsaturated Flow above a Recharging or Discharging Groundwater Flow System," *Water Resources Res.* 5:153-171, 1969.

Freeze, R. A., " Three-dimensional, Transient, Saturated-Unsaturated Flow in a Groundwater Basin," *Water Resources Res.* 7:347-366, 1971.

Freeze R. A.,and J. A. Cherry, *Groundwater*, Prentice Hall, Englewood Cliffs, NJ, 1979.

Gierke, J. S., Hutzler, N. J., and J. C. Crittenden, "Modeling the Movement of Volatile Organic Chemicals in Columns of Unsaturated Soil." *Water Resources Res.*, 26(7), 1529-1547.

Green, W. H. and G. A. Ampt, 1911, "Studies of Soil Physics, 1: The Flow of Air and Water Through Soils," *J. of Agriculture Science*, Vol. 4, No. 1, pp. 1-24.

Gupta, S. C. and W. E. Larson, 1979, "Estimating Soil Water Retention Characteristics from Particle Size Distribution, Organic Matter Percent, and Bulk Density," *Water Resources Res.*, vol. 15, pp. 1633-1635.

Guymon, Gary L., *Unsaturated Zone Hydrology,* Englewood Cliffs, NJ, Prentice Hall, 1994.

Hinchee, R. E., et al., "Underground Fuel Contamination, Investigation, and Remediation a Risk Assessment Approach to How Clean Is Clean," *Proceedings* Petroleum Hydrocarbons and Organic Chemicals in Ground Water, Dublin, OH, NWWA, pp. 539-563, 1986.

Ho, C. K., and K. S. Udell, "An Experimental Investigation of Air Venting of Volatile Liquid Hydrocarbon Mixtures from Homogeneous Porous Media." *Journal of Contaminant Hydrology*, 11, 291-316, 1992.

Hoag, G. H., and M. C. Marley, "Gasoline Residual Saturation in Unsaturated Uniform Aquifer Materials." *Environmental Engineering*, 112(3), 586-604, 1986.

Holtan, H. N., "A Concept for Infiltration Estimates in Watershed Engineering," *USDA Bull.*, 41-51, 1961.

Horton, R. E., "An Approach toward a Physical Interpretation of Infiltration Capacity," *Soil Science Society Amer. J.* 5:399-417, 1940.

"Approach toward a Physical Interpretation of Infiltration-Capacity," *Soil Sci, Soc. Am. J.*, vol. 5, pp. 399-417.

Johnson, P. C., Kemblowski, J. D., and J. D. Colthart, "Practical Screening Models for Soil Venting Applications." *Petroleum Hydrocarbons and Organic Chemicals in Ground Water*, Houston, Texas, 521-546, 1988.

Johnson, P. C., C. C. Stanley, M. W. Kemblowski, D. L. Byers, and J. D. Colthart, "A practical approach to the design, operation, and monitoring of in-situ soil-venting systems," *Ground Water Monitoring Review,* 10:2:159-178, 1990a.

Johnson, P. C., Hyper Ventilate User's Manual, Shell Oil Company, 1991.

Jordan, D. L., Mercer, J. W., and R. M. Cohen, "Review of Mathematical Modeling for Evaluating Soil Vapor Extraction Systems." *540/R-95/513*, National Risk Management Research Laboratory, Office of Research and Development, USEPA, 1995.

Jury, W. A., W. F. Spencer and W. J. Farmer, "Chapter 4: Chemical Transport Modeling: Current Approaches and Unresolved Problems," *Chemical Mobility and Reactivity in Soil Systems,* ASA, Madison, WI, pp. 49-64, 1983.

Klute, A., and C. Dirksen, "Hydraulic Conductivity and Diffusivity--Laboratory Methods," in A. Klute, ed., *Methods of Soil Analysis, Part I -- Physical and Mineralogical Methods*, American Society of Agronomy Monograph 9, 2d ed., pp. 687-734, 1986.

Konikow, L. F., and T. D. Bredehoeft, "Computer Model of Two-Dimensional Solute Transport and Dispersion in Ground Water," Techniques of Water Resources Investigations of the United States Geological Survey, 90, 1978.

Marley, M. C. and G. E. Hoag, Induced soil venting for the recovery/restoration of gasoline hydrocarbons in the vadose zone. Petroleum Hydrocarbons and Organic Chemicals in Ground Water--Prevention, Detection and Restoration, NWWA, Dublin, OH, pp. 473-503, 1984.

Massmann, J. W., "Applying Ground Water Flow Models in Vapor Extraction System Design," *Journal of Environmental Engineering*, 115(1), 129-149, 1989.

Massmann, J., and D. F. Farrier, "Effects of Atmospheric Pressures on Gas Transport in the Vadose Zone." *Water Resources Res.*, 28(3), 777-791, 1992.

McCray, J. E., and R. W. Falta, "Numerical Simulation of Air Sparging for Remediation of NAPL Contamination," *Ground Water*, 35(1), 99-110, 1997.

McCarthy, K. A., and R. L. Johnson, "Transport of Volatile Organic Compounds Across the Capillary Fringe," *Water Resources Res.,* 29(6), 1675-1683, 1993.

Mein, R. G. and C. L. Larson, "Modeling Infiltration During a Steady Rain," *Water Resources Res.*, Vol. 9, No. 2, pp. 384-394, 1973.

Mendoza, C., A., and E. O. Frind, "Advective-Dispersive Transport of Dense Organic Vapors in the Unsaturated Zone: 1. Model Development." *Water Resources Res.*, 26(3), 379-387, 1990a.

Mendoza, C. A., and E. O. Frind, "Advective-Dispersive Transport of Dense Organic Vapors in the Unsaturated Zone: 2. Sensitivity Analysis." *Water Resources Res.*, 26(3), 388-398, 1990b.

Metcalfe, D. E., and G. J. Farquhar, "Modeling Gas Migration through Unsaturated Soils from Waste Disposal Sites," *Water Air and Soil Pollution,* 32, 247-259, 1987.

Millington R. J., and J. M. Quirk, "Permeability of Porous Media," *Trans Faraday Soc.* 57:1200-1207, 1961.

Neuman, S. P., "Saturated-Unsaturated Seepage by Finite Elements," *J. Hydraul. Eng.*, Vol. 99 (HY12), pp. 2233-2251, 1986.

Nielsen, D. R., M. Th. van Genuchten, and J. W. Biggar, "Water Flow and Solute Transport Processes in the Unsaturated Zone," *Water Resour. Res.*, vol. 22, no. 9, pp. 89S-108S, 1986.

Nofziger, D. L., J. R. Williams and T. E. Short, "Interactive Simulation of the Fate of Hazardous Chemicals During Land Treatment of Oily Wastes," EPA/600/8-88/001, 1988.

Nofziger D. L., K. Rajender, S. K. Nayudu and P. Su, "Chemflo: One-Dimensional Water and Chemical Movement in Unsaturated Soils," EPA/600/8-89/076, 1989.

Olson, R. S., and D. E. Daniel, "Measurement of Hydraulic Conductivity of Fine-grained Soils," in T. F. Zimmie and C. O. Riggs, eds., *Permeability and Groundwater Contaminant Transport*, STP 746, Philadelphia, American Society of Testing and Materials, pp. 18-64, 1981.

Panday, S. and M. T. Corapcioglu, "Reservoir Transport Equations by Compositional Approach," *Trans. Porous Media,* Vol. 4, pp. 369-393, 1989.

Pankow, J. F. and J. A. Cherry, Dense Chlorinated Solvents and Other DNAPLS in Ground Water: History, Behavior, and Remediation, Portland, Oregon, Waterloo Press, 1996.

Philip, J. R. and D. A. de Vries, "Moisture Movement in Porous Media Under Temperature Gradients," *Eos Trans,* AGU, Vol. 38(2), pp. 222-232, 1957.

Powers, S. E., C. O. Loureiro, L. M. Abriola, and W. J. Weber, "Theoretical Study of the Significance of Nonequilibrium Dissolution of Nonaqueous Phase Liquids in Subsurface Systems," *Water Resources Res.,* 27(4), 463-477, 1991.

Richards, L. A., "Capillary Conduction of Liquids in Porous Mediums," *Physics*, Vol. 1, pp. 318-333, 1931.

Rathfelder, K., Yeh, W. W.-G., and D. Mackay, "Mathematical Simulation of Soil Vapor Extraction Systems: Model Development and Numerical Examples." *Contaminant Hydrology*, 8, 263-297, 1991.

Rathfelder, K., Lang, J. R., and L. M. Abriola, "Soil Vapor Extraction and Bioventing: Applications, Limitations and Future Research Directions," *Reviews of Geophysics, Supplement*, 1067-1081, 1995.

Rawls, W. J., D. L. Brakensiek and N. Miller, "Green-Ampt Infiltration Parameters From Soils Data," *J. Hydraulic Engineering*, ASCE, Vol. 109, No. 1, pp. 62-70, 1983.

Rawls, W. J., Ahuja, L. R., Brakensiek, A., and A. Shirmohammadi, "Infiltration Parameters from Soils Data," *J. Hydraulic Engineering*, American Society of Civil Engineers 109(1):62-70, 1993.

Rubin, J. And R. Steinhardt, "Soil Water Relations During Rain Infiltration, I, Theory," *Soil Sci. Soc. Am. Proc.*, Vol 27(3), Pp. 246-251, 1963.

Soil Conservation Service, *Urban Hydrology for Small Watersheds*, Technical Release 55, pp. 2.5-2.8, 1986.

Short, T. E., "Modeling of Processes in the Unsaturated Zone," in R. C. Loehr and J. F. Malina, Jr., eds., *Land Treatment: A Hazardous Waste Management Alternative*, Water Resources Symposium Number Thirteen, U.S. EPA and University of Texas at Austin, pp. 211-240, 1986.

Short, T. E., "Movement of Contaminants from Oily Wastes during Land Treatment," in E. J. Calabrese and P. J. Kostecki, eds., *Soils Contaminated by Petroleum: Environmental and Public Health Effects*, New York, John S. Wiley and Sons, pp. 317-330, 1988.

Skaggs, R. W. and R. Khaleel, "Chapter 4, Infiltration," *Hydrologic Modeling of Small Watersheds*, C. T. Haan, J. P. Johnson and D. L. Brakensiek (eds.), American Society of Agricultural Engineers, St. Joseph Michigan, Monograph No. 5, 1982.

Sleep, B. E., and J. F. Sykes, "Modeling the Transport of Volatile Organics in Variably Saturated Media." *Water Resources Res.*, 25(1), 81-92, 1989.

Smith, R. E., "Approximate Soil Water Movement by Kinetic Characteristics," *Soil Sci. Soc. Am. J.*, Vol. 47 (1), pp. 3-8, 1983.

Swartzendruber, D., "A Quasi Solution of Richards' Equation for Downward Infiltration of Water into Soil," *Water Resources Res.*, vol. 5, pp. 809-817, 1987.

Thibodeaux, L. J. and S. T. Hwang, "Landfarming of Petroleum Wastes - Modeling of the Air Emissions Problem." *Env. Progress*, 1, Vol. 1, pp. 42-46, 1982.

Van Genuchten, M. Th., "A Closed-Form Equation for Predicting the Hydraulic Conductivity of Unsaturated Soils," *Soil Sci. Soc. Am. J.*, vol. 44, pp. 892-898, 1980.

Verschueren, K., *Handbook of Environmental Data on Organic Chemicals*, New York, Van Nostrand Reinhold, 1983.

C H A P T E R   1 0

NUMERICAL MODELING OF CONTAMINANT TRANSPORT

10.1 INTRODUCTION

A ground water model is a tool designed to represent a simplified version of a real field site. It is an attempt to take our understanding of the physical, chemical, and biological processes and translate them into mathematical terms. The resulting model is only as good as the conceptual understanding of the processes. The goal of modeling is to predict the value of an unknown variable such as head in an aquifer system or the concentration distribution of a given chemical in the aquifer in time and space. Models can be used as:

1. Predictive Tools. These are site specific applications of models with the objective of determining future conditions or the impact of a proposed action on existing conditions in the subsurface.

2. Interpretive or Research Tools. These models are usually used for studying system dynamics and understanding processes.

3. Generic or Screening Tools. These models generally incorporate uncertainty in aquifer parameters and are used in a regulatory mode for the purpose of developing management standards and guidelines.

In developing a ground water flow or solute transport model, the first step is to develop a **conceptual model** consisting of a description of the physical, chemical and biological processes which are thought to be governing the behavior of the system being analyzed (Istok, 1989). The next step is to translate the conceptual model into mathematical terms or a **mathematical model**, that is, a set of partial differential equations and an associated set of auxiliary boundary conditions. Finally, solutions of the equations subject to the auxiliary conditions can be obtained using analytical or numerical methods.

If analytical methods are used, the solution is called an **analytical model**. Analytical solutions are usually possible only for simple geometries, homogeneous aquifers, and simple boundary conditions. If numerical methods are used, the solution to the collection of partial differential equations and auxiliary conditions is referred to as a **numerical model**. A computer program that implements the numerical model is referred to as a **computer code** or **computer model**. Computer models are essential for analyzing subsurface flow and contamination problems because they are designed to incorporate the spatial variability within the aquifer, as well as spatial and temporal trends in hydrologic parameters that an analytical model cannot incorporate.

Much discussion has been presented over the past decade regarding the usefulness and drawbacks of modeling. The main complaint of models is that they require great quantities of data and are therefore too expensive to assemble and run. Furthermore, models can never be proven to be correct. On the other hand, some argue that models are essential for performing complex analyses and for making informed decisions. Models allow more effective use of the available data; the implications of proposed courses of action at the field scale can be analyzed and evaluated with them.

Both arguments are well justified. The prospective modeler, however, needs to keep in mind that a good modeling methodology will increase confidence in modeling results. In addition, establishing the purpose of the modeling effort at the outset and establishing realistic expectations will provide for a much more effective utilization of modeling. Prior to initiating the modeling process, the following questions need to be addressed:

1. What is the problem that is being solved or answered through modeling?

2. Is modeling the most appropriate method for establishing the answer to the problem at hand?

3. What level of sophistication in modeling would be required to answer the question?

4. What level of confidence can be associated with the available field data and the anticipated results from the modeling effort?

The responses to these questions will allow the prospective modeler to determine the magnitude of the modeling effort, that is, whether the model is one-, two-, or three-dimensional, analytical or numerical, and whether a steady-state or transient analysis is necessary. Answering question #4 allows the modeler to anticipate the benefits to be gained from the modeling effort and to weigh those benefits against the costs that would be incurred for the modeling study. Finally, keep in mind that modeling is only one component in a hydrogeologic assessment and not an end in itself. The proposed modeling effort should be integrated within the framework for action at a given field site.

The field of ground water flow and transport modeling has grown tremendously over the past fifteen years. This is mostly due to the need for quantitative estimates of flow and mass transport in the subsurface. Many articles and books have been written about the science of modeling in ground water. The reader is referred to Mercer and Faust (1986), Wang and Anderson (1982), Huyakorn and Pinder (1983), Hunt (1983), Javandel et al. (1984), Bear and Verruijt (1987), Istok (1989), National Research Council (1990), and Anderson and Woessner (1992) as a starting point. Anderson and Woessner (1992) propose a modeling protocol that can be summarized as follows:

1. Establish the purpose of the model.

2. Develop a conceptual model of the system.

3. Select the governing equation and a computer code. Both the governing equation and code should be verified. Verification of the governing equation demonstrates that it describes the physical, chemical, and biological processes occurring. Code verification can be accomplished by comparing the model results to an analytical solution of a known problem.

4. Design the model. This step includes selection of a grid design, time parameters, initial and boundary conditions, and developing estimates of model parameters.

5. Calibrate the designed model. Calibration refers to the process of determining a set of model input parameters that approximates field measured heads, flows and/or concentrations. The purpose of calibration is to establish that the model can reproduce field-measured values of the unknown variable. It is noted that calibration is quite subjective and in many cases does not yield a unique set of parameters that reproduce field conditions. This topic will be discussed in more detail in Section 10.9.

6. Determine the effects of uncertainty on model results. This is sometimes referred to as a sensitivity analysis. The model parameters are varied individually within a range of possible values, and the effect on model results is evaluated.

7. Verify designed and calibrated model. This step involves testing the model's ability to reproduce another set of field measurements using the model parameters that were developed in the calibration process.

8. Predict results based on calibrated model.

9. Determine the effects of uncertainty on model predictions.

10. Present modeling design and results.

11. Post audit and redesign model as necessary. As more data is collected beyond model development, it is possible to compare the model predictions against the new field data. This may lead to further modifications and refinements of the site model.

Steps 1 through 4 of Anderson and Woessner's protocol are discussed in this section. The remaining steps are discussed in Section 10.9 within the context of applying models to field sites.

10.1.1 Purpose of Model

It is essential to identify clearly the purpose of the modeling effort at the outset in order to maximize the benefits from the analysis. Stating the purpose of modeling also helps focus the study, determine expectations, and limit the unnecessary expenditure of resources. Typical objectives for modeling studies include:

1. Testing a hypothesis, or improving knowledge of a given aquifer system

2. Understanding physical, chemical or biological processes

3. Designing remediation systems

4. Predicting future conditions or the impact of a proposed stress on a ground water system

5. Resource management

10.1.2 Conceptual Models

A key step in the modeling process is to formulate a conceptual model of the system being modeled. A conceptual model is a pictorial representation of the ground water flow and transport system, frequently in the form of a block diagram or a cross section (Anderson and Woessner, 1992). The nature of the conceptual model will determine the dimensions of the numerical model and the design of the grid.

The purpose of building a conceptual model is to simplify the field problem and make it more amenable to modeling. For example, consider the geologic framework shown in Figure 10.1. A complete reconstruction of this system in a ground water flow model is not feasible; however, a conceptual model of the system can be constructed by identifying the pertinent hydrologic features of the geologic framework as shown in Figure 10.1.

Formulating a conceptual model for flow and/or transport includes one or more of the following steps depending on the nature of the problem being simulated:

1. Define hydrogeologic features of interest, (e.g., the aquifers to be modeled). The conceptual model may combine several geologic formations into a single unit or may subdivide a single formation into aquifers and confining units.

2. Define the flow system and sources and sinks of water in the system. Sources or inflows may include recharge from infiltration, recharge from surface water bodies, or artificial recharge of ground water. Sinks or outflows may include springflow, baseflow to streams, evapotranspiration, and pumping. Defining the flow system involves determining the direction of ground water flow and the hydrologic interaction between the different modeled units.

3. Define the transport system and sources and sinks of chemicals in the system. The conceptual model has to include a representation of the time-variant chemical source concentration, mass or volume of spill, and the chemical and biological processes affecting those chemicals.

Recent advances in software development have resulted in the ability to build a conceptual model and manage site data within a model pre- and post-processor or a Geographical Information System (GIS), which can interact with the pre-processor. This type of software is discussed in Section 10.8.

10.1.3 Equations of Flow and Transport

As mentioned earlier, one of the steps in the modeling protocol is to determine the governing equation to be solved. This is extremely important, especially when the modeler is applying a model that has been acquired from a commercial source. A review of three of the classes of models based on the processes being modeled and the associated governing equations is presented next. The reader is referred to Chapters 9 and 11 for the immiscible/multiphase flow and transport equations.

Saturated Ground Water Flow in Three Dimensions:

$$\frac{\partial}{\partial x}\left(K_x \frac{\partial h}{\partial x}\right) + \frac{\partial}{\partial y}\left(K_y \frac{\partial h}{\partial y}\right) + \frac{\partial}{\partial z}\left(K_z \frac{\partial h}{\partial z}\right) = S_s \frac{\partial h}{\partial t} + W^* \tag{10.1}$$

where h is head, K_x, K_y, K_z, denote hydraulic conductivity in the x-, y-, and z- directions, respectively, S_s is specific storage, t is time, and W^* is a general source/sink term.

Unsaturated Ground Water Flow Equation in Three Dimensions:

$$\frac{\partial}{\partial x}\left(K_x(\psi) \frac{\partial \psi}{\partial x}\right) + \frac{\partial}{\partial y}\left(K_y(\psi) \frac{\partial \psi}{\partial y}\right) + \frac{\partial}{\partial z}\left(K_z(\psi)\left(\frac{\partial \psi}{\partial z}\right)\right) = C(\psi) \frac{\partial \psi}{\partial t} \pm Q \tag{10.2}$$

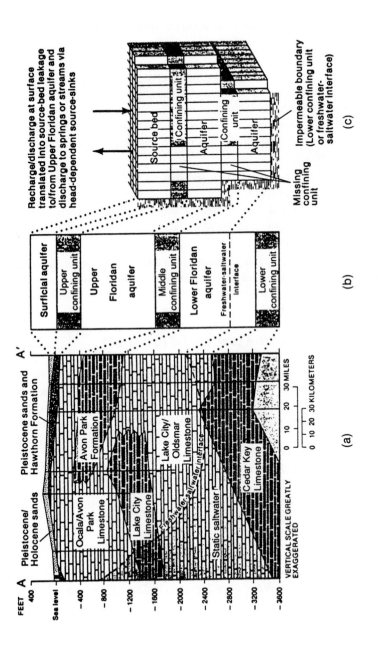

Figure 10.1 Developing a hydrogeologic conceptual model. (a) Geologic units in hydrogeologic framework. (b) Hydrogeological units in conceptual model. c) Equivalent units in digital ground water flow model. Source: Anderson and Woessner, 1992.

where ψ is pressure head; $K_x(\psi)$, $K_y(\psi)$, $K_z(\psi)$, are the components of the unsaturated hydraulic conductivity in the x-, y-, and z- directions, respectively; $C(\psi)$ is the specific moisture capacity, and Q is a source or sink of volumetric fluid flow per unit volume.

Solute Transport in the Saturated Zone in Three Dimensions

$$D_x \frac{\partial^2 C}{\partial x^2} + D_y \frac{\partial^2 C}{\partial y^2} + D_z \frac{\partial^2 C}{\partial z^2} - \frac{\partial(CV_x)}{\partial x} - \frac{\partial(CV_y)}{\partial y} - \frac{\partial(CV_z)}{\partial z} \pm \sum_k R_k = \frac{\partial C}{\partial t} \qquad (10.3)$$

where C is the concentration of the chemical; V is the seepage velocity; D_x, D_y, and D_z are the dispersion coefficients in the x, y, and z directions, respectively; t is time; and R_k is the rate of addition or removal of solute due to chemical and biological reactions.

10.1.4 Discretization

In numerical models, the physical layout of the area in question is replaced with a discretized model domain referred to as a grid and consisting of cells, blocks, or elements depending on whether finite difference or finite element methods are used. Some of the key issues in setting up numerical models have to do with the design of the grid system: How large of a grid to use? How many cells or elements within the grid would be necessary? What impact, if any, does grid discretization have, on model results?

Generally, the grid should be drawn on an overlay of a map of the area to be modeled. It is preferable to align the horizontal plane of the grid such that the x and y axes are colinear with K_x and K_y, respectively. The vertical axis of the model, when present, should be aligned with K_z (Anderson and Woessner, 1992). Selecting the size of the cells/elements to be used is a critical step in grid design that depends on many factors such as: spatial variability in model parameters, physical boundaries of system, type of model being used (finite difference or finite element), computer model limitations, data handling limitations, runtime, and associated computer costs. Spatial discretization may affect model results. While detailed discussion of this issue is beyond the scope of this chapter, the prospective modeler is encouraged to evaluate discretization effects on model results.

Discretization decisions also need to be made for the time parameter. The majority of numerical models calculate results at time t by subdividing the total time into time steps, Δt. Generally, smaller time steps are preferable, but the computational time and cost involved in the modeling process increases as the time step is decreased. Time steps may be influenced by the requirements of the model. Some models suffer from **numerical instabilities,** which cause unrealistic oscillating solutions if a sufficiently small time step is not used. It is a good modeling practice to test the sensitivity of the model results to the size of the time step. Many transport models calculate the maximum time step size based on model conditions, such as grid size and flow velocity. This enables the transport model to eliminate some numerical instability; however, flow models cannot use this method, and must be carefully checked by the user.

10.1.5 Dimensionality

Another issue closely linked to discretization is that of the dimensionality of the problem: is a 1-D model sufficient to achieve the purposes of modeling or is it necessary to develop a 2-D or 3-D model? Would an analytical solution provide the required answer or is it necessary to utilize a numerical model? Is a steady-state assumption adequate or does the problem necessitate a transient analysis?

A good rule of thumb to use when deciding the dimensionality of the model is to avoid complexity if at all possible. For example, air pollution modeling might require a three-dimensional analysis of pollutant dispersion and diffusion. Ground water contamination at a field site where the data has been collected using conventional monitoring wells, however, can be simulated only as a 2-D problem because there is not a 3-D definition of the plume of contamination.

10.1.6 Boundary and Initial Conditions

The governing equation alone is not sufficient to describe a specific physical system. This is because a general solution of an nth order differential equation will involve n independent arbitrary constants or functions. In order to define uniquely a given physical problem, the values of the constants or forms of the functions must be specified. Initial and boundary conditions can be used to provide this required additional information. Generally, boundary conditions specify the value of the dependent variable, or the value of the first derivative of the dependent variable, along the boundaries of the system being modeled.

Correct selection of boundary conditions is a critical step in model design. In steady-state simulations, for example, the boundaries largely determine the flow pattern. Boundary conditions affect transient solutions when the effects of the transient stress reach the boundary. In this case, the boundaries must be selected such that the simulated effect is realistic.

Boundary conditions are typically derived from physical and/or hydraulic boundaries of ground water flow systems, for example, the presence of an impermeable body of rock or a river in connection with the ground water aquifer. Hydrogeologic boundaries are represented by three types of mathematical formulations: specified head, specified flux, and head dependent flux boundaries.

Specified head. (Dirichlet conditions). A specified head boundary is simulated by setting the head at the relevant locations equal to known values:

$$H(x, y, z) = H_0 \tag{10.4}$$

where $H(x, y, z)$ is the head at a point with coordinates (x, y, z) and H_0 is a specified head value. It is important to recognize that a specified head boundary represents an inexhaustible supply of water.

Specified flux boundaries. (Neumann conditions). Specified flux boundaries are defined by giving the derivative of the head across the boundary:

$$q_x = \frac{\partial H}{\partial x} = \text{Constant} \qquad (10.5)$$

This type of boundary is used to describe fluxes to surface water bodies, springflow and seepage to and from bedrock underlying the system. A special type of specified flux boundaries is a no-flow boundary which is set by specifying flux to be zero. A no-flow boundary may represent impermeable bedrock, an impermeable fault zone, a ground water divide or a streamline.

Head-dependent flux boundaries. (Cauchy or mixed conditions). For this type of boundary, the flux across the boundary is calculated given a boundary head value:

$$\frac{\partial H}{\partial x} + aH = C \qquad (10.6)$$

where a and C are constants. Leakage to or from a river, for instance, can be simulated using this type of boundary condition.

In some instances, it may not be possible to use physical boundaries and regional ground water divides. Other hydraulic boundaries can be defined from information on the configuration of the flow system. However, care must be taken when establishing such boundaries to ensure that the model boundaries will not cause the solution to differ significantly from the response that would occur in the field. For example, hydraulic boundaries may be defined from a water table map of the area to be modeled. The model grid is superimposed on the water table contour map, and specified head boundary conditions can be interpolated. It is important to verify, however, that these boundary conditions will not be impacted by stresses imposed on the model, such as pumping from a location near the boundary.

The above mentioned boundary conditions used to represent flow may also be used as sources of chemicals into a ground water aquifer. For example, a specified head boundary may be used to represent a contaminant source releasing chemicals into the aquifer at a specified concentration. Similarly, a flux boundary can be used to simulate the flux of contaminants across the boundary. More typically, however, injection wells are used to represent sources of contamination as discussed in the following paragraphs.

10.1.7 Sources and Sinks

Water as well as chemicals may enter the grid in one of two ways — through the boundaries, as determined by the boundary conditions, or through sources and sinks within the interior of the grid. Even though the same model options may be used to represent boundary sources and sinks as to represent internal sources and sinks, the reader should remember that internal sources and sinks are not boundary conditions. For example, specified head cells are used to represent specified head boundary conditions, but specified head nodes may be placed within the grid to represent lakes and rivers or some other type of source.

An injection or pumping well is a point source or sink and is represented in a ground water model by specifying an injection or pumping rate at a designated node or cell. In a 2-D model, an assumption of a fully penetrating well over the aquifer thickness is made. The prospective modeler is cautioned when modeling wells with models that allow only a uniform grid (i.e., all cells have the same size), and when the cell size in the model greatly exceeds the actual diameter of the well. The head calculated by the model is not an accurate approximation of the head measured in the well, but rather the head value predicted by the model is closer to an average of the heads measured as one moves outward from the well toward the edge of the cell.

10.1.8 Source and Types of Errors: Accuracy of Numerical Models

One of the key components in computer modeling of ground water flow and contaminant transport that is often neglected is an assessment of the error introduced due to the selected modeling methodology. There are two types of error resulting from a modeling study that need to be clearly distinguished:

1. Computational errors. These errors occur because of the numerical approximation procedures that are used to solve the governing equations. Computational errors are usually estimated by applying the continuity equation or the principle of conservation of mass (input – output = accumulation).

2. Calibration errors. These errors occur due to model assumptions and limitations in parameter estimation. Calibration errors can be quantified by comparing the model's predicted values to observed values of the unknown variable (see Section 10.9).

10.1.9 Limitations of Models

Mathematical models have several limitations, which can be conceptual or application-related. Conceptual limitations are those that relate to representation of the actual process or system with a mathematical model. For example, analytical models are limited by the simplifying assumptions that are required to develop the solution. The analytical models that are available are limited to certain idealized conditions and may not be applicable to a field problem with complex boundary conditions. Another limitation of analytical models is that spatial or temporal variation of system properties such as permeability and dispersivity cannot be handled.

Application-related limitations have to do with the solution procedure that is utilized in the model development or with the amount of effort required to implement the solution. For example, the approximation of a differential equation by a numerical solution introduces two types of computational errors: numerical and residual. The numerical errors are due to the solution method used in solving the differential equations. The residual errors are a result of approximating the differential equation with a series of mathematical expressions.

Numerical models are also limited by their complexity so that the user needs a certain level of knowledge to be able to apply those models. Achievement of the required familiarity level is time consuming and could be prohibitive when funding is limited or when dealing with a time constraint. Preparation of input data for numerical models often takes a long time, even with the recently developed pre-processors discussed in Section 10.8. A relatively fast computer is necessary when using a numerical model, especially for large, complex problems.

10.2 NUMERICAL METHODS

Numerical or computerized solutions of the flow and/or transport equation in two dimensions are the most plentiful and commonly used techniques. These solutions are generally more flexible than analytical solutions because the user can approximate complex geometries and combinations of recharge and withdrawal wells by judicious arrangement of grid cells. The general method of solution is to break up the flow field into small cells, approximate the governing partial differential equations by differences between the values of parameters over the network of time t, then predict new values for time $t + \Delta t$. This continues forward in time in small increments Δt.

The most common mathematical formulations for approximating the partial differential equations of flow and solute transport include:

- Finite difference methods
- Finite element methods
- Method of characteristics
- Collocation methods
- Boundary element methods

Before defining these methods, it is necessary to define the different types of Partial Differential Equations (PDEs). All PDEs of the form $L(u) = f$ can be classified as **elliptic, parabolic, or hyperbolic.** The PDE can be written as:

$$a\frac{\partial^2 u}{\partial x^2} + 2b\frac{\partial^2 u}{\partial x \partial y} + c\frac{\partial^2 u}{\partial y^2} = F\left(x, y, u, \frac{\partial u}{\partial x}, \frac{\partial u}{\partial y}\right) \qquad (10.7)$$

where a, b, and c are functions of x and y only and the equation is classified as linear if F is linear. The PDE is referred to as:

- Hyperbolic,   if $b^2 - ac > 0$
- Parabolic,   if $b^2 - ac = 0$
- Elliptic,   if $b^2 - ac < 0$

The finite difference method is the most popular method for simulating problems of ground water flow and transport. Finite difference methods are conceptually straightforward and easily understood. Moreover, much research has been done on developing a variety of algorithms for solving finite difference equations. The earlier finite-difference methods operate by dividing space into rectilinear cells along the coordinate axes. Homogeneous values within each cell are represented by values at a single node. Partial differentials can then be approximated by differences and the resulting set of equations solved by iteration (Mercer and Faust, 1986; Carnahan et al., 1969; Prickett, 1975). Approximating the differentials by a difference requires neglecting remaining terms, which results in **truncation** error.

Finite-difference models have been developed for a variety of field situations including saturated and unsaturated flow, and for transient and constant pollutant sources. The primary disadvantage of these methods is that the truncation error in approximating the partial differential equations be significant (Anderson, 1979). More details about the finite difference method are included in Section 10.3, and the reader is referred to Peaceman and Rachford (1955), Forsythe and Wasow (1960), Aziz and Settari (1979), Crichlow (1977), Peaceman (1977), Remson et al. (1965), Freeze and Witherspoon (1966), Bittinger et al. (1967), Pinder and Bredehoeft (1968), Cooley (1971), Freeze (1971), Brutsaert (1973), Green et al. (1970), Peaceman and Rachford (1962), Shamir and Harleman (1967), Oster et al. (1970), Tanji et al. (1967), and Zheng and Bennett, (1995) for additional information.

The finite element method also operates by breaking the flow field into elements, but in this case the elements may vary in size and shape. In the case of a triangular element, the geometry would be described by the three corner nodes where heads and concentrations are computed. The head or concentration within an element can vary in proportion to the distance to these nodes. Sometimes complex interpolating schemes are used to predict parameter values accurately within an element and thereby reduce the truncation errors common in finite difference procedures. Some numerical dispersion may still occur but is usually much less significant. The use of variable size and shape elements also allows greater flexibility in the analysis of moving boundary problems, such as those related to a moving water table or when contaminant and flow transport must be analyzed as a coupled problem.

A disadvantage of the finite element method is the need for formal mathematical training to understand the procedures properly. Finite element methods generally have higher computing costs (Pinder and Gray, 1977; Pinder, 1973; Wang and Anderson, 1982). More details on the finite element method are presented in Section 10.4, and the reader is additionally referred to Bathe and Wilson (1976), Chung (1979), Clough (1960), Cook (1974), Finlayson (1972), Huebner (1975), Hinton and Owen (1979), Norrie and De Vries (1978), Segerlind (1976), Zienkiewicz (1977), Gallagher (1975), and Zheng and Bennett (1995).

The method of characteristics (MOC) is a variant of the finite difference method and is particularly suitable for solving hyperbolic equations. The method of characteristics was developed to simulate advection-dominated transport by Garder et al. (1964). In ground water hydrology, Pinder and Cooper (1970) and Reddell and Sunada (1970) used the method to solve the density-dependent transport equations. Later, MOC was used widely to simulate the movement of contaminants in the subsurface (Bredehoeft and Pinder, 1973). The method of characteristics is most useful where solute transport is dominated by advective transport. The most common procedure is to track idealized particles through the flow field. In step one, a particle and an associated mass of contaminant are translated a certain distance according to the flow velocity. The second step adds the effects of longitudinal and transverse dispersion. This procedure is computationally efficient and minimizes numerical dispersion problems (Konikow and Bredehoeft, 1978). The method of characteristics is discussed in more detail in Section 10.5.

The collocation method provides the advantage of the finite element method with additional attractive features. Collocation methods do not require integration procedures in the formulation of the approximating equations. Moreover, the resulting matrix equation exhibits a coefficient structure that may be amenable to efficient solution using modern methods in matrix algebra (Huyakorn and Pinder, 1983). The collocation method will not be discussed in detail in this book; however, the reader is referred to Finlayson (1972), Chang and Finlayson (1977), Houstis et al. (1979), Douglas and Dupont (1974), Sincovec (1977), Allen and Pinder (1983), Bangia et al. (1978), Pinder et al. (1978), Frind and Pinder (1979), Lapidus and Pinder (1982), and Celia and Pinder (1980).

The boundary element method, a variant of the finite element method, is especially useful in the solution of elliptic equations for which Green's functions exist. The boundary element method reduces a 2-D or 3-D problem to one defined in one or two dimensions, respectively. The boundary element method is a relative newcomer in applied numerical analysis and not very popular yet in subsurface hydrology. The boundary element method will not be discussed in this book, but the interested reader is referred to Jawson and Ponter (1963), Liggett (1977), Brebbia and Walker (1980), Lapidus and Pinder (1982), Liggett and Liu (1983), Benarjee et al. (1981), Rizzo and Shippy (1970), Dubois and Buysee (1980), Jawson and Symm (1977), Lennon et al. (1979), and Liggett and Liu (1979).

10.2.1 Fundamental Concepts

The following summary is not intended to be a thorough discussion of numerical methods. It is included to familiarize the reader with some of the more common terminology used in numerical modeling. For detailed discussions on numerical methods, the reader is referred to Kelly (1967), Carnahan et al. (1969), Celia and Gray (1992), and Mathews (1992).

Iteration means that a process is repeated until an answer is achieved. Iterative techniques can be used to find roots of equations, solutions of linear and nonlinear systems of equations and solutions of differential equations. Iteration methods require that an initial guess be made and that a rule or function for computing successive terms exists.

Convergence is characterized by the question, "Does the numerical solution approach the true solution as a chosen numerical procedure is applied?" The convergence problem may arise from using an iterative technique or a numerical technique that involves truncation of an infinite series.

A **stable** numerical procedure is one where as the solution marches forward in time, the errors are not amplified such that the solution becomes invalid.

Curve fitting techniques attempt to fit a given set of data with a mathematical expression or function. For example, one of the most common curve fitting methods is a **least squares fit,** where the function $f(x)$ is approximated using:

$$f(x) \approx \sum_{k=0}^{n} a_k \phi_k(x) \equiv y(x) \tag{10.8}$$

where $\phi_0(x), ..., \phi_n(x)$ are $n+1$ appropriately chosen functions. The exact values of $f(x)$ are known over a certain domain, which consists of a discrete set of points $x_0, x_1, ..., x_n$ or of a continuous interval (a, b). The least squares approximation is defined to be that for which the a_k's are determined so that the sum of $w(x)r^2(x)$ the domain is as small as possible, where $w(x)$ is a nonnegative weighting function and $r(x) = f(x) - y(x)$.

Newton-Raphson Iteration involves finding a root of $f(x) = 0$ given one initial approximation p_0 and using the iteration

$$p_k = p_{k-1} - \frac{f(p_{k-1})}{f'(p_{k-1})} \qquad \text{for } k = 1, 2,... \tag{10.9}$$

Secant Method is applied to finding a root of $f(x) = 0$ given two initial approximations p_0 and p_1 and using the iteration

$$p_{k+1} = p_k - \frac{f(p_k)[p_k - p_{k-1}]}{f(p_k) - f(p_{k-1})} \qquad \text{for } k = 1, 2,... \tag{10.10}$$

Gaussian Elimination and Back-Substitution refers to the simplest method of solving a set of equations of the form:

$$\begin{aligned}
a_{11}x_1 + a_{12}x_2 + a_{13}x_3 + \cdots + a_{1n}x_n &= b_1 \\
a_{21}x_1 + a_{22}x_2 + a_{23}x_3 + \cdots + a_{2n}x_n &= b_2 \\
a_{31}x_1 + a_{32}x_2 + a_{33}x_3 + \cdots + a_{3n}x_n &= b_3 \\
a_{n1}x_1 + a_{n2}x_2 + a_{n3}x_3 + \cdots + a_{nn}x_n &= b_n
\end{aligned} \tag{10.11}$$

Gaussian elimination consists of dividing the first equation by a_{11} and using the result to eliminate x_1 from all succeeding equations. Next, the modified second equation is used to eliminate x_2 from the succeeding equations, and so on. After this elimination has been effected n times, the resultant set of equations is solved by backward substitution.

10.2.2 The Numerical Solution of Partial Differential Equations

The purpose of this example is to present an introductory account of the numerical methods by which approximate solutions to partial differential equations can be obtained. The fundamental idea on which the numerical solution of partial differential equations is based is this: each of the partial derivatives that appears in the equation is replaced by a finite-difference approximation. When these differences are evaluated at each of the mesh points, the result is a set of simultaneous equations that can be solved either directly or by various iterative procedures.

Specifically, in a plane grid, if the coordinates of the mesh points (named neutrally for the moment) are $p_i = p_0 + ih$ and $q_j = q_0 + jk$, then from the usual difference quotient approximation to the first derivative, we have

$$\left.\frac{\partial u}{\partial p}\right|_{p_i,q_j} = \frac{u_{p_{i+1},q_j} - u_{p_i,q_j}}{h} = \frac{u_{i+1,j} - u_{i,j}}{h} \tag{10.12}$$

Similarly

$$\left.\frac{\partial u}{\partial q}\right|_{p_i,q_j} = \frac{u_{i,j+1} - u_{i,j}}{k} \tag{10.13}$$

Furthermore, for the case of a second derivative, we obtain

$$\left.\frac{\partial^2 u}{\partial p^2}\right|_{p_i,q_j} = \frac{u_{p_{i+1},q_j} - 2u_{p_i,q_j} + u_{p_{i-1},q_j}}{h^2} = \frac{u_{i+1,j} - 2u_{i,j} + u_{i-1,j}}{h^2} \tag{10.14}$$

Similarly

$$\left.\frac{\partial^2 u}{\partial q^2}\right|_{p_i,q_j} = \frac{u_{i,j+1} - 2u_{i,j} + u_{i,j-1}}{k^2} \tag{10.15}$$

Elliptic Equations (Laplace's Equation In Two Dimensions). Using Eqs. (10.14) and (10.15) to approximate each of the partial derivatives in the 2-D form of Laplace's equation, namely

$$\frac{\partial^2 u}{\partial x^2} + \frac{\partial^2 u}{\partial y^2} = 0 \tag{10.16}$$

We obtain, as a difference equation approximating the actual equation

$$\frac{u_{i+1,j} - 2u_{i,j} + u_{i-1,j}}{h^2} + \frac{u_{i,j+1} - 2u_{i,j} + u_{i,j-1}}{k^2} = 0 \tag{10.17}$$

or, making the natural and convenient assumption that $h = k$ and solving for $u_{i,j}$

$$u_{i,j} = \frac{u_{i+1,j} + u_{i,j+1} + u_{i-1,j} + u_{i,j-1}}{4} \tag{10.18}$$

This asserts that the value of u at any mesh point is equal to the average of the values of u at the four adjacent mesh points.

If Eq. (10.18) is evaluated at each of the mesh points, which are not boundary points, where the value of the solution u is initially given, the result is a system of simultaneous linear equations in the unknown functional values $u_{i,j}$. The number of equations is, of course, just equal to the number of mesh points at which the value of u is to be calculated; and (at least for rectangular regions) it can be shown that this system of equations always has a unique nontrivial solution.

Example 10.1   STEADY STATE HEAD IN A SQUARE REGION

To illustrate the formulation and solution of such a system, let us attempt to approximate the steady-state head distribution $u(x,y)$ in the square region shown in Figure 10.2, using the grid obtained by dividing each edge into four equal parts. The unknowns in this problem are the heads at the nine points of the grid which are not boundary points.

Solution.   At the outset, we note that from symmetry $u_{11} = u_{31}$, $u_{12} = u_{32}$, and $u_{13} = u_{33}$, so that our problem actually involves only six equations in the six unknowns u_{11}, u_{12}, u_{13}, u_{21}, u_{22}, and u_{23}. Applying Eq. (10.18) at each of the six mesh points P_{11}, P_{12}, P_{13}, P_{21}, P_{22}, P_{23} and taking into account the symmetries we have just noted and the known values of u on the boundary, we have at P_{11}

$$4u_{11} - u_{01} - u_{10} - u_{21} - u_{12} = 0$$

or noting that by hypothesis $u_{01} = u_{10} = 0$

$$4u_{11} - u_{21} - u_{12} = 0 \tag{10.19}$$

Similarly, at P_{12}, P_{13}, P_{21}, P_{22}, P_{23} we have, respectively

$$4u_{12} - u_{11} - u_{22} - u_{13} = 0 \tag{10.20}$$

$$4u_{13} - u_{12} - u_{23} = 3/16 \tag{10.21}$$

$$4u_{21} - 2u_{11} - u_{22} = 0 \tag{10.22}$$

$$4u_{22} - u_{21} - 2u_{12} - u_{23} = 0 \tag{10.23}$$

$$4u_{23} - u_{22} - 2u_{13} = 1/4 \tag{10.24}$$

Using Eqs. (10.19), (10.20), and (10.21) to eliminate u_{21}, u_{22}, and u_{23} from Eqs. (10.22), (10.23), and (10.24), we obtain the system

$$15u_{11} - 8u_{12} + u_{13} = 0$$

$$-8u_{11} + 16u_{12} - 8u_{13} = -\frac{3}{16}$$

$$15u_{13} - 8u_{12} + u_{11} = 1$$

Yielding $u_{11} = 0.0154$, $u_{12} = 0.0396$, $u_{13} = 0.0872$.

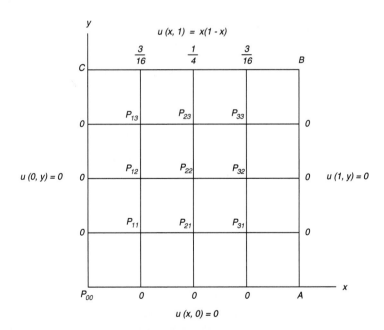

Figure 10.2 A typical lattice used in the approximate solution of Laplace's equation in the unit square. Source: Wylie and Barrett, 1982.

There is another way in which the finite-difference approximation to the Laplacian can be used to determine the value of the solution at the points of the grid. It is a simple iterative method, which proceeds as follows. We first recall that the finite-difference approximation to the Laplacian [Eq. (10.18)] expresses the value of the solution at any mesh point as the average of the values at the four adjacent points. Thus, after an initial estimate for the value of the solution at each mesh point has been made, they can be corrected and improved by systematically moving through the grid and replacing each value according to Eq. (10.18). In doing this, each value, as soon as it is corrected, should be used in all subsequent calculations.

As an illustration of this method, let us reconsider the problem we have just worked. Beginning with the estimates shown in Figure 10.3a, we have for the first refinement of u_{13} the value

$$u_{13} = \frac{0.1875 + 0.0000 + 0.1200 + 0.0600}{4} = 0.0919$$

Continuing through the grid as indicated using the corrected values as soon as they become available (but taking no advantage of the symmetry of the problem), we obtain the values shown in Figure 10.3b. Values bearing the subscript 1 were obtained by a single iteration; values bearing the subscript 5 were obtained after five iterations.

Parabolic Equations (The One-Dimensional Heat Equation). For the 1-D transport equation,

$$\frac{\partial^2 c}{\partial x^2} = a^2 \frac{\partial c}{\partial t} \tag{10.25}$$

the region of the x–t plane over which a solution is sought is always infinite, because of the infinite increase of time. As a finite-difference approximation to Eq. (10.25) we have, using Eqs. (10.13) and (10.14),

$$\frac{1}{h^2}(c_{i+1,j} - 2c_{i,j} + c_{i-1,j}) = \frac{a^2}{k}(c_{i,j+1} - c_{i,j}) \tag{10.26}$$

or, setting $m = k/a^2 h^2$ and solving for $c_{i,j+1}$,

$$c_{i,j+1} = mc_{i+1,j} + (1 - 2m)c_{i,j} + mc_{i-1,j} \tag{10.27}$$

Clearly, it would be convenient to choose h and k so that the value of m is 1/2. The values of c on the boundary are of course provided by the data of the problem. Thus the given initial condition $c(x,0)$ provides the values of c_{00}, c_{10}, c_{20}, ... Similarly, end conditions of the form

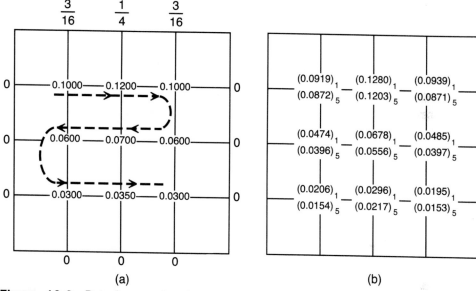

Figure 10.3 Data from an iterative solution of Laplace's equation. Source: Wylie and Barrett, 1982.

$$c(0,t) = g_1(t), \qquad c(l,t) = g_2(t) \tag{10.28}$$

where g_1 and g_2 are usually, though not necessarily, constant, furnish the values of c_{01}, c_{02}, c_{03}, ... and c_{l1}, c_{l2}, c_{l3}, ... No flow boundary conditions can, of course, be handled as outlined above in the discussion of Laplace's equation.

The determination of the solution over the rest of the grid proceeds in a straightforward way, using the extrapolation pattern provided by Eq. (10.26). First, the values of c_{11}, c_{21}, ..., $c_{l-1,1}$ are calculated from the known values of c_{00}, c_{10}, c_{20}, ..., c_{l0}. Then using these new values and the boundary values c_{01} and c_{l1}, the solution is "marched" forward by calculating the values of c at the grid points in the third row, and so on for the remainder of the grid.

10.3 FINITE DIFFERENCE METHODS

In general, a finite difference model is developed by superimposing a system of nodal points over the problem domain. In the finite difference method, nodes may be located inside cells (block-centered, Figure 10.4) or at the intersection of grid lines (mesh centered, Figure 10.5). Aquifer properties and head values are assumed to be constant within each cell in a block-

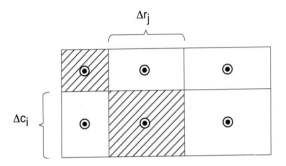

Figure 10.4 Block-centered grid system.

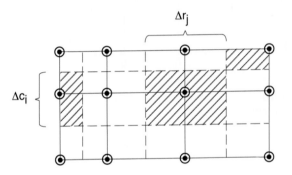

Figure 10.5 Point or mesh-centered grid system.

centered finite difference model. An equation is written in terms of each nodal point in finite difference models because the area surrounding a node is not directly involved in the development of the finite difference equations (Wang and Anderson, 1982).

The principles behind finite difference approximations will be illustrated using Laplace's equation in two dimensions:

$$\frac{\partial^2 h}{\partial x^2} + \frac{\partial^2 h}{\partial y^2} = 0 \qquad (10.29)$$

Consider a finite set of points on a regularly spaced grid (Figure 10.6). In the finite difference approximation, derivatives are replaced by differences taken between nodal points. A central approximation to $\partial^2 h/\partial x^2$ at (x_0, y_0) is obtained by approximating the first derivative at $(x_0 + \Delta x/2, y_0)$ and at $(x_0 - \Delta x/2, y_0)$ and then obtaining the second derivative by taking a difference between the first derivatives at those points

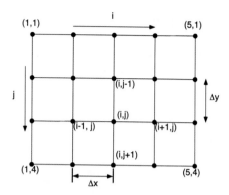

Figure 10.6 Finite-difference grid system.

$$\frac{\partial^2 h}{\partial x^2} \approx \frac{\dfrac{h_{i+1,j} - h_{i,j}}{\Delta x} - \dfrac{h_{i,j} - h_{i-1,j}}{\Delta x}}{\Delta x} \tag{10.30}$$

which simplifies to

$$\frac{\partial^2 h}{\partial x^2} \approx \frac{h_{i-1,j} - 2h_{i,j} + h_{i+1,j}}{\Delta x^2} \tag{10.31}$$

Similarly,

$$\frac{\partial^2 h}{\partial y^2} \approx \frac{h_{i,j-1} - 2h_{i,j} + h_{i,j+1}}{\Delta y^2} \tag{10.32}$$

By adding the expressions in Eqs. (10.31) and (10.32), and assuming that $\Delta x = \Delta y$, we obtain the finite difference approximation to Laplace's equation:

$$h_{i-1,j} + h_{i+1,j} + h_{i,j-1} + h_{i,j+1} - 4h_{i,j} = 0 \tag{10.33}$$

The generalized form of Eq. (10.33) is the most widely used equation in finite difference solutions of steady-state problems. There will be one equation of the form of Eq. (10.33) for each interior point (i,j) of the problem.

10.3.1 Explicit Finite Difference Approximation

For transient conditions, the head in an aquifer is a function of time; therefore, in addition to the spatial finite difference approximation for head, a finite difference approximation for $\partial h / \partial t$ is also needed. An **explicit** finite difference approximation is one where $h_{i,j}^{n+1}$ is calculated using only values of h known at time n. Explicit formulations are easily solved, because there is only one unknown variable in each equation. An explicit, **forward** difference approximation is given by

$$\frac{\partial h}{\partial t} \approx \frac{h_{i,j}^{n+1} - h_{i,j}^{n}}{\Delta t} \tag{10.34}$$

where n and $n+1$ represent two consecutive time levels. Similarly, an explicit, **backward** difference approximation is given by

$$\frac{\partial h}{\partial t} \approx \frac{h_{i,j}^{n} - h_{i,j}^{n-1}}{\Delta t} \tag{10.35}$$

Finally, an explicit, **central** difference approximation in time is given by

$$\frac{\partial h}{\partial t} \approx \frac{h_{i,j}^{n+1} - h_{i,j}^{n-1}}{2\Delta t} \tag{10.36}$$

The central difference approximation was found to be unconditionally unstable by Remson et al. (1971) and therefore should be avoided. For the case of transient flow, given by

$$\frac{\partial^2 h}{\partial x^2} + \frac{\partial^2 h}{\partial y^2} = \frac{S}{T} \frac{\partial h}{\partial t} \tag{10.37}$$

an explicit approximation yields a stable solution if the value of the ratio $(T\Delta t)/[S(\Delta x)^2]$ is kept sufficiently small. In the 1-D case where flow occurs only in the x direction, the parameter $(T\Delta t)/[S(\Delta x)^2]$ must be ≤ 0.5 (Remson et al., 1971) to ensure numerical stability. For the 2-D case where $\Delta x = \Delta y = a$, $(T\Delta t)/[S(\Delta x)^2]$ must be ≤ 0.25 (Rushton and Redshaw, 1979).

10.3.2 Implicit Finite Difference Approximation

An **implicit** finite difference formulation is one where the heads h at time $n+1$ are evaluated using other values of head at time $n+1$. The solution to an implicit finite difference approximation involves a matrix of equations that must be solved simultaneously, because there are several unknown variables in each equation. Implicit formulations will often use a weighted average of the approximations at n and $n+1$. The weighting parameter is represented by α, and it lies between 0 and 1. If the time step $n+1$ is weighted by α and time step n is weighted by $(1-\alpha)$, then:

$$\frac{\partial^2 h}{\partial x^2} \approx \alpha \frac{h_{i+1,j}^{n+1} - 2h_{i,j}^{n+1} + h_{i-1,j}^{n+1}}{(\Delta x)^2} + (1-\alpha) \frac{h_{i+1,j}^{n} - 2h_{i,j}^{n} + h_{i-1,j}^{n}}{(\Delta x)^2} \tag{10.38}$$

A similar expression is written for $\partial^2 h / \partial y^2$. The parameter α is selected by the modeler. For $\alpha = 1$, the space derivatives are approximated at $n+1$, and the finite difference scheme is said to be fully implicit. If a value of 0.5 is selected for α, then the scheme is referred to as the **Crank-Nicolson method**.

10.3.3 Alternating Direction Implicit (ADI)

The derivation and solution of the finite-difference equation and the use of the iterative ADI have been discussed extensively by Pinder and Bredehoeft (1968), Prickett and Lonnquist (1971), and Trescott et al. (1976). In general, the basis of the ADI method is to obtain a solution to the flow equation by alternately writing the finite-difference equation, first implicitly along columns and explicitly along rows, and then vice versa. In order to reduce the errors that may result from the ADI method, an iterative procedure is added so that within a single time step, the solution would converge within a specified error tolerance. The ADI method will be illustrated by approximating the 2-D transient equation for a confined aquifer:

$$\frac{\partial^2 h}{\partial x^2} + \frac{\partial^2 h}{\partial y^2} = \frac{S}{T} \frac{\partial h}{\partial t} \tag{10.39}$$

where S is the storage coefficient and T is the transmissivity. Assuming $\Delta x = \Delta y = a$, the fully implicit finite difference approximation is:

$$h_{i+1,j}^{n+1} + h_{i-1,j}^{n+1} + h_{i,j+1}^{n+1} + h_{i,j-1}^{n+1} - 4h_{i,j}^{n+1} = \frac{Sa^2}{T} \frac{h_{i,j}^{n+1} - h_{i,j}^{n}}{\Delta t} \tag{10.40}$$

In the first step of ADI, Eq. (10.40) is rewritten such that heads along columns are on one side of the equation and heads along rows are on the other side (also referred to as rewriting the equation, first implicitly along columns and explicitly along rows) results in:

$$h_{i,j-1}^{n+1} + \left(-4 - \frac{Sa^2}{T\Delta t}\right) h_{i,j}^{n+1} + h_{i,j+1}^{n+1} = -\frac{Sa^2}{T\Delta t} h_{i,j}^{n} - h_{i+1,j}^{n} - h_{i-1,j}^{n} \tag{10.41}$$

Eq. (10.41) will yield a tridiagonal coefficient matrix (one that has nonzero entries only along the three center diagonals) along any column (see Example 10.2). The second step of ADI involves rewriting Eq. (10.40) implicitly along rows and explicitly along columns:

$$h_{i-1,j}^{n+1} + \left(-4 - \frac{Sa^2}{T\Delta t}\right)h_{i,j}^{n+1} + h_{i+1,j}^{n+1} = -\frac{Sa^2}{T\Delta t}h_{i,j}^{n} - h_{i,j+1}^{n} - h_{i,j-1}^{n} \qquad (10.42)$$

The explicit approximation along columns uncouples one row from another. Therefore, Eq. (10.42) will also generate a set of matrix equations—one for each interior row—with tridiagonal coefficient matrices. Alternating the explicit approximation between columns and rows is an attempt to compensate for errors generated in either direction.

10.3.4 Iterative Methods

A set of simultaneous finite difference equations could be solved directly; however, in problems having a large number of nodes, simultaneous solutions are impractical. Instead, iterative procedures can be used where an initial guess of the solution is made. Further improvements on the initial guess are then calculated. There are three commonly used iterative techniques: the **Jacobi iteration, Gauss-Seidel iteration,** and **Successive Over Relaxation (SOR).** Of the three, Jacobi iteration is the least efficient and Successive over relaxation is the most efficient.

Jacobi iteration. If Eq. (10.33) were solved for $h_{i,j}$, then:

$$h_{i,j} = \frac{h_{i-1,j} + h_{i+1,j} + h_{i,j-1} + h_{i,j+1}}{4} \qquad (10.43)$$

The value of $h_{i,j}$ at any point is the average value of head computed from its four nearest neighbors.

The Jacobi iteration associates an **iteration index (m)** with the finite difference equation for head:

$$h_{i,j}^{m+1} = \frac{h_{i-1,j}^{m} + h_{i+1,j}^{m} + h_{i,j-1}^{m} + h_{i,j+1}^{m}}{4} \qquad (10.44)$$

For $m = 1$, an initial guess of $h_{2,2}^1$, $h_{3,2}^1$, $h_{2,3}^1$, and $h_{3,3}^1$ is made. Eq. (10.44) is used to calculate head values for $m = 2, 3,\dots, n$. Iteration continues until the solution converges to the preset error tolerance level, that is, the difference between the answers for $m = n$ and m = $n+1$ is less than the convergence criterion.

Gauss-Seidel iteration. The Gauss-Seidel iteration formula is:

$$h_{i,j}^{m+1} = \frac{h_{i-1,j}^{m+1} + h_{i,j-1}^{m+1} + h_{i+1,j}^{m+1} + h_{i,j+1}^{m+1}}{4} \tag{10.45}$$

Successive Over Relaxation (SOR). The SOR iteration is tied to the residual (c) or change between two successive Gauss-Seidel iterations:

$$c = h_{i,j}^{m+1} - h_{i,j}^{m} \tag{10.46}$$

The Gauss-Seidel iteration eliminates or **relaxes** the residual (c) by replacing $h_{i,j}^{m}$ with $h_{i,j}^{m+1}$ after each calculation. In the SOR method, on the other hand, the residual is multiplied by a relaxation factor ω, where ω 1. The value of $h_{i,j}^{m+1}$ is given by:

$$h_{i,j}^{m+1} = h_{i,j}^{m} + \omega c \tag{10.47}$$

A value of ω between 1 and 2 has been recommended (Wang and Anderson, 1982).

Example 10.2. TRIDIAGONAL MATRICES

Consider the 1-D transient flow equation:

$$\frac{\partial^2 h}{\partial x^2} = \frac{S}{T} \frac{\partial h}{\partial t} \tag{10.48}$$

The implicit or backward finite difference approximation, where the space derivative is evaluated at the ($n+1$) time level, is

$$\frac{h_{i-1}^{n+1} - 2h_i^{n+1} + h_{i+1}^{n+1}}{(\Delta x)^2} = \frac{S}{T} \frac{h_i^{n+1} - h_i^{n}}{\Delta t} \tag{10.49}$$

Assume that we have a problem domain with six nodes where the first and last nodes are boundary nodes of known head. We wish to write the set of algebraic equations that would be generated by applying Eq. (10.49) to these nodes, and we wish to write it in matrix form.

Solution. First, we rearrange Eq. (10.49) and put unknowns, that is, heads at the ($n+1$) time level, on the left-hand side and put knowns on the right-hand side.

$$h_{i-1}^{n+1} + \left(-2 - \frac{S(\Delta x)^2}{T\Delta t}\right) h_i^{n+1} + h_{i+1}^{n+1} = -\frac{S(\Delta x)^2}{T\Delta t} h_i^{n} \tag{10.50}$$

If the head values h_1 and h_6, which are known from the boundary conditions, are transferred to the right-hand side, then the matrix form of the set of algebraic equations for the six-node problem is

$$
\begin{bmatrix}
-2 - \dfrac{S(\Delta x)^2}{T\Delta t} & 1 & 0 & 0 \\[2ex]
1 & -2 - \dfrac{S(\Delta x)^2}{T\Delta t} & 1 & 0 \\[2ex]
0 & 1 & -2 - \dfrac{S(\Delta x)^2}{T\Delta t} & 1 \\[2ex]
0 & 0 & 1 & -2 - \dfrac{S(\Delta x)^2}{T\Delta t}
\end{bmatrix}
\begin{Bmatrix}
h_2^{n+1} \\[2ex]
h_3^{n+1} \\[2ex]
h_4^{n+1} \\[2ex]
h_5^{n+1}
\end{Bmatrix}
=
$$

$$
\begin{Bmatrix}
-\dfrac{S(\Delta x)^2}{T\Delta t} & h_2^n - h_1 \\[2ex]
-\dfrac{S(\Delta x)^2}{T\Delta t} & h_3^n \\[2ex]
-\dfrac{S(\Delta x)^2}{T\Delta t} & h_4^n \\[2ex]
-\dfrac{S(\Delta x)^2}{T\Delta t} & h_5^n - h_6
\end{Bmatrix}
$$

The coefficient matrix has nonzero entries only along the three center diagonals. This type of matrix is known as a tridiagonal matrix, which is easily solved.

Example 10.3.   FINITE DIFFERENCE APPROXIMATION TO THE DIFFUSION EQUATION

A finite difference approximation to the equation that describes steady-state diffusion of a dissolved substance into a quiescent fluid body in which a first-order reaction occurs has been derived by Celia and Gray (1992) as follows:

$$
D\frac{d^2 u}{dx^2} - Ku = 0 \qquad 0 < x < 1 \; cm \tag{10.51}
$$

$$
u(0) = 0 \qquad u(1) = C_1
$$

where $u(x)$ [M/L^3] is the concentration of the dissolved substance, D [L^2/T] is the diffusion coefficient, K [1/T] is the reaction rate, and C_1 [L^2/T] is a specified concentration at the right boundary. The coefficients D, K, and C_1 are constants that, for this calculation, will be assigned the following values: $D = 0.01$ cm^2/s, $K=0.1$ sec^{-1}, and C_1 = 1.0 g/cm^3.

The first step in deriving an approximate solution to Eq. (10.51) is the discretization step. First, three nodes are chosen, one at each boundary point and a third at $x = 0.5$. Thus three discrete values, (U_1, U_2, U_3), will be computed to approximate the true solution values $(u(0), u(0.5), u(1)) = (u_1, u_2, u_3)$. Because three unknowns are to be determined, three algebraic equations are needed. Two equations come directly from the boundary conditions, namely

$$U_1 = 0 \tag{10.52}$$

$$U_3 = C_1 \tag{10.53}$$

The finite difference approximation to the exact solution is thus required to exactly satisfy the first-type boundary (or Dirichlet) conditions. For all other nodes (in this case, only node 2), finite difference equations are written. Because the governing equation must hold at all points in the region $0 < x < 1$, it must be the case that the equation holds at $x = x_2 = 0.5$. Thus

$$D\frac{d^2u}{dx^2}\bigg|_{x_2} - Ku\big|_{x_2} = 0$$

Taylor series expansion for the second derivative leads to the equality

$$D\left[\frac{u_1 - 2u_2 + u_3}{(\Delta x)^2} + \text{T.E.}\right] - Ku_2 = 0 \tag{10.54}$$

where T.E. is the truncation error, T.E., $u\big|_{x_2}$ is represented without error as u_2, and the constant spacing is denoted by Δx, with $\Delta x = 0.5$. Eq. (10.54) involves exact nodal values u_j ($j = 1,2,3$). To write the appropriate finite difference approximation, the truncation error terms are neglected, resulting in the finite difference equation

$$D\frac{U_1 - 2U_2 + U_3}{(\Delta x)^2} - KU_2 = 0 \tag{10.55}$$

(Note that for this problem $U_1 = u_1$ and $U_3 = u_3$ while $U_2 = u_2$.) Eq. (10.55) is the algebraic equation used to solve for the nodal (finite difference) approximations U_j ($j = 1,2,3$). Combination of Eqs. (10.52), (10.53) and (10.55) leads to

$$
\begin{bmatrix}
1 & 0 & 0 \\
\dfrac{D}{(\Delta x)^2} & -K-\dfrac{2D}{(\Delta x)^2} & \dfrac{D}{(\Delta x)^2} \\
0 & 0 & 1
\end{bmatrix}
\begin{bmatrix} U_1 \\ U_2 \\ U_3 \end{bmatrix}
=
\begin{bmatrix} 0 \\ 0 \\ C_1 \end{bmatrix}
\qquad (10.56)
$$

The solution of this set of equations is $U_1 = 0$, $U_2 = C_1 D/[2D + K(\Delta x)^2]$, $U_3 = C_1$. Using values of $D = 0.01$, $K = 0.1$, $C_1 = 1$, and $\Delta x = 0.5$, the solution is $U_2 = 0.222$. This compares to the exact solution $u(0.5) = 0.171$.

If four nodes are chosen instead such that $\Delta x = 1/3$, then the boundary conditions produce

$$U_1 = 0 \qquad (10.57)$$

$$U_4 = 1 \qquad (10.58)$$

and the two interior finite difference equations must be written, one corresponding to each interior node. The finite difference approximations analogous to Eq. (10.55) are

$$D\frac{U_1 - 2U_2 + U_3}{(\Delta x)^2} - KU_2 = 0 \qquad (10.59)$$

$$D\frac{U_2 - 2U_3 + U_4}{(\Delta x)^2} - KU_3 = 0 \qquad (10.60)$$

Given $\Delta x = 1/3$, and the previous values of D, K, and C_1, the approximation step produces the following set of linear algebraic equations:

$$
\begin{bmatrix}
1 & 0 & 0 & 0 \\
0.09 & -0.28 & 0.09 & 0 \\
0 & 0.09 & -0.28 & 0.09 \\
0 & 0 & 0 & 1
\end{bmatrix}
\begin{bmatrix} U_1 \\ U_2 \\ U_3 \\ U_4 \end{bmatrix}
=
\begin{bmatrix} 0 \\ 0 \\ 0 \\ 1 \end{bmatrix}
\qquad (10.61)
$$

The solution step then produces the approximate solution $U = (0, 0.094, 0.291, 1)$; this compares to the analytical solution $(0, 0.083, 0.320, 1)$.

Example 10.4. NUMERICAL SOLUTION FOR DRAWDOWN TO A WELL, TRANSIENT CONDITIONS

A FORTRAN program for solving the governing equation for drawdown to a well in a confined aquifer under transient conditions (Eq. 10.62) is available (Bedient and Huber,

1992). Assume T = 500 ft²/d and initial head = 20 ft. First, Eq. (10.62) can be written in finite difference form as

$$\frac{\partial^2 h}{\partial x^2} + \frac{\partial^2 h}{\partial y^2} = -\frac{R(x,y)}{T} \tag{10.62}$$

$$\alpha\left(\bar{h}_{i,j}^{n+1} - h_{i,j}^{n+1}\right) + (1-\alpha)\left(\bar{h}_{i,j}^{n} - h_{i,j}^{n}\right) = \frac{a^2 S}{4T} \frac{h_{i,j}^{n+1} - h_{i,j}^{n}}{\Delta t} - \frac{a^2 R_{i,j}^{n}}{4T} \tag{10.63}$$

where

$$\bar{h}_{i,j}^{n+1} = \frac{h_{i-1,j}^{n} + h_{i+1,j}^{n} + h_{i,j-1}^{n} + h_{i,j+1}^{n}}{4}$$

The iterative form of Eq. (10.63) is

$$h_{i,j}^{n+1} = \frac{\left[\alpha\bar{h}_{i,j}^{n+1}\right] + \frac{a^2 S}{4T\Delta t} h_{i,j}^{n} + (1-\alpha)\left[\bar{h}_{i,j}^{n} - h_{i,j}^{n} + \frac{a^2 R_{i,j}^{n}}{4T}\right]}{\frac{a^2 S}{4T\Delta t} + \alpha} \tag{10.64}$$

Assume that flow to the well in the aquifer described is transient. The well is pumping at a rate of 2500 ft³/d. If the storativity of the aquifer is 0.005, the drawdown near the well after one week can be determined. A starting time period of 0.05 days, a factor of 1.4 to increase the time increment (12 time iterations will equal about 7 days), the Crank-Nicolson scheme with $\alpha = 0.5$, a tolerance of 0.001, and no more than 200 iterations in the drawdown computation will be used for each time step. The computed drawdowns from the model are shown in Table 10.1. The solution can be compared

TABLE 10.1 Computed drawdown for Example 10.4

The Drawdown Array at Time = 6.96 is:									
0.88	0.88	0.87	0.85	0.82	0.80	0.78	0.76	0.75	0.74
0.90	0.89	0.88	0.86	0.83	0.81	0.78	0.76	0.75	0.75
0.93	0.93	0.91	0.89	0.86	0.83	0.80	0.78	0.76	0.76
1.00	0.99	0.97	0.93	0.90	0.86	0.82	0.80	0.78	0.78
1.10	1.09	1.05	1.00	0.95	0.90	0.86	0.83	0.81	0.80
1.24	1.22	1.16	1.09	1.02	0.95	0.90	0.86	0.83	0.82
1.45	1.40	1.30	1.19	1.09	1.00	0.93	0.89	0.86	0.85
1.76	1.65	1.47	1.30	1.16	1.05	0.97	0.91	0.88	0.87
2.32	1.98	1.65	1.40	1.22	1.09	0.99	0.93	0.89	0.88
3.56	2.32	1.76	1.45	1.25	1.10	1.00	0.94	0.90	0.89

TABLE 10.2 Comparison of Drawdown at 100 m from a Well using Numerical Solutions with Selected α and Theis Analytical Solutions

Time (days)	Δt	Drawdown in Feet for			Theis
		$\alpha = 0$	$\alpha = 0.5$	$\alpha = 1$	
0.05	0.05	0.00	0.19 (4)	0.33(4)	0.011
0.12	0.07	0.68	1.03 (4)	1.28(5)	0.56
0.24	0.11	2.66	2.98 (5)	3.20(5)	3.00
0.41	0.17	6.57	6.41 (5)	6.37(6)	6.90
0.66	0.25	12.35	11.40 (6)	10.85(8)	11.82
1.04	0.38	18.95	17.54 (7)	16.43(10)	17.56
1.61	0.57	25.90	24.26 (9)	22.76(12)	23.79
2.46	0.85	32.60	31.21 (11)	29.52(16)	30.30
3.74	1.28	42.29	38.25 (14)	36.48(21)	37.06

The numbers in parenthesis indicate the number of iterations used.

against the analytical Theis method at various points in time. It can be shown that the selection of Δx, Δy, Δt, and α will strongly influence the accuracy of the numerical results.

For the explicit case, if Δt is too large, the scheme becomes unstable and yields useless answers. Boundary conditions and choice of error tolerance in the iterative method also contribute to numerical errors. Results in Table 10.2 show the comparison of a numerical example with $Q = 1000$ m³/day, $T = 4.50$ m²/day, $S = 0.0005$, for various values of Δt and α. Values of $\Delta x = \Delta y = 100$ m were chosen. Theis results are also shown.

10.4 FINITE ELEMENT METHODS

One of the difficult problems in flow through porous media involves sharp fronts. A sharp front refers to a large change in a dependent variable over a small distance. Sharp front problems are encountered in both miscible (advective-dispersive flow) and immiscible (multifluid and multiphase flow) problems. The most common complaint about low order, finite-difference methods applied to sharp front problems is that the computed front is "smeared out." The process by which the front becomes smeared is referred to as **numerical dispersion**.

In general, for linear problems, the finite element method can track sharp fronts more accurately, which reduces considerably the numerical diffusion problem. The finite element method, however, has several numerical problems, which include: numerical oscillation, instability, and large computation time requirements as will be seen later.

The finite element analysis of a physical problem can be described as follows (Huyakorn and Pinder, 1983):

1. The physical system is subdivided into a series of finite elements that are connected at a number of nodal points. Each element is identified by its element number and the lines connecting the nodal points situated on the boundaries of the element.

2. A matrix expression, known as the **element matrix**, is developed to relate the nodal variables of each element. The element matrix may be obtained via a mathematical formulation that makes use of either a variational or weighted residual method.

3. The element matrices are combined or assembled to form a set of algebraic equations that describe the entire system. The coefficient matrix of this final set of equations is called the global matrix.

4. Boundary conditions are incorporated into the global matrix equation.

5. The resulting set of simultaneous equations is solved using a variety of techniques such as the Gauss elimination.

Finite element methods will not be covered in this text.

10.5 METHOD OF CHARACTERISTICS (MOC)

The method of characteristics was developed by Garder et al. in 1964 mainly to overcome the numerical dispersion problem resulting from solving the advection-dispersion equation with conventional finite-difference techniques. The MOC has been widely used for simulating the transport of miscible compounds in ground water (Reddell and Sunada, 1970; Bredehoeft and Pinder, 1973; Konikow and Bredehoeft, 1974 and 1978).

The method of characteristics will be illustrated using the 1-D form of the transport equation for a conservative tracer:

$$D_x \frac{\partial^2 C}{\partial x^2} - V \frac{\partial C}{\partial x} = \frac{\partial C}{\partial t} \tag{10.65}$$

where C is the tracer concentration, V is the velocity, D_x is the coefficient of hydrodynamic dispersion, and t is the time.

Equation (10.65) becomes hyperbolic as the dispersion term becomes small with respect to the advection term. The simplified set of equations in terms of an arbitrary curve parameter is associated with the hyperbolic Eq. (10.65) is the MOC. Therefore, Eq. (10.65) can be simplified into the following system of Ordinary Differential Equations (ODEs):

$$\frac{dx}{dt} = V \qquad (10.66)$$

$$\frac{dC}{dt} = D_x \frac{\partial^2 C}{\partial x^2} \qquad (10.67)$$

The solutions of the simplified set of equations are called the characteristic curves of the differential equation. The numerical procedure proposed by Garder et al. (1964) involves both a stationary grid and a set of moving points. The stationary grid is obtained by subdividing the axis into intervals such that:

$$x_i = i \, \Delta x \quad \text{for} \quad i = 0, 1, ..., m - 1 \qquad (10.68)$$

A set of moving points or representative fluid particles with density of P points per grid interval is introduced into the numerical solution. The rate of change in concentration in the ground water is observed in the aquifer when moving with the fluid particle.

The location of each moving point is specified by its coordinate in the finite-difference grid. Initially, the moving points are uniformly distributed throughout the grid system. The initial concentration assigned to each point is the initial concentration associated with the interval containing the point. At each time interval, the moving points in the system are relocated in the flow field in proportion to the flow velocity at their respective location:

$$x_{p,n+1} = x_{p,n} + \Delta t_{n+1/2} V \qquad (10.69)$$

where $x_{p,n+1}$, $x_{p,n}$ are the locations of particle p at time $n+1$ and n, respectively. After moving each point, the coordinates for the points are examined to determine in which interval the point lies. Each interval is assigned a concentration $C_{i,n}^*$ equal to the concentration of all the points that lie in the interval, after having been moved.

Next, the change in concentration due to dispersion is calculated for each interval:

$$\Delta C_{i,n+1/2} = \Delta t_{n+1/2} D_x \Delta x^2 C_{i,n}^* \qquad (10.70)$$

Each moving point is then assigned a new concentration:

$$C_{p,n+1} = C_{p,n} + \Delta C_{i,n+1/2} \qquad (10.71)$$

All points falling within an interval at a given time undergo the same change in concentration due to dispersion. Finally, the concentrations at the stationary grid points are computed for the new time step:

$$C_{i,n+1} = C^*_{i,n} + \Delta C_{i,n+1/2} \tag{10.72}$$

This completes the step from t_n to t_{n+1}, and the procedure is repeated for each subsequent time step.

Khaleel and Reddell (1986) provided listings of MOC programs for solving 1-D and 2-D tracer flow problems. They tested MOC for four cases: (1) longitudinal dispersion in 1-D flow; (2) longitudinal dispersion in 2-D flow; (3) longitudinal and lateral dispersion in 1-D flow; and (4) longitudinal and lateral dispersion in 2-D flow. For example, results from the 1-D MOC solution were compared to the analytical solution for the same problem provided by Ogata and Banks (1961) (see Chapter 6). Khaleel and Reddell's (1986) results showed good agreement between the analytical solution and the MOC numerical solution.

Similar results were obtained for the three other test cases. The reader is referred to the paper for more details on the test cases. It should be mentioned, however, that Khaleel and Reddell found it necessary to use a coordinate transformation to simulate 2-D flow fields more accurately. The coordinate axes were rotated so that an angle of 45° existed between the velocity vector and the transformed coordinate axes.

10.6 NUMERICAL FLOW MODELS

Computer models to simulate saturated ground water flow are typically 2-D or 3-D. Two-dimensional models may be used to simulate flow in the x-y plane or flow in a vertical cross section of the subsurface, and may simulate unsaturated or saturated water flow. Table 10.3 is a list of some of the available flow and contaminant transport models. Models that have seen extensive use include MOC and BIOPLUME II for 2-D contaminant transport with biodegradation (see Chapter 8). MT3D and RT3D are 3-D contaminant transport models that allow the user to incorporate reaction schemes. RT3D has been used to simulate chlorinated solvent reactions (Example 10.5). A detailed presentation of the MODFLOW model, one of the most widely used ground water flow models, serves to illustrate the main concepts involved in flow modeling.

TABLE 10.3   Selected Ground Water Flow and Contaminant Transport Models

Model Name	Model Description	Model Processes	Author(s)
BIOPLUME II (1987)	A two-dimensional model for simulating transport of a single dissolved hydrocarbon species under the influence of oxygen-limited biodegradation, first-order decay, linear sorption, advection, and dispersion.	decay dispersion advection adsorption	H.S. Rifai P.B. Bedient R.B. Borden J.F. Haasbeek
BIOPLUME III (1998)	Successor to BIOPLUME II. Two-dimensional model for reactive transport of multiple hydrocarbons under the influence of advection, dispersion, sorption, first-order decay, and reactant-limited biodegradation.	decay dispersion advection adsorption	H.S. Rifai C.J. Newell J.R. Gonzales S. Dendrou B. Dendrou L. Kennedy J.T. Wilson
CFEST (1987)	A three-dimensional finite-element model to simulate coupled transient flow, solute- and heat-transport in saturated porous media.	advection, dispersion diffusion, adsorption decay	S.K. Gupta C.T. Kinkaid P.R. Meyer C.A. Newbill C.R. Cole
FE3DGW (1985)	Transient or steady-state, finite-element three-dimensional simulation of flow in a large multi-layered groundwater basin.	leakage delayed yield compaction infiltration	S.K. Gupta C.R. Cole F.W. Bond
FEMWASTE/ FECWASTE (1981, 1987)	Two-dimensional transient finite-element model simulates areal or cross-sectional transport of dissolved constituents for a given velocity field in an anisotropic, heterogeneous porous medium	capillarity, convection dispersion, diffusion adsorption, decay	G.T. Yeh D.S. Ward
FLONET, FLOTRANS (1985)	Two-dimensional steady-state groundwater flow (FLONET) and transient solute transport (FLOTRANS) models for cross-sectional problems. FLOTRANS is an extension of FLONET.	decay, dispersion advection, adsorption	E.O. Frind
HELP (1987)	A water budget model for the Hydrologic Evaluation of Landfill Performance.	surface storage, runoff infiltration, percolation evapotranspiration, storage, soil moisture, lateral drainage	P.R. Schroeder J.M. Morgan T.M. Walski A.C. Gibson
MOC (1988)	To simulate transient, two-dimensional, horizontal ground water flow and solute transport in confined/ semiconfined aquifers using finite differences and method of characteristics.	advection, conduction dispersion, diffusion adsorption	L.F Konikow J.D. Bredehoeft

Table 10.3 Selected Ground Water Flow and Contaminant Transport Models (Continued)

Model Name	Model Description	Model Processes	Author(s)
MODFLOW (1988)	A modular three-dimensional finite-difference groundwater model to simulate transient flow in anisotropic, heterogeneous, layered aquifer systems.	evapotranspiration drainage	M.G. McDonald A.W. Harbaugh
MOTIF (1986)	Finite-element model for 1, 2, and 3-D saturated/unsaturated groundwater flow, heat transport, and solute transport in fractured porous media; facilitates single-species radionuclide transport and solute diffusion from fracture to rock matrix.	convection, dispersion diffusion, adsorption decay, advection	V. Guvanasen
MT3D (1990) **MT3DMS** (1998)	A three-dimensional transport model that uses flow fields. Particle tracking and finite difference methods are available to simulate anisotropic, heterogeneous, layered aquifer systems (MT3DMS is a multi-species update).	Advection, dispersion, sorption, decay	C. Zheng
Random Walk (1981)	To simulate one- or two-dimensional, steady/nonsteady flow and solute transport problems in a heterogeneous aquifer with water table and/or confined or semiconfined conditions, using a "random-walk" technique.	advection, dispersion diffusion, adsorption decay, chemical reaction	T.A. Prickett T.G. Naymik C.G. Lonnquist
RT3D (1998)	A three-dimensional reactive transport model. It uses the numerical engine of MT3D for multiple species and contains several pre-defined reaction schemes. User-defined reaction schemes can also be used.	Advection, dispersion, bio-degradation, decay, sorption, monod, user-defined	T.P. Clement Y.Sun B.S. Hooker J.N. Petersen
SEFTRAN (1985)	A two-dimensional finite-element model for simulation of transient flow and transport of heat or solutes in anisotropic, heterogeneous porous media.	advection, dispersion diffusion, adsorption decay	P. Huyakorn
SUTRA (1984)	A finite-element simulation model for two-dimensional, transient or steady-state, saturated-unsaturated, density-dependent ground water flow with transport of energy or chemically reactive single species solutes.	capillarity, convection dispersion, diffusion adsorption, reactions	C.I. Voss
SWIFT II (1982)	A cross-sectional finite-element model for transient horizontal flow of salt and fresh water and analysis of upconing of an interface in a homogeneous aquifer.	buoyancy leakage	A. Verruijt J.B.S. Gan
USGS-3D-FLOW (1982)	A finite-difference model to simulate transient, three-dimensional and quasi-three-dimensional, saturated flow in anisotropic, heterogeneous groundwater systems.	evapotranspiration leakage	P.C. Trescott S.P. Larson

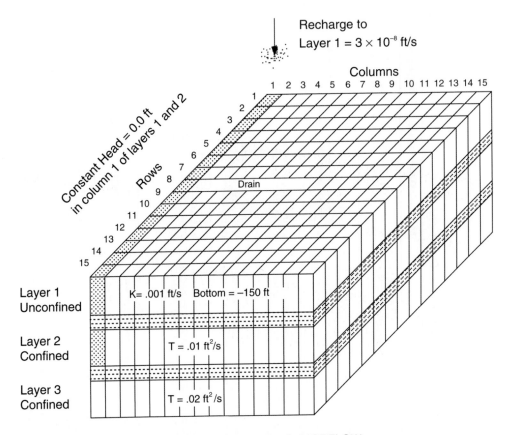

Figure 10.7 Schematic of an aquifer system in MODFLOW.

MODFLOW. MODFLOW, a modular 3-D finite-difference flow code developed by the U. S. Geological Survey (McDonald and Harbaugh, 1988), simulates saturated flow in three dimensions. It was designed such that the user can select a series of packages or modules to be used during a given simulation. Each module or package deals with a specific feature of the hydrologic system which is to be simulated, (e.g., wells, recharge, and rivers). The model contains several interdependent modules, of which the basic, block centered flow, and one of the three solution packages (strongly implicit, slice-successive overrelaxation, or pre-conditioned gradient) are required for every simulation.

MODFLOW can be used to simulate fully 3-D systems (Figure 10.7) and quasi three-dimensional systems in which the flow in aquifers is horizontal and flow through confining beds is vertical. The model can also be used in a two-dimensional mode for simulating flow in a single layer or two-dimensional flow in a vertical cross section. An aquifer can be confined, unconfined or a mixed confined/unconfined. Flow from external stresses, such as flow to wells, areal recharge, evapotranspiration, flow to drains, and flow through riverbeds, can also be simulated.

For unconfined and mixed confined/unconfined aquifers, the elevations of the top and bottom of the aquifer are input and used in the model to calculate the saturated thickness based on the location of the water table within the aquifer. For confined aquifers, thickness is incorporated in the transmissivity distribution specified for the layers (Figure 10.7). Low-conductivity units or clay units are typically not included in the vertical discretization of the system, but rather are included through the use of a conductance term between the upper and lower units separated by the clay. Boundary conditions handled by the model include constant head, no flow and flux boundaries, and general head boundaries (in which a constant head is applied some distance from the edge of the model). Simulation time is divided into stress periods, which are in turn divided into time steps. A stress period is a time during which aquifer stresses (such as pumping and recharge rates) do not change. For transient simulations, the time steps may form a geometric series in which the parameters of the series, the number of time steps, and the multiplier are specified.

The primary output from the model is the head distribution. In addition, a volumetric water budget is provided as a check on the numerical accuracy of the simulation. The model was designed to provide a cell-by-cell flow distribution if required by the user. MODFLOW can also output a "head and flow file" which can be used by several transport models as described in the next section. An example is presented in section 10.8.

10.7 CONTAMINANT TRANSPORT MODELS

Many numerical transport models have been developed over the past 30 years. These models utilize a variety of numerical techniques and solve various forms of the governing transport equation, each subject to a certain set of boundary conditions. In addition, these models may simulate transport in one, two, or three dimensions; in the saturated or unsaturated zone; and miscible or immiscible transport. Table 10.3 provides a listing of some of these models. One should consult the International Ground Water Modeling Center (http://www.mines.edu/research/igwmc/) for other listings of available models. Additional information about modeling, and a listing of publicly available groundwater models is available at the US EPA's Center for Subsurface Modeling Support (http://www.epa.gov/ada/csmos.html), and the USGS's groundwater software information center at http://water.usgs.gov/software.

Reviewing each one of the contaminant transport models listed in Table 10.3 is beyond the scope of this chapter. One class of transport models, however, that is currently evolving and needs to be briefly mentioned is that of 3-D models which use the flow results of MODFLOW. These models use the same grid definitions defined for a MODFLOW run, and perform contaminant transport calculations with assigned sources, sinks, etc. They include:

- MODPATH (Pollock, 1988 and 1989)
- PATH3D (Zheng, 1989)

- MT3D (Zheng, 1990; Zheng, 1992)
- SEAM3D (Widdowson et al., 1997)
- RT3D (Clement, 1998),
- MT3DMS (Zheng and Wang, 1998)

In particular, SEAM3D, MT3DMS, and RT3D are all based on the MT3D engine, and offer similar multi-species contaminant transport support. The remainder of the section will focus on reviewing the MOC model, the MT3D model and MT3Ds successors in an effort to demonstrate the utility of ground water contaminant transport models.

10.7.1 USGS Two-Dimensional Solute Transport Model — MOC

The method of characteristics (MOC) is used in the USGS model to solve the solute transport equation (Figure 10.8). In order to apply the model to a field site, it is necessary to superimpose a block-centered finite-difference grid over the site by specifying the number of cells in the x and y directions (note that the y-axis should be oriented along the main direction of flow at the site). The values of the various parameters in the model can be uniform over the whole domain, or varying over each cell in the domain (see Section 10.5).

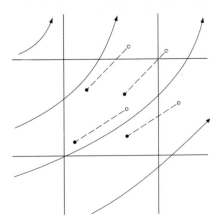

- • Initial location of particle
- ○ New location of particle
- ➔ Flow line and direction of flow
- --- Computed path of particle

Figure 10.8 Particle tracking in USGS two-dimensional Model.

The finite-difference flow equation is solved numerically in MOC using an iterative alternating-direction implicit (ADI) procedure. The aquifer specific parameters in MOC include porosity, longitudinal and transverse dispersivity, thickness of the aquifer, transmissivity, and recharge. There are several model parameters that relate to the numerical methods used in MOC.

Two control parameters are used for the transport equation. The first parameter is used to limit the maximum distance within a cell that a particle can move during a time step. The time step is determined internally in the model and is controlled by four stability criteria that are discussed later in this section. The second parameter is the number of particles in a cell (up to 16). A related parameter is utilized to specify the maximum number of particles in the whole grid. The length of time for which modeling is required is specified in MOC using three parameters: the number of pumping periods in the simulation time, the actual time in years for each pumping period, and the number of time steps in a pumping period.

Source parameters include injection wells, constant concentration cells, and recharge cells. Injection wells and recharge cells basically define a source that leaks into an aquifer, that is, a source that has a flow rate and a concentration associated with it ($Q = Q_0$ and $C = C_0$). A constant concentration cell ($C = C_0$ boundary condition) simulates a source that adds contaminant mass at natural gradients into the aquifer. The MOC model allows the specification of up to five observation wells or monitoring wells at a given site. The history of chemical concentrations in those wells is included in the output from the model.

Boundary conditions in MOC are specified by the user. Types of boundary conditions that can be used include constant head cells or constant flux cells. A constant flux boundary can be used to represent aquifer underflow, well withdrawals, or well injection. A constant head boundary can represent parts of the aquifer where the head will not change in time. Constant head boundaries are simulated by using a high leakage term (1.0 s^{-1}). The resulting rate of leakage into or out of the constant head cell would equal the flux required to maintain the head in the aquifer at the specified altitude. If a constant flux or constant head boundary represents a source, then the chemical concentration must be specified.

The numerical procedure in MOC requires that a no-flow boundary surrounds the modeled site. No-flow boundaries simply preclude the flow of water or contaminants across the boundaries of the cell. Initial conditions in the aquifer also have to be specified: the initial water table, and the initial contaminant concentrations.

The output from the MOC model consists generally of a head map and a chemical concentration map for each node in the grid. Immediately following the head and concentration maps is a listing of the hydraulic and transport errors. If observation wells had been specified, a concentration history for those wells would be included in the output. Detailed examples using BIOPLUME II and III, which are based on the MOC code, modified for biodegradation, are presented in Chapters 8 and 13.

10.7.2 MT3D: A Modular Three-Dimensional Transport Model

MT3D is a transport model that complements the MODFLOW flow simulation model. MT3D solves the advection-dispersion equation with first-order reaction and sorption, using flow fields calculated during a corresponding MODFLOW model run. THE MODEL requires an identical grid layout to MODFLOW, to ensure correspondence between the flow simulation and the transport simulation. Therefore, MT3D can simulate the same range of 2-D and 3-D scenarios as MODFLOW.

MT3D includes five packages that control various aspects of ground water contaminant transport. The basic package contains basic model information, including grid size, and timing information, and is required for all model runs. The advection package controls the solution scheme to be used. MT3D contains four different solution packages, including: Method of Characteristics (MOC), as described in **Section 10.5**; Modified Method of Characteristics (MMOC), a particle tracking method that combines 'backward' particle tracking with an interpolation scheme to reduce the computational burden of a simulation, but does not handle sharp fronts very well; Hybrid Method of Characteristics (HMOC), which combines the standard MOC and the MMOC methods, alternating back and forth depending on the presence of sharp concentration fronts; and Upstream Finite Difference, a nonparticle based method, similar to the forward-differencing scheme described in Section 10.3.

The dispersion package controls the amount of dispersion introduced by the model, while the source-sink mixing package controls sources and sinks of concentration due to wells, drains, recharge, rivers/streams, general head boundaries, and evapotranspiration. MT3D requires only the concentration information for these processes, as the flow characteristics of the sources/sinks are contained in the 'head and flow file' written by MODFLOW. The sources/sinks, however, must correspond to sources and sinks entered into the MODFLOW model. Finally, the reaction model controls radioactive decay or biodegradation that is treated as first-order decay, and sorption using the linear, Freundlich, or Langmuir models.

10.7.3 RT3D: Reactive Transport in 3 Dimensions

RT3D, developed at Battelle Laboratories, is the first and most widely known of the multi-species models which use the numerical engine developed in MT3D (Clement et al, 1998). RT3D is based on the 1997 version of MT3D (DOD Version 1.5), but has extended MT3Ds capabilities with the addition of several reaction packages. RT3D can accommodate multiple sorbed and aqueous phase species with any one of seven pre-defined reaction frameworks, or any other novel framework that the user may define. This allows, for example, natural attenuation processes or an active remediation to be evaluated, and simulations can be applied to modeling contaminants such as heavy metals, explosive, petroleum hydrocarbons, and/or chlorinated solvents. Most of the reactions modeled by RT3D are for simulation of various biodegradation processes.

RT3D's preprogrammed reaction packages include: Instantaneous aerobic decay of BTEX; Instantaneous degradation of BTEX using multiple electron acceptors; Kinetically limited hydrocarbon biodegradation using multiple electron acceptors; Rate-limited sorption reactions; Double Monod method; Sequential decay reactions

$$(PCE \to TCE \to DCE \to VC \to Ethene)$$

and an Aerobic/anaerobic model for PCE/TCE degradation.

RT3D is used in the modeling example which follows (**Example 10.5**) to simulate the sequential biotransformation of PCE at a typical dry cleaner site.

10.7.4 MT3DMS: Multiple-Species Version Of MT3D

MT3DMS includes several enhancements over MT3D, besides multiple species capabilities (Zheng & Wang, 1998). A new advection solver method, called the total variation diminishing scheme (TVD) is included, which allows the user to select from three different solution methods, depending on the requirements of the system being modeled. Other new features are a new implicit generalized conjugate gradient solution method, nonequilibrium sorption, and the multiple-species structure that will accommodate add-on reaction packages, such as those in RT3D or SEAM3D. MT3DMS does not contain any reaction packages in its basic distribution.

10.7.5 SEAM3D: Sequential Electron Acceptor Model for 3D

SEAM3D, developed with funding from the U.S. military, is designed to simulate subsurface transport of multiple solutes under the same aquifer conditions as MODFLOW and MT3D (Widdowson et al., 1997). It includes the following extensions: multiple electron acceptors are simulated (O_2, NO_3^-, Mn(IV), Fe(III), SO_4^{2-}, and CO_2), with biodegradation occurring in sequence, according to laboratory observations; biodegradation is accomplished following Monod kinetics; immobile nonaqueous phase liquid (NAPL) mass can be placed in any cell, and it will dissolve according to equilibrium assumptions. SEAM3D is based on the MT3D transport engine.

10.8 MODELING WITH GRAPHICAL PRE-PROCESSORS

One of the greatest advances in ground water modeling (and surface water modeling) in the last decade is the advent of the graphical pre- and post-processor. Several systems have been developed recently that allow the user to create a conceptual model of subsurface conditions which can then be used to export aquifer parameters into ground water flow and contaminant transport models, such as MODFLOW and MT3D. These systems aid the modeler by assisting in data management. They include the Groundwater Modeling System (GMS) created by the Engineering Computer Graphics Laboratory at Brigham Young University (http://www.ecgl.byu.edu) for the Department of Defense (DoD), and Visual MODFLOW, created by Waterloo Hydrogeologic Software (http://www.flowpath.com). The authors will focus on GMS as an example of this type of software due its utility and general acceptance. The general functionality of the different packages is very similar.

The GMS package is divided into several modules, including the Map module, for creating conceptual models, and for working with observed data; the 3-D grid module, for working with MODFLOW, MT3D, and several other models based on MODFLOW, as well as other 3-D grid data sets; the 3-D scatter module for working with 3-D scatter data sets, such as concentrations and conductivities; the 2-D grid and scatter modules for working with 2-D scatter data and gridded data sets; the borehole module for working with borehole information, including cone penetrometer data; the triangular interconnected network module, for working with surfaces; the solid module for working with stratigraphy; and the 2-D and 3-D mesh modules for working with finite element meshes (which can be used to run finite element models, such as FEMWATER).

In order to create a MODFLOW/MT3D model of a field site, the user will need to create a conceptual model of the site. Often, this will involve importing a base map via an image or a CAD file. The base map can be "registered" to the coordinate system desired by the user by locating three known points on the map. After the base map has been imported, the user can import or hand-place other relevant information, such as boreholes, well locations and observed concentrations, and source zones. Much of this information can be entered into the conceptual model before a model grid has been created. This allows for greater flexibility in deciding what the optimal model grid will be, before the process of assigning values to specific grid cells begins, and allows the user to change grid definitions without losing the information entered into the grid.

GMS also offers several interpolation/extrapolation options for spatially variable data. For example, one might have hydraulic conductivity observations at several locations in the model area (from slug tests or pump tests). Using the interpolation methods (inverse distance weighted, nearest neighbor, kriging, etc.), the software will estimate the values for each point on the model grid. Data calculators are available to manipulate 2-D and 3-D data sets, with standard mathematical functions, as well as minimum, maximum, etc.

Once the model is built, the user can run MODFLOW, MT3D, RT3D, and other models directly from GMS, and read the output into GMS for post-analysis. Post-analysis can consist of drawing 2-D layer contours, taking cross sections, drawing 3-D contours, comparisons with observed data, and several other options. One of the major advantages of using an integrated pre- and post-processor is the ease of calibration of a model. The integration of observed data into the modeling system allows the user to compare model outputs with observed data in several ways, either through plotting contours of modeled and observed data, or by plotting x-y scatter plots of modeled versus observed values, in which a 45° angle represents a direct match, or by plotting a time series of observed and modeled concentrations for a single observation point (Holder et al., 1998).

Example 10.5   MODELING A DRY CLEANER SITE WITH GMS

GMS was used to create MODFLOW and RT3D models of a dry cleaner site in Houston, Texas, in which PCE contamination has impacted a local neighborhood. Contamination related to dry cleaning facilities has become an issue in the 1990s analogous to LPST releases in the 1980s. Dry cleaners are generally small and located near residential neighborhoods, making chemical discharges a serious health concern since the solvent used to dry clean, perchloroethylene (PCE) is a suspected carcinogen with a drinking water maximum contaminant level of 5 μg/L. Dry cleaners use 56% of the perchlorethylene in the United States (Izzo, 1992)

Aside from obvious contamination sources typically associated with any chemical operation, such as tank storage areas, process equipment, and loading docks, dry cleaners have additional sources that may contaminate the subsurface. Inadequate PCE recovery equipment may lead to PCE entering the sanitary sewer lines. PCE may then be released to the subsurface from flaws and joints in the piping, or by degrading certain types of polymer piping, such as ABS or PVC (Ranney and Parker, 1995). Many dry cleaners also have below ground lint traps, usually constructed from concrete. PCE may migrate through cracks in the concrete as well. Contamination from these sources may not be easily detectable and may constitute the bulk of the chemical release from the dry cleaner (See Figure 4.10).

PCE in the organic phase is a dense nonaqueous phase liquid (DNAPL), as described in Chapter 11, and will pass through the soil matrix, leaving small droplets of residual NAPL behind. As ground water sweeps through the aquifer, the PCE will slowly dissolve into the fresh ground water, with a solubility of about 150 mg/L. The residual PCE is a continuing source of contamination to the aquifer that may affect ground water quality long after the dry cleaner closes. The pools are difficult to find so it is generally accepted as a rule of thumb that if ground water concentrations greater than 1% of the aqueous solubility are detected, it is a strong possibility that a nonaqueous phase exists (Pankow and Cherry, 1996 and Chapter 11).

Two dry cleaner facilities were located in the contaminated area at the Houston site (Figure 10.9). The first operated from the mid-1970s until 1996, while the second opened in 1993 and is still in operation. Beneath the surficial clay in Houston, the affected aquifer is silty/sandy with a hydraulic conductivity of 5 × 10^{-3} cm/s. The aquifer is unconfined with the water table at about 20 ft below ground surface (BGS), and a clay layer approximately 30 - 35 ft BGS. The gradient of the ground water is approximately 0.005, in a generally southward direction. A stream north/northeast of the facilities provides shallow ground water recharge in the region.

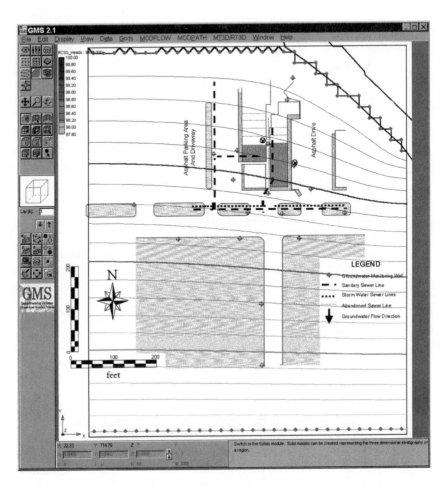

Figure 10.9 Ground water contours at two dry cleaner sites in Houston. The dry cleaners are the dark gray buildings.

Samples taken from the site show the primary concentration of the plume to be located in the area between the two cleaners. Contamination has moved off-site and migrated at least 2000 ft downgradient, and the plume is approximately 500 ft wide. The presence of TCE, the primary product of a PCE dechlorination, indicates that *in situ* biotransformation is occurring at this site. The site does not show direct evidence of a DNAPL since the maximum concentrations are less than the 1.5 mg/L rule of thumb (1% of 150 mg/L). However, the PCE concentrations are still much higher than the 5 μg/L limit needed to comply with drinking water standards.

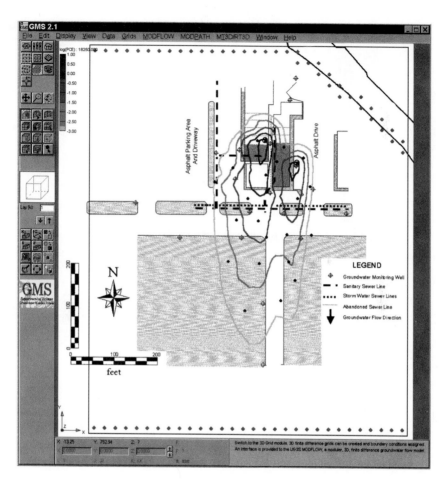

Figure 10.10 PCE concentrations modeled at the two dry cleaner sites.

The shallow aquifer characteristics were entered into the "map" module of GMS, along with two wells, representing sources of contamination at each site. Using resources such as site maps and USGS Digital Raster Graphics (DRGs) to locate relevant features, such as the stream, model boundaries were chosen, a grid was created, and the aquifer information from the map module was transferred to the MODFLOW and RT3D models. After the MODFLOW and RT3D models were created, they were checked with a built-in model checker, which looks for common modeling errors (e.g., zeros in the hydraulic conductivity field, etc.), and several model runs were performed. First, MODFLOW was run to get the head and flow values, which were checked against observed data. At this time, modifications needed to calibrate the flow modeling are done (see Section 10.9), then RT3D is run, using the heads and flows calculated in MODFLOW. Figure 10.10 shows the resulting PCE concentrations for 1998.

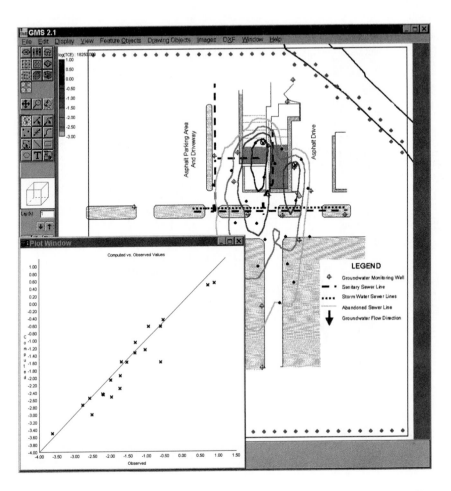

Figure 10.11 TCE concentrations at the dry cleaner sites, along with a calibration plot showing a comparison of computed v. measured data.

Several methods of comparison between modeled and observed values are possible. A visual comparison of contours can give a general sense of the plume size, maxima locations, etc. An *x-y* plot of modeled vs. observed data (Figure 10.11) provides a different comparison, which can be extremely useful in determining goodness of fit. From the general closeness of the data to the 45° line, the dry cleaner model fits the observed data reasonably well. Due to the wide variation in measured values of concentrations and hydraulic conductivities, it is often useful to plot these variables on a logarithmic scale, as shown in Figure 10.11. The logarithmic scale emphasizes the difference between measurements that span several orders of magnitude. In this case, using a linear scale would make concentrations of 0.001 mg/L and 0.1 mg/L almost indistinguishable.

The modeling of this site was made simpler and more effective using the pre- and post-processor GMS; which represents a significant improvement in time and effort over earlier methods in the 1980s. The calibration tools and the integrated visualization methods were used to help assure the model's accuracy. The prospective modeler must remember, however, that the accuracy and usefulness of a model are dependent on the available input data, and on the proper application of the modeling techniques described in Section 10.9.

10.9 APPLYING NUMERICAL MODELS TO FIELD SITES

Good field data are essential when using a model for simulating existing flow and/or contaminant conditions at a site or when using a model for predictive purposes. However, an attempt to model a system with insufficient data may be useful because it may serve as a method for identifying those areas where detailed field information needs to be collected. As mentioned earlier, a good modeling methodology will increase confidence in modeling results. In this section, emphasis is placed on outlining the procedure of designing and applying a selected ground water model to a field site. This step corresponds to item #4 in the modeling protocol established by Anderson and Woessner (1992), which was discussed in Section 10.1.

10.9.1 Model Set-Up

Once a conceptual model has been developed for the site and a computer model selected, it becomes necessary to interpret the conceptual model, and translate it into an input file that can then be used by the model. The interpretation process begins by analyzing the hydrogeologic and water quality data collected at the site, with the objective of predicting trends in the data and estimating the parameters required to run the model.

Data collection and analysis. Most site characterization efforts include identification of the subsurface geology, history of contamination, and water quality at the site. The stratigraphy is determined using soil borings, well logs, and geophysical tools. The subsurface geologic data usually has to be interpreted into values of the hydraulic conductivity and/or transmissivity, thickness of unit, and porosity, which can then be used as input to the model. The elevation of the water table and/or the potentiometric surface measured at discrete monitoring wells can be interpreted by constructing water level contours to determine the general direction of ground water flow.

Water quality data collected at specified time intervals from monitoring wells are generally analyzed to determine the trends in the spatial and temporal distributions of chemicals at the site. In many cases, the collected water quality data for a specific chemical are contoured to determine the extent of the plume of contamination.

For transport models, additional parameters that describe the physical, chemical, and biological properties of the chemicals of concern are necessary. A history of the chemical release (when it happened, how much was released) is an input requirement when one is attempting to simulate an existing contaminant plume. Defining whether a chemical is subject to biotic (or biological) and/or abiotic (chemical) reactions is essential for developing more representative models.

Parameter estimation. Obtaining the information necessary for modeling is not an easy task. Some data may be obtained from existing reports and studies, but more often it is necessary to rely on field characterization efforts. Transmissivity and the storage coefficient are typically obtained from pumping test results. Alternatively, the hydraulic conductivity is obtained from slug tests. For unconsolidated sands, the hydraulic conductivity may be obtained from laboratory grain size analyses or from permeability tests using permeameters.

Caution must be exercised when interpreting field measurements of hydraulic conductivity for use as input in ground water models. For instance, transmissivity values from pump tests are volume averaged; thus, the measured transmissivity is representative of the average properties of the aquifer zone influenced by the pump test. Hydraulic conductivity values, on the other hand, determined from slug tests are point values and only representative of the local zone where the slug test was conducted. Also, hydraulic conductivity values obtained from permeameter tests typically are several orders of magnitude smaller than values measured in situ.

Hydrologic stresses include pumping, recharge, and evapotranspiration. Of the three, pumping rates are the easiest to estimate. Recharge is one of the most difficult parameters to estimate. Recharge refers to the volume of infiltrated water that crosses the water table and becomes part of the ground water flow system (Anderson and Woessner, 1992). Discharge, on the other hand, refers to ground water that moves upward across the water table and discharges directly to the surface or the unsaturated zone. It is common for modelers to simulate recharge as a spatially uniform rate across the water table equal to some percentage of average annual precipitation. It is important to note, however, that this approach is very simplistic and does not take into account the spatial and temporal variations in recharge rates. Evapotranspiration may be determined from field measurements using lysimeters and/or studies of the vegetation.

10.9.2 Calibration

Calibrating a model is the process of demonstrating that the model is capable of producing field-measured values of the unknown model variable. For the case of ground water flow, for example, calibration is accomplished by finding a set of parameters, boundary and initial conditions, and stresses that produce simulated values of heads and/or fluxes that match measured values within a specified range of error.

Finding this set of parameter values has been compared by Anderson and Woessner (1992) to solving what is known as the **inverse problem**. In the ground water flow inverse problem, for instance, the objective is to determine values of the parameters from information about heads. The inverse problem contrasts with the forward problem, in which the specified model parameters are used to calculate heads.

There are two ways to achieve model calibration: (1) manual trial-and-error selection of parameters; and (2) automated parameter estimation. In trial-and-error calibration, parameter values are initially assigned to the grid. The initial parameter values are adjusted in sequential model runs to match simulated data to the calibration targets. Trial-and-error calibration may produce non-unique solutions because different combinations of parameters can yield essentially the same results. Also the trial-and-error process is quite subjective and is influenced by the modeler's expertise.

Automated inverse modeling may not be subjective and is not influenced by the modeler; however, it suffers from being complicated and computer intensive. Automated inverse modeling is also associated with instability problems and non-uniqueness in some cases. With the indirect approach, an inverse code automatically checks the head solution and adjusts parameters in a systematic way so as to minimize an objective function which compares the model calculated values of head to the measured values.

The results of the calibration should be evaluated relative to the measured values both qualitatively and quantitatively. To date, there is no standard protocol for evaluating model calibrations. A qualitative evaluation of the calibration involves comparing trends in the simulated results to those observed from the measured data. For example, a visual comparison could be made between contour maps of measured and simulated heads or concentrations to determine the similarities and differences between them. However, contour maps of field data themselves may include some error introduced by contouring and therefore should not be used as the only evaluation measure of calibration.

A quantitative evaluation of the calibration involves listing the measured and simulated values and determining some average of the algebraic differences between them. Two methods are commonly used to express this difference:

$$\text{Mean Error} = \frac{1}{n}\sum_{i=1}^{n}(x_m - x_s)_i \tag{10.94}$$

$$\text{Root Mean Squared Error} = \sqrt{\frac{1}{n}\sum_{i=1}^{n}(x_m - x_s)_i^2} \tag{10.95}$$

where x_m and x_s are the measured and simulated values, respectively.

10.9.3 Sensitivity Analysis

The purpose of a sensitivity analysis is to quantify the effects of uncertainty in the estimates of model parameters on model results. During a sensitivity analysis, calibrated values for hydraulic conductivity, recharge, boundary conditions, etc., are systematically changed within a pre-established range of applicable values. The magnitude of change in heads and/or concentrations from the calibrated solution is a measure of the sensitivity of the solution to that particular parameter. The results of the sensitivity analysis are expressed as the effects of the parameter change on the average measurer of error (mean error or root mean square error) and on the spatial distribution of heads and/or concentrations.

10.9.4 Model Verification

Because of uncertainties in parameter estimates for a given site, the calibrated model parameters may not accurately represent the system under a different set of boundary conditions or hydrologic stresses. In a typical verification exercise, values of parameters and hydrologic stresses determined during calibration are used to simulate a transient response for which a set of field data exists (Anderson and Woessner, 1992). Examples of transient data sets include pumping test data and changes in water levels in response to pumping. In the absence of a transient data set, however, the model can be tested using a second set of steady-state data.

Unfortunately, sometimes it is not possible to verify a model because only one data set exists and it is usually used in the calibration process. A calibrated but unverified model can still be used to make predictions as long as sensitivity analyses of both the calibrated and predictive model are performed and evaluated.

10.9.5 Prediction

Prediction is one of the more common motivations for modeling. In a predictive simulation, the parameters determined during calibration are used to predict future conditions or the response of the system to future events. The length of time for which prediction may be required is an important consideration in model selection and design. For example, permitting for deep well injection of hazardous wastes requires contaminant transport modeling horizontally and vertically for 10,000 years. This implies that if a numerical model is used, care should be taken to ensure a large enough grid to allow for 10,000 years of transport.

The prediction process should be associated with a sensitivity analysis similar to that completed after calibration. Even though the calibrated model has been verified and subjected to a sensitivity analysis, the model may not give accurate results when stressed in some new way.

SUMMARY

Numerical models of groundwater flow and contaminant transport are designed to allow a modeler to simulate the groundwater conditions in an aquifer based on measurable aquifer and contaminant characteristics. The model is a mathematical representation of real-world physical, chemical, and/or biological processes, and can be used to predict future contamination, to interpret system dynamics, or to screen field sites for possible contamination problems. The mathematical representation is implemented using approximation techniques known as Finite Element, Finite Difference, or Method of Characteristics. An important part of modeling a site is the development of a conceptual model, which represents the parameters and processes that are important at the site. This conceptual model can be designed on paper or with the aid of new modeling software. The numerical model is assembled by interpreting information from the conceptual model.

REFERENCES

Allen, M. B. and G. F. Pinder, "Collocation Simulation of Multiphase Porous-Medium Flow," *Soc. Pet. Eng.* J. 23, 135-142. 1983.

Anderson, M. P., "Using models to simulate the movement of contaminants through ground water flow systems," Critical Reviews in Environmental Control, 9 (2) 97-156, 1979.

Anderson, M. P. and W. W. Woessner, *Applied Ground Water Modeling*, San Diego, CA, Academic Press, Inc., 1992.

Aziz, K. and A. Settari, *Petroleum Reservoir Simulation*, England, Essex, Applied Sci. Publ., 1979.

Banerjee, P. K., R. Butterfield and G. R. Tomlin, "Boundary Element Methods for Two-Dimensional Problems of Transient Ground Water Flow," *Int. J. Num. Anal. Method. Geomech.* 5, 15-31, 1981.

Bangia, V. K., C. Bennett, A. Reynolds, R. Raghavan and G. Thomas, "Alternating Direction Collocation Methods for Simulating Reservoir Performance," Paper SPE 7414, *Proc.*, 53rd Annual Technical Conference and Exhibition of Soc. Pet. Eng. AIME, Houston, Texas, 1978.

Bathe, K. J., and E. L. Wilson, *Numerical Methods in Finite Element Analysis*, Englewood Cliffs, New Jersey, Prentice-Hall, 1976.

Bear, J. and A. Verruijt, *Modeling Ground Water Flow and Pollution*, Dordrecht, Holland, D. Reidel Publishing Company, 1987.

Bedient, P. B. and W. C. Huber, *Hydrology and Floodplain Analysis,* 2nd Ed., New York, Addison-Wesley, 1992.

Bittinger, M. W., H. R. Duke and R. A. Longenbaugh, "Mathematical Simulations for Better Aquifer Management," Publ. no. 72 IASH, pp. 509-519, 1967.

Brebbia, C. A. and S. Walker, *Boundary Element Techniques in Engineering,* London Butterworths, 1980.

Bredehoeft, J.D. and G. F. Pinder, "Mass Transport in Flowing Ground Water," *Water Resources Res.* 9, 192-210, 1973.

Brutsaert, W., "Numerical Solutions of Multiphase Well Flow," *ASCE J. Hydraul. Div.*, 99 (HY1), 1981-2001, 1973.

Carnahan, B., H. A. Luther, and J. O. Wilkes, *Applied Numerical Methods*, New York, John Wiley and Sons, 1969.

Celia, M. A. and G. F. Pinder, "Alternating Direction Collocation Solution to the Transport Equation," *Proc.*, of the 3rd International Conference on Finite Elements in Water Resources, S. Y.

Wang, C. V. Alsonso, C. A. Brebbia, W. G. Gray, and G. F. Pinder, eds., pp. 3.36-3.48. University of Mississippi, 1980.

Celia, M.A. and W. G. Gray, *Numerical Methods for Differential Equations*, New Jersey, Prentice Hall, 1992.

Chang, P. W. and B. A. Finlayson, "Orthogonal Collocation on Finite Elements for Elliptic Equations," *Advances in Computer Methods for Partial Differential Equations III*, R. Vichnevetsky, ed., 79-86. New Brunswick, New Jersey, IMACS, 1977.

Chung, T. J., *Finite Element Analysis in Fluid Dynamics*, New York, McGraw-Hill, 1979.

Clement, T. P., Y. Sun, B. S. Hooker, and J. N. Petersen, "Modeling Multispecies Reactive Transport in Ground Water." *Ground Water Monitoring & Remediation*, 18 (2): 79-92, 1998.

Clough, R. W., "The Finite Element Method in Plane Stress Analysis," *ASCE J. Struc. Div. Proc. 2nd Conf. Electronic Computation*, 345-378, 1960.

Cook, R. D., *Concepts and Applications of Finite Element Analysis*, New York, John Wiley and Sons, 1974.

Cooley, R. L., "A Finite Difference Method for Unsteady Flow in Variably Saturated Porous Media: Application to a Single Pumping Well," *Water Resources Res.*, 7 (6), 1607-1625, 1971.

Crichlow, H. B., *Modern Reservoir Engineering- A Simulation Approach*, Englewood Cliffs, New Jersey, Prentice-Hall, 1977.

Douglas, J., Jr., and T. Dupont, *Collocation Methods for Parabolic Equations in a Single Space Variable,* Berlin and New York, Springer-Verlag, 1974.

Dubois, M. and M. Buysee, "Transient Heat Transfer Analysis by the Boundary Integral Method," *Proc.* Second Int. Seminar on Recent Advances in Boundary Element Methods, 137-154. C. Brebbia, ed., CML Publications, University of Southampton, 1980.

Finlayson, B. A., *The Method of Weighted Residuals and Variational Principles with Application in Fluid Mechanics, Heat and Mass Transfer*, New York, Academic Press, 1972.

Forsythe, G.E. and W. R. Wasow, *Finite-Difference Methods for Partial Differential Equations*, New York, John Wiley & Sons, Inc., 1960.

Freeze, R. A. and P. A. Witherspoon, "Theoretical Analysis of Regional Ground Water Flow; 1. Analytical and Numerical Solutions to the Mathematical Model," *Water Resources Res.*, 2, 641-656, 1966.

Freeze, R. A., "Three-Dimensional, Transient, Saturated-Unsaturated Flow in a Ground Water Basin," *Water Resources Res.*, 7 (2), 347-366, 1971.

Frind, E. O. and G. F. Pinder, "A Collocation Finite Element Methods for Potential Problems in Irregular Domains," *Int. J. Num. Methods Eng.*, 14, 681-701, 1979.

Gallagher, R. H., *Finite Element Analysis Fundamentals*, Englewood Cliffs, New Jersey, Prentice-Hall, 1975.

Garder, A. O., D. W. Peaceman and A. L. Pozzi, Jr., "Numerical Calculation of Multidimensional Miscible Displacement by the Method of Characteristics," *Soc. Pet. Eng. J.*, 4(1), 26-36, 1964.

Green, D. W., H. Dabiri, and C. F. Weinaug, "Numerical Modeling of Unsaturated Ground Water Flow and Comparison to a Field Experiment," *Water Resources Res.*, 6, 862-874, 1970.

Hinton, E. and D. R. J. Owen, *An Introduction to the Finite Element Computations*, Chapter 1-4, Swansea, United Kingdom Pineridge Press, 1979.

Holder, Anthony W., P. B. Bedient and J. B. Hughes, "TCE and 1,2-DCE Biotransformation Inside a Biologically Active Zone," *Proceedings* The First International Conference on Remediation of Chlorinated and Recalcitrant Compounds, Monterey, CA, May 18-21, 1:219-224, 1998.

Houstis, E. N. W. F. Mitchell, and T. S. Papatheodorou, "A C^1-collocation Method for Mildly Nonlinear Elliptic Equations on General 2-D Domains," *Advances in Computer Methods for Partial Differential Equations III*, R. Vichnevetsky and R. S. Stepleman, Eds., New Brunswick, New Jersey, IMACS, 1979.

Huebner, K. H., *Finite Element Method for Engineers*, New York, John S. Wiley and Sons, 1975.

Hunt, B., *Mathematical Analysis of Ground Water Resources*, London, Butterworths, 1983.

Huyakorn, P. S. and G. F. Pinder, *Computational Methods in Subsurface Flow*, San Diego, California, Academic Press, Inc., 1983.

Istok, J., *Ground Water Modeling by the Finite Element Method*, Water Resources Monograph 13, American Geophysical Union, Washington, D.C, 1989.

Izzo, V.J. *Dry Cleaners—A Major Source of PCE in Groundwater*, California Regional Water Quality Control Board. Central Valley Region. March 1992.

Jawson, M. A. and A. R. Ponter, "An Integral Equation Solution of the Torsion Problem," *Proc. R. Soc. London, Ser. A* 273, 237-246, 1963.

Jawson, M. A., and G. T. Symm, *Integral Equation Methods in Potential Theory and Elastostatics*, New York, Academic Press, 1977.

Javandel, I., C. Doughty, and C. F. Tsang, "Ground Water Transport: Handbook of Mathematical Models," American Geophysical Union, Washington, D.C. *Water Resources Monograph* 10. 228 pp, 1984.

Kelly, L.G., *Handbook of Numerical Methods and Applications*, Reading, MA, Addison-Wesley Publ. Co., 1967.

Khaleel, R. and D. L. Reddell, "MOC Solutions of Convective-Dispersion Problems," *Ground Water*, vol. 24, no. 6, pp. 798-807, 1986.

Konikow, L. F. and J. D. Bredehoeft, "Modeling Flow and Chemical Quality Changes in an Irrigated Stream-aquifer System," *Water Resources Res.*, v. 10, no. 3, pp. 546-562, 1974.

Konikow, L. F. and J. D. Bredehoeft, "Comptuer Model of Two Dimensional Solute Transport and Dispersion in Ground Water," *Techniques of Water Resources Investigation*, Book 7, Chapter C2, U.S. Geological Survey, Reston, VA,, 1978.

Lapidus, L. and G. F. Pinder, *Numerical Solution of Partial Differential Equations in Science and Engineering*, New York, John S. Wiley and Son, 1982.

Lennon, G. P., P. L-F Liu, and J. A. Liggett, "Boundary Integral Equation Solution to Axisymmetric Potential Flows: 1. Basic Formulation," *Water Resources Res.*, 15(5), 1102-1106, 1979.

Liggett, J. A. and P. L-F Liu, *The Boundary Integral Equation Method for Porous Media Flow*, London, George Allen and Unwin, 1983.

Liggett, J. A. and P. L-F. Liu, "Unsteady Flow in Confined Aquifers--A Comparison of Two Boundary Integral Methods," *Water Resources Res.*, 15(4), 861-866, 1979.

Liggett, J. A., "Location of Free Surface in Porous Media," *ASCE Hydraul. Div*, 103 (HY4), 353-365, 1977.

Mathews, J. H., *Numerical Methods for Mathematics, Science, and Engineering*, 2nd Edition, New Jersey, Prentice Hall, 1992.

McDonald, M.G. and A. W. Harbaugh, *A Modular Three-Dimensional Finite-Difference Ground-Water Flow Model*, Book 6 Modeling Techniques, Scientific Software Group, Washington, DC, 1988.

Mercer, J. W. and C. R. Faust, *Ground-Water Modeling*, NWWA, 2nd Ed. 1986.

National Research Council, *Ground Water Models: Scientific and Regulatory Applications*, Schwartz, F. W., et al., eds., Washington, D.C., National Academy Press, 1990.

Norrie, D. H. and G. DeVries, *An Introduction to Finite Element Methods*, New York, Academic Press, 1978.

Ogata, A., and R. B. Banks, "A Solution of the Differential Equation of Longitudinal Dispersion in Porous Media," U.S. Geol. Survey Prof. Paper 411-A. U. S. G. P. O., Washington, DC. 7 pp, 1961.

Oster, C. A., J. C. Sonnichsen, and P. T. Jaske, "Numerical Solution of the Convective Diffusion Equation," *Water Resources Res.*, 6, 1746-1752, 1970.

Pankow, J.F., Cherry, J. A. *Dense Chlorinated Solvents and Other DNAPLs in Groundwater*, Portland, Waterloo Press, 1996.

Peaceman, D. W. and H. H. Rachford, Jr., "The Numerical Solution of Parabolic and Elliptic Differential Equations," *J. Soc. Ind. Appl. Math.*, 3, 28-41, 1955.

Peaceman, D. W. and H. H. Rachford, Jr., "Numerical Calculation of Multidimensional Miscible Displacement," *Soc. Pet. Eng. J.*, 2, 327-339, 1962.

Peaceman, D. W., *Fundamentals of Numerical Reservoir Simulation*, Amsterdam, Elsevier, 1977.

Pinder, G. F. and J. D. Bredehoeft, "Application of the Digital Computer for Aquifer Evaluation," *Water Resources Res.*, 4, 1069-1093, 1968.

Pinder, G. F., and H. H. Cooper, Jr., "A Numerical Technique for Calculating the Transient Position of the Salt Water Front," *Water Resources Res.* 6 (3), 875-882, 1970.

Pinder, G. F., E. O. Frind, M. A. Celia, "Ground Water Flow Simulation Using Collocation Finite Elements," *Proc.* of the 2nd International Conference on Finite Elements in Water Resources, C. A. Brebbia, W. G. Gray and G. F. Pinder, eds., 1.171-1.185. Plymouth, England, Pentech Press, 1978.

Pinder, G.F. and W. G. Gray, *Finite Element Simulation in Surface and Subsurface Hydrology*, New York, Academic Press, 1977.

Pinder, G. F., "A Galerkin-Finite Element Simulation of Ground Water Contamination on Long Island, New York," *Water Resources Res.*, 9, 1657-1669, 1973.

Pollock, D. W., "Semianalytical Computation of Path Lines of Finite-Difference Models," *Ground Water* 26(6), pp. 743-750, 1988.

Pollock, D. W., "Documentation of Computer Programs to Complete and Display Pathlines Using Results from the U.S. Geological Survey Modular Three-Dimensional Finite-Difference Ground-Water Model," USGS, Open File Report 89-381, 1989.

Prickett, T. A. and C. G. Lonnquist, "Selected Digital Computer Techniques for Ground Water Resource Evaluation," *Illinois Water Survey Bull*, 55, 62 p, 1971.

Prickett, T.A., "Modeling Techniques for Ground Water Evaluation," *Advances in Hydroscience*, vol. 10, New York, Academic Press, pp. 1-143, 1975.

Ranney, T.A., Parker, L.V. *Susceptability of ABS, FEP, FRE, FRP PTFE, and PVC Well Casing to Degradation by Chemicals,* US Army Corps of Engineers, Cold Regions Research and Engineering Laboratory, Special Report 95-1, January 1995.

Reddell, D. L. and D. K. Sunada, "Numerical Simulation of Dispersion in Ground Water Aquifers," *Hydrol*, Paper 41, Fort Collins, Colorado, Colorado State University, 1970.

Remson, I., G. M. Hornberger, and F. J. Molz, *Numerical Methods in Subsurface Hydrology*, New York, Wiley-Interscience, 1971.

Remson, I., C. A. Appel, and R. A. Webster, "Ground Water Models Solved by Digital Computer," *ASCE J. Hydraul. Div.*, 91 (HY3), 133-147, 1965.

Rizzo, F. J. and D. J. Shippy, "A Method of Solution for Certain Problems of Transient Heat Conduction," *AIAA J.* 89(11), 2004-2009, 1970.

Rushton, K. R. and S. C. Redshaw, *Seepage and Ground Water Flow*, New York, John S. Wiley and Sons, 1979.

Segerlind, L. J., *Applied Finite Element Analysis*, New York, Wiley, 1976.

Shamir, U. Y. and D. F. Harleman, "Dispersion in Layered Porous Media," *ASCE J. Hydraul. Div.*, 93, 237-260, 1967.

Sincovec, R. F., "Generalized Collocation Methods for Time-Dependent, Nonlinear Boundary-Value Problems, *Soc. Pet. Eng. J.*, 345-352, 1977.

Tanji, K. K., G. R. Dutt, J. L. Paul and L. D. Donen, "II. A Computer Method for Predicting Salt Concentrations in Soils at Variable Moisture Contents," *Hilgardia* 38, 307-318, 1967.

Trescott, P.C., G. F. Pinder and S. P. Larson, "Finite-Difference Model for Aquifer Simulation in Two Dimensions with Results of Numerical Experiments," *U.S. Geological Survey Techniques of Water Resources Investigations*, Book 7, Chapter C1, 116 p., 1976

van der Heijde, P. K. M., A. I. El-Kadi and S. A. Williams, *Ground Water Modeling: An Overview and Status Report*, U. S. Environmental Protection Agency, Ada, OK, 1988.

Wang, H. F., and M. P. Anderson, *Introduction to Ground Water Modeling Finite Difference and Finite Element Methods*, San Francisco, CA., W. H. Freeman and Company, 237 p., 1982

Widdowson, M. A., D. W. Waddill, Ruiz, C. E., "SEAM3D: A Numerical Model For Three-Dimensional Solute Transport And Sequential Electron Acceptor-Based Bioremediation In Groundwater," *Proceedings* Congress of the International Association of Hydraulic Research, Volume C, San Francisco, CA, USA, 1997.

Wylie, C. R., and L. C. Barrett, *Advanced Engineering Mathematics,*, 5th E., New York, McGraw-Hill, 1982.

Zheng, C., MT3D: A Modular Three-Dimensional Transport Model for Simulation of Advection, Dispersion and Chemical Reactions of Contaminants in Groundwater Systems. Report to the USEPA, 170 pp., 1990.

Zheng, C., M. P. Anderson, and K. R. Bradbury, "Effectiveness of Hydraulic Methods for Controlling Groundwater Pollution," In *Groundwater Contamination,* L. M. Abriola, ed., IAHS Publication No. 185, pp. 173-179, 1989.

Zheng, C., G. C. Bennett, and C. B. Andrews, Reply to Discussion of "Analysis of Ground Water Remedial Alternatives at a Superfund Site," *Ground Water,* vol. 30, no. 3, pp. 440-442, 1992.

Zheng, C., and G. D. Bennett, *Applied Contaminant Transport Modeling: Theory and Practice,* New York, Van Nostrand Reinhold, 1995.

Zheng, C. and P.P. Wang, MT3DMS, A Modular Three-Dimensional Transport Model, Technical Report, US Army Corps of Engineers Waterways Experiment Station, Vicksburg, MS., 1998.

Zienkiewicz, O. C., *The Finite Element Method*, 3rd ed., London, McGraw-Hill, 1977.

CHAPTER 11

NONAQUEOUS PHASE LIQUIDS

11.1 INTRODUCTION

Nonaqueous Phase Liquids (NAPLs) are immiscible (undissolved) hydrocarbons in the subsurface that exhibit different behavior and properties from those of dissolved contaminant plumes. While dissolved plumes are invisible to the naked eye and travel with the flow of ground water, NAPLs form a visible, separate oily phase in the subsurface whose migration is governed by gravity, buoyancy, and capillary forces. Because of the variety in their chemical composition, the behavior of NAPLs can be very different: Some light NAPLs (LNAPLs), after moving downward through the vadose zone, can float and move on top the water table, while other, more dense NAPLs (DNAPLs) can move downward past the water table and penetrate deep into the saturated zone.

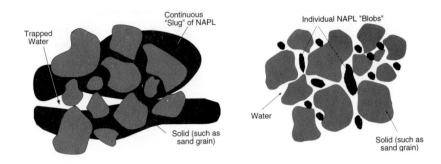

Figure 11.1 Conceptual representation of: (a) free-phase vs. (b) residual NAPL.

When released at the surface, **free-phase** or **mobile** NAPL is forced into the pores of the soil/aquifer matrix by the hydrostatic pressure on the continuous body of NAPL. Because the NAPL is under pressure, it can enter even very small pores and fractures in the subsurface as long as the original NAPL entry point, such as a waste pond or leaking underground storage tank, is active. When the supply of new NAPL is exhausted, however, the pressure on the free-phase NAPL is removed and small blobs (or "ganglia") of NAPL "snap-off" or "bypass" the once continuous NAPL body and become trapped in individual pores or small groups of pores by capillary forces (see Figure 11.1). The **residual saturation**, defined as the fraction of total pore volume occupied by residual NAPL under ambient ground water flow conditions, is an important parameter in ground water remediation problems because it indicates the amount of NAPL that is trapped in the subsurface. The actual residual saturation value at a particular location is determined by the type of chemicals that comprise the NAPL, whether the NAPLs are in the saturated zone or vadose zone, and most importantly, the structure and hydrogeologic characteristics of the soil/aquifer matrix.

NAPLs have a tremendous impact on the remediation of contaminated aquifers, because it is very difficult or impossible to remove all of the residual NAPL blobs once they are trapped in individual pores. Although many NAPL removal technologies are currently being tested, to date there have been few field demonstrations where sufficient NAPL has been successfully removed from the subsurface to restore an aquifer to drinking water quality. The NAPL that remains trapped in the soil/aquifer matrix acts as a continuing source of dissolved contaminants to ground water, greatly complicating the restoration of affected aquifers for many years. Because NAPLs act so differently from dissolved constituents in ground water, several key concepts are introduced below.

11.1.1 Single Component NAPLs vs. Mixed NAPLs

NAPLs are either comprised of a single chemical or as a complex mixture of several or hundreds of chemicals. For example, a spill of pure trichloroethylene (TCE) can produce a single component NAPL comprised of TCE. A gasoline spill, on the other hand, will yield a NAPL comprised of a number of different aromatic and aliphatic hydrocarbons. As one might expect, understanding and predicting the behavior of a mixed-NAPL is much more complex than doing so for a single-component NAPL.

11.1.2 Saturation and Residual Saturation

Saturation (S_i where "i" is an index representing a fluid, and can represent oil (o), water (w), or air (a)) is the fraction of total pore space containing a particular fluid "i" in a representative volume of a porous media:

$$S_i = V_i / V_{\text{pore space}} \tag{11.1}$$

where

$\quad V_i \quad$ = the volume of fluid and
$\quad V_{\text{pore space}}$ = the volume of open pore space

Saturation values for free-phase, continuous masses of NAPLs have been reported as low as 15% to 25%. A controlled release of PCE at a Canadian research site indicated that the final saturations in a 3m × 3m × 3m test cell ranged from 1% to 38%, and that saturations greater than 15% appeared to be related to free-phase DNAPL (Pankow and Cherry, 1996). A study of an LNAPL site in San Diego showed typical LNAPL saturations between 5% and 20%, with several wells showing free-phase LNAPL, even in zones with LNAPL saturations less than 25% (Huntley et al. 1994).

The saturation where a continuous NAPL becomes discontinuous and is immobilized by capillary forces is known as the residual saturation (S_{or}). In unsaturated soils, residual saturation of NAPL fluids, defined as the fraction of the total pore volume occupied by NAPL under ambient condition, typically ranges from 5% to 20%. In the saturated zone, residual saturation values are typically higher because NAPL serves as a "nonwetting" fluid when in contact with water (see Section 11.3), and residual saturation values range from 15% to 50% of the total pore volume (Mercer and Cohen, 1990; Schwille, 1988). Residual saturation appears to be relatively insensitive to the type of chemicals that comprise a NAPL but is very sensitive to soil properties and heterogeneities (USEPA, 1990). Figure 11.2 describes the difference between saturation and residual saturation.

NAPL saturation can be estimated by the following equation if laboratory analysis of the total amount of organic material on the soil (such as a Total Petroleum Hydrocarbon or TPH analysis) is available (Parker et al., 1994) (see Example 11.1).

$$S_o = \frac{\rho_b \cdot TPH}{\rho_n \cdot n \cdot 10^6} \tag{11.2}$$

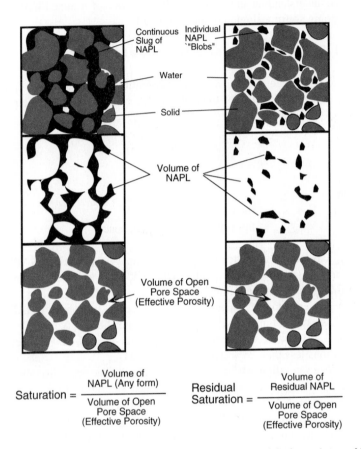

Figure 11.2 Saturation and residual saturation. (a) free-phase NAPL. (b) residual NAPL.

where

S_o = NAPL saturation (unitless)
ρ_b = Soil bulk density (g/cm^3)
ρ_n = NAPL density (g/cm^3)
TPH = Total Petroleum Hydrocarbons (mg$_{hydrocarbon}$/kg$_{dry\ soil}$)
n = porosity

Example 11.1   CONVERSION FROM TPH TO SATURATION

What is the approximate NAPL saturation of a soil with a TPH value of 10,000 mg/kg? Assume soil bulk density = 1.7 g/cm^3 and porosity = 0.40. The NAPL, gasoline, has a density of 0.75 g/cm^3. Disregard the small concentrations of hydrocarbon present in the dissolved or sorbed phases in the sample.

Solution. Apply Eq. (11.2) to calculate the NAPL saturation of this sample:

$$S_o = \frac{1.7x\ 10,000}{0.75x\ 0.40\ x\ 10^6} = 0.06$$

Analysis. 6% of pore space is filled with NAPL, indicating that the NAPL is probably in a residual state and is immobile.

11.1.3 Role of NAPLs as Long-Term Sources

At many sites, the total contaminant mass in the NAPL phase is often many times larger than the total mass of even a large dissolved contaminant plume. To illustrate this point, consider that concentrations of dissolved hydrocarbon plumes are typically reported in units of **parts per million** (ppm) or **parts per billion** (ppb), which represent 1 gram of hydrocarbon per every million or billion grams of water. The amount of NAPL in an aquifer, on the other hand, is reported as a **percentage** of open pore space occupied by NAPL (the saturation value). For a comparison of the relative masses of hydrocarbon in the dissolved versus NAPL phases at a hypothetical hazardous waste site, see Example 11.2.

Because many sites involve hundreds, thousands, or even hundreds of thousands of gallons of NAPLs released to the subsurface, the relative importance of the NAPL phase should not be overlooked. While the dissolved phase is important because it can migrate off-site relatively quickly, NAPLs serve as continuing long-term sources of dissolved organic contaminants to ground water.

A detailed technical evaluation was conducted by the EPA at 24 ground water pump-and-treat sites (U.S. EPA, 1989; 1992d). This study concluded that, indeed, the key factor in the poor performance of pump-and-treat systems was the presence of NAPLs in the water-bearing units. Residual NAPLs were found to serve as continuing sources of constituents to ground water at these sites, undermining the feasibility of aquifer restoration by ground water extraction methods. In response to these findings, the EPA modified the guidelines for remedial actions at Superfund sites affected by NAPLs. In an EPA directive issued in May 1992 (U.S. EPA, 1992c), the agency recognizes that full remediation of ground water impacted by NAPLs, particularly DNAPLs, may be technically impracticable at many sites.

Example 11.2   COMPARING DISSOLVED MASS VS. NAPL MASS

A leaking underground storage tank released 1000 gal of gasoline (density approximately 0.9 g/mL and approximately 1% benzene) to the subsurface. After one year, the resulting dissolved benzene plume is 100 ft long, 50 ft wide, and 10 ft deep. The average benzene concentration of the plume is 0.10 mg/L, and the porosity of the aquifer is 0.30. If no hydrocarbon is lost from volatilization or biodegradation, how much of the original release is in the dissolved phase, and how much is in the NAPL phase?

Solution.

1. Mass of Benzene Released in Gasoline

    NAPL Mass = [1000 gal gasoline] [3.78 L/gal] [1000 mL/L] [0.9 g/mL]

    $\qquad$ [1 kg/1000 mg] [0.01 kg benzene/kg gasoline]

    $\qquad$ =34.02 kg = (74.84 lb)

2. Volume of Contaminated Ground Water in Plume

    Volume = [100 ft] [50 ft] [10 ft] [0.30] [28.3 L/ft^3]

    $\qquad$ = 429,000 L

3. Mass of Dissolved Benzene

    Dissolved Mass = [429,000 L] [0.1 mg/L] [kg/10^6 mg]

    $\qquad$ = 0.0429 kg Benzene

4. Comparison

    NAPL Mass $\quad$ = 34.02 kg (99.9%)

    Dissolved Mass = 0.0429 kg (0.1 %)

Analysis. As this example shows, most of the organic mass at a NAPL site is found in the NAPL phase. NAPLs can act as long-term sources of dissolved contaminants to ground water.

11.1.4 Difficulty In Confirming Presence or Absence of NAPLs

Knowing whether a site is contaminated by NAPL is important in order to properly develop site characterization studies and to design reliable ground water remediation systems. At some sites the presence of NAPLs can be confirmed by visually observing if free-phase hydrocarbons have accumulated in wells or are present in soil cores. At many sites, however, the presence of NAPLs are difficult to confirm because residual NAPL will not flow into a monitoring well (it is trapped in the pores of the soil) and is even difficult to see by visual inspection of soil cores. Although several indirect methods are available to estimate the potential for NAPL occurrence, such as measuring the concentrations of hydrocarbons on soil, it is still difficult to confirm the presence or absence of NAPLs at many sites.

11.1.5 Difficulty in Removing Trapped Residual NAPLs

Capillary forces make it very difficult or impossible to remove all the NAPLs that have been released to the subsurface. For example, oil-recovery operations at oil fields that employ pumping alone typically remove less than one-third of the oil in a petroleum reservoir. Enhanced oil recovery techniques, such as waterflooding or the application of surfactants, can only bring 50% to 80% of the original in-place oil (NAPL) to the surface under optimum conditions. These recovery rates are acceptable to the oil industry, where economics determine the ultimate amount of oil recovered from a reservoir. At hazardous waste sites, however, removal of much more than 99% of NAPL is probably required in order to restore a contaminated aquifer to drinking water standards (i.e. low part-per-billion range for most organics). At most sites, this level of recovery is impractical when using pumping and injecting alone. Wilson and Conrad (1984) made a prescient summary of the problems posed by residual NAPL in 1984 when they said:

"The migration of hydrocarbon essentially immiscible with water occurs as a continuous multiphase flow under the influence of capillary, viscous, and gravity forces. Once the source of hydrocarbon is disrupted, and the main body of hydrocarbon displaced, some of it is trapped in the porous media because of capillary forces. Hydrocarbon migration halts as this lower, residual saturation is reached. The trapped hydrocarbon remains as pendular rings and/or isolated, essentially immobile blobs. Residual hydrocarbons act as a continual source of contaminants as, for example, water coming into contact with the trapped immiscible phase leaches soluble hydrocarbon components."

11.2 TYPES OF NAPLs

Although NAPLs are associated with a diverse group of industries and have a wide range of physical properties, they are generally classified by specific gravity (density relative to water) into light NAPLs (LNAPL or dense NAPLs (DNAPLs). LNAPLs have a specific gravity less than water, and will float on the water table. DNAPLs, on the other hand, have specific gravities greater than water and can sink deep into the saturated zone. This simple classification system, although based only on density, is a very useful framework for evaluating the migration pathway, related chemicals and industries, and the ultimate fate of NAPLs in the subsurface.

11.2.1 LNAPLs (Light Nonaqueous Phase Liquids)

LNAPLs are primarily associated with petroleum production, refining, and wholesale distribution and retail distribution (service stations) of petroleum products (Newell et al. 1995). Spills and accidental releases of gasoline, kerosene, diesel, and associated condensate are common sources of LNAPLs to ground water; Wiedemeier et al., (1999) summarized results from two studies that indicated that free-phase LNAPL was found at 40% to 65% of petro-leum hydrocarbon sites. When LNAPL is released at the surface, it first migrates downward through the unsaturated zone under the force of gravity. After encountering a water-bearing unit, the LNAPL forms a pancake-like pool on top of the capillary fringe and top portion of the saturated zone (see Figure 11.3). Ground water flowing past the trapped residual DNAPL dissolves soluble components of the DNAPL, forming a dissolved plume downgradient of the LNAPL zone. Typical chemicals of interest resulting from the dissolution of petroleum products include benzene, toluene, ethyl benzene, and xylene (BTEX) as well as other aro-matic hydrocarbons (see Table 11.1).

Because LNAPLs do not penetrate very deep into the water table and are biodegradable under natural conditions, they are generally thought to be a more manageable environmental problem than a DNAPL release. With small-scale releases such as those associated with serv-ice stations, natural processes will usually attenuate the environmental impacts within a span of several years.

TABLE 11.1   Chemicals Typically Associated with an LNAPL Release

Aromatics
Benzene
Ethyl Benzene
Toluene
Xylenes
Naphthalene
Aliphatic Alkanes
Octane
Decane

11.2.2 DNAPLs (Dense Nonaqueous Phase Liquids)

DNAPLs are related to a wide variety of industrial activities, including almost any facility where degreasing, metal stripping, chemical manufacturing, pesticide production, coal gasifi-cation plants, creosote operations, or other activities involving chlorinated solvents were performed. As with LNAPLs, the main chemicals of concern are the dissolution products of the DNAPL; for solvent-type DNAPLs, these chemicals include a wide range of chlorinated aliphatic hydrocarbons and other organics such as some polyaromatic hydrocarbons (PAHs), and pentachlorobiphenyls (PCBs) (see Table 11.2).

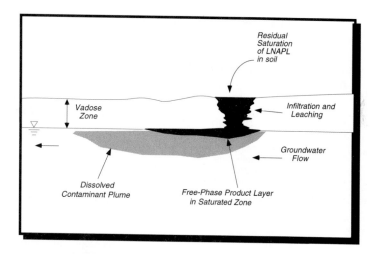

Figure 11.3 Conceptual model of LNAPL release.

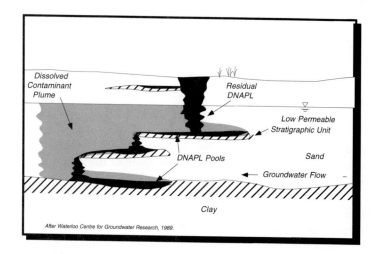

Figure 11.4 Conceptual model of DNAPL release. Source: Waterloo Centre for Groundwater Research, 1991.

After being released at the surface, DNAPLs move vertically downward through the vadose zone. If large quantities of DNAPL have been released, mobile DNAPL will continue vertical migration until it is trapped as a residual hydrocarbon or until low-permeability stratigraphic units are encountered, which can create DNAPL "pools" in the soil/aquifer matrix. However, pools are rarely observed at actual field sites.

In Figure 11.4 a perched DNAPL pool fills up and then spills over the lip of the low-

TABLE 11.2   Chemicals Typically Associated with a DNAPL Release

Halogenated Volatiles	Non-Halogenated Semi-Volatiles
Chlorobenzene	2-Methyl naphthalene
1,2-Dichloropropane	o-Cresol
1,1-Dichloroethane	p-Cresol
1,1-Dichloroethylene	2,4-Dimethylphenol
1,2-Dichloroethane	m-Cresol
Trans-1,2-Dichloroethylene	Phenol
Cis-1,2-Dichloroethylene	Naphthalene
1,1,1-Trichloroethane	Benzo(a)anthracene
Methylene chloride	Fluorene
1,1,2-Trichloroethane	Acenaphthene
Trichloroethylene	Anthracene
Chloroform	Dibenzo(a,h)anthracene
Carbon tetrachloride	Fluoranthene
1,1,2,2-Tetrachloroethane	Pyrene
Tetrachloroethylene	Chrysene
Ethylene dibromide	2,4-Dinitrophenol
Halogenated Semi-Volatiles	**Miscellaneous**
1,4-Dichlorobenzene	Coal tar
1,2-Dichlorobenzene	Creosote
Aroclor 1242, 1254, 1260	
Chlordane	
Dieldrin	
2,3,4,6-Tetrachlorophenol	
Pentachlorophenol	

permeability stratigraphic unit. This example demonstrates how the movement of DNAPL is controlled by the density forces and the structure of the subsurface, and typically not by the movement of ground water.

DNAPLs are observed much less frequently than LNAPLs. Wiedemeier et al. (1999) compiled data from two studies that showed that DNAPL was observed at only 15% to 22% of sites contaminated with chlorinated solvents in ground water. An EPA study of 310 Superfund sites found DNAPL present at only 13% of the sites (U.S. EPA, 1993). The EPA study concluded that 57% of all Superfund sites in the United States have a high or moderate potential for the presence of DNAPL, even though DNAPL was observed at only 5% of all Superfund sites in the study. In other words, DNAPL is probably an important source of ground water contamination at almost all chlorinated-solvent-contaminated sites, despite the fact that it is rarely detected in site monitoring wells.

DNAPLs, particularly if comprised of chlorinated solvents, usually present a much more formidable remediation challenge than LNAPLs for three reasons: (1) dissolved chlorinated solvents do not biodegrade as readily as petroleum hydrocarbons at some sites, and therefore can travel for longer distances in the subsurface; (2) the density and low viscosity of chlorinated solvent DNAPLs spreads the contaminated zone below the water table compared to LNAPL releases, which remain near the surface of the water table; and (3) the chlorinated solvents density, interfacial tension, and viscosity allow them to move through small preferential flowpaths in the subsurface, so that DNAPL can move into low permeability zones that are hard to remediate. Aquifers contaminated with large quantities of DNAPLs are almost impossible to restore to original conditions using any current proven ground water clean-up technologies (Pankow and Cherry, 1996).

11.3 NAPL TRANSPORT — GENERAL PROCESSES

11.3.1 NAPL Transport at the Pore Level

At the pore level, NAPL movement occurs when enough pressure is available to force free-phase NAPL through a small pore throat and thereby displace air and/or water that once occupied the pore. The amount of pressure that is required depends on the **capillary forces** that act on the different fluids on either side of the pore throat. For example, capillary forces will draw some fluids through a pore throat and displace a second fluid residing in the pore. The way that capillary forces act on these two fluids is partially explained by wettability: The fluid drawn into the pore is referred to as the **wetting fluid** while the fluid repelled by capillary forces is the **non-wetting fluid** (Bear, 1972).

Wettability is defined as the tendency of one fluid to spread preferentially over a solid surface in favor of the second fluid. It is measured by observing the contact angle of a test fluid on a surface when surrounded by a larger volume of a background fluid (see Figure 11.5): a **contact angle** of < 70° indicates that the small amount of the test fluid is wetting and the background fluid is nonwetting. A contact angle >110° indicates that the test fluid is nonwetting, and contact angles between 70° and 110° are neutral-wetting systems (Mercer and Cohen, 1990).

Wettability is closely related to another physical property, **interfacial tension**, which is defined as the free surface energy at the interface between two immiscible fluids (Villaume, 1985). The interaction between similar molecules on one side of the interface and dissimilar molecules on either side of the interface produces capillary forces when the two fluids come in contact with a solid phase, such as a pore throat. Interfacial tension values have been reported for many organic hydrocarbons in contact with water and curves relating to capillary pressure, interfacial tension, and wettability have been developed by Mercer and Cohen, 1990.

To apply the concept of wettability to NAPL transport in specific field situations requires considerable information regarding the physical properties of each fluid in the system and the solid, that is, the soil grains or aquifer media. However, the following generalizations can be made:

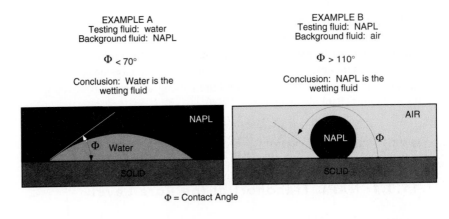

Figure 11.5 Wettability configurations for NAPL, showing a water-wet example and a NAPL-wet example.

- Water is almost always the wetting fluid when mixed with air or NAPLs in the subsurface.

- NAPLs serve as the wetting fluid when mixed with air, but act as the nonwetting fluid when combined with water in the subsurface (Domenico and Schwartz, 1990).

These general rules can be elaborated using three examples of NAPL movement: downward migration of DNAPLs through the saturated zone, NAPL movement through the vadose zone, and LNAPL behavior at the water table.

11.3.2 Downward Migration of DNAPLs in the Saturated Zone

When DNAPLs migrate through the saturated zone, a three-phase system consisting of solid, water, and DNAPL is formed. The DNAPL acts as a nonwetting fluid that must overcome capillary forces in order to squeeze through the pore throat of a pore filled with a wetting fluid, in this case water. The pressure that must be exceeded is called the **entry pressure**. To enter the pore, sufficient driving force must be provided from the combination of (1)

DNAPL density forces and (2) pressure forces present in the continuous DNAPL mass. If the driving force is greater than the entry pressure, then the DNAPL will move forward and enter the pore. When the driving force is removed, the continuous DNAPL mass can split up into countless blobs of residual NAPLs, located mostly in the larger pores of the aquifer matrix (see Figure 11.1).

Unlike the lighter-than-water chemicals, DNAPLs will continue to move vertically downward until they reach a stratigraphic barrier or until the original supply of DNAPL is exhausted and the DNAPL mass is converted to residual DNAPL. In some cases, the downward migration can continue hundreds of feet below the surface.

11.3.3 NAPLs in the Vadose Zone

NAPL infiltration into the vadose zone results in a four-phase system consisting of the air phase, water phase, solid phase, and NAPL phase (U.S. EPA, 1990; Huling and Weaver, 1991). Water on the soil grains serves as a wetting fluid, and NAPL acts as a wetting fluid with respect to air on the water film and a nonwetting fluid with respect to the water (Domenico and Schwartz, 1998). In other words, downward migrating NAPL infiltrates relatively easily into the porous media because it is a partial wetting fluid in this four-phase system, and capillary forces do not repel the movement of NAPLs when entering a pore largely filled with air. If sufficient NAPL is available, it continues to move downward from the source area by forming (1) films between the gas and water phases and/or (2) blobs of NAPL that replace gas in the pores, or water in the pore throats (U.S. EPA, 1990). The tendency of a certain chemical to form films or blobs is dependent of the physical properties of the chemical. Chlorinated solvents, for example, will generally not to form large, continuous films when released to the vadose zone and will respond differently to remediation techniques such as soil venting and in-situ biodegradation than chemicals, which will form films (U.S. EPA, 1990).

When the original supply of NAPL is exhausted, some of the pore space in the vadose zone will be occupied by the remaining residual NAPL in films and/or blobs, with the rest of the pore space filled by air/vapor (located primarily in the larger pores) and water (spread out on the surface of the soil grains and filling the smaller pores).

The residual saturation of NAPLs (either LNAPLs or DNAPLs) in the saturated zone is usually higher than that in the unsaturated zone by a factor from two to five (Domenico and Schwartz, 1990). The reason for the higher concentration of residual NAPLs in saturated media is due to the following factors (Mercer and Cohen, 1990; U.S. EPA, 1990):

- The NAPL/air density ratio is greater than the NAPL/water density ratio, favoring drainage of NAPLs from the vadose zone.

- In the saturated zone, NAPLs are the nonwetting fluid and are trapped in the larger pores.

- NAPLs tend to spread out farther in the vadose zone because of the favorable capillary conditions.

11.3.4 LNAPL Behavior at the Water Table

The interaction between water, air, and NAPLs becomes more complex once the NAPLs approach the water table and associated capillary fringe. In a completely saturated system, water is the wetting fluid and NAPL is the nonwetting fluid whose movement is hindered by repellent capillary forces. The capillary fringe represents the transition zone between a system where NAPLs are a partial wetting fluid (the vadose zone) and where they are the nonwetting fluid (the saturated zone). If the density of a NAPL is less than water, then it will accumulate on top of the capillary fringe and eventually flow in thin sheets along the water table once a certain minimum thickness is achieved (Domenico and Schwartz, 1990). If the LNAPL flowrate through the vadose zone is fast enough, then capillary fringe will collapse and the LNAPL will move deeper and penetrate a short way past the water table. Once the LNAPL supply is exhausted, however, the continuous mass of LNAPL in the capillary fringe will begin to break up into individual blobs and convert from a free-phase mass of LNAPL to a zone containing residual LNAPL.

11.3.5 NAPL Transport Through Fractures and Heterogeneities

The previous section discussed theoretical models for movement of immiscible fluids through a porous media by moving through the primary porosity of the system, the open pore spaces. In the field, however, NAPL typically moves through preferential pathways (large pores, small-scale fractures, rootholes, etc.) in the soil and aquifer matrix. For example, many studies have shown how DNAPL will migrate preferentially through secondary porosity features in the soil/aquifer matrix, that is, larger fractures, partings, rootholes, slickensides, coarse-grained layers, and other micro-stratigraphic features rather than saturating the open pore volume of a porous media (see Pankow and Cherry, 1996). In general, heterogeneities will have the following effects on NAPL movement in the subsurface:

- **Increased residual saturation:** Even small amounts of clay or silt in a soil (as little as 2% by weight) can have a dramatic effect on NAPL migration by creating much more complex, branching migration pathways and by increasing the final residual saturation (U.S. EPA, 1990).

- **Increased penetration depth into vadose zone:** The presence of heterogeneities permit the NAPL to penetrate much deeper into the vadose zone than would be predicted from using typical residual saturation values and assuming uniform saturation of the aquifer media (see Figure 11.6). One research field study showed that even small releases of DNAPL can penetrate quickly through preferential flowpaths in the vadose zone before reaching the water table (Poulson and Kueper, 1992, Pankow and Cherry, 1996) (see Figure 11.7).

- **Make fine-grained confining units ineffective barriers to NAPL flow:** Clay aquitards that serve as effective "confining units" in the context of ground water flow may not serve as effective barriers to migration of some DNAPLs (primarily the chlorinated solvents) because of micro-scale heterogeneities (U.S. EPA 1992d; Pankow and Cherry, 1996). Modeling studies have indicated that some low-viscosity DNAPLs can penetrate and migrate through hairline fractures as small as 20 microns wide. At one Superfund site, for example, large volumes of DNAPL were observed to have moved significant distances (~50 ft vertically and ~300 ft laterally) in the secondary porosity features of various clay and silt units underlying the site (Connor, Newell, and Wilson, 1989). Pankow and Cherry provide a detailed overview of DNAPL migration through fractures.

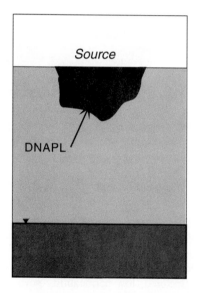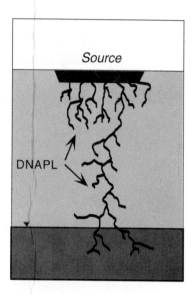

Figure 11.6 NAPL migration in primary vs. secondary porosity. (a) NAPL migration through primary porosity. (b) NAPL migration through secondary porosity features (fractures, root holes, etc.) the more common transport mechanism.

The ability of DNAPLs (primarily chlorinated solvent DNAPLs) to penetrate small fractures has enormous implications with regard to remediation. Parker et al. (1994) demonstrated how some DNAPLs that become trapped in naturally-occurring fractures in clays or rocks can dissolve relatively rapidly (on the order of a few years) into the clay or rock, leaving a geologic media that is almost impossible to restore. The physics of this type of system can be very favorable to DNAPL dissolution, as DNAPL spreads along planar fractures with very large surface areas. Large surface areas, when combined with a powerful diffusive driving

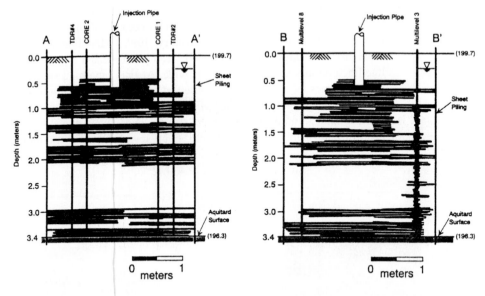

Figure 11.7 Probable distribution of PCE migration pathways after controlled release of 230.9 liters of PCE into Borden sand test cell. Shown are two perpendicular vertical cross-sections (cross-sections intersect in middle of each cross-section). Source: Kueper et al., 1993.

force between the high-concentration fracture and the lower concentration-matrix results in a rapid diffusive disappearance of DNAPLs (Parker et al., 1994; Pankow and Cherry, 1996).

Freeze and McWhorter (1997) developed a conceptual framework to qualitatively evaluate the potential benefits of DNAPL removal from fractured, low-permeability soils, a relatively common hydrogeologic setting as chlorinated solvents are often found to penetrate small fractures in clay units at site. The authors concluded that "very high mass removal efficiencies are required to achieve significant long-term risk reduction with technology applications of finite duration. Further, it is unlikely that current technologies can achieve such efficiencies in heterogeneous low-permeability soils that exhibit dual porosity properties and preferential pathways."

11.3.6 NAPL Transport at the Site Level

Beyond the scale of the individual pore, NAPL migration becomes much more difficult to predict. At the scale of an entire hazardous waste site, for example, the path taken by a NAPL as it migrates through the subsurface is dominated by factors related to the NAPL release, physical properties of the NAPL, and most importantly geological factors (Feenstra and Cherry 1991; U.S. EPA, 1992a):

- the volume of NAPL released
- properties of the soil/aquifer media, such as pore size and permeability
- micro-stratigraphic features, such as root holes, small fractures, and slickensides found in silt/clay layers
- general stratigraphy, such as the location and topography of low-permeability units
- properties of the NAPL, such as wettability, density, viscosity, and interfacial tension
- the duration of release, such as a one-time "slug" event or a long-term continual discharge
- the area of infiltration at the NAPL entry point to the subsurface

To illustrate the movement of NAPLs at hazardous waste sites, several conceptual models are presented in Figures 11.8 to 11.15.

11.3.7 LNAPL Conceptual Models

After a spill or leak near the surface, both LNAPLs and DNAPLs move vertically downward under the force of gravity and soil capillarity. When only a small amount of NAPL was released, however, all of the free-phase NAPL is eventually trapped in pores and fractures in

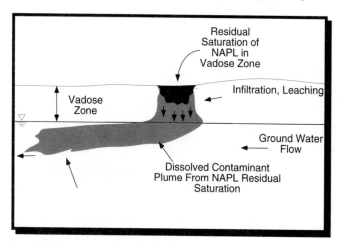

Figure 11.8 LNAPL release to vadose zone only.

the unsaturated zone (see Figure 11.8). Infiltration through the NAPL zone dissolves some of the soluble organic constituents in the NAPL, carrying organics to the water table and forming a dissolved organic plume in the aquifer. This type of release scenario is relatively rare compared to sites where NAPL has penetrated all the way to a water bearing unit (Wiedemeier et al., 1999).

When enough LNAPL is released to reach the water table, the LNAPL will spread along the capillary fringe and the top of the water table because of buoyancy forces. Moving ground water will move past this thin, pancake-like LNAPL layer will dissolve soluble contaminants to form a dissolved hydrocarbon plume (see Figure 11.3).

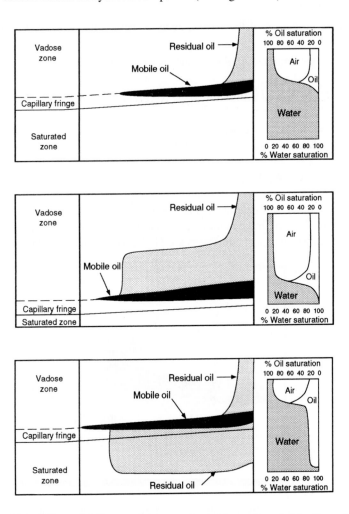

Figure 11.9 Effect of falling and rising water table on the distribution of mobile and residual phases on an LNAPL. Source: Fetter, 1993.

If a free-phase LNAPL is present, a falling water table will lower the floating LNAPL layer, leaving an emplaced source of residual NAPL behind in the saturated zone when the water table recovers (see Figure 11.9). Similarly, a rising water table will lift the free-phase layer into the vadose zone and can increase the residual saturation of the affected soils after the water table drops. This movement is a cause for concern because it will increase the residual hydrocarbon zone, and therefore greatly increase the concentration of dissolved organics.

As shown in Figure 11.10, LNAPL that is forced into confined aquifers by high-entry pressures can migrate under buoyancy forces in directions other than the direction of ground water flow. This phenomenon is very similar to the trapping of oil in petroleum reservoirs. To increase the recovery of LNAPL, recovery wells should be installed near the tops of any stratigraphic traps and screened through the confining unit/aquifer boundary.

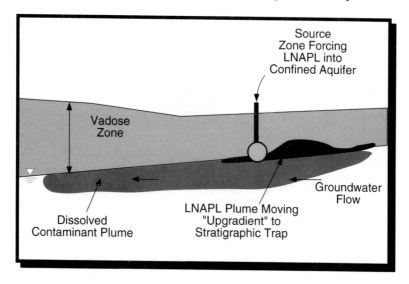

Figure 11.10 LNAPL accumulating in stratigraphic trap in confined aquifer.

11.3.8 DNAPL Conceptual Models

A DNAPL release at the surface can migrate all the way through the unsaturated zone and then continue downward until the mobile DNAPL is exhausted and is trapped as a residual hydrocarbon in the porous media (see Figure 11.4). Ground water flowing past the trapped residual DNAPL dissolves soluble components of the DNAPL, forming a dissolved plume downgradient of the DNAPL zone.

Mobile DNAPL will continue vertical migration until it is converted a residual state or until low-permeability stratigraphic units are encountered which can create DNAPL "pools" in the soil/aquifer matrix (see Figure 11.4), although pools are rarely observed at field sites. In this figure, a perched DNAPL pool fills up and then spills over the lip of the low-permeability stratigraphic unit. The spill-over point (or points) can be some distance away from the original source, greatly complicating the process of tracking the DNAPL migration. Pankow and Cherry (1996) concluded that lateral movement from the input location can be large.

DNAPL introduced into a fractured rock or fractured clay system follows a complex pathway based on the distribution of fractures in the original matrix (see Figure 11.11). The number, density, size, and direction of the fractures usually cannot be determined due to the extreme heterogeneity of a fractured system and the lack of economical aquifer characterization technologies. Relatively small volumes of DNAPL can penetrate deeply into fractured systems due to the low retention capacity of the fractures and the ability of some DNAPLs

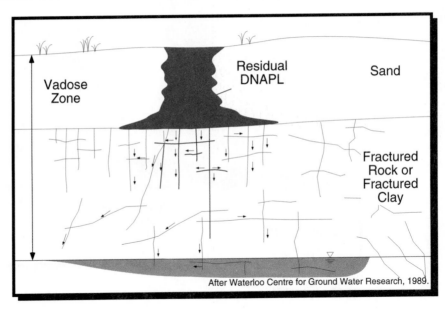

Figure 11.11 Fractured rock or fractured clay system. Waterloo Centre for Groundwater Research, 1991.

to migrate through very small (< 20 microns) fractures. Many clay units, once considered to be relatively impermeable to DNAPL migration, often act as fractured media with preferential pathways for vertical and horizontal DNAPL migration (Pankow and Cherry, 1996).

In the case of a composite DNAPL site, mobile DNAPL migrates vertically downward through the unsaturated zone and the first saturated zone, producing a dissolved constituent plume in the upper aquifer (see Figure 11.12). Although a DNAPL pool is formed on the fractured clay unit, the fractures are large enough to permit vertical migration downward to the deeper aquifer. The DNAPL then pools in a topographic low in the underlying impermeable unit, and a second dissolved constituent plume is formed.

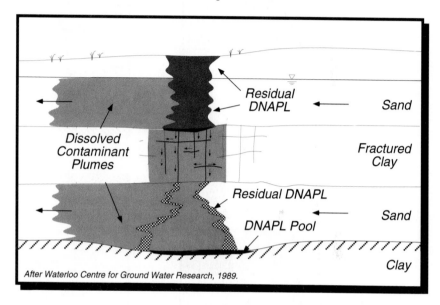

Figure 11.12 Composite DNAPL site. Source: Waterloo Centre for Groundwater research.

The reader should note that these diagrams depict general patterns of NAPL behavior only. The actual path taken by NAPLs at actual hazardous waste sites is usually much more complex due to the large-scale and small-scale heterogeneities found at the site. At many sites the final distribution of NAPLs in the subsurface may never be fully characterized due the complex distribution of countless small-scale heterogeneities in the subsurface.

11.3.9 Conceptual Models — Scale Effects

Wiedemeier et al. (1999) developed a group of conceptual models of NAPL source zones that telescope from the site level (typically hundreds of feet in size) down to the sub-pore level (typically millimeters or smaller in size). This model, shown in Figure 11.13, is described below (adapted with permission from Wiedemeier et al., 1999). The **site-wide models** for LNAPL and DNAPL (top "a" panels) are quite similar, as both LNAPL and DNAPL migrate down through the vadose zone, spread out at changes in soil texture, and then penetrate further downward in fingers. When the LNAPL hits the water table, however, buoyancy forces cause the LNAPL to spread out in a thin, pancake-like layer, and later to smear vertically with the changing water table, leaving residual LNAPL throughout the smear zone. An aqueous-phase plume flows from the smear zone, migrating with the moving ground water close to the water table.

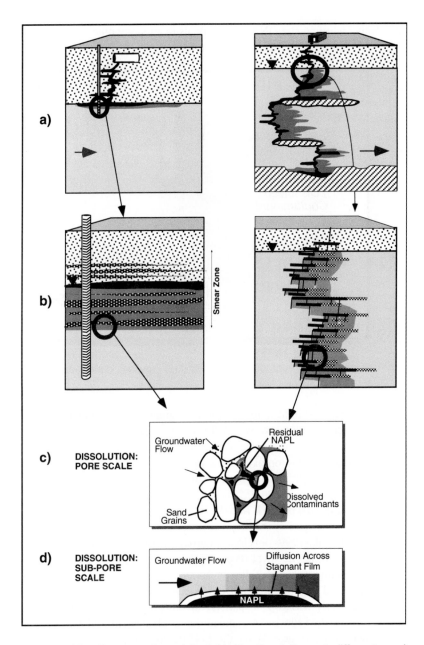

Figure 11.13 Conceptual model of NAPL dissolution at different scales.
Source: Wiedemeier et al., 1999 and Pankow and Cherry, 1996.

DNAPL penetrates through the water table and fingers into the saturated zone, forming lenses at subtle changes in aquifer material and more major, macro-scale heterogeneities. In the conceptual model, the DNAPL spills down from the lenses and eventually forms a pool on a capillary barrier (in this case, an unfractured clay layer) at the bottom of the water-bearing unit. Based on a theoretical treatment of fingering phenomena, Kueper and Frind (1988) suggested that the fingers formed by chlorinated solvent DNAPLs in saturated sands or finer media are often less than 10 cm wide. Dissolved plumes are created by every finger and pool, with the plumes associated with the discrete fingers being very thin in the y direction (the direction coming out of the page), and the plumes created by the pools being very thin in the z direction (vertically up and down).

In the second "b" panels of the conceptual model, closer, **core-scale views** on the order of a few feet are shown for the LNAPL and DNAPL releases, corresponding to the size observed when a typical saturated soil core is brought to the surface for evaluation. Note that NAPL can be present, but not observed, in a core, as the amount of NAPL can be small and lack a strong color contrast with the soil. With the LNAPL release, the entire smear zone is visible, and it is apparent that subtle changes in the aquifer material cause a nonuniform distribution of residual LNAPL. In the DNAPL conceptual model, a similar process occurs where subtle changes in the aquifer materials cause the DNAPL to form an apparently random sequence of fingers leading down to thin horizontal lenses from which more fingers emanate.

The amount of dissolution that occurs at this scale is dependent on (1) the surface area of the NAPL that is exposed to moving ground water, (2) the size of the NAPL blobs, and (3) the chemical characteristics of the NAPL (e.g., the mole fraction of soluble components and the solubility of NAPL compounds). Note that the presence of residual NAPL in a porous medium can reduce the relative permeability of the residual NAPL zone. In one laboratory experiment performed by Anderson et al. (1992a), the flow through the residual DNAPL zone was reduced by about 20%. Kueper and Frind (1992), using a range of residual saturations between 14% and 40%, estimated that the corresponding reduction in relative permeability (and therefore ground water flow) for a PCE/water system is between 20% and 70%.

In the **pore scale** (millimeters or less) conceptual model, either residual LNAPL and DNAPL blobs are shown in panel "c"). Both the LNAPL and DNAPL residual blobs have the same general appearance, and ground water flow between the sand grains of the porous medium will come into contact with a NAPL blob, and dissolve the soluble contaminants. Note that the LNAPL and DNAPL will usually be "nonwetting" in the saturated system. In this case, water (the wetting agent) will be in direct contact with the solid (sand grains in this case) and occupy the smallest pore spaces, whereas the NAPL blobs will occupy the larger pores. In a LNAPL smear zone or a DNAPL pool, the percentage of the pore space occupied by the NAPL (called saturation) will be greater than that occupied by water, such that the NAPL may form a continuous mass that could migrate as a body. Under most conditions, however, water will continue to occupy some fraction of the pore space (called the residual water content), and it is rare for large volumes of the porous media to be completely occupied by the NAPL at most contaminated sites.

At the **sub-pore scale** (see the "d" panel), the surface of the LNAPL or DNAPL blob is in contact with ground water, and dissolution is actively taking place. Here a thin film of stagnant water is formed on the blob, and diffusion occurs through the stagnant film to transport soluble contaminants to the film's surface. Moving ground water mixes with the dissolved compounds leaving the film, forming a dissolved plume. At many parts of each residual NAPL blob, however, there is no moving ground water near the blob (e.g., the part of the blob adjacent to sand grains) and, therefore, there is little or no mass transport across the film.

If the NAPL consists of a single compound, the NAPL blob will slowly shrink over time as dissolution continues. If the NAPL consists largely of nonsoluble components with a small fraction of soluble compounds (such as gasoline), dissolution will be affected by effective solubility considerations (see below), and the residual NAPL blob will not shrink appreciably.

11.4 NAPL TRANSPORT — COMPUTATIONAL METHODS

Although the exact path of NAPL movement through the subsurface is difficult or impossible to predict, several general relationships are available for planning and conceptual design purposes.

11.4.1 Pore Level Calculations

Capillary Pressure. Several researchers have summarized the relationships between capillary forces and NAPL movement under hydrostatic and hydrodynamic conditions (Mercer and Cohen, 1990; Bear, 1979). A simple definition of capillary pressure is that it is the pressure difference between the nonwetting and wetting fluid:

$$P_c = P_{nw} - P_w \qquad (11.3)$$

where,

P_c = capillary pressure
P_{nw} = pressure of nonwetting fluid (such as a NAPL)
P_w = pressure of wetting fluid (such as water)

Bear (1979) provides a more detailed definition of capillary pressure for the case of a nonwetting NAPL sphere in a water-filled porous media:

$$P_c = (2\sigma \cos \phi) / r \qquad (11.4)$$

where

P_c = capillary pressure

σ = interfacial tension between NAPL and water

ϕ = contact angle

r = radius of the water filled pore that the NAPL must move through to exit or enter pore

Using this relationship, one can see that as the radius of the soil pores gets smaller, the capillary pressure required to force NAPL into or out of the pore increases. In other words, NAPLs have more difficulty moving through fine-grained soils such as silts and clays than through coarse-grained sands and gravels, corresponding to observations from numerous field sites.

The capillary pressure relationship shown in Eq. (11.4) can be expanded to provide estimates of the hydrostatic and hydrodynamic conditions required for NAPL migration. Some of the more important NAPL migration relationships, listed below, are presented in Table 11.3 (Mercer and Cohen, 1990):

- Critical NAPL height required for NAPL penetration into the vadose zone (see Eq. (11.5))

- Critical NAPL height required for DNAPL penetration into a saturated aquifer (Eq. (11.6))

- Critical NAPL height required for DNAPL penetration from a coarse-grained material into a fine-grained material (Eq. (11.7) and Example 11.3)

- Minimum hydraulic gradient required to prevent downward DNAPL migration or upward LNAPL migration (Eq. (11.8))

TABLE 11.3   Additional Capillary Pressure Relationships

$$Z_n(est) = \frac{2\sigma \cos \phi}{r_t g \rho_n} \qquad \text{(Eqn. 11.5)}$$

where: Zn (est) =Critical NAPL height required for NAPL penetration into the vadose zone

$$Z_n(est) = \frac{2\sigma \cos \phi}{r_t g (\rho_n - \rho_w)} \qquad \text{(Eqn. 11.6)}$$

where: Zn (est) = Critical NAPL height required for DNAPL penetration into a saturated aquifer

TABLE 11.3 *continued*

$$Z_n(est) = \frac{2\sigma\cos\phi\left(\frac{1}{r_t} - \frac{1}{r}\right)}{gabs(\rho_n - \rho_w)} \tag{Eqn. 11.7}$$

$$= \frac{P_{c(fine)} - P_{c(coarse)}}{gabs(\rho_n - \rho_w)}$$

$$= \frac{P_{c(fine)} - P_{c(coarse)}}{gabs(\rho_n - \rho_w)}$$

where: Zn (est) = Critical NAPL height required for downward DNAPL penetration or upward LNAPL migration from a coarse-grained material into a fine-grained material

$$\frac{\Delta h}{\Delta z_n} = \frac{\rho_n - \rho_w}{\rho_w} \tag{Eqn. 11.8}$$

where: h / z_n = Minimum hydraulic gradient required to prevent downward DNAPL migration or upward LNAPL migration

σ = interfacial tension between NAPL and water
ϕ = contact angle
r = radius of the water filled pore that the NAPL must move through to exit or enter pore
r_t = radius of the water filled pore throat that the NAPL must move through to exit or enter pore
ρ_n = density of NAPL (gm/cc)
ρ_w = density of water (1 gm/cc)
g = force of gravity (980 cm/sec2)
μ= dynamic viscosity (centipoise)

Example 11.3 illustrates how to apply a capillary force relationship to a NAPL problem.

Example 11.3   CRITICAL NAPL HEIGHT REQUIRED FOR NAPL PENETRATION INTO THE VADOSE ZONE

Assume that a mobile DNAPL pool is perched above an unsaturated fine-grained silt layer with a pore radius of 0.005 mm. The DNAPL has a specific gravity of 1.3, an interfacial tension with water of 0.04 N/m, and a contact angle to a mineral solid phase of 35°. How thick must the DNAPL have to be before it penetrates the fine-grained silt layer? Assume the residual DNAPL saturation is located above the DNAPL pool.

Solution. Apply Eq. 11.5.

$$Z_n(\text{est}) = \frac{2s \cos f}{r_{\text{fine}} g(r_n - r_w)}$$

$$= \frac{2(0.040 \text{ N/m})(\cos 35°)}{(0.000005 \text{ m})(9.8 \text{ m/sec}^2)(1300 \text{ kg/m}^3 - 1000 \text{ kg/m}^3)}$$

$$= 4.5 \text{ m}$$

Analysis. Based on this theoretical analysis, substantial accumulation (i.e., 4.5 m) of DNAPL on top of the silt layer is required to penetrate the silt. Because the capillary pressure relationships are dependent on pore radius, microscale heterogeneities (such as fractures) will often control the overall migration pathway taken by mobile DNAPL. At actual sites, the above can overpredict DNAPL ponding on acquitards (Stephens et al., 1998; Tuck et al., 1999).

Darcy's Law. Movement of free-phase NAPLs through a porous medium can be evaluated by using Darcy's equation. If all or almost all of the open pore space is filled with a continuous, free-phase NAPL mass, then Darcy's equation can be applied to NAPL movement in a similar way that Darcy's equation is used for ground water flow. The most important exception, however, is that hydraulic conductivity (K) must be replaced by the intrinsic permeabilities (k) to account for the different hydraulic characteristics differences related to the NAPL fluid. For the simple one-dimensional (1-D) case:

$$v = -(k\rho g/\mu)(dh/dl) \tag{11.9}$$

where

$$dh/dl = \frac{z + P}{\rho g} dl \tag{11.10}$$

v	=	darcy velocity (cm/sec)
k	=	intrinsic permeability (cm^2; 1 cm^2 = 10^8 darcies)
ρ	=	density of NAPL (g/cm^3)
g	=	force of gravity (980 cm/sec^2)
μ	=	dynamic viscosity (poise; 1 poise = 1 g/cm-sec)
dh/dl	=	hydraulic gradient of NAPL mass
z	=	reference elevation
P	=	pressure (atm)

Relative Permeability. When both water and NAPL are present in the aquifer, however, multiphase flow regime is established. Multiphase flow occurs when two different fluids flow through a porous medium, compete for available pore space, and thereby reduce the mobility of both fluids (Mercer and Cohen, 1990). This reduction in mobility is defined by the **relative permeability**, the ratio of the effective permeability of a fluid at a given saturation to the intrinsic permeability of the medium. In a specific porous medium, relative permeability of a fluid ranges from 0 to 1.0 based on a complex function of the saturation of the fluid, whether the fluid is wetting or nonwetting, and whether a wetting fluid is displacing a nonwetting fluid (called **imbibition**) or a nonwetting fluid is displacing a wetting fluid (called **drainage**). NAPL moving into the saturated zone is an example of drainage (the water is draining away from the pore). Forcing NAPL out of the pore with water pressure is an example of imbibition.

Figure 11.14 shows a typical relative permeability diagram for a two-fluid system comprised of NAPL and water and illustrates how the two fluids interfere with each other to reduce mobility. At most parts of the relative saturation curve, adding the relative permeabilities of the NAPL (the nonwetting fluid in a NAPL/water mixture) and the water (the wetting fluid) do not equal one; thus the interference reduces the overall mobility of both fluids in the porous medium (see Example 11.4). One additional point shown on this relative permeability curve is the difference in relative permeability for NAPLs undergoing drainage versus imbibition. As one might expect, it is easier for NAPL to enter a pore than it is to leave a pore, meaning that a relatively permeability diagram for drainage will show higher relative permeability than will the relative permeability diagram for imbibition.

Example 11.4   RELATIVE PERMEABILITY

A NAPL has entered an aquifer and a laboratory study of cores taken from the site yielded the relative permeability curves shown in Figure 11.14. If the average NAPL saturation (S_{in}) is 0.50, what are the relative permeabilities of the NAPL and the water? What are the implications of those relative permeability numbers?

Solution. From Figure 11.14, the relative permeability of NAPL is 0.25, and the relative permeability of water is 0.05. A relative permeability of 0.25 means that the NAPL will flow through the current mixture of sand/water/NAPL at only 25% the rate that it would flow through a sand/NAPL mixture with no water present. Similarly, water will flow through this sand/water/NAPL mixture at a rate that is only 5% of the flowrate for a sand/water mixture (i.e., no NAPL).

Analysis. The movement of NAPL and water through a porous media slows down significantly when oil and water are mixed together. To maximize the removal of a

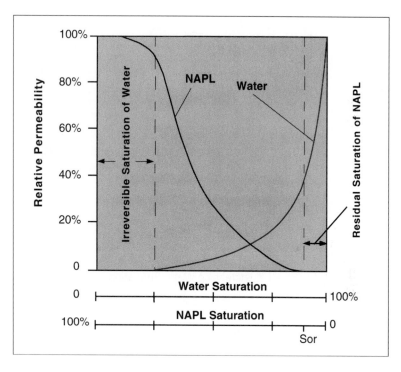

Figure 11.14 Residual Saturation curve. Source: Schwille, 1998. 1999 by Lewis Publishers, a subsidiary of CRC Press.

large free-phase NAPL pool, keep the NAPL pool intact for as long as possible to avoid the interference caused by pumping a combined NAPL and water mixture.

With the same relative permeability curve, the type of flow regime can be described as a function of saturation, as shown in Figure 11.15 (Williams and Wilder, 1971). When the NAPL saturation is high (Zone I), the NAPL mass is continuous and NAPL transport dominates. Because the water is trapped in small, isolated pores, water phase is noncontinuous and the relative permeability of water is very low or zero. In Zone II, both NAPL and water are continuous but do not share the same pore spaces. Due to interference, however, the relative permeabilities of both fluids are greatly reduced. Zone III represents the case where the NAPL is discontinuous and is trapped as a residual hydrocarbon in isolated pores. Water movement in this region dominates flow, and there is little or no NAPL flow under these conditions. The saturation where the relative permeability of the NAPL phase becomes zero is defined as the residual saturation for NAPL; all of the NAPL is discontinuous and no NAPL flow is observed.

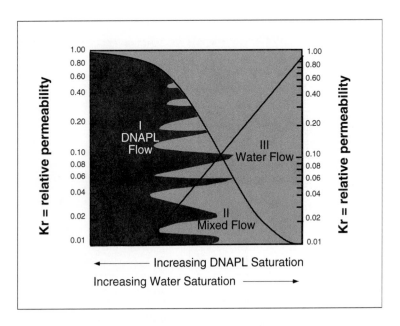

Figure 11.15 Different flow regimes in NAPL/water system. Source: Williams and Wilder, 1971.

Typical relative permeability data are available in the technical literature (Saraf and McCafferty, 1982 and Honarpour et al. 1987) and are useful for illustrating the general relationship between permeability and saturation. The shape of the relative permeability curve is related to (1) intrinsic permeability, (2) pore-size distribution, (3) ratio of fluid viscosity, (4) interfacial tension, and (5) wettability (Domenico and Schwartz, 1990; Demond and Roberts, 1987). In actual practice, however, relative permeability relationships are rarely developed from individual field studies (Mercer and Cohen, 1990).

11.4.2 NAPL Computations At The Site Level

Computer Models for Continuous-Phase NAPL Migration. The petroleum industry pioneered the development of computer models that simulated the migration of NAPLs in the subsurface in the 1960s, and during the 1980s environmental scientists and engineers began to adapt these types of codes to ground water problems. While the current family of environmental multiphase models can simulate a variety of ground water problems, the data requirements are significant and difficult to estimate accurately (Mercer and Cohen, 1990). Due to extreme field complexity associated with NAPL migration, most models are used for conceptual studies only or for prediction of general migration patterns of NAPL in the subsurface. Pankow and Cherry (1996) provide reviews of existing computer models for simulating NAPL flow for ground water problems.

Residual NAPL Relationships for Design of Remediation Systems. While the capillary forces that hold residual NAPL in pores are relatively strong, they can be overcome by gravity forces associated with buoyancy/density forces, or by viscous forces associated with ground water flow. The ratio of capillary forces to gravity forces is known as the bond number (N_b) while the ratio of capillary forces to viscous forces is called the capillary number (N_c):

$$N_b = k\Delta\rho g/\sigma \tag{11.11}$$

$$N_c = (k\rho g/\sigma)(\Delta h/\Delta l) \tag{11.12}$$

$$N_c = (K\mu/\sigma)(\Delta h/\Delta l) \tag{11.13}$$

where,

k	=	intrinsic permeability (cm^2)
ρ	=	density of water (g/cm^3)
σ	=	interfacial tension (dyne/cm)
g	=	gravitational acceleration (g/cm^2)
$\Delta\rho$	=	fluid-fluid density difference (g/cm^3)
$\Delta h/\Delta l$	=	hydraulic gradient
μ	=	dynamic viscosity of water (g/cm-sec)
K	=	hydraulic conductivity (cm/sec)

The bond and capillary number relationships can be used with empirical data to estimate the change in residual saturation due to gravity or viscous forces. Figure 11.16 shows an example of a residual saturation/capillary number curve for a sandstone material. As the capillary number increases, either from an increase in ground water velocity or a reduction in interfacial tension, the amount of residual saturation decreases. On this curve, the change in residual saturation is represented by the ratio of current saturation (S_i) to initial residual saturation (S_{ir}). The first residual hydrocarbon blobs are mobilized when $N_c = 2 \times 10^{-5}$, and all the residual hydrocarbon blobs are mobilized when $N_c = 2 \times 10^{-3}$. Please note that this curve is for one particular sandstone, and that other porous media will have curves with different shapes and endpoints.

Capillary numbers can be used to estimate the potential efficiency of a hydrocarbon removal scheme employing either high hydraulic gradients or reduced interfacial tension, or both. With the empirical data from the sandstone material in Figure 11.16, Wilson and Conrad (1986) showed the magnitude of the hydraulic gradient required to mobilize NAPL

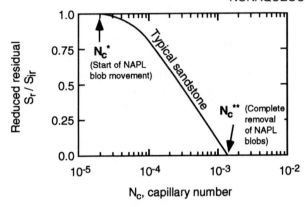

Figure 11.16 Residual hydrocarbon saturation ration, relating final residual saturation to initial residual saturation as a function of capillary number Nc. Source: Wilson and Conrad, 1984.

blobs (see Figure 11.17). These data show that complete mobilization of residual hydrocarbons is very difficult or impossible to achieve in most aquifers using hydraulic gradient alone (Wilson and Conrad, 1986). The required hydraulic gradients are so high for many aquifers (> 1 ft/ft) that no reasonable configuration of pumping and injection wells could be designed to sweep all of the residual NAPL trapped in the pores of the aquifer. In a few cases where permeability is exceptionally high, such as aquifers comprised of coarse-grained material such as gravel, it may be possible to remove all or most of the residual hydrocarbons using the force of water alone.

Addition of surfactants and cosolvents (agents such as polymers, alcohols, or detergents) can also increase the capillary number by reducing the interfacial tension of the NAPL/water blobs. See Chapter 13 for additional information regarding the use of surfactant agents.

11.5 FATE OF NAPLs IN THE SUBSURFACE

As indicated by the transport relationships described in the preceding section, much of the NAPL that is released in the subsurface becomes tightly trapped by capillary forces in the pores and fractures of the soil/aquifer matrix. Eventually, however, the hydrocarbons that comprise the NAPLs are either (1) transferred to the air, (2) transformed to carbon dioxide and water, or (3) transferred to the water. These three processes are called **volatilization, in-situ biodegradation/hydrolysis**, and **dissolution.**

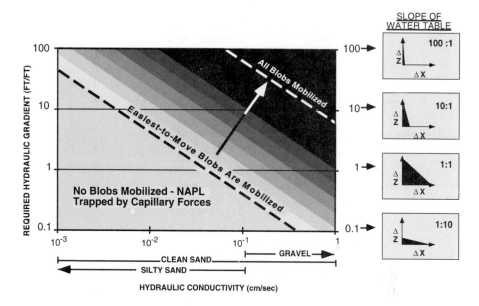

Figure 11.17 Hydraulic gradient required to initiate or completely mobilize residual NAPL blobs vs. hydraulic conductivity of porous media. Note the median hydraulic gradient from a nation-wide survey of 400 aquifers was 0.007 ft/ft, and the median hydraulic conductivity was 0.005 cm/sec. These conditions are well below the values required for blob mobilization. Source: Wiedemeier et al., 1999.

11.5.1 Volatilization

In the vadose zone, volatilization can occur when contaminated water, soil containing sorbed hydrocarbons, or NAPL comes in contact with air. As described in Chapter 7, one of the most important volatilization relationship is Henry's law, which is based on a local equilibrium assumption and yields the concentration of an organic in air if one knows the total concentration of the organic in water.

NAPLs in the subsurface will also volatilize, but in a different fashion than that of a mixture of dissolved organics in water. For a pure-phase NAPL, the vapor pressure defines the equilibrium between the NAPL phase and air phase. For NAPL mixtures, equilibrium conditions for a hydrocarbon are described by principles from Raoult's law:

$$P_a = X_a P_0^a \tag{11.14}$$

where

P_a = vapor pressure of the hydrocarbon "a" in the NAPL mixture (atm)

X_a = mole fraction of hydrocarbon "a" in the NAPL mixture

P_0^a = vapor pressure of a pure hydrocarbon "a" NAPL (atm)

Note that if the NAPL is a single component, the mole fraction equals 1.0 and the pure phase vapor pressure can be used to estimate the vapor pressure in the system of interest. See Example 11.5 for more details on the application of Raoult's Law.

Example 11.5   RAOULT'S LAW

A NAPL of pure benzene is released to the unsaturated zone. What is the *theoretical* concentration of benzene in an air stream that passes through the contaminated zone? What is the concentration of benzene in the air if the NAPL is comprised of only 20% by mole fraction NAPL and 80% nonvolatile organics?

Solution. The theoretical concentration of benzene in air for the pure benzene NAPL can be expressed in two ways, either as a volumetric concentration in units of parts per million volume (ppmv) or as a unit of mg/L (note this is not equivalent to ppm when air is the solvent). To calculate a volumetrically-based concentration for the pure benzene, convert from the vapor pressure expressed in atmospheres using Eq. 11.14:

$$P_a = X_a P_0^a$$
$$P_a = (1)(0.10 \text{ atm})$$
$$P_a = 0.10 \text{ atm}$$
$$C = P_a \text{ (atm)} \times 1{,}000{,}000 = 100{,}000 \text{ ppmv}$$

where

X_a = mole fraction of benzene in NAPL (1.0 for a pure benzene NAPL)

P_0^a = vapor pressure of pure-phase component (0.10 atm or 76 mm Hg)

C = volumetric concentrations of benzene in air (ppmv)

To calculate the concentration in mg of benzene per liter of air, use the expression

$$C \text{ (mg/l)} = \frac{[X_a][P_0^a][MW]}{RT}$$

$$= \frac{[1.0 \text{ mole/mole}][0.10 \text{ atm}][78.1 \text{ g/mole}][1000 \text{ mg/g}]}{[0.0821 \text{ L} - \text{atm/mole} - \text{K}][293 \text{ K}]}$$

$$= 325 \text{ mg/L}$$

If the NAPL contains only 20% mole fraction of benzene, use Raoult's law to estimate the actual vapor pressure:

$$P_a = X_a P_0^a$$

$$= 0.20(0.10 \text{ atm})$$

$$= 0.02 \text{ atm}$$

To convert to a mass-based concentration, use this expression:

$$C \text{ (mg/l)} = \frac{[X_a][P_0^a][\text{MW}]}{RT}$$

$$= \frac{[0.2 \text{ mole/mole}][0.10 \text{ atm}][78.1 \text{ g/mole}][1000 \text{ mg/g}]}{[0.0821 \text{ L} - \text{atm/mole} - \text{K}][293 \text{ K}]}$$

$$= 65 \text{ mg/L}$$

Analysis: Different concentrations have different practical applications: Volumetric concentrations are often compared against health-based standards, while the mass-based concentrations are important for remediation design.

Vapor transport through the soil under ambient conditions is usually limited by diffusion because there is considerable "dead end" spaces in the subsurface that will be partially filled with NAPL but will not allow air to pass by directly. Therefore, volatilization occurs as the vapors leave the NAPL and move to diffusion towards the zones with lower concentrations, that is, the pathways carrying air. Several software packages are available to describe diffusion-limited volatilization from contaminated soils that are exposed to the atmosphere (e.g., Connor and Bowers, 1998). A simple diffusion model developed by Hamaker (Lyman et al., 1982) assumes the soil column to be semi-infinite (the total depth of the zone undergoing removal of organics by volatilization is small compared to the total contaminated depth) and estimates mass loss over time in soils with:

$$Q_t = 2C_0(D_t / \pi)^{-0.5} \tag{11.15}$$

where

Q_t = mass loss over time per unit area of exposed soil for some time t [M/L^2]
C_0 = initial concentration of soil [M/L^3]
D_t = Diffusion coefficient of vapor through soil [L^2/T]

11.5.2 Chemical And Biological Degradation

Hydrolysis. Hydrolysis (see Chapter 7) is probably the most important nonbiological reaction for many NAPL-related chemicals, and is probably the most significant environmental fate process for certain families of chemicals, such as selected chlorinated solvents (i.e., 1,1,1-trichlorethane, chloroethane). Hydrolysis is a nonbiological transformation where an organic chemical reacts with water (or a component ion of water) to form a derivative organic chemical (Domenico and Schwartz, 1990):

$$R{-}X \;\Rightarrow\; R{-}OH + X^{-} + H^{+} \qquad\qquad (11.16)$$

In this reaction, $R{-}X$ is a hydrocarbon with X representing an attached halogen, carbon, phosphorous, or nitrogen group. Lyman et al. (1982) lists functional groups that are particularly susceptible to hydrolysis reactions and groups that are resistant to hydrolysis. When considering the effect of hydrolysis on NAPLs, note that only the molecules on the surface of a NAPL blob are in contact with water, thereby preventing the hydrolysis of the hydrocarbon molecules on the inside of the blob. Similarly, NAPLs in the vadose zone will not undergo hydrolysis when they are only in contact with air (see Chapter 7).

Dissolution. The transfer of soluble organics from an immiscible liquid (such as a NAPL) to the water is called **dissolution** (see Figure 11.18). In the vadose zone, infiltration water moving past NAPL will dissolve soluble hydrocarbons and transport them to the saturated zone. In aquifers, dissolution occurs when NAPL slowly dissolves as ground water flows past residual NAPL blobs or a large continuous-phase NAPL pool. Because most sites are probably affected by NAPLs, the dissolved plumes are a symptom of NAPL contamination either in the vadose zone or the saturated zone (Weidemeier et al. 1999).

The most important factors controlling the dissolution rate are the saturation of the NAPL in the subsurface and the **effective solubility** of the dissolving hydrocarbons. Simply put, higher dissolution rates are associated with more soluble hydrocarbons in a NAPL and/or large amounts of NAPL in the subsurface. Secondary parameters that influence the dissolution rate include ground water seepage velocity and porosity. With several of these key values estimated from engineering judgment or obtained from the field, an estimate of dissolution rate can be obtained and used for the purpose of predicting how long the NAPL will serve as an active source of dissolved hydrocarbons to ground water.

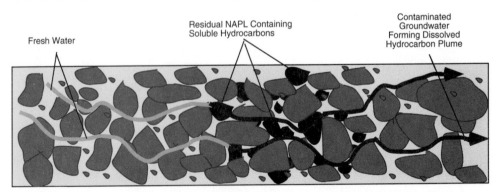

Figure 11.18 NAPL dissolution of residual NAPL, forming dissolved hydrocarbon plume.

Effective Solubility Relationship. For single-component NAPLs, the pure-phase solubility of the organic constituent can be used to estimate the theoretical upper-level concentration of organics in aquifers or for performing dissolution calculations. For NAPLs comprised of a mixture of chemicals, however, the **effective solubility** concept should be employed. **Effective solubility** is defined as the theoretical aqueous solubility of an organic constituent in ground water that is in chemical equilibrium with a mixed NAPL (a NAPL containing several organic chemicals). The effective solubility of a particular organic chemical can be estimated by multiplying its mole fraction in the NAPL mixture by its pure phase solubility, based on principles from Raoult's law (see Borden, et al., 1992; Feenstra, Mackay, and Cherry, 1991; Pankow and Cherry, 1996):

$$S_i^e = X_{oi} S_i \qquad (11.17)$$

where

S_i^e = the effective solubility of indicator constituent i in the water phase (mg/L)
X_{oi} = the mole fraction of indicator constituent i in the DNAPL phase (unitless)
S_i = the solubility of indicator constituent i in water (mg/L)

Effective solubilities can be calculated for all components in a DNAPL mixture (see Example 11.6). Insoluble organics in the mixture (such as long-chained alkanes) will reduce the mole fraction and effective solubility of more soluble organics but will not contribute dissolved-phase organics to ground water. Please note that this relationship is approximate and does not account for nonideal behavior of mixtures, such as cosolvency, etc.

The initial mole fraction of the soluble organic in the NAPL phase is determined through laboratory analysis.

Example 11.6 EFFECTIVE SOLUBILITY

Calculate the effective solubility of a DNAPL with a mole fraction of trichloroethylene (TCE) equal to 0.10.

Solution. Apply Eq. (11.17):

$S_i^e = X_{oi} S_i$
$S_i^e = (0.10)\ (1100\ \text{mg/l})$
$S_i^e = 110\ \text{mg/l}$

Analysis. When soluble organics are found in mixed DNAPLs, they have a lower theoretical solubility in water than they would if the organics were found as a pure-component DNAPL. This is one reason why near-solubility concentrations are never found in the field, as many of the DNAPLs causing dissolved plumes are mixed DNAPLs. The other main reason for never observing near-saturation conditions in the field is dilution with clean water. Even in an area of high DNAPL saturation, there are still some streamlines that never come into contact with the DNAPL (see Anderson et al., 1992a; Anderson et al., 1992b; Pankow and Cherry, 1996; Wiedemeier et al., 1999).

Predicting Dissolution Rates Over Time. As with the volatilization of NAPLs, the dissolution rate of a mixed NAPL will decline over time, due to the reduction in mole fraction of soluble components in the NAPL. Simple models (e.g., see discussion in Wiedemeier et al., 1999) can be used to simulate the slow decline in dissolved hydrocarbon concentration over time that is originating from a NAPL zone. A method developed by Feenstra (Pankow and Cherry, 1996) uses dissolution data from multi-component NAPLs to estimate the mass of NAPL in a source zone.

In-Situ Biodegradation. Current conceptual models of biodegradation assume that significant biological transformation does not occur in the NAPLs themselves. However, vigorous biodegradation reactions can serve to reduce dissolved contaminants that result from dissolution, thereby increasing the driving force for dissolution and increasing the rate that NAPLs are depleted. The dissolution products from fuel NAPLs, such as the BTEX compounds from gasoline, are readily biodegradable both aerobically and anaerobically (Wiedemeier et al. 1999). Computer models such as BIOPLUME and BIOSCREEN (see Chapter 8) account for the available biodegradation capacity (also called the expressed assimilative capacity) of the ground water to simulate the biodegradation of fuel components (e.g., see Newell et al., 1996). Example 11.7 illustrates the mass balance between available electron acceptors that flow through a residual NAPL source zone and the mass of dissolvable contaminants in the source zone.

Many chlorinated solvents are now known to biodegrade in the subsurface. For example, the chlorinated ethenes (PCE, TCE, DCE, and VC) and chlorinated ethenes (TCE, DCA) are biodegraded by dechlorinating bacteria called halorespirators that consume dissolved hydrogen along with chlorinated solvents. The dissolved hydrogen itself is either produced by naturally occurring bacteria that ferment nonchlorinated organics, or can be added directly (Newell et al., 1998).

Example 11.7   IN-SITU BIODEGRADATION OF LNAPL SOURCE ZONE

How long does it take to for clean ground water to biodegrade the mass in an LNAPL source zone? Use the following assumptions:

Depth of LNAPL penetration into saturated zone: 2 m

Width of LNAPL release in saturated zone: 10 m

LNAPL mass: 1000 gallons of gasoline (~2500 kg)

Fraction of BTEX in gasoline: 10%

Ground water darcy velocity: 0.1 m/day

Equivalent amount of BTEX that can be consumed by clean ground water flowing through source zone (this is based on the expressed assimilative capacity of the clean ground water, such as the amount of oxygen and other electron acceptors available for biodegradation) : 10 mg/l

Solution.

Time to degrade (t) may be calculated as follows:

$$t = \frac{\left[2500 \text{ kg LNAPL}\right] \cdot \left[\dfrac{0.1 \text{ kg BTEX}}{1 \text{ kg LNAPL}}\right] \cdot \left[\dfrac{10^6 \text{ mg BTEX}}{\text{kg BTEX}}\right]}{\left[\dfrac{0.1 \text{ m}}{\text{day}} \cdot 10 \text{ m} \cdot 2 \text{ m}\right] \cdot \left[\dfrac{10^3 \text{ L}}{\text{m}^3}\right] \cdot \left[\dfrac{10 \text{ mg e}^- \text{ acceptors}}{1 \text{ L clean water}}\right] \left[\dfrac{1 \text{ mg BTEX removed}}{3.14 \text{ mg e}^- \text{ acceptor}}\right] \cdot \left[\dfrac{365 \text{ day}}{\text{yr}}\right]}$$

$= 34$ years

Analysis. This calculation indicates that clean ground water has the capacity to biodegrade all of the dissolved BTEX contaminants in the LNAPL source zone in 34 years at this site. The actual time may be longer, however, if the rate of BTEX dissolution is slower than the rate that the clean ground water delivers electron acceptors to the source zone.

11.6 CHARACTERIZING NAPLs AT REMEDIATION SITES

Although the presence of NAPLs can dominate the remediation process at a site, it is often difficult to locate NAPL zones or even to confirm that NAPL is present at site. The following sections summarize the most important techniques, both direct and indirect, that can be employed to characterize the distribution of NAPLs at a hazardous waste site. Cohen and Mercer (1993) provide a rich collection of procedures for evaluating DNAPL sites, many of which can also be applied to investigation of LNAPL problems. The U.S. EPA (1992a) provides a worksheet and flowcharts to help determine the potential for occurrence of DNAPL at hazardous waste sites.

11.6.1 Direct Measure

Apparent vs. Actual LNAPL Thickness. Analysis of free-phase hydrocarbons in a well is the best evidence that NAPLs are present in the subsurface. As would be expected, a floating layer in a monitoring well indicates the presence of a LNAPL layer floating on top of the water table, while a dense layer at the bottom of a well indicates a heavy DNAPL in the formation. The thickness of the LNAPL layer in the well can provide an order-of-magnitude indication of the thickness of the LNAPL floating layer, with the "apparent thickness" in the well usually being two to ten times thicker than the actual product thickness in the aquifer (Cohen and Mercer, 1993). The primary reason for this difference is seen in Figure 11.19, where the LNAPL in the formation is shown floating on top of the capillary fringe while the LNAPL in the well floats on top of, and partially depresses, the actual water table.

The actual relationship between the apparent and true LNAPL thickness is very difficult to predict. Based on a review of many of these methods, Hampton and Miller (1988) proposed the use of the following simplified relationship for approximating the true thickness of LNAPL-saturated formation. LNAPL thickness in a formation (h_f) may be approximated by:

$$h_f \approx h_w \left(\rho_{\text{water}} - \rho_{\text{LNAPL}} \right) / \rho_{\text{LNAPL}} \tag{11.18}$$

where

   h_f is the thickness of LNAPL in formation
   h_w is the thickness of LNAPL in well
   ρ_{water} is the density of water
   ρ_{LNAPL} is the density of LNAPL

Note that this relationship is only an approximation of actual conditions in the field. Some specialized field procedures, such as dielectric logging, may be more useful for estimating the true product thickness in the formation (Kemblowski and Chiang, 1989; Keech, 1988).

DNAPL Thickness in Wells. While apparent product thickness can provide a general indication of the amount of LNAPL conditions in the field, DNAPL thickness data is much more difficult to interpret and use. Unless the DNAPL observation well is screened

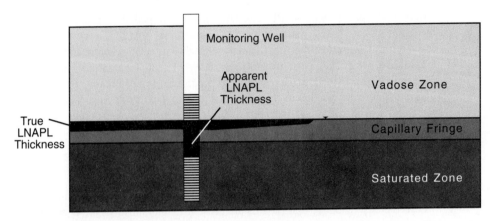

Figure 11.19 LNAPL floating on top of capillary fringe in formation and accumulating on top of water table in well.

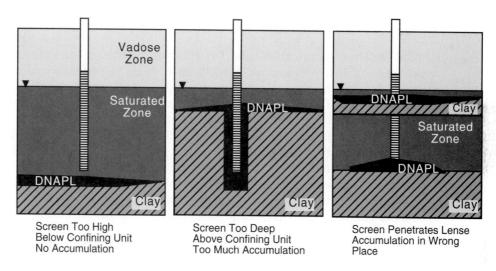

Figure 11.20 Problems with measuring DNAPL in monitoring wells.

directly within a DNAPL pool or lens and is constructed correctly, the apparent DNAPL thickness can give erroneous indications of the quantity of DNAPL in the formation (see Figure 11.20). In general, DNAPL accumulation in wells only proves that mobile DNAPL is present in the subsurface (Pankow and Cherry, 1996).

One important point to remember is that the absence of NAPL in a well does not confirm that the subsurface is free of NAPL, however. If a screen is set below the surface of the water table, for example, the floating LNAPL layer will ride above the screen and buoyancy forces will prevent the LNAPL from entering the well. Similarly, a well that does not intersect any DNAPL-flowing zones, or is screened above a DNAPL pool or lens, will not indicate the presence of DNAPL. Considerable care must be taken to make sure that the well screen will intersect the zone that may have NAPLs. Most importantly, a well will not exhibit any NAPL if the screened interval contains only residual NAPL. The residual NAPL is trapped in the porous media and is prevented by capillary forces from migrating into the well.

Visual examination of soil samples. In cases of gross NAPL contamination, a visual inspection of a soil core can prove that NAPLs are present in the subsurface. A core that is saturated with oil, for example, is usually fairly easy to discern with the naked eye. NAPL that is present in small secondary porosity features or tied up as small residual blobs may be very difficult to observe, however, particularly if the NAPL has a similar color to the soil matrix. Some field investigators recommend shaking the soil core in a jar with water to separate the DNAPL from the soil or performing a paint filter test to increase the chance for visual detection. In addition, use of a black light will help to identify many NAPLs containing aromatic and other florescent hydrocarbons, and Sudan IV hydrophobic dye can be used to help see NAPLs in soil samples (Cohen and Mercer, 1993).

11.6.2 Indirect Measures

Ground Water Concentration and Distribution. Although one might expect that concentrations of dissolved chemicals in NAPL zones would be near the solubility of these chemicals, in actual practice concentrations this high are rarely observed in the field. Two main explanations are often given for this phenomenon: (1) the effective solubility relationship limits the actual concentration of dissolved constituents in ground water in contact with mixed NAPLs; and (2) the typical monitoring well, constructed with a 10 to 20 ft-long screen, intersects many "clean" flowlines that do no contact NAPL, resulting in a dilution of the "dirty" NAPL-related flowlines that are sampled.

Because of these factors, an often-employed rule of thumb for NAPL states that if concentrations of NAPL-related chemicals in ground water are greater than 1% of the pure-phase or effective solubility, then NAPLs are probably present at the site (U.S. EPA, 1992a, Pankow and Cherry, 1996) (Example 11.8). Note that this is a general rule and therefore it should be used in conjunction with other indicators of NAPL presence. The EPA (1992) states "however, certain concentrations are generally accepted as indicating a highly likelihood of a subsurface DNAPL source across a wide range of sites (i.e., 1% or more of a compounds solubility). However, concentrations representing less than 1% of a compounds solubility do not indicate the absence of a subsurface DNAPL source." A modified version of the rule that considers the presence of multi-component NAPLs was used by the U.S. EPA (1992a).

Example 11.8   INDIRECT MEASURES OF DNAPL PRESENCE: 1% RULE

Site A has a monitoring well with dissolved trichloroethene concentrations on the order of 15 mg/L. What does the 1% rule indicate for DNAPLs at this site?

Solution.
Pure-phase solubility of TCE = 1100 mg/L
1% of pure phase solubility = 11 mg/L
Concentrations at this well exceed 1% of the pure phase solubility

Analysis. The site concentrations at this well suggest that DNAPL is present at the site, even though free-phase DNAPL was not observed in the well. Although the presence of DNAPL cannot be proven explicitly at this site, the data from this well indicate a likelihood of DNAPL presence.

The distribution of dissolved constituents at a site can also be used as an indicator of the presence of NAPLs. If dissolved NAPL-related chemicals appear in an anomalous upgradient/across gradient location, or are variable over time, then either a free-phase floating LNAPL layer or DNAPL mass may have been moving across the site and that NAPLs are currently serving as a source of dissolved constituents to ground water. Finally, if DNAPL-related chemical concentrations appear to increase with depth, then the presence of DNAPLs is indicated.

Chemical Analysis of Soil/Aquifer Matrix Samples. A general rule of thumb for soil samples is that if greater than 10,000 mg/kg of hydrocarbon contamination (1% of soil mass) is observed in the soil or aquifer matrix sample, then that sample probably contains some NAPL (Feenstra et al., 1991). A more exact method employs a partitioning calculation based on the chemical analyses of soil samples from the saturated zone and the effective solubility concept. This method tests the initial hypothesis that all of the organics in the subsurface are either dissolved in ground water or adsorbed to soil (assuming dissolved-phase sorption, not the presence of NAPL). By using the concentration of organics on the soil and the partitioning calculation, a theoretical pore-water concentration of organics in ground water is determined. If the theoretical pore-water concentration is greater than the estimated solubility of the organic constituent of interest, then NAPL may be present at the site (Feenstra et al., 1991):

Step 1: Calculate S_i^e, the effective solubility of organic constituent of interest.

Step 2: Determine K_{oc}, the organic carbon-water partition coefficient from literature sources or from empirical relationships based on K_{ow}, the octanol-water partition coefficient, which is also found in the literature. For example, K_{oc} can be estimated from K_{ow} using the following expression developed for polyaromatic hydrocarbons (Karickhoff et al, 1979):

$$\log K_{oc} = \log K_{ow} - 0.21 \qquad (11.19)$$

Other empirical relationships between K_{oc} and K_{ow} are presented in Chapter 7.

Step 3: Determine f_{oc}, the fraction of organic carbon on the soil, from a laboratory analysis of clean soils from the site. Values for f_{oc} typically range from 0.03 to 0.00017 mg/mg (Domenico and Schwartz, 1990). Convert values reported in percent to mg/mg.

Step 4: Determine or estimate ρ_b, the dry bulk density of the soil, from a soil analysis. Typical values range for ρ_b from 1.8 to 2.1 g/mL (kg/L). Determine or estimate θ_w, the water-filled porosity.

Step 5: Determine K_d, the partition (or distribution) coefficient between the pore water (ground water) and the soil solids:

$$K_d = K_{oc} \cdot f_{oc} \qquad (11.20)$$

Step 6: Using C_t, the measured concentration of the organic compound in saturated soil in mg/kg, calculate the theoretical pore water concentration assuming no NAPL (i.e., C_w in mg/L):

$$C_w = (C_t \cdot \rho_b)/(K_d \rho_b + \theta_w) \qquad (11.21)$$

Step 7: Compare C_w and S_i^e (from Step 1):

$$C_w < S_i^e \text{ suggests possible absence of NAPL} \qquad (11.22)$$

$$C_w > S_i^e \text{ suggests possible presence of NAPL} \qquad (11.23)$$

Example 11.9 shows how this partitioning procedure is applied to field data to help determine whether NAPLs are present in the subsurface.

Example 11.9   INDIRECT MEASURES OF DNAPL PRESENCE: SOILS DATA

A soil sample extracted from a site with a gasoline release shows 100 mg/kg benzene. Does this indicate that the benzene is present as a NAPL? The fraction of natural organic carbon on the soil (f_{oc}) is 0.1% or 0.001 gm/gm. Assume that the gasoline is 2% benzene, the K_{oc} for benzene is 38 L/kg, and the soil bulk density is 1.8 kg/L.

Solution. Using Eqs. (11.20) and (11.21):

Pure-phase solubility of benzene = 1,740 mg/L

Effective solubility = S_i^e = 0.02 · 1740 = 34.8 mg/L

$K_d = f_{oc} \cdot K_{oc}$ = (0.001) (38 L/kg) = 0.038 L/kg

$$C_w = \frac{\left(100 \, \frac{mg}{kg}\right)\left(1.7 \, \frac{kg}{L}\right)}{\left[\left(0.038 \, \frac{L}{kg}\right)\left(1.7 \, \frac{kg}{L}\right) + 0.35\right]}$$

C_w = 414 mg/L

S_i^e = 34.8 mg/L

$C_w > S_i^e$ (the presence of NAPL is indicated in this soil sample)

Analysis. Because the residual NAPL blobs are so small, often they cannot be seen. This simple analysis can be used to help determine whether NAPL is present in the soil. C_w represents the theoretical pore water concentration if there were no NAPL present. S_i^e represents the effective solubility in the presence of NAPL, that is, the lowest concentration that would be expected if NAPL were there. Since C_w is greater than S_i^e then the presence of NAPL is indicated.

Geophysics. Because of the difficulty in locating NAPLs in the subsurface, borehole and surface geophysics are becoming more popular for site characterizations. Ground penetrating radar, complex resistivity, and electromagnetic induction have been applied to detect aqueous and nonaqueous hydrocarbons at some sites (U.S. EPA, 1992b). The value of these methods increases with the number of applications at a particular site; these geophysical techniques are better suited for detecting subtle changes in subsurface composition, such as a moving free-phase NAPL mass, than in assessing static conditions. Currently the application of geophysics at hazardous waste sites is limited by the paucity of results from research sites and by the small number of personnel that are trained to use geophysics for ground water remediation problems.

11.6.3 Integrated Approach for Determining Potential Occurrence of DNAPLs

In practice, data from several sources are used together to determine whether NAPLs are present at a hazardous waste site. One example of an integrated approach for determining whether DNAPL is present at Superfund sites uses both direct and indirect evidence (U.S. EPA, 1992a). This preliminary screening approach can be employed to determine the need for implementation of a full-scale DNAPL detection/delineation program.

11.6.4 Special Considerations for Designing DNAPL Delineation Programs

Special precautions are required to avoid inadvertent creation or enhancement of DNAPL migration pathways during the course of hydrogeologic investigations conducted at DNAPL-contaminated sites. Given the ability of DNAPL materials to move downward through very small fractures (e.g., 20 microns) within the soil mass, conventional grouting procedures may not prove effective for soil borings or wells drilled directly through a DNAPL perching stratum and into an underlying, clean unit. In developing a DNAPL detection / delineation workplan, the following concepts should be applied:

- "Outside-In" Approach: Prior to penetrating a suspected DNAPL zone, critical stratigraphic features should first be identified by investigations conducted outside of the area of concern. These preliminary data should be analyzed to identify potential perching strata or "safety nets" beneath the DNAPL zone. All drilling subsequently conducted within the area of DNAPL occurrence must be terminated at the depth of the uppermost, continuous "safety net" stratum. In thick, fractured rock settings, such perching strata may not be present, and the risks associated with drilling inside the DNAPL zone must be carefully weighed against the need for vertical delineation data.

- Soil Borings and Wells: To avoid inadvertent penetration of perching layers within DNAPL zones, soil borings should be sampled continuously with depth and terminated at or near the surface of such confining strata. For detection of free-phase DNAPL, observation wells must be screened across the upper surface of a perching layer (see Figure 11.5). However, under no conditions should the well boring penetrate the full thickness of the base stratum. Wells should be constructed with short screen sections and double-cased through the depth of any overlying DNAPL -contaminated sections.

- Non-Invasive Site Investigation Techniques: Where applicable, non-invasive techniques should be employed to indicate DNAPL presence or characterize site stratigraphy. Geophysical methods can be applied to define the presence and topography of perching strata. In addition, shallow soil gas sampling above the zone DNAPL occurrence has proven a useful indicator of DNAPL presence in some cases.

In general, the risks involved with LNAPL delineation techniques are much smaller than for DNAPL, largely because the downward migration of LNAPL is restricted by the water table and associated capillary fringe.

SUMMARY

Nonaqueous phase liquids (NAPLs) are contaminants that exist in a separate immiscible (nondissolved) phase in the subsurface. Because they are a separate phase, NAPLs have different fate and transport properties from those of dissolved contaminant plumes. NAPLs migrate through the subsurface under gravity and buoyancy forces and do not move along the general flow of ground water. While NAPLs can migrate through the subsurface as a continuous organic mass, it is almost impossible to extract all the NAPL. The NAPL breaks up into countless blobs in individual pores that are trapped so tightly by capillary forces that typical pumping measures cannot dislodge them. Because of this phenomenon, it is common to never observe NAPL during site investigations. Therefore, indirect indicators are often be used to determine if NAPL is present or not.

NAPLs can be divided into two major types based on density: LNAPLs (lighter-than-water NAPLs) will move downward and then float on top of the water table, whereas DNAPLs (denser-than-water NAPLs) can sink far below the water table. Although this classification system is based on density, it is also a good predictor of where NAPLs come from and their fate in the subsurface. In general, LNAPLs are associated with petroleum product spills and have chemicals that, once dissolved, are readily biodegraded by naturally occurring microorganisms at almost all sites. Many DNAPL releases are related to the manufacture and use of chlorinated solvents, once dissolved these chemicals appear to biodegrade under some but not all natural conditions.

Sites containing NAPLs usually have many times the contaminant mass as a site with only a dissolved plume. Therefore, it is much more difficult to restore ground water at NAPL-affected sites, particularly if a DNAPL comprised of chlorinated solvents is present. These solvent sites cannot be restored to drinking-water standards using any proven technologies, so the trapped DNAPL can act as a continuing source of ground water contamination for tens or hundreds of years. To effectively manage ground water problems at hazardous-waste sites, the effects of NAPLs should be considered very carefully during site characterization and remediation system design.

REFERENCES

Anderson, M.R., R.L. Johnson, and J.F. Pankow, "Dissolution of Dense Chlorinated Solvents into Groundwater: 1. Dissolution from a well-defined residual source," Ground Water, 30(2), 1992a.

Anderson, M.R., R.L. Johnson, and J.F. Pankow, "Dissolution of Dense Chlorinated Solvents into Groundwater. 3. Modeling Contaminant Plumes from Fingers and Pools of Solvent." Environmental Science Technology, 26: 901-908, 1992b.

Bear, J., *Dynamics of Fluids In Porous Media*, New York, American Elsevier, 1972.

Bear, J., *Hydraulics of Groundwater*, New York, McGraw-Hill, 1979.

Borden, R.C., and C. Kao, "Evaluation of Groundwater Extraction for Remediation of Petroleum-Contaminated Aquifers," *Water Environment Research,* 64(2): 28-35, 1992.

Cohen, R. M., and J. W. Mercer, DNAPL Site Evaluation, Boca Raton, Florida, C.K. Smoley, 1993.

Connor, J. A. and R. L. Bowers, *Guidelines for Risk-Based Corrective Action Modeling for Chemical Release Sites*, NGWA Petroleum Hydrocarbons Conf., Houston, TX, 1998. ww.gsi-net.com

Connor, J. A., C. J. Newell, and D. K. Wilson, Assessment, Field Testing, and Conceptual Design for Managing Dense Nonaqueous Phase Liquids (DNAPL) at a Superfund Site, Petroleum Hydrocarbon and Organic Chemicals in Ground Water, NWWA, Houston, Texas, 1989.

Demond, A. H., "An Examination of Relative Permeability Relations for Two-Phase Flow in Porous Media," *Water Resources Bulletin*, 23(4): 616-628, 1987.

Domenico, P. A., and F. W. Schwartz, *Physical and Chemical Hydrogeology*, New York, John Wiley and Sons, 1998.

Feenstra, S., D. M. MacKay, and J. A. Cherry, "A Method for Assessing Residual NAPL Based on Organic Chemical Concentrations in Soil Samples," *Groundwater Monitoring Review*, 11(2), 1991.

Freeze, R. A., and D. B. McWhorter, "A Framework for Assessing Risk Reduction During DNAPL Mass Removal from Low-Permeability Soils," Ground Water, 35(1): 111-123, 1997.

Hampton, D. R., and P. D. G. Miller, Laboratory Investigation of the Relationship Between Actual and Apparent Product Thickness in Sands, Petroleum Hydrocarbons and Organic Chemicals in Ground Water, Houston, Texas, NWW, 1988.

Honarpour, M., and S.M. Mahmood, "Relative-Permeability Measurements: An Overview." *Journal of Pet. Technology*, 40(8): 963-966, 1987.

Huling, S., and J. Weaver, Dense Nonaqueous Phase Liquids, EPA Groundwater Issue Paper, U.S. Environmental Protection Agency, EPA/540/4-91-002, 1991.

Huntley, D. H., R. N. Corley, H. P., "Nonaqueous Phase Hydrocarbon in a Fine-Grained Sandstone, 1. Comparison Between Measured and Predicted Saturations and Mobility." *Ground Water,* 32(4):626-634, 1994.

Karickhoff, S. W., D. S. Brown, and T. A. Scott, "Sorption of Hydrophobic Pollutants on Natural Sediments," *Water Res.,* 13:241-248, 1979.

Keech, D. A., Hydrocarbon Thickness on Groundwater By Dielectric Well Logging, *Petroleum Hydrocarbons and Organic Chemicals in Groundwater,* Houston, Texas, NWWA, 1988.

Kemblowski, M. W., and C. Y. Chiang, "Hydrocarbon Thickness Fluctuations in Monitoring Wells." *Ground Water,* 28(2): 244-252, 1989.

Kueper, B. H., and E. O. Frind, "An Overview of Immiscible Fingering in Porous Media," *Journal of Cont. Hydrology,* 2, 1988.

Lyman, W. J., W. F. Reehl, and D. H. Rosenblatt, *Handbook of Chemical Property Estimation Methods-Environmental Behavior of Organic Compounds*, New York, McGraw-Hill, 1982.

Mercer, J. W., and R. M. Cohen, "A Review of Immiscible Fluids in the Subsurface: Properties, Models, Characterization and Remediation," *Journal of Contaminant Hydrology,* 6:107-163, 1990.

Newell, C. J., S. D. Acree, R. R. Ross, and S. G. Huling, Light Nonaqueous Phase Liquids, Ada, OK, U.S. Environmental Protection Agency, 1995.

Pankow, J. F., and J. A. Cherry, *Dense Chlorinated Solvents and other DNAPLs in Groundwater*, Ontario, Waterloo Press, 1996.

Parker, B. L., R. W. Gillham, and J. A. Cherry, "Diffusive Disappearance of Dense, Immiscible Phase Organic Liquids in Fractured Geologic Media," *Ground Water*, 32:805-820, 1994.

Parker, J. C., D. W. Waddill, and J. Johnson, UST Corrective Action Technologies: Engineering Design of Free Product Recovery Systems, Blacksburg, VA, Environmental Systems & Technologies, Inc, 1994.

Poulson, M. M., and B. H. Kueper, "A Field Experiment to Study the Behavior of Tetrachloroethylene in Unsaturated Porous Media." *Environmental Science and Technology*, 26:889-895, 1992.

Saraf, D. N., and F. G. McCafferty, Two- and Three-Phase Relative Permeabilities: A Review, Calgary, Alta., Pet. Recov. Inst, 1982.

Schwille, F., *Dense Chlorinated Solvents in Porous and Fractured Media: Model Experiments*, Chelsea, Michigan, Lewis Publishers, 1988.

Stephens, D. B., J. A. Kelsey, M. A. Prieksat, M. G. Piepho, C. Shan,. and M. D. Ankeny, "DNAPL Migration Through a Fractured Perching Layer," *Ground Water*, 36(4): 605-611, 1998.

Tuck, D. M., Discussion of "DNAPL Migration Through a Fractured Perching Layer," *Ground Water*, 37(4): 485, 1999.

U.S. Environmental Protection Agency, Evaluation of Ground-Water Extraction Remedies, Volume 1 Summary Report. EPA/540/2-89/054, 1989.

U.S. Environmental Protection Agency, Laboratory Investigation of Residual Liquid Organics from Spills, Leaks, and the Disposal of Hazardous Wastes in Groundwater. EPA/600/6-90/004, 1990.

U.S. Environmental Protection Agency, Evaluation of Ground-Water Extraction Remedies: Phase II, Volume 1 Summary Report, Office of Emergency and Remedial Response. Publication 9355.4-05, 1992.

U.S. Environmental Protection Agency, Considerations in Ground-Water Remediation at Superfund Sites and RCRA Facilities-Update. EPA OSWER 9283.1-06, 1992.

U.S. Environmental Protection Agency, Dense Nonaqueous Phase Liquids - A Workshop Summary. EPA/600-R-92/030, 1992.

U.S. Environmental Protection Agency, Estimating Potential for Occurrence of DNAPL at Superfund Sites, R.S. Kerr Environmental Research Laboratory. EPA 9355.4-07FS. EPA Quick Reference Fact Sheet, 1992.

U.S. Environmental Protection Agency, Evaluation of the Likelihood of DNAPL Presence at NPL Sites, National Results, 1993.

Wiedemeier, T. H., H. S. Rifai, C. J. Newell, and J. T. Wilson, *Natural Attenuation of Fuel Hydrocarbons and Chlorinated Solvents*, New York, John Wiley and Sons, 1999.

Williams, D.E., and D.G. Wilder, "Gasoline Pollution of a Ground-Water Reservoir - A Case History." *Groundwater*, 9(6): 50-54, 1971.

Wilson, J. L., and S. H. Conrad, "Is Physical Displacement of Residual Hydrocarbons a Realistic Possibility in Aquifer Restoration?" *Petroleum Hydrocarbon and Organic Chemicals in Ground Water*, NWWA, Houston, Texas, 1984.

CHAPTER 12

NATURAL ATTENUATION AND RISK BASED CORRECTIVE ACTION

12.1 INTRODUCTION

Natural attenuation is a remediation approach that relies on naturally occurring processes such as dispersion, sorption, and biodegradation to control the migration of contaminants dissolved in ground water. A related approach, Risk-Based Corrective Action (RBCA), involves determining the risks to human health and the environment associated with ground water plumes and remediating the plumes to that protective level. This chapter summarizes why these technologies are being used and how they are implemented.

12.1.1 Why Natural Attenuation Has Emerged

Two converging factors have prompted the increased use of natural attenuation as a plume management technique. First, our understanding of subsurface properties has increased tremendously over the past ten years, and we now realize that many active remediation technologies are not as effective as once thought. For example, studies of multiple operating pump-and-treat systems performed by the EPA in 1989 (U. S. EPA, 1989 and 1992a) and by the National Research Council (NRC) in 1994 indicated that most pump-and-treat systems were unable to achieve the remediation goals (most commonly, ground water restoration) that were established when the systems were installed.

The EPA studies concluded that three factors created the poor performance of pump-and-treat systems: (1) the presence of hydrogeologic controls, such as low permeability zones; (2) design problems, and most importantly, (3) the presence of NAPLs in the water-bearing units. Residual NAPLs were found to serve as continuing sources of constituents to ground water at most of the sites studied, undermining aquifer restoration efforts. In response to these findings, the EPA modified the guidelines for remedial actions at Superfund sites affected by NAPLs. In an EPA Directive issued in May 1992   (U. S. EPA, 1992b), the agency recognized that full remediation of ground water impacted by NAPLs, particularly DNAPLs, will be technically impracticable at many sites.

The NRC Committee on Ground Water Cleanup Alternatives also evaluated the effectiveness of ground water pump-and-treat systems (NRC, 1994). Out of 77 sites with active pump-and-treat systems, only eight had achieved their prescribed cleanup goals. A four-category site rating system characterized the relative practicability of ground water cleanup based on site hydrogeologic conditions, constituent type, and other factors (see Table 1). Only five of the 16 sites classified as Category 1 or 2 (easier to cleanup) had achieved their

TABLE 12.1 Relative Ease of Cleaning Up Contaminated Aquifers as a Function of Contaminant Chemistry and Hydrogeology (from National Research Council, 1994)

Hydrogeology	Mobile, Dissolved (degrades / volatilizes)	Mobile, Dissolved	Strongly Sorbed, dissolved (degrades / volatilizes)	Strongly Sorbed, dissolved	Separate Phase LNAPL	Separate Phase DNAPL
Homogeneous, single layer	1[a]	1-2	2	2-3	2-3	3
Heterogeneous, single layer	1	1-2	2	2-3	2-3	3
Homogeneous, multiple layers	2	2	3	3	3	4
Heterogeneous, multiple layers	2	2	3	3	3	4
Fractured	3	3	3	3	4	4

[a] Relative ease of cleanup, where 1 is the easiest and 4 is most difficult

original cleanup goals, while none of the 42 sites categorized as Category 4 (hardest to cleanup) were successful. The presence of NAPLs, difficult hydrogeologic conditions, and nondegrading contaminants, were identified as key obstacles to restoring contaminated ground water. Overall, the NRC concluded that ground water pump-and-treat methods could require very long operating periods (in some cases, centuries) to restore ground water to drinking water standards at some sites (NRC, 1994).

The second reason for the emergence of natural attenuation as a viable remediation alternative is that our understanding of how natural processes impact plume migration has increased significantly over the past several years. For example, the U.S. Air Force initiated a Natural Attenuation Initiative in the mid-1990s that involved collecting natural attenuation data from over 30 different petroleum hydrocarbon sites (see discussion in Wiedemeier et al., 1999). The results showed that biodegradation processes at fuel sites were much more vigorous and widespread than once thought. In addition, "plume-a-thon" studies performed by several researchers (e.g., Rice et al., 1995; Mace et al., 1997; Newell and Connor, 1998) indicated that most dissolved hydrocarbon plumes from leaking underground storage tanks (primarily located at gas stations) were relatively short (see Figures 12.1 and 12.2), and that the majority of the plumes were either stable or shrinking. These studies, and other natural attenuation research efforts, showed that natural attenuation processes could contain many contaminant plumes without posing a risk to human health or the environment.

In summary, the limitations of ground water pump-and-treat technologies, combined with the realization that many plumes exhibited little or no risk, have led to increased application of natural attenuation as an approach to manage contaminated ground water.

12.1.2 Plume Life-Cycle

One of the most important studies supporting the concept of natural attenuation was a multiple site study performed by Rice et al., (1995), also referred to as the Lawrence Livermore National Laboratory (LLNL) Study. In this study, benzene plume lengths and trends over time were evaluated from 271 underground storage tank sites in California (primarily gas station tanks). After analyzing the trend data from sites with at least 8 sampling episodes, the authors defined a plume life cycle with four different stages:

- **Expanding**: Residual source present. Mass flux of contaminants exceeds assimilative capacity of aquifer.
- **Stable:** Insignificant changes. Active or passive remediation processes are controlling plume length.
- **Shrinking:** Residual source nearly exhausted and active or passive remediation processes significantly reducing plume mass.
- **Exhausted:** Average plume concentration very low (e.g., 1 ppb) and unchanging over time. Final stages of source zone dissolution over a relatively small area at a site.

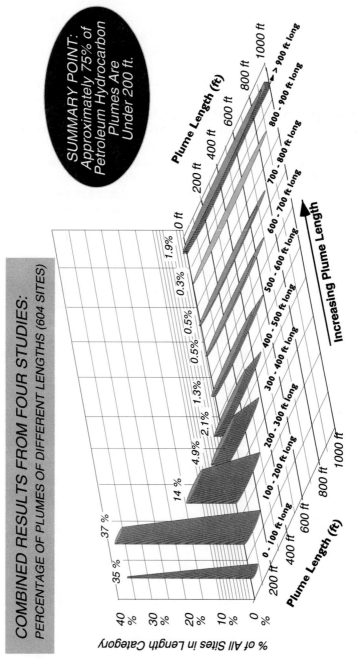

Figure 12.1 *Dissolved Hydrocarbon Plume Lengths from Four Studies. Source: Newell and Connor, 1998.*

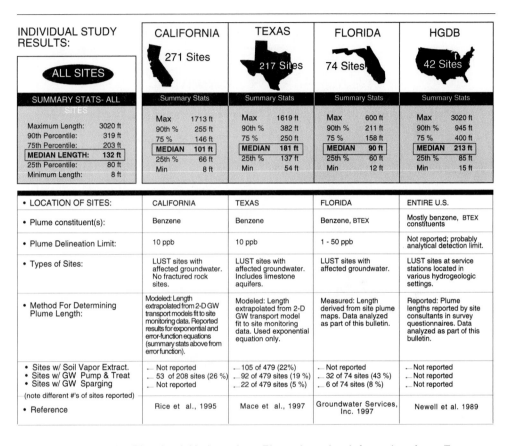

Figure 12.2 Dissolved Hydrocarbon Plume Lengths Information from Four Studies. Source: Newell and Connor, 1998.

This type of plume life-cycle analysis was repeated by Mace et al. (1997) for 217 sites in Texas.

As shown in the conceptual plume lifecycle figures conceived by Rice and presented by Newell and Connor (1998) (see Figure 12.3), of the approximately 500 petroleum hydrocarbon sites addressed by this analysis, nearly 75% were found to be in either a stable or a shrinking condition, based on analyses of both plume length and concentration. Fewer than 10% of the plumes were found to be expanding in length (8% for the California study, only 3% for the Texas study). Plume lengths were frequently stable (42% to 61%), while average plume concentrations were predominantly shrinking (47% to 59%). These results suggest that dissolved hydrocarbon plumes tend to reduce more rapidly in concentration than in

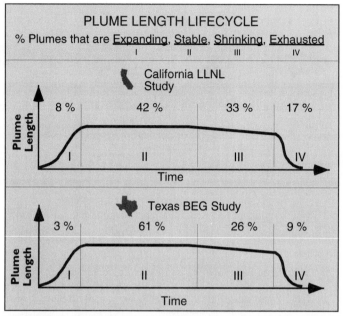

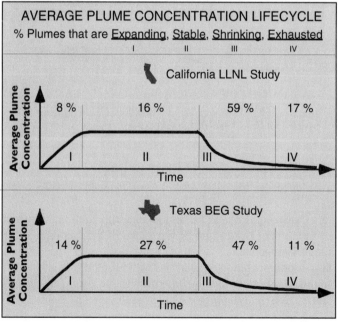

Figure 12.3 Summary of Trends for Plume Length and Plume Concentration from California and Texas. Source: Rice et al., 1995 and Mace et al., 1997.

length. Similar results were observed in a plume study performed by Buscheck et al. (1996), where 67% of 119 plumes in northern California were found to be stable/shrinking in length, and 91% had stable/diminishing concentrations.

McNab et al. (1999) applied a similar approach to chlorinated solvent sites. In this study, 29% percent of the 65 sites appeared to have expanding plumes, 55% of the plumes had no trends, and 16% of the plumes appeared to be shrinking.

These plume-a-thon studies have shown that most dissolved contaminant plumes are not expanding, and that natural attenuation processes have the potential to manage ground water contamination at many sites.

12.1.3 Advantages and Disadvantages

In 1997, the Environmental Protection Agency released a directive regarding Monitoring Natural Attenuation (see Section 12.3) that concluded that "Monitored natural attenuation has several potential advantages and disadvantages, and its use should be carefully considered during site characterization and evaluation of remediation alternatives." The policy memorandum listed several advantages and disadvantages (EPA, 1997):

Potential advantages of monitored natural attenuation include:

- As with any *in situ* process, generation of fewer remediation wastes, reduced potential for cross-media transfer of contaminants commonly associated with *ex situ* treatment, and reduced risk of human exposure to contaminated media
- Less intrusion as few surface structures are required
- Application to all or part of a given site, depending on site conditions and cleanup objectives
- Use in conjunction with, or as a follow-up to, other (active) remedial measures
- Lower overall remediation costs than those associated with active remediation

The potential disadvantages of monitored natural attenuation include:

- Longer time frames to achieve remediation objectives, compared to active remediation
- Complex and costly site characterization
- Toxicity of transformation products may exceed that of the parent compound;
- Need for long-term monitoring
- Need for institutional controls may be necessary to ensure long-term protectiveness
- Continued contamination migration, and/or cross-media transfer of contaminants

As with any remediation technology, natural attenuation is viable at some sites but not at others. Some of the key factors that determine whether natural attenuation is appropriate include:

1. plume stability
2. required remediation time frame
3. risk associated with contaminants and natural attenuation processes
4. economics of natural attenuation versus other technologies
5. off-site contamination issues
6. the degree of understanding regarding site processes

For example, a site with a stable or shrinking plume, no immediate need for restoration of ground water, no apparent risk from ground water contaminants, expensive active remediation alternatives, no off-site contamination, and well understood natural attenuation processes (i.e., BTEX biodegradation) is probably an excellent candidate for natural attenuation. On the other hand, a site with an expanding plume, a short remediation time frame (perhaps due to an impending property transaction), risks above state-mandated risk targets, relatively inexpensive active remediation alternatives (such as a very small plume), an off-site plume, or complicated natural attenuation processes might be a less suitable candidate.

12.2 GENERAL PRINCIPLES BEHIND NATURAL ATTENUATION

Natural attenuation controls contaminants released from source zones via dispersion, diffusion, sorption, degradation (either biodegradation or abiotic processes such as hydrolysis), volatilization, and dilution. Volatilization and diffusion are relatively unimportant in most non-clay ground water systems (Wiedemeier et al., 1999); therefore, the main attenuation process are dispersion, sorption, degradation, and dilution. These key natural attenuation processes are discussed in Chapters 6, 7, and 8 and in more detail below.

12.2.1 Dispersion

Dispersion is subsurface mixing due to ground water movement and aquifer heterogeneities, and can occur in the longitudinal, transverse, and vertical directions (see Section 6.3). The amount of attenuation provided by dispersion can be estimated using computer models. As an example the BIOCHLOR model (Aziz et al., 1999; see Chapter 8) was used to predict the attenuation caused by longitudinal and transverse dispersion alone (no vertical dispersion or biodegradation or sorption) for a plume produced by a vertical plane source zone 200 ft wide with discharge into a water-bearing unit with 100 ft/yr seepage velocity. As shown in Table 12.2, longitudinal and transverse dispersion have only a minor effect in this typical example (11% reduction in concentration) over the first 1000 ft of plume length. For a 5000-ft long plume, the reduction in concentration is more substantial (48%). Vertical dispersion, if included in the model, has a much more dramatic effect, but may not be present to this extent at many actual field sites.

TABLE 12.2 Reduction in Plume Concentration vs. Plume Length Due to Dispersion Only

DISPERSIVITY (FT)	BASE CASE	LOWER LONGITUDINAL TRANSVERSE DISPERSIVITY	HIGHER LONGITUDINAL TRANSVERSE DISPERSIVITY	BASE CASE WITH LOWER TRANSVERSE DISPERSIVITY	BASE CASE WITH VERTICAL DISPERSIVITY
Longitudinal	20	10	50	20	20
Transverse	2	1	5	0.2	2
Vertical	none	none	none	none	0.2

DISTANCE FROM SOURCE (ft)	REDUCTION IN CENTERLINE CONCENTRATION DUE TO DISPERSION ONLY (%)				
500	2.5%	0.2%	16%	0%	48%
1000	11%	2.5%	32%	0%	66%
2000	26%	11%	48%	0%	80%
5000	48%	32%	65%	2.5%	91%

12.2.2 Sorption

Sorption is a nondestructive process in which organic compounds and metals are sorbed to the aquifer matrix, and it is represented by a retardation factor (see Chapter 7). The retardation factor indicates two processes: (1) the degree to which a particular constituent moves slower than ground water seepage velocity, and (2) the ratio of total constituent mass per volume of aquifer matrix to the volume of dissolved constituents.

Sorption serves as an attenuation process by effectively reducing the mass available to the dissolved phase. Assuming a linear isotherm (a conservative assumption; see Chapter 7), a retardation factor of 3 means that only one-third of the released material will ever be dissolved in ground water. Therefore, for finite releases of contaminants to ground water (i.e., a pulse source), the resulting plume for the sorbed contaminants will have lower concentrations than a plume for contaminants that do not sorb.

12.2.3 Degradation

Biodegradation and abiotic degradation involve chemical transformation of the constituent (see Chapter 7). Biodegradation is a biochemical reaction that occurs in two different ways (McCarty, 1996): (1) use of the organic compound as a primary growth substrate, and (2) co-metabolism. The use of the organic constituent as a primary growth substrate is the dominant mechanism resulting in the degradation of contaminants and occurs when microorganisms gain energy by transferring electrons from an electron donor to an electron acceptor. Co-metabolism is typically not important under naturally-occurring conditions.

Depending on the geochemical characteristics of the ground water (such as redox conditions) and the type of microorganisms present, organic compounds can be either the electron donor or acceptor. If the redox conditions are appropriate, biodegradation is expected, but it can be fast or slow depending on the reaction rate. One way to determine whether biodegradation is occurring is to evaluate site data to demonstrate the consumption of electron acceptors, the presence of metabolic by-products, and that the geochemical conditions (primarily redox conditions) are appropriate for biodegradation reactions (see Section 12.2 and Chapter 7).

Hydrolysis is a naturally-occurring chemical process where dissolved constituents will degrade and form other compounds. It is important for a handful of compounds, primarily chlorinated solvents such as 1,1,1-TCA (half-life of 1-2 years) and chloroethane (half-life of 0.12 years). Other compounds such as the chlorinated ethenes (PCE, TCE, DCE) have hydrolysis half-lives greater than 10^6 years.

12.2.4 Dilution

Dilution can be an important attenuation process under several different circumstances, such as a slowly moving ground water plume that flows into a zone where significant surface recharge enters the water-bearing unit. Note that because mixing is limited in the subsurface, high concentration zones will probably still be present even with this influx of clean water, as the plume will be driven downwards by the recharge. Another example of dilution is when contaminants migrate vertically through a low-permeability layer, and then mix with faster moving ground water traveling horizontally through a more permeable, underlying water-bearing unit. Finally, many ground water plumes are diluted when they discharge to surface water, and the surface water mixes with ground water to reduce overall concentrations. If the surface water system has a high flowrate relative to the ground water discharge (a common occurrence) then considerable attenuation occurs. The BIOSCREEN and BIOCHLOR models contain mass flux calculators to facilitate surface water dilution calculations (Newell et al., 1997; Aziz et al., 1999).

12.2.5 Summary

Natural attenuation processes, primarily dispersion, sorption, degradation, and dilution, can reduce contaminant concentrations that leave plume source zones. A useful classification system described by Rice et al. (1995) defines contaminant plumes as either being expanding (source loading exceeds attenuation capacity), stable (source loading equal to attenuation capacity), shrinking (source loading smaller than attenuation capacity), or exhausted (only small zones of dissolved contaminants present in depleted source zones). Geochemical indicators can be used to indicate the presence of degradation processes that are destroying chemical mass. The goal of a natural attenuation study is to demonstrate that natural attenuation processes are ongoing, and that they can manage the dissolved contaminants leaving a source zone.

12.3 NATURAL ATTENUATION PROTOCOLS AND GUIDANCE

Several technical protocols have been developed to demonstrate natural attenuation of contaminants in ground water, with the most commonly used approaches being the ASTM Remediation by Natural Attenuation (RNA) standard and two air force protocols. In addition, the EPA has issued a directive for use of "monitored natural attenuation." These protocols are discussed in more detail below.

12.3.1 ASTM Standard for Petroleum Release Sites

The American Society for Testing and Materials (ASTM) has developed a standard for a systematic approach to evaluating the effectiveness of remediation by natural attenuation (RNA) at petroleum release sites (ASTM, 1998a), employing three lines of evidence (see Table 12.3). For the **primary line of evidence,** current and historical ground water monitoring data are analyzed to establish the relationship of constituent concentration over time. The ASTM Standard indicates that at some petroleum release sites, evaluation of historical data may be sufficient to indicate stable or diminishing plume area and constituent concentration.

TABLE 12.3 Lines of Evidence in ASTM RNA Standard for Petroleum Release Sites

ASTM LINES OF EVIDENCE	
Primary	• Contaminant data to define plume as shrinking, stable, or expanding.
Secondary	• Geochemical indicators of naturally-occurring biodegradation.
	• Estimates of attenuation rates.
Optional	• GW solute transport modeling.
	• Microbiological studies.
	• Estimates of assimilative capacity.

In other cases, the secondary and optional lines of evidence are developed to adequately demonstrate that natural attenuation is effectively controlling plume growth.

The **secondary line of evidence** consists of (1) an evaluation of geochemical indicators of biodegradation (e.g., the consumption of electron acceptors), and (2) calculation of lumped attenuation rate calculations. **The optional line of evidence** entails construction of comprehensive calibrated site models to quantify natural attenuation processes, including the combined effects of physical processes, (e.g., dispersion and dilution), chemical processes (e.g., sorption), and biological processes (including both aerobic and anaerobic processes).

Although developed for fuel sites, the basic approach of using historical data, geochemical/rate indicators, and modeling tools can be applied to other types of sites besides petroleum hydrocarbon sites. While analysis of concentration trend data should be similar for all types of sites, different types of geochemical analysis and different types of solute transport models may be required for fuels versus solvents versus metals sites.

12.3.2 Air Force Fuel Contamination Protocol

The Air Force Center for Environmental Excellence (AFCEE) issued the first comprehensive natural attenuation protocol in 1995 (Wiedemeier, et al., 1995). This protocol, designed for fuel hydrocarbon sites, is based on a strategy where up to three lines of evidence are employed to demonstrate natural attenuation: (1) documented loss of contaminants at the field scale; (2) contaminant and geochemical analytical data, and (3) direct microbial evidence. The protocol emphasizes the first two lines of evidence, and states that direct microbial evidence can be used to "further document intrinsic remediation."

The document included a detailed discussion of the site characterization data needed to demonstrate natural attenuation. At that time, interest in anaerobic biodegradation of fuels was increasing (e.g., see Wilson, 1994). The protocol was based on the conclusion that anaerobic pathways could be a significant, or even the dominant, degradation mechanism at many petroleum fuel sites (Wilson, 1994). The AFCEE natural attenuation protocol was designed to illustrate how natural attenuation processes, particularly anaerobic biodegradation, could control the migration of plumes at petroleum release sites.

Besides emphasizing site characterization requirements, the protocol also discussed the development of conceptual models, required data analysis techniques, and the application of solute transport models such as BIOPLUME (see Chapter 10).

12.3.3 Air Force and EPA Chlorinated Solvents Protocols

In 1996, AFCEE issued a protocol for evaluating natural attenuation of chlorinated solvents in ground water (Wiedemeier et al., 1996). This document used the same three lines of evidence as the fuels protocol, but stressed that the third line (direct microbial evidence) should be used only "when absolutely necessary." The chlorinated protocol included a new discussion of geochemical indicators and a screening system to determine whether biodegradation of chlorinated solvents via reductive dechlorination (the most important biodegradation pathway for chlorinated solvents) was occurring at a particular site. In addition, a new classification system was introduced where chlorinated solvent plumes (or portions of plumes) are classified as one of three types of environments (Wiedemeier et al., 1999) :

- **Type 1:** Anaerobic Systems Due to Anthropogenic Carbon. Anaerobic conditions are typical at sites contaminated with fuel hydrocarbons, landfill leachate, or other anthropogenic carbon because these organics exert a electron-acceptor demand on the system (see Figure 12.4).

- **Type 2:** Anaerobic Systems Due to Naturally-Occurring Carbon. This environment occurs in hydrogeologic settings that have inherently high organic car-

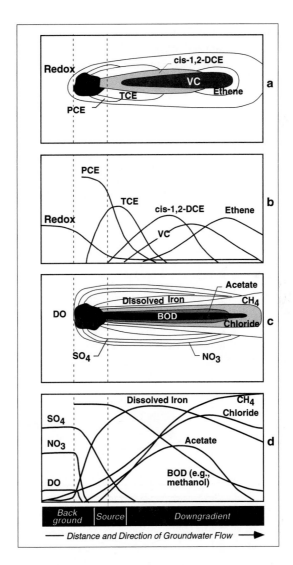

Figure 12.4 Conceptual Model of Type 1 Environment for Chlorinated Solvent Plumes. Source: Wiedemeier et al, 1999.

bon concentrations, such as coastal or stream/river deposits with high concentrations of organics, shallow aquifers with recharge zones in organic-rich environments (such as swamps), or zones impacted by natural oil seeps.

- **Type 3:** Aerobic Systems Due to No Fermentation Substrate. A Type 3 environment is characterized by a well-oxygenated ground water system with little or no organic matter (see Figure 12.5). Concentrations of dissolved oxygen typically are greater than 1.0 mg/L. In such an environment, halorespiration will

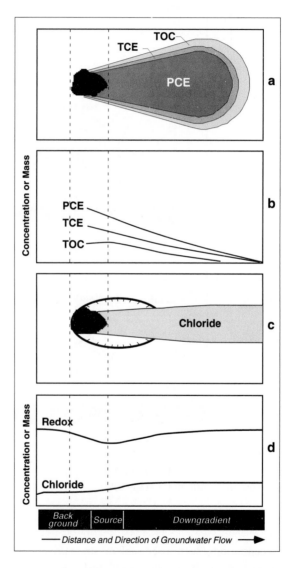

Figure 12.5 Conceptual Model of Type 3 Environment for Chlorinated Solvent Plume due to PCE and TCE Release. Source: Wiedemeier et al, 1999.

not occur and chlorinated solvents such as perchloroethene, trichloroethene, trichloroethane, and carbon tetrachloride will not biodegrade. In this environment, very long dissolved-phase plumes are likely to form.

In 1998, the EPA issued a technical protocol for chlorinated solvents based on the air force protocol (Wiedemeier et al., 1998). While much of the two documents are similar, the EPA document includes additional information on the use of natural attenuation from a regulatory perspective. Some technical information was also modified, such as the screening system to determine the presence of biodegradation processes at chlorinated solvent sites.

12.3.4 EPA Monitored Natural Attenuation Directive

In 1997, the EPA issued a directive to clarify the use of "monitored natural attenuation" (MNA) at Superfund, RCRA, UST, and other contaminated sites (EPA, 1997). While natural attenuation had been used occasionally for ground water remediation, it was not widely applied until the late 1990s. The 1997 directive stated that MNA will serve as only one component of the total remedy for the majority of cases, and it should be "used very cautiously as the sole remedy at contaminated sites." In addition, EPA reiterated that it did not change EPA's remediation directive related to source control and ground water restoration, and any application of MNA must be supported by a careful technical demonstration and subsequent performance monitoring.

Some key directives in the memorandum are:

- "Monitored natural attenuation is an appropriate remediation method only where its use will be protective of human health and the environment and it will be capable of achieving site-specific remediation objectives within a reasonable timeframe."

- "Decisions to employ natural attenuation as a remedy or remedy component should be thoroughly and adequately supported with site-specific characterization data and analysis."

- "Three types of site-specific information or 'evidence' should be used in such as evaluation: These are (1) Historical ground water and/or soil chemistry data that demonstrate a clear and meaningful trend of declining contaminant mass and/or concentrations at appropriate monitoring or sampling points; (2) Hydrogeologic or geochemical data that can be used to indirectly demonstrate the type(s) of natural attenuation processes active at the site, and the rate at which such processes will reduce contaminant concentrations to required levels; and (3) Data from field or microcosm studies that directly demonstrate the occurrence of a particular natural attenuation process at a site."

- "Unless EPA or the implementing State agency determines that historical data (number 1 above) are of sufficient quality and duration to support a decision to use monitored natural attenuation, EPA expects that data characterizing the nature and rates of natural attenuation processes at the site (number 2 above) should be provided. Where the latter are also inadequate or inconclusive, data from microcosm studies (number 3 above) may also be necessary."

12.3.5 Modeling Tools

Software products have recently been introduced to help people perform natural attenuation studies. For example, the RNA Tool Kit (Groundwater Services, 1999) provides statistical, graphing, and geochemical tools to help analyze and present natural attenuation data. Key modeling tools include the BIOSCREEN, BIOCHLOR, and BIOPLUME III models (see Chapter 8). Another useful web source, The Natural Attenuation Tool Kit web page (http://members.aol.com/jacrosby1/home.htm), provides key links to natural attenuation resources.

12.4 DEMONSTRATING NATURAL ATTENUATION

While the different protocols all place a different emphasis on how to demonstrate natural attenuation, three key elements are:

- **plume history** (to demonstrate loss of contaminant mass that leaves the source)
- **geochemical indicators and rates** (to demonstrate conditions are favorable for mass loss)
- **computer modeling** (to demonstrate that site data are consistent with loss via natural attenuation)

These three components of a natural attenuation demonstration are discussed in more detail below.

12.4.1 Plume History

Analysis of plume history is intended to define a ground water plume as stable, shrinking, or expanding. RNA is appropriate at sites with shrinking or stable plumes if the remediation goals and timeframe are constant with the expected performance of RNA at the site.

Guidelines developed as part of the ASTM RNA Standard (ASTM,1998a; Nevin et al., 1998) suggest that at least one upgradient well, one downgradient well, and at minimum two wells located within the ground water plume, and that data must be available from at least four independent sampling events. (Note that the requirements were developed for small fuel sites such as gas stations, and may not be appropriate for larger, more complex sites).

Methods for analysis plume history are shown in Table 12.4. At some sites, the plume status may be apparent from a visual inspection of the contour maps or concentration and plume length graphs (see Figure 12.6 for an example). However, at many sites a statistical evaluation of the historical monitoring data may be desired to provide an objective measure of plume status or to resolve differences in interpretation of the data between site stakeholders.

TABLE 12.4 Methods to Analyze Plume History Data to Determine Plume Stability

SCOPE and DATA REQUIREMENTS: Involves graphical analysis of historical plume concentration measurements to define plume status as either stable, shrinking, or expanding. Requires data from multiple well locations, 4 or more sampling episodes. Methods include:

• *Plume contour maps*	Plot plume contours over time to illustrate **stable, shrinking, or expanding condition**.
• *Centerline concentration plots*	Plot centerline plume concentration data for multiple time periods, showing **concentration trends** from plume source to plume edge.
• *Well concentration plots*	Plot **concentration vs. time** data for individual monitoring wells, and provide linear regression to define concentration trend. When performed in source areas, an estimate of the **lifetime of the source** can be derived.
• *Average plume concentration plots*	Define **average plume concentration vs. time** based on data collected from several monitoring wells.
• *Statistical trend analysis*	Quantify **groundwater concentrations trends** using Mann-Whitney or Mann-Kendall statistical methods.

Key statistical tools for analyzing monitoring data trends that are not confirmed by a visual inspection of site data over time include the **Mann-Whitney** and the **Mann-Kendall** tests (Gilbert, 1987, Groundwater Services, 1999). These are statistical approaches for evaluating trends in a data set, such as concentration versus time data, at discreet locations.

The **Mann-Whitney U Test** (also called the Wilcoxon Rank-Sum Test, Gilbert, 1987) employs a **non-parametric** ranking procedure where a trend is reported from the overall ranking of different measurements, but not the magnitude of the measurements. It is currently being used by the State of New Jersey to determine plume stability (28 N.J.R. 1143). The test is performed for every contaminant at every monitoring well at a site where plume stability test is desired.

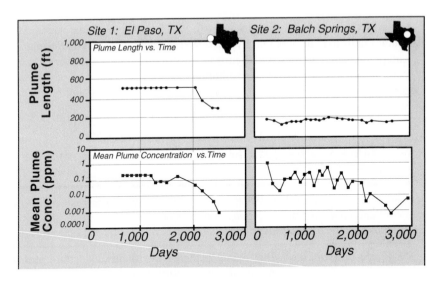

Figure 12.6 Example of Plume History Data for Two Petroleum Hydrocarbon Sites in Texas. Source: Newell and Connor, 1998 and Mace et al, 1997.

The **Mann-Kendall Test** is another non-parametric test (Gilbert, 1987) that can be used to define the trends in data using a ranking procedure. It requires four or more independent sampling events and compares each sampling event against every other sampling event. The worksheet on Figure 12.7 shows how to calculate the Mann-Kendall S statistic, where a positive S value indicates an increasing trend, and a negative S value indicates a declining trend. The S value and the total number of sampling events are used to determine whether a trend is probably present in the data.

The Mann-Kendall Test has been incorporated into an existing natural attenuation software package, the RNA Tool Kit, that uses an expanded implementation with three types of statistical information: the Mann-Kendall S statistic, a calculated confidence level, and the coefficient of variance for the sample data (Groundwater Services, 1999). Figure 12.8 shows a conceptual representation of the three types of information, where the S statistic shows the direction of the trend, the confidence factor shows how strong the trend is, and the coefficient of variation indicates how much scatter there is in the data. With this approach, sites can be classified as: expanding, probably expanding, stable, probably declining, declining, or not indicating a trend.

Example 12.1   PLUME HISTORY

A quarterly monitoring program shows the following benzene concentrations from a well at a site. Does the Mann-Kendall analysis S Statistic indicate the benzene concentration as Increasing, Decreasing, or as having No Trend?

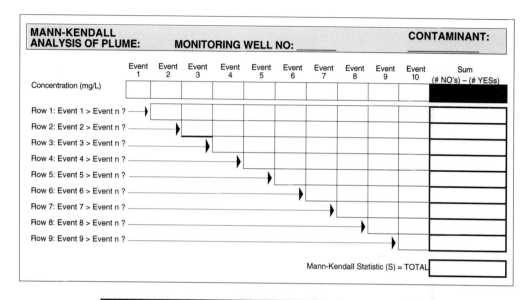

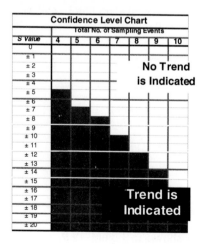

Figure 12.7 Worksheet for Mann-Kendall S-Statistic. Source: Groundwater Services, 1999.

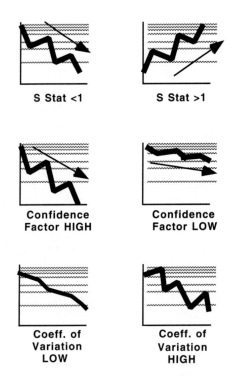

Figure 12.8 Conceptual Model for use of Mann-Kendall Test in Plume Stability Analysis. Source: Groundwater Services, 1999.

Date Sampled	Benzene Concentration (mg/L)
11/1/93	3.18
2/1/94	3.455
5/1/94	3.022
8/1/94	4.876
11/1/94	1.635
2/1/95	2.561
6/1/95	2.329
8/1/95	0.95

Solution. As shown in Figure 12.9, the Mann-Kendall worksheet indicates that the benzene in this well exhibits a DECLINING trend. To provide a more detailed interpretation of the results, the confidence factor and coefficient of variation can also be analyzed.

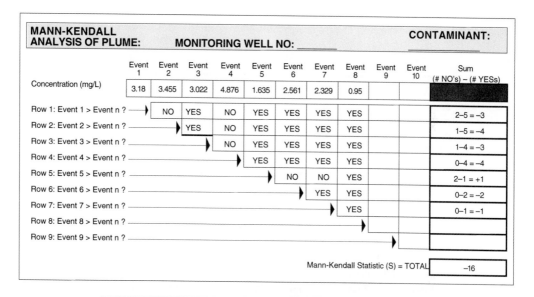

MANN-KENDALL ANALYSIS OF PLUME:	MONITORING WELL NO: _____									CONTAMINANT: _____
	Event 1	Event 2	Event 3	Event 4	Event 5	Event 6	Event 7	Event 8	Event 9	Event 10	Sum (# NO's) − (# YESs)
Concentration (mg/L)	3.18	3.455	3.022	4.876	1.635	2.561	2.329	0.95			
Row 1: Event 1 > Event n ? →		NO	YES	NO	YES	YES	YES	YES			2−5 = −3
Row 2: Event 2 > Event n ?			YES	NO	YES	YES	YES	YES			1−5 = −4
Row 3: Event 3 > Event n ?				NO	YES	YES	YES	YES			1−4 = −3
Row 4: Event 4 > Event n ?					YES	YES	YES	YES			0−4 = −4
Row 5: Event 5 > Event n ?						NO	NO	YES			2−1 = +1
Row 6: Event 6 > Event n ?							YES	YES			0−2 = −2
Row 7: Event 7 > Event n ?								YES			0−1 = −1
Row 8: Event 8 > Event n ?											
Row 9: Event 9 > Event n ?											
							Mann-Kendall Statistic (S) = TOTAL				−16

CHARACTERIZATION OF GROUNDWATER PLUME BASED ON DATA FROM THIS WELL

Use the Confidence Level Chart with the Mann-Kendall Statistic computed above (S) and the number of sampling events to estimate confidence level in the presence of a trend. S<0 indicates a declining trend, while S>0 indicates an increasing trend.

Confidence Level Chart

Total No. of Sampling Events

S Value: 4 5 6 7 8 9 10

Data From This Well is Probably Declining

Figure 12.9 Example of Mann-Kendall S-Statistic Calculation. S Statistic is −16, indicating that a declining trend is probably present.

TABLE 12.5 Geochemical and Rate Indicators of Natural Attenuation

SCOPE and DATA REQUIRMENTS: In the absence of an adequate historical database, secondary evidence of plume attenuation may be established based on geochemical indicator measurements or calculation of a site-specific first-order decay rate.   Requires plume delineation and geochemical analyses.

• *Geochemical Indicators of Bioremediation*	Quantify on-going **natural attenuation processes** based on comparison of electron acceptor and metabolic by-product concentrations between upgradient wells and plume wells. Also use indicators such as dissolved hydrogen to determine if microbial environment (e.g., aerobic, nitrate reducing, iron reducing, sulfate reducing vs. methanogenic conditions).
• *Site-Specific First-Order Decay Rate from Centerline Concentration vs. Distance Plots*	Derive **site-specific biological natural attenuation rates** for organic constituents dissolved in groundwater using centerline concentration data vs. distance. The result is a lumped decay rate, where all attenuation processes (sorption, dispersion, and biodegradation) are lumped together. Note that this decay rate **is not** equivalent to a biodegradation rate used in solute transport models or rates derived from concentration vs. time plots.

12.4.2 Geochemical Indicators and Rates

Geochemical Indicators. Geochemical indicators and rates provide supplement information that natural attenuation processes are active at the site (see Table 12.5). There are three general types of geochemical indicators:

1. Consumption of electron acceptors used for direct oxidative reactions. The apparent loss of dissolved oxygen, nitrate, and sulfate in the plume area is typically used as a geochemical indicator of direct oxidation of petroleum hydrocarbons, but does not relate to the direct loss of chlorinated solvents (see Tables 12.6 and 12.7).

2. Production of metabolic by-products. At petroleum hydrocarbon sites, ferrous iron and methane are typically used as indicators of anaerobic biodegradation of dissolved petroleum hydrocarbon contaminants. At chlorinated solvent sites, the presence of daughter products is evaluated. For example, key chlorinated solvent daughter products for chlorinated ethenes are cis-DCE (cis-DCE is a strong indicator of biodegradation of TCE, while trans-DCE typi-

cally originates from released source materials); vinyl chloride (the daughter product of DCE biodegradation under anaerobic biodegradation), and ethene (the daughter product of vinyl chloride biodegradation). (For a more detailed discussion of daughter products, see Chapter 7 or Wiedemeier et al., 1999).

3. Presence of appropriate redox/microbial environments. At some chlorinated solvent sites, dissolved hydrogen is measured to indicate whether the site is under nitrate reducing, iron reducing, sulfate reducing, or methanogenic conditions. Biodegradation of chlorinated solvents via reductive dechlorination (the most important dechlorination reaction for many chlorinated solvents) is favored in sulfate reducing and methanogenic environments (Wiedemeier et al., 1999).

TABLE 12.6 Geochemical Indicators at Petroleum Hydrocarbon (Fuel) Sites With Naturally Occuring Biodegradation

GEOCHEMICAL INDICATOR	GEOCHEMICAL INDICATOR CONCENTRATION	
	Inside of Plume	Outside of Plume
Dissolved Oxygen	Low	Higher
Nitrate	Low	Higher
Manganese	Higher	Low
Ferrous Iron (dissolved)	Higher	Low/ND
Sulfate	Low	Higher
Methane	Higher	Low/ND

ND: Non-detect

Note that different geochemical indicators are used at petroleum hydrocarbon rather than chlorinated solvent sites. For petroleum hydrocarbon plumes, the dissolved contaminants (primarily BTEX compounds) serve as electron donors and dissolved oxygen, nitrate, solid ferric iron, sulfate, and carbon dioxide serve as electron acceptors (see Table 12.6). The disappearance of the electron acceptors in the plume indicates active biodegradation processes that are consuming the dissolved petroleum hydrocarbons. Because ferric iron is a solid phase, and because carbon dioxide has numerous other sources and sinks, the presence of their metabolic by-products (ferrous iron and methane, respectively) are used to indicate that these reactions are ongoing (Wiedemeier et al., 1999). Newell et al. (1996) shows a statistical evaluation of geochemical indicators for 28 air force petroleum hydrocarbon sites.

TABLE 12.7 Geochemical Indicators at Sites with Chlorinated Solvents That Undergo Naturally Occuring Biodegradation via Reductive Dechlorination (e.g., PCE, TCE, TCA, Carbon Tetrachloride)

GEOCHEMICAL INDICATOR	GEOCHEMICAL INDICATOR CONCENTRATION	
	Inside of Plume	Outside of Plume
Dissolved Oxygen	Low	Higher
Nitrate	Low	Higher
Manganese	Higher	Low
Ferrous Iron (dissolved)	Higher	Low/ND
Sulfate	Low	Higher
Methane	Higher	Low/ND
Daughter Products	Present	ND
Dissolved Hydrogen	Higher	Low/ND

ND: Non-detect

For chlorinated solvent plumes, the dissolved contaminants (e.g., PCE, TCE, DCE, TCA, DCA, etc.) serve as electron acceptors and dissolved hydrogen (produced from fermentation of other organics) is used as the electron donor (Wiedemeier et al., 1999). This type of reaction occurs only under deeply anaerobic conditions, and therefore the redox state of the aquifer is an important indicator for determining the likelihood of biodegradation. The redox state can be determined using field measurements by evaluating the presence of inorganic species (e.g., presence of oxygen indicates the site is not anaerobic), by evaluating the presence of organic by-products (i.e., methane), or by evaluating the presence of dissolved hydrogen concentrations. Table 12.7 shows the types of geochemical indicators at sites where biodegradation of chlorinated solvents is indicated.

Rate Calculations. In some natural attenuation protocols, rate calculations are used as evidence to demonstrate that natural attenuation processes are active. There are different kinds of rates, and application of rate calculations should be performed carefully to ensure proper interpretation (Rifai and Newell, 1998).

One of the most common type of rate calculations uses centerline plume concentrations that are plotted on semi-log paper against distance from the source (ASTM, 1998a; Rifai and Newell, 1998). A bulk attenuation rate (referred to as "k") is then calculated using the slope and ground water seepage velocity (see Figure 12.10). The resulting rate value, if positive, indicates that concentrations are declining between the source and the edge of plume due to the combined effects of dispersion, biodegradation, and other natural attenuation proc-

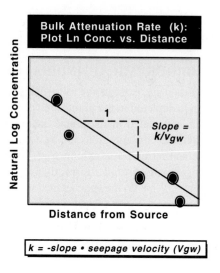

Figure 12.10 Calculation Approach for Site-Specific Lumped Attenuation Rates.

esses acting on dissolved contaminants that have left the source zone. Note that this calculation is appropriate only when the plume is known to be stable or shrinking, and that the process of calculating a rate provides a value that typically is not used for any further calculations or compared to anything. In effect, the rate calculation just indicates that concentrations are declining.

A second type of rate calculation is the plotting of concentrations at a particular well against time. This rate (referred to as "k_s" for k of source) primarily reflects how the source loading has changed over time. For stable plumes, k_s will be zero. For shrinking plumes, the k_s term will indicate how quickly the loading rate from the source (primarily from dissolution from nonaqueous phase hydrocarbons at most sites) is declining over time. Note that this type of rate is very different from the bulk attenuation rate described above. The k_s term can be used in other calculations, such as to estimate what concentrations will be in the future by extrapolating past concentration vs. time trends.

A third type of rate calculation uses a computer model or a specialized calculation to remove the effects of sorption and dispersion, and to determine the biodegradation rate λ. The λ rate reflects the rate of biodegradation of the contaminant and nothing else. As with the bulk attenuation rate, this calculation is appropriate only when the plume is known to be stable or shrinking. It has been the author's experience that for many fuel release sites with BTEX plumes, biodegradation is the primary attenuation process and therefore λ will be close to the bulk attenuation rate k.

The biodegradation rate λ can be calculated using different calculation approaches based on tracers or analytical models (Wiedemeier et al., 1999). An automated **attenuation rate**

model, FATE V, is also available to calculate λ from site specific contaminant and hydrogeologic data (Nevin et al., 1997).

Example 12.2 GEOCHEMICAL INDICATORS

A fuel hydrocarbon site exhibits the following pattern of geochemical indicators: Dissolved oxygen is depleted in the plume area (2.5 mg/L outside plume, 0.7 mg/L inside plume). Sulfate is depleted in the plume area (120 mg/L outside plume, 10 mg/L inside plume). Nitrate concentrations are low (< 1 mg/L) outside and inside the plume area. Methane and ferrous iron exhibit high concentrations in the source area of the plume (4.2 mg/L and 16 mg/L, respectively), but have no detectable concentrations outside the plume. What do the geochemical indicators indicate?

Solution. These geochemical indicators show that vigorous aerobic and anaerobic biodegradation of petroleum hydrocarbons is ongoing at this site.

Example 12.3 GEOCHEMICAL INDICATORS

A chlorinated solvent site with PCE exhibits the following pattern of geochemical indicators: Dissolved oxygen is slightly depressed in the plume area (2.5 mg/L outside the plume vs. 2.0 mg/L inside plume). Nitrate and sulfate concentrations are unchanged inside versus outside the plume. No methane or dissolved hydrogen or daughter products were observed. What do the geochemical indicators indicate?

Solution. These geochemical indicators show that the site is aerobic, and it is unlikely that PCE will biodegrade.

Example 12.4 BULK ATTENUATION RATE CALCULATION

A site has BTEX concentration versus distance data for four wells located 160 ft apart. What is the bulk attenuation rate (i.e., the rate that reflects the combined effect of dispersion, sorption, and biodegradation)? The site has a ground water seepage velocity of 58 ft/yr.

Solution. Plotting the *natural logarithm* of the concentration versus distance yields the plot below, with a best-fit line having a slope of –0.05 (unitless) (see Figure 12.11). The seepage velocity is 58 ft/yr, or 0.16 ft/day. When multiplied together, this yields a bulk attenuation rate k of:

$k = -$ slope $\cdot$ seepage velocity

$k = -(-0.05) \cdot (0.16 \text{ ft/day})$

$k = 0.008 \text{ day}^{-1}$

bulk attenuation half-life $= \ln(2)/k$ (see Chapter 7)

bulk attenuation half-life = 0.693/0.008/day

bulk attenuation half-life = 87 days

The effects of sorption, dispersion, and biodegradation combine to reduce dissolved BTEX concentrations by half every 87 days once the BTEX leaves the source (and assuming the BTEX is no longer flowing through any other source zones).

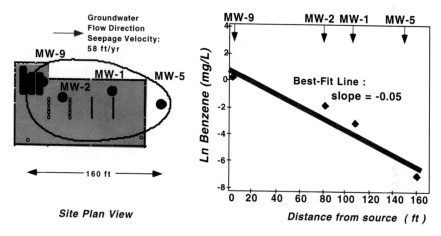

Figure 12.11 Site Plan View with Data Used for Rate Calculation.

12.4.3 Modeling Studies

Solute transport models are often used as a line of evidence for natural attenuation studies to support claims that the plume is stable and that geochemical indicators show ongoing bio-degradation (see Table 12.8). Perhaps the most important task for a modeling study is to determine whether natural attenuation processes are sufficient to prevent further migration of the plume. The modeling approach is to build a transient (time dependent) model with a best-guess time for the source release. After calibrating the model to the observed plume, the simulation time is increased. If the plume does not expand in the model, then modeling supports the contention that natural attenuation processes are controlling the plume. If the model indicates that the plume has the potential to expand, then this line of evidence is not supportive that the plume is controlled.

In general, plume history data provides more reliable indication of plume stability than models if the plume history is long relative to the time required for the contaminants to

Table 12.8 Use of Models to Demonstrate Lines of Evidence

SCOPE and DATA REQUIREMENTS: When applicable, support primary and secondary evidence using modeling studies.	
• *Use of Natural Attenuation Models*	**Compile data** regarding source size and strength, time since release, advection, dispersion, adsorption, and biodegradation processes occurring at the site and **enter into model.** Increase simulation period in model to determine if plume has potential to expand based on best understanding of site attenuation processes. Representative models for fuel sites: BIOSCREEN, BIOPLUME III. Representative models for chlorinated solvent sites: BIOCHLOR, MODFLOW/RT3D.

travel between key monitoring wells near the edge of the plume. Modeling plays a more important role in sites where natural attenuation processes are more complex or where there is limited or no historical data.

Commonly used natural attenuation models include BIOSCREEN and BIOPLUME II or III for fuel sites, and BIOCHLOR and MODFLOW/RT3D for chlorinated solvent sites (see Chapters 8 and 10).

12.4.4 Case Study

Key results from a natural attenuation study performed at Keesler AFB site in Biloxi, Mississippi by Newell et al. (1995) are shown below. Additional case studies of natural attenuation studies at both fuel and chlorinated sites are presented by Wiedemeier et al. (1999).

At Keesler AFB, a gasoline service tank at the base released gasoline into Coastal Deposit sands, an unconfined water bearing unit. One tank was removed in 1987 and then three more tanks were removed in 1996. Although no free product was observed in the monitoring wells, residual NAPL was detected in two soil samples using short-wave ultraviolet light and Sudan IV hydrophobic dye. A ground water monitoring system installed in 1995 was used to delineate a BTEX plume that was determined to be approximately 41,000 sq ft in area (about 320 ft in length by 140 ft in width). The highest concentration of benzene observed at the site in 1995 was 3.55 mg/L.

Plume History. Plume history data were available for only one location. Total BTEX concentrations in this area were 1.5 mg/L in 1991 and 1.2 mg/L in 1995, which indicate a stable or slowly shrinking plume.

Geochemical Indicators. Geochemical data indicated that both aerobic and anaerobic biodegradation are occurring at the site. Dissolved oxygen concentrations fell from background levels of over 2.0 mg/L outside the plume area to approximately 0.4 mg/L inside the plume, indicating anaerobic conditions in the core of the BTEX plume (see Figure 12.12).

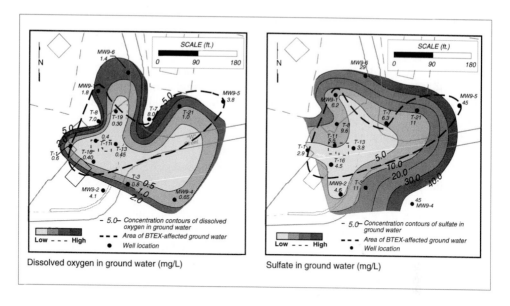

Figure 12.12 Distribution of electron acceptors in ground water, April 1995, Keesler AFB, Mississippi. Source: Wiedemeier et al., 1999.

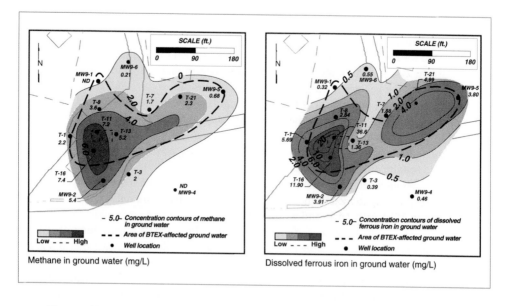

Figure 12.13 Metabolic by-products in ground water, April 1995, Keesler AFB, Mississippi. Source: Wiedemeier et al., 1999.

Sulfate data showed considerable depletion of this electron acceptor in the center of the plume, with background levels of 26.2 mg/L falling to 3.8 mg/L inside the plume (see Figure 12.12).

Metabolic by-product data also showed extensive anaerobic biodegradation processes. Both ferrous iron and methane showed strong correlation with the dissolved plume (see Figure 12.13). Maximum concentrations of ferrous iron and methane at the site were 36.6 mg/L and 7.4 mg/L, respectively, compared to non-detect or near non-detect concentrations in clean background wells for both compounds. No rate calculations were performed for the natural attenuation demonstration at this site.

Based on the geochemical indicators, the ground water contains significant biodegradation capacity (also called expressed assimilative capacity, defined as the mass of contaminant that can be removed by one liter of ground water moving from a clean background zone through the plume area. The calculated biodegradation capacity at the site was 16.7 mg/L, with most of this capacity coming from sulfate reduction and methanogenesis.

Ground Water Modeling. The BIOSCREEN Natural Attenuation Model (Newell et al., 1996) (see Chapter 8) was used as an additional line of evidence at the site (Newell et al., 1996; Wiedemeier et al., 1999). The model was calibrated to match the observed data using two different biodegradation models (both the first order decay and instantaneous reaction model). The model was then used to indicate that the plume was "no longer growing in size," and that the source mass was slowly being degraded by natural attenuation processes.

12.4.5 Key Natural Attenuation Issues

Implementation of natural attenuation often brings up three important issues regarding the need for source remediation, the natural and duration of long-term monitoring, and the appropriateness of natural attenuation for expanding plumes. The discussion below summarizes some of the key arguments relevant to each question.

Source Remediation. From a regulatory perspective, source removal is often still prescribed as a requirement before natural attenuation is implemented. For example, the EPA MNA directive (EPA, 1997) states that source control is a "fundamental component of any monitored natural attenuation remedy," and it is expected that source control "will be evaluated for all contaminated sites and that source control measures will be taken at most sites."

From a technical and risk perspective, however, the applicability of source control is more difficult to determine. At most sites that have organic contaminants, much of the source is actually in the form of residual nonaqueous phase liquids (NAPLs) that are very difficult to remove with current technologies. In practical terms, removal of these sources would entail relatively large expensive excavation projects to ensure that the source has been removed. Removal of mobile NAPL or areas of contaminated vadose zone soils is possible, but at many sites these sources do not increase the risk associated with the site. For example, Freeze and McWhorter (1997) concluded that at sites with DNAPL in low permeability units, "very high mass removal efficiencies are required to achieve significant long-term risk reduction with technology applications of finite duration. Further, it is unlikely that current technologies can achieve such efficiencies in heterogeneous low-permeability soils that exhibit dual porosity properties and preferential pathways." At these types of sites, source removal would be very difficult and not provide any reduction in risk at the site.

Performance Monitoring. At many sites, the questions are of how long monitoring should continue and in what form is asked. The EPA's MNA directive (EPA, 1997) states that "Performance monitoring is required as long as contamination levels remain above required cleanup levels on any portion of the site. Typically, monitoring is continued for a specified period (e.g., one to three years) after cleanup levels have been achieved to ensure that concentration levels are stable and remain below target levels."

At many sites, however, site managers make the case that once a plume has been shown to be shrinking, and if the concentrations are all below risk-based levels, and if no off-property issues or discharge issues are present, then long-term monitoring need not extend for years and years. The rationale is that strong scientific evidence and extended empirical data demonstrate that the plume will behave predictably, and that additional data collection does not increase the reliability of the remedy or provide any other beneficial effect. In summary, there are a wide variety of views on how much long-term monitoring is enough. This question typically is resolved on a site-by-site basis.

Expanding Plumes. The focus of this chapter has been on using plume stability to indicate that natural attenuation is a viable remediation alternative. In theory, natural attenuation can be used for expanding plumes, and some states such as Texas are exploring the use of natural attenuation for expanding plumes as long as the plumes do not expand too much (i.e., less than a couple of hundred feet). The 1997 EPA directive states that "monitored natural attenuation would more likely be appropriate if the plume is not expanding...".

In practice, the use of natural attenuation for rapidly expanding plumes is more difficult to apply, as it is difficult to predict how long the plume will extend before stabilizing. The best applications of natural attenuation to expanding plumes are for cases where the plume, if expanding, is expanding slowly (such as for a chemical with a very high retardation factor or one undergoing biodegradation).

12.5 RISK-BASED CORRECTIVE ACTION (RBCA)

The Risk-Based Corrective Action (RBCA) process was developed by an ASTM Committee (ASTM, 1995, 1998b) to establish a comprehensive process for management of both human health and ecological risks associated with chemical releases to soil or ground water. The RBCA program was originally devised for petroleum release sites (ASTM, 1995), and was extended for chemical release sites (non-petroleum sites) in 1998. This section reviews the key concepts behind RBCA and its application to ground water problems.

Natural attenuation and RBCA are similar in two ways: (1) They are both relatively new methods for managing contaminants in the environment; and (2) They both account for the ability of nature to attenuate contaminants as they move through the environment.

Effective risk management via RBCA at chemical release sites entails (1) identification of applicable risk factors on a site-specific basis and (2) development and implementation of appropriate protective measures in the timeframe necessary to prevent unsafe conditions. Key elements of the risk-based site evaluation process include:

- **Exposure Pathway Screening**: Identify potential mechanisms for exposure of human or ecological receptors on a site-specific basis. For many contaminated sites, the ground water pathway with ingestion of ground water will be important. Other pathways that are typically reviewed include inhalation of vapor and particulates, dermal contact with soil, ingestion of soil and dust leaching from soils to ground water, and discharge to surface water
- **Risk-Based Cleanup Objectives**: For each complete exposure pathway, evaluate potential for exposure in excess of safe limits based on tiered evaluation of soil and ground water cleanup limits. For example, a common risk level for carcinogenic chemicals is 1 excess cancer death per 100,000 or 1,000,000 exposed persons.
- **Remedy Selection**: Develop risk-based exposure control strategy based on the nature and timing of the potential impact. The remedy might be active remediation or natural attenuation to reduce concentrations, containment to interrupt exposure pathways, or institutional controls to remove potential receptors.

12.5.1 RBCA Tools

Modeling tools can prove helpful at various points of the RBCA site evaluation process, including exposure pathway screening, tiered evaluation of clean-up standards, remedy selection, and design of the compliance monitoring program. Software tools combine fate and transport models (which help quantify the effects of natural attenuation between source and receptor), exposure factors (which indicate how much chemical gets ingested by potential receptors, chemical and toxicological properties (which determine how mobile and how toxic a contaminant is) and risk levels (which are typically determined by regulatory agencies). Figure 12.14 shows how site information, exposure data, toxicity factors, and risk levels perform RBCA calculations in one commonly used software package (Connor et al., 1998; Connor and Bowers, 1998).

12.5.2 Key Concept: Natural Attenuation Factor (NAF)

For a given exposure pathway, the clean up standard (referred to in RBCA studies as a Site-Specific Target Level or SSTL) represents a in source zone soils or ground water that is protective of a human or ecological receptor located some distance away at the **point of exposure** (POE). For example, for the ground water exposure pathway, the SSTL is the contaminant concentration in ground water at the source zone that will prevent unsafe exposure to a receptor located at the POE (e.g., a person who uses a drinking water well located some distance downgradient).

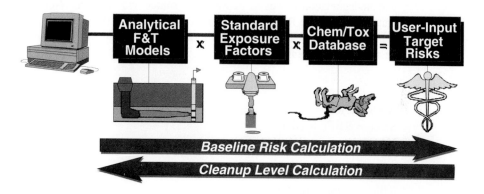

Figure 12.14 Calculation Scheme for RBCA Software Calculation. Forward Calculation Involves Entering Site Concentrations To Determine Risk at Site. Backward Calculation Involves Entering Safe Risk Levels To Determine Safe Concentration Levels at Site. Source: Connor et al., 1998.

For each complete exposure pathway, SSTL values for the source medium can be back-calculated from safe exposure levels at the POE using the following general expression: SSTL = RBEL × NAF

Where

$$\begin{aligned}
\text{RBEL} &= \text{Risk-based exposure limit at POE} \\
\text{NAF} &= \text{Natural attenuation factor defining natural reduction in} \\
&\quad \text{contaminant concentrations during transport from source} \\
&\quad \text{to POE.}
\end{aligned}$$

In the case of the ground water pathway, the NAF can be calculated by simply comparing the source concentration and concentration at the POE if the data are available and if the plume is no longer expanding. If these conditions are not met, then natural attenuation models are used to estimate the NAF. Most RBCA software packages (e.g., Connor et al., 1998) use analytical solute transport for most RBCA calculations.

Example 12.5 RBCA Calculation.

A site containing benzene and toluene in ground water has a domestic ground water well located 1000 ft downgradient from the source zone. If this well is the closest ground water Point of Exposure (POE) for this site, what are the SSTLs (site specific target level) for benzene and toluene that will protect the people using the downgradient well? Assume that the BIOSCREEN model predicts that both benzene and toluene concentrations are reduced by a factor of 100 times by advection, dispersion, sorption, and biodegradation processes between the source and the POE. Note that the drinking water standard (the RBEL in this case) for benzene is 0.005 mg/L and that of toluene is 1 mg/L (in other words benzene is much more hazardous to human heath when ingested than toluene is).

ANSWER:
SSTL = RBEL × NAF
NAF = 100 from BIOSCREEN

RBEL = 0.005 mg/L for benzene
RBEL = 1 mg/L for toluene

SSTL for benzene = 0.050 mg/L
SSTL for toluene = 10 mg/L

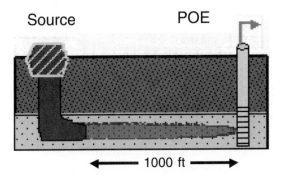

If the ground water at the source has concentrations less than these SSTLs, then no further action is required, and natural attenuation can be used to manage the plume. If source ground water concentrations are greater than one or both SSTLs, then either (1) the source needs to be remediated to reduce concentrations, (2) the plume needs to be cut off using pumping or some other containment approach, or (3) an institutional remedy needs to be implemented where the receptors need to be moved off well water and future ground water use is prohibited. The RBCA process does have limitations; for example, ecological risk is not explicitly calculated in many RBCA studies and off-site property damages issues complicate the implementation of RBCA. However, RBCA is becoming an accepted approach for managing contaminants in ground water at many sites.

SUMMARY

Natural attenuation and risked-based corrective action (RBCA) have emerged as accepted methods for managing contaminated ground water at many sites. Both approaches account for naturally occurring processes that reduce the concentration of contaminants in the subsurface. Natural attenuation is demonstrated by evaluating plume history, geochemical indicators, and model predictions. A RBCA evaluation calculates the risk associated with a site and using models, exposure data, and toxicity data, yields a safe clean-up standard at the source zone.

REFERENCES

Aziz, C.E., C. J. Newell, J. R. Gonzales, P. Haas, T.P. Clement, and Y. Sun, *BIOCHLOR Natural Attenuaton Decision Support System vers. 1.0 User's Manual*, Air Force Center for Environmental Excellence, Brooks AFB, Texas, 1999. www.gsi-net.com

American Society for Testing and Materials, Standard Guide for Risk-Based Corrective Action Applied at Petroleum Release Sites, ASTM E-1739-95, Philadelphia, PA, 1995.

American Society for Testing and Materials, *Remediation of Ground Water by Natural Attenuation at Petroleum Release Sites*, ASTM E-1943-98, Philadelphia, PA, 1998a.

American Society for Testing and Materials, *Standard Provisional Guide for Risk-Based Corrective Action,* ASTM PS 104-98, Philadelphia, PA, 1998b.

Buscheck, T. E., D. C. Wickland, and D. L. Kuehne, "Multiple Lines of Evidence to Demonstrate Natural Attenuation of Petroleum Hydrocarbons," *NGWA Petroleum Hydrocarbons Conference,* Houston, TX, November 1996.

Connor, J.A. and R.L. Bowers, "Guidelines for Risk-Based Corrective Action Modeling for Chemical Release Sites," *NGWA Petroleum Hydrocarbons Conference*, Houston, TX, Nov. 1998, ww.gsi-net.com.

Connor, J. A., R. L. Bowers, and J .P. Nevin, *User's Guide: RBCA Tool Kit for Chemical Releases,* Groundwater Services, Inc., Houston, Texas, 1998. www.gsi-net.com

Freeze, R. A. and D. B. McWhorter, "A Framework for Assessing Risk Reduction During DNAPL Mass Removal from Low-Permeability Soils," *Ground Water*, Vol. 35, No. 1, Jan.-Feb. 1997, pp. 111-123, 1997.

Gilbert, R. O., *Statistical Methods for Environmental Pollution Monitoring*, New York, Van Nostrand Reinhold, 1987.

Groundwater Services, Inc., *Florida RBCA Planning Study*, Groundwater Services, Inc., Houston, Texas, 1997. www.gsi-net.com.

Groundwater Services, Inc., *The RNA Tool Kit User's Manual*, Groundwater Services, Inc., Houston, Texas, 1999. www.gsi-net.com.

Mace, R. E., R. S. Fisher, D. M. Welch, and S. P. Parra, *Extent, Mass, and Duration of Hydrocarbon Plumes from Leaking Petroleum Storage Tank Sites in Texas*, Bureau of Economic Geology, University of Texas at Austin, Geologic Circular, 97-1, 1997.

McCarty, P. L., "Biotic and Abiotic Transformations of Chlorinated Solvents in Ground Water," *Symposium on Natural Attenuation of Chlorinated Organics in Ground Water*, EPA/540/R-96/509, p. 5-9, 1996.

McNab, W. W., D. W. Rice, J. Bear, R. Ragaini, C. Tuckfield, and C. Oldenburg, "Historical Case Analysis of Chlorinated Volatile Organic Compound Plumes," Lawrence Livermore Laboratory, University of California, Livermore, Ca, 1999.

National Research Council. *Alternatives for Ground Water Cleanup*, Washington, D.C, National Research Council, 1994.

Nevin, J. P., C. J. Newell, J. A. Connor, T. E. McHugh, and N. J. Novick, "Practical Methods For Demonstration Of Groundwater Remediation By Natural Attenuation (RNA)," *NGWA Petroleum Hydrocarbons Conference*, Houston, TX, November, 1998.

Nevin, J. P., Connor, J. A., Newell, C. J., Gustfuson, J. B., Lyons, K. A., "Fate 5: A Natural Attenuation Calibration Tool for Groundwater Fate and Transport Modeling," *Petroleum Hydrocarbons and Organic Chemicals in Ground Water*, Houston, Texas, 1997. www-gsi-net.com

Newell, C. J., and J. A. Connor, *Characteristics Of Dissolved Hydrocarbon Plumes: Results of Four Studies*, Washington D.C., American Petroleum Institute, 1998.

Newell, C. J., J. Gonzales, and R. McLeod, *BIOSCREEN Natural Attenuation Decision Support System*, U.S. Environmental Protection Agency. EPA/600/R-96/087, August, 1996.

Newell, C .J., J. Gonzales, and R. McLeod, *BIOSCREEN Natural Attenuation Decision Support System, Version 1.4* Revisions, U.S. Environmental Protection Agency, 1997. www.epa.gov/ada/kerrlab.html

Rice, D. W., R. D. Grose, J. C. Michaelsen, B. P. Dooher, D. H. MacQueen, S. J. Cullen, W. E. Kastenberg, L. G. Everett, M. A. Marino, *California Leaking Underground Fuel Tank (LUFT) Historical Case Analysis*, Environmental Protection Dept., Nov. 16, 1995.

Rifai, H. S. and C. J. Newell, "Estimating First-Order Decay Rates for BTEX Using Data from 115 Sites," *NGWA Petroleum Hydrocarbons Conference*, Houston, TX, November 1998.

U.S. Environmental Protection Agency, *Evaluation of Ground-Water Extraction Remedies*, Volume 1 Summary Report, Office of Emergency and Remedial Response, EPA/540/2-89/054, September 1989.

U. S. Environmental Protection Agency, *Evaluation of Ground-Water Extraction Remedies: Phase II*, Volume 1 Summary Report, EPA OERR 9355.4-05, Washington, D.C., February 1992a.

U. S. Environmental Protection Agency, *Considerations in Ground-Water Remediation at Superfund Sites and RCRA Facilities–Update*, EPA OSWER 9283.1-06, Washington, D.C., May 27, 1992b.

U.S. Environmental Protection Agency, *Monitored Natural Attenuation at Superfund, RCRA Corrective Action, and Underground Storage Tank Site, Draft Interim Final Policy*, Office of Solid Waste and Emergency Response (OSWER), Washington, D.C., 1997.

Wiedemeier, T. H., H. S. Rifai, C. J. Newell, and J. W. Wilson, *Natural Attenuation of Fuels and Chlorinated Solvents*, New York, John Wiley & Sons, 1999.

Wiedemeier, T. H., M. A. Swanson, D. E. Moutoux, E. K. Gordon, J. T. Wilson, B.H. Wilson, D. H. Kampbell, J. E. Hansen, and P. Haas, *Technical Protocol for Evaluation Natural Attenuation of Chlorinated Solvents in Groundwater*, Air Force Center for Environmental Excellence, November, 1996.

Wiedemeier, T. H., M. A. Swanson, D. E. Moutoux, E. K. Gordon, J. T. Wilson, B. H. Wilson, D. H. Kampbell, P. Haas, J. E. Hansen, and F. S. Chappelle, *Technical Protocol for Evaluation*

Natural Attenuation of Chlorinated Solvents in Groundwater, U.S. Environmental Protection Agency, EPA/600R-98/128, 1998.

Wiedemeier, T. H., J. T. Wilson, D. H. Kampbell, R. N. Miller, and J. E. Hansen, *Technical Protocol for Implementing Intrinsic Remediation With Long-Term Monitoring for Natural Attenuation of Fuel Contamination Dissolved in Groundwater (Revision 0)*, Air Force Center for Environmental Excellence, April, 1995.

Wilson J. T., Presentation at Symposium on Intrinsic Bioremediation of Ground Water, Denver, Colorado, EPA 600/R-94-162, August 1-Sept. 1, 1994.

C H A P T E R   1 3

GROUND WATER
REMEDIATION ALTERNATIVES

13.1 INTRODUCTION TO REMEDIATION METHODS

During the past decade, ground water scientists and engineers have devised a number of methods to contain and/or remediate soil and ground water contamination. This technology has been largely driven by ground water regulations (i.e., RCRA, CERCLA, and HSWA) relating to the transport and fate of contaminants at waste sites (see Chapter 14). Ground water remediation has gone through a revolution since 1993 due to a number of complicating issues that were discovered at numerous waste sites. Many of the original pump-and-treat systems that were installed to remove soluble contaminated plumes from the subsurface simply failed to clean up shallow ground water to acceptable water quality levels. These problems were first documented in reports by the EPA (1989; 1992), and mostly relate to difficulties in site characterization and the lack of recognition of the NAPLs problem de-scribed in detail in Chapter 11. A National Research Council publication on Alternatives to Ground Water Cleanup (NRC, 1994) indicated that the nation may be wasting large amounts of money on ineffective remediation efforts. Other findings from the NRC are summarized below.

The remediation of a site must address two major issues: the soluble plume of contamination, which responds to site hydrogeology and may be migrating off site, and the source zone, which may contain NAPLs or residual oils where the original spill or leak occurred. It is now recognized that these source areas and soluble plumes may have to be addressed in very different ways, with greater levels of remediation or containment designed for the source area.

Examples of sources include leaking landfills, leaking pipes or tanks, spills that have sorbed to the subsurface near the water table, and either LNAPLs floating near the capillary fringe or DNAPLS residing on clay lenses below the water table or at the bottom of an aquifer (Chapter 11). The control of these complex source areas is a major challenge at every hazardous waste site and spill. Soluble plumes, on the other hand, were studied extensively over the past two decades, and traditional pump and treat systems can provide some level of control off-site or at a site boundary.

Recently ground water scientists and engineers investigated the ability of current ground water remediation technology to meet specified clean-up standards, typically the restoration of ground water to drinking water standards. An important study, completed by the EPA in 1989, evaluated the performance of 22 ground water remediation systems that had been in operation at least five years (U.S. EPA, 1989). Although contaminant removal of significant hydrocarbon mass was realized, the decrease in contaminant concentration over time was much slower than originally anticipated. Factors that were identified as major impediments to ground water restoration include:

- Contaminant factors such as nonaqueous phase liquids (NAPLs), high sorption potential, and continued leaching from source areas
- Hydrogeologic factors such as heterogeneities, low permeability units, and fractures
- Design factors such as pumping rates, recovery well locations, and screened intervals

Additional EPA research and directives have focused on the problems associated with NAPLs in the subsurface, and have concluded that "NAPLs will have significant influence on the timeframe required and/or the likelihood of achieving clean-up standards" (EPA, 1992). The NRC study (1994) concluded that it may be impractical to restore many difficult hazardous waste sites using current technology, and emerging methods may be required. For sites where conditions preclude restoration to mandated cleanup standards, the general remediation strategy described in this chapter might be applied.

The goals of a ground water remediation effort may include a range of objectives such as limiting the migration of a soluble plume off-site, isolating and containing a source area from further leaking, or treating the affected ground water aquifer down to some drinking water standard. As was discovered in the 1970s, for the control of water quality of surface lakes and streams, it may not be technologically or economically feasible to remediate a contaminated aquifer to drinking water standards of quality. Rather, some level of protection at the fence line (or at a receptor well) to control off-site migration combined with intensive source controls may be acceptable in many cases. EPA is beginning to define a new set of goals for many hazardous waste site remediations nationwide as ground water professionals learn more about the actual performance of standard remediation methods, such as pump and treat (EPA, 1992). Figure 13.1 summarizes several remedial measures currently being practiced.

Natural attenuation methods and risk-based corrective action have received enormous attention in recent years (Chapter 12). These methods give more credit to the attenuation (dispersion, dilution, biodegradation, etc.) processes that might be operating in an aquifer between the point of disposal and any downgradient receptors. But care must be taken to assure, through well-designed monitoring programs, that concentrations are decreasing in time and that plumes are shrinking in size. Otherwise, we may end up with even more complex problems to deal with in the future.

13.2 REMEDIAL ALTERNATIVES

Once a site has been well characterized for hydrogeology and contaminant concentrations, alternatives for control and remediation can be selected and combined to provide an overall cleanup strategy. Choosing a remedial technology is a function of the type of contaminant, site hydrogeology, source characteristics, and the location of the contaminant in the subsurface. The variation of hydraulic conductivity (K) or transmissivity (T) of a formation is one of the most important parameters of interest. Thus, the ultimate success or failure of any remediation system is a direct function of the ability of the aquifer to transport fluids, both water and contaminant, nutrients, NAPLs, and vapor or air. Well mechanics dictate that pumping and injection rates of liquids and vapors are directly related to aquifer properties. Many of these issues will be addressed in detail in this chapter.

Knowledge of the reactivity or biodegradability of a contaminant in the subsurface is vital for determining whether in situ treatment processes will work. Chapters 7 and 8 indicated that levels of electron acceptors, such as dissolved oxygen, are crucial to the design of a bioremediation system. The ability of an injection system or infiltration system to deliver nutrients or additional electron acceptors to a desired location in a plume is a function of both hydraulic conditions and reactions in the subsurface. Chemical reactions and sorption of organics onto the soil matrix, which might occur during a remediation effort, must also be addressed in detail as part of the design phase of any remediation (Chapter 7).

If pure product or NAPL exists at or near the water table in the form of separate phase fluid, the problem of removal may be greatly complicated. As described in Chapter 11, float-

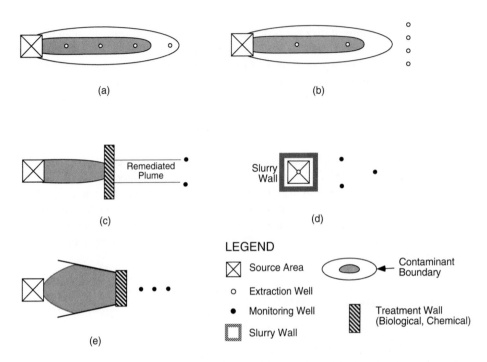

Figure 13.1 Remedial options and source control. (a) Standard pump and treat. (b) Fence line pump and treat. (c) Treatment wall system. (d) slurry wall system. (e) Funnel and gate system.

ing product on the water table (LNAPL) is easier to deal with than denser than water contaminants (DNAPLs), which can sink to lower regions of the aquifer and cannot be easily removed. Thus, depending on the site hydrogeology, it is often necessary to combine a limited pumping system with other techniques (bioremediation, soil vapor extraction, skimming of NAPL) in order to complete remediation in the saturated and vadose zones near a hazardous waste site.

The generally accepted remediation strategies for cleanup of subsurface contamination problems include:

1. Complete source removal (i.e., excavation)

2. Source or plume containment (barriers, hydraulic control)

3. Mass reduction methods
    A. Bioremediation
    B. Soil vapor extraction
    C. Natural attenuation

The above methods, while not the only ones in use, represent the most prevalent and successful ones being applied at many hazardous waste sites today. The remainder of the chapter describes various classes and specific emerging remediation methods in detail. Section 13.3 addresses issues of source control where NAPLs may be present. Section 13.4 reviews traditional pump and treat and hydraulic containment, since so many of the older systems are still in existence. Section 13.5 explains the basics of bioremediation as it applies and has been implemented at field sites. A case study is presented at the end of the chapter. Section 13.6 describes soil vapor extraction with a detailed case study at the end of the chapter. Section 13.7 presents NAPL issues and a detailed case study. Section 13.8 discusses some of the new and emerging technologies that have been tried at a number of experimental sites such as Hill Air Force Base (AFB) in Utah and Dover AFB in Delaware. Section 13.9 presents several detailed case studies of actual field site remediation efforts.

The field of remediation technology is changing rapidly, and new methods are constantly being devised and tested by many research and development groups in the United States and abroad. Several major conferences each year provide a forum for presenting and comparing new methods of ground water cleanup. In particular, the Battelle conferences on *In Situ* and On-Site Bioremediation (1991 to 1999) and on Remediation of Chlorinated and Recalcitrant Compounds (1998) contain many excellent up-to-date methodologies and examples from field sites and laboratory settings that should be of interest. The interested reader should consult the general literature from the Association of Ground Water Scientists and Engineers, the American Society of Civil Engineers, the American Geophysical Union, and the American Chemical Society.

13.3 CONTAINMENT METHODS FOR SOURCE CONTROL

Because of the limitations of conventional pump and treat systems, interest in physical containment methods has increased, primarily for isolating source zones to limit migration of plumes. The containment option is designed to control the spread of contaminants in the subsurface by the use of physical containment methods or hydrodynamic controls. Containment is usually restricted to source areas of a spill or leak from a pond, tank, or landfill, or to contaminated ground water in the immediate vicinity of a source. Hydraulic or hydrodynamic controls usually involve some injection or pumping of ground water via a series of wells surrounding the source or in the immediate plume area (Section 13.4). Physical containment measures are designed to isolate contaminated soil and ground water from the local environment and to minimize any downgradient migration.

Isolation techniques for the surface and subsurface include excavation and removal of the contaminated soil and ground water; barriers to ground water flow such as caps, liners, and cutoff walls; and surface water controls, which are described in order. The NRC (1994; 1997) and Pankow and Cherry (1996) provide thorough reviews of remedial methods for NAPLs, contaminated ground water, and contaminated soils. The Battelle conferences described above also present numerous examples of successful and unsuccessful remediation schemes.

13.3.1 Excavation Methods

A pit is usually dug to remove the soil, or pumping wells are installed to control the plume, and the excavated soil is transported to a secured site, such as a landfill or surface impoundment, for disposal (Ehrenfeld and Bass, 1984). This practice is generally no longer permitted in most areas. In recent years, contaminated soil is often sent to a hazardous waste incinerator for complete thermal destruction of organic contaminants. The ground water is pumped out and can be treated using a variety of techniques. The problem in excavation and removal to another location is the high cost, except for small amounts of soil as in the case of underground storage tanks. However, removal of contaminated soil and ground water to a more environmentally appropriate location may be necessary if *in situ* containment or treatment poses problems or initiates litigation. An obvious difficulty associated with excavation and removal is that total removal may be impossible when the contamination extends deep into the subsurface, the contaminants occur beneath a facility or building, or NAPLs are present.

13.3.2 Barriers to Ground Water Flow

Physical barriers used to prevent the flow of ground water include slurry walls, grout curtains, sheet piling, and compacted liners or geomembranes (NRC, 1994). Low permeability barriers for NAPL control are described in Section 13.7. Typical barriers may be used to contain contaminated ground water or leachate or prevent the flow of clean ground water into a zone of contamination. A barrier that completely encircles a contaminated region will provide better containment than a straight barrier, because ground water can flow around the ends. Some of these barriers should be used along with a pumping or collection system for improved hydraulic control across the liner or slurry wall.

Slurry wall aquifers with sandy surficial soil less than 60 ft in depth and underlain by an impermeable layer of fine grain deposits or bedrock are most amenable to slurry wall construction (Need and Costello, 1984). Construction of a slurry wall entails excavating a narrow trench (2 to 5 ft wide) surrounding the contaminated zone (Figure 13.2). The slurry acts to maintain the trench during excavation and is usually a mixture of soil or cement, bentonite, and water (Ehrenfeld and Bass, 1984). The trench is generally excavated through the aquifer and into the bedrock. Installation of a slurry wall at depths greater than 60 ft is difficult. Several books are available on detailed design issues related to slurry wall construction. (Johnson et al., 1985) provides a useful series of papers on slurry walls, based on a symposium sponsored by the ASTM.

There are two different methods for construction of slurry walls. Trenches constructed using a cement-bentonite (C-B) mixture are allowed to set whereas those constructed with a soil-bentonite (S-B) mixture are backfilled and solidified with appropriate materials. Solidification of the trench may be accomplished by backfilling with soil mixed with bentonite, soil

Figure 13.2 Trenching in progress. Source: Ryan, 1985 © ASTM.

mixed with cement, concrete, and asphaltic emulsion, or a combination of these with synthetic membranes (Tallard, 1985; Lynch et al., 1984). The chosen materials should be compatible with the *in situ* soil and contaminant regime. Depending on the backfill material used, the permeability of the resulting barrier may range from 10^{-6} to 10^{-8} cm/sec (Nielson, 1983). An S-B slurry cutoff wall was chosen for the first cleanup financed by the EPA's Superfund program (Ayres et al., 1983).

Grout curtains are another type of physical barrier. They are constructed by injecting grout (liquid, slurry, or emulsion) under pressure into the ground through well points (Canter and Knox, 1986). Ground water flow is impeded by the grout that solidifies in the interstitial pore space. The curtain is made contiguous by injecting the grout into staggered well points that form a two- or three-row grid pattern (Ehrenfeld and Bass, 1984). Spacing of the well points for grout injection and the rates of injection are critical. Premature solidification occurs when the injection rate is too slow, whereas the soil formation is fractured when the rate is too fast. Soil permeability is decreased and soil-bearing capacity is increased after the grout properly solidifies. Chemical or particulate grouting is most effective in soils that are of sand-sized grains or larger. The expense of grouting and the potential for contamination-related problems in the grout limit its usefulness in the ground water area.

Sheet piling involves driving interlocking sections of steel sheet piling into the ground. The sheets are assembled before use by slotted or ball-and-socket type connections and are driven into the soil in sections. The piles are driven through the unsaturated zone and the aquifer down into the consolidated zone using a pile driver. After driving the barrier into the consolidated material, the piles remaining above ground are usually cut off. The connections between the steel sheets are not initially watertight; however, fine grained soil particles eventually fill the gaps and the barrier generally becomes more impermeable to ground water flow. The interlocks can be grouted to seal the joints between individual sheets. Sheet piling may be less effective in coarse, dense material because the interlocking web may be disrupted during construction. New developments in the technology have significantly reduced the potential for leakage through these walls (Starr and Cherry, 1994). Sheet piles have been used at a number of experimental sites to isolate contaminated zones from one another with some success (Bedient et al., 1999).

Liners represent another type of physical barrier and are often used in conjunction with surface water controls and caps (Canter and Knox, 1986). Liners are often used to protect ground water from leachate resulting from landfills containing hazardous materials. The type of liner used depends on the type of soil and contaminants that are present. Liners include polyethylene, polyvinyl chloride (PVC), many asphalt-based materials, and soil-bentonite or cement mixtures. Polyvinyl chloride liners have hydraulic conductivities of less than 3.0×10^{-11} ft/sec; however, little is known about the service life of the PVC membranes (Threlfall and Dowiak, 1980). The membrane should be installed over fine-grained soil to prevent punctures. A typical liner for a landfill is depicted in Figure 13.3.

13.3.3 Surface Water Controls

These methods alter vertical migration of contaminants by controlling infiltration of surface water through the vadose zone. Caps, dikes, terraces, vegetation, and grading are used to reduce the amount of infiltration into a site and control erosion, such as at a landfill. Channels, chutes, downpipes, seepage basins, dikes, and ditches that are used to divert uncontaminated surface water away from waste sites, collect contaminated leachate, or direct contaminated water away from clean areas (Ehrenfeld and Bass, 1984; Thomas et al., 1987). Many of these techniques may be used in combinations with each other.

Surface capping usually involves covering the contaminated area with an impermeable material, regrading to minimize infiltration of surface water, and revegetating the site (Canter and Knox, 1986). Surface caps are usually constructed using materials from one of three groups: (1) natural soils, (2) commercially designed materials, or (3) waste materials. The material used should be compatible with the soil type and contaminant regime. Examples include clay, concrete, asphalt, lime, fly ash, and mixed layers or synthetic liners. Fine-textured soils, often from on-site, are most commonly used. Several types of materials are used in combination to create a multilayer cap for a landfill (Figure 13.4).

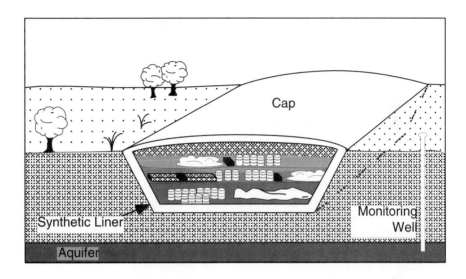

Figure 13.3 Example of synthetic liner for a hazardous-waste landfill.

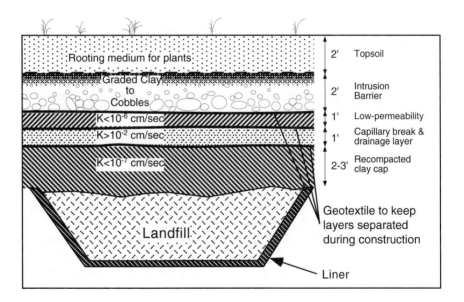

Figure 13.4 Typical multilayered cap constructed of natural soil materials.

13.4 HYDRAULIC CONTROLS AND PUMP AND TREAT SYSTEMS

Hydraulic control of ground water contamination can be designed to generally lower the water table or potentiometric surface to prevent discharge off-site, to reduce the rate of migration by removing contaminated waste, or to confine the plume to a potentiometric low created by a combination of pumping and injection wells. Maintenance on wells and pumps is particularly important for this method, and as ground water levels change, the system design may have to respond accordingly. Above ground biological or physical treatment units may be necessary to handle any contaminated water pumped by the wells.

In recent years, especially since about 1990, studies of pump and treat systems have indicated that drinking water standards may be essentially impossible to achieve in a reasonable time frame at many sites (EPA, 1989 and 1992; NRC, 1994). Between 1982 and 1992, 73% of the cleanups at Superfund sites with contaminated ground water specified the use of pump and treat technology. The effectiveness of pump and treat depends strongly on hydrogeologic and contaminant properties. For increasingly complex sites, the possibility of cleanup success decreases as discussed by the National Research Council (1994).

Several alternatives for removing contaminants via hydraulic control in the subsurface may all be part of an overall strategy for site remediation. The most popular methods have included interceptor systems, soil venting or vapor extraction (Section 13.6), and pumping or injection wells. It is not uncommon to find some or all of these methods being used at a single site, depending on the mix of chemicals and the hydrogeology of the site.

Interceptor systems use drains, a line of buried perforated pipe, and/or trenches, or an open excavation usually backfilled with gravel, to collect contaminated ground water close to the water table. These systems operate as a line of wells near the shallow water table, and are efficient at removing contamination along a linear boundary. Trenches are often used to collect nonaqueous phase liquids (LNAPLs) like crude oil or gasoline, that are light and tend to move near the capillary fringe just above the water table. Figure 13.5 shows a skimmer pump designed to selectively remove LNAPL entering the trench from a leaking UST. Trenches have also been used to collect DNAPLs from fractured limestone where a trench cuts across the fractures, is backfilled and pumped, and creates a significant zone of depression for ground water withdrawal (Figure 13.6). The trench should be designed long enough to avoid product flow around the end, and deep enough for hydraulic control to avoid the water table falling beneath the bottom of the trench during dry periods.

Pumping wells are used to extract water from the saturated zone by creating a capture zone for migrating contaminants (Figure 13.7). A major problem is the proper treatment and disposal of the contaminated water. On-site treatment facilities are usually required before water can be reinjected to the aquifer or released to the surface sanitary system. The number of wells, their locations, and the required pumping rates are the key design parameters of interest, and methods of analysis for wells are described in more detail in Chapter 3. Pumping contaminated water containing dissolved constituents can be addressed using standard well mechanics and capture zone theory which is well understood (Mercer et al., 1990). If the hy-

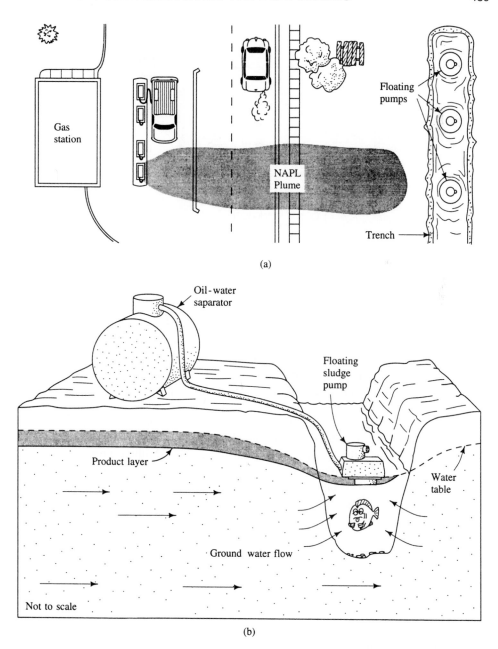

(a)

(b)

Figure 13.5 (a) Top view of LNAPL plume and interceptor trench. (b) Cross section of trench and floating pump used to capture floating product and depress the water table. Source Fetter, 1999.

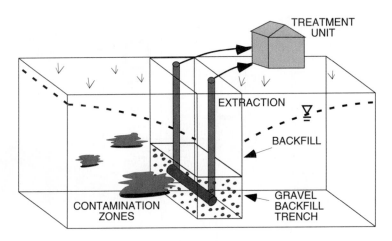

Figure 13.6 Collection Trench for DNAPL Source Zones.

drogeology is conducive to an injection or pumping system, then several design approaches can be used to develop an efficient and reliable system for contaminant removal. The most successful designs have been for relatively sandy or silty sand soils, that are very well-characterized, and ones where cleanup goals have not been too stringent.

Pilot scale pumping systems or small field demonstration projects have been used at a number of sites to evaluate the pump rates and the placement of wells in a small area of the site, before expanding to the entire site. In this way, operational policies, mechanical problems, and costs can be evaluated before attempting the larger cleanup. Careful monitoring of the system is the key to understanding how the injection/pumping pattern will respond over time. Many of the systems were originally designed without properly addressing the source area, where NAPL issues can create serious problems for standard pump and treat, vapor extraction or NAPL controls. Even with the problems associated with pump and treat designs, many sites still have these systems in place, and are providing some measure of control for off site areas.

13.4.1 Capture Zone Techniques

Pumping water containing dissolved contaminants can be addressed using standard well mechanics and capture zone theory (Chapter 3). If the hydraulic conductivity is too low or the geology is overly complex and heterogeneous, then pumping or hydraulic control may not be a feasible alternative for hazardous waste cleanup. If the hydrogeology is permeable enough for an injection pumping system, then both analytical and numerical models are available to evaluate placement and efficiency of remediation.

Javandel and Tsang (1986) developed a useful analytical method for the design of recovery well systems, based on the concept of a capture zone (Figure 13.7). More sophisticated modeling approaches are described in Chapter 10 and Section 13.9 for the case of more complex sites where numerical models must be employed. The capture zone for a well depends on the pumping rate and the aquifer conditions. Ideally, the capture zone should be somewhat larger than the plume to be cleaned up, so wells can be added until sufficient pumping capacity is provided to create a useful capture zone. However, with more wells, some contaminants may pass between the wells, so well spacing becomes an important parameter as well as pumping rate. The greater the pumping rate, the larger the capture zone, so the closer the wells are placed, the better the chance of complete plume capture. Overall, the method minimizes the pumping injection rates through a proper choice of well location and distance between wells.

Javandel and Tsang (1986) use complex potential theory as the basis for a simple graphical procedure to determine the pumping rate, the number of wells, and the distance between wells. The method requires type curves for one to four wells (Figure 13.8) and values for two parameters, B the aquifer thickness (assumed to be constant) and U the specific discharge or Darcy velocity (also assumed constant) for the regional flow system. The method involves the following five steps:

1. Construct a map of the contaminant plume at the same scale as the type curves. The edge or perimeter of the plume should be clearly indicated together with the direction of regional ground water flow.

2. Superimpose the type curve for one well on the plume, keeping the x-axis parallel to the direction of regional ground water flow and along the midline of the plume so that approximately equal proportions of the plume lie on each side of the x-axis. The pumped well on the type curve will be at the

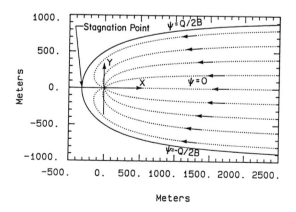

Figure 13.7 Paths of some water particles within the capture zone with Q/BU = 2000, leading to the pumping well located at the origin. Source: Javandel and Tsang, 1986.

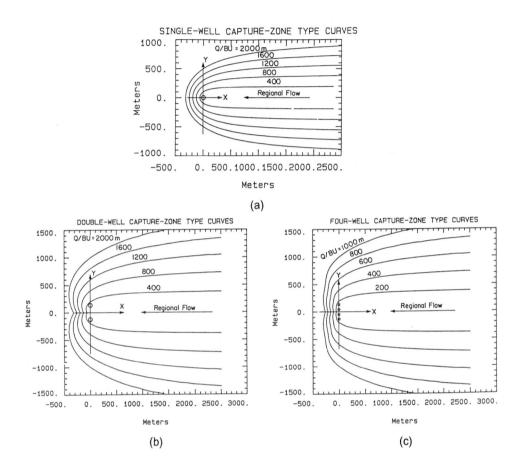

Figure 13.8 Set of type curves showing the capture zones for various values of Q/Bu. (a) Single pumping well at the origin. (b) Two pumping wells located on the Y axis. (c) Four pumping wells located on the Y axis. Source: Javandel and Tsang, 1986.

downstream end of the plume. The type curve is adjusted so that the plume is enclosed by a single Q/BU curve.

3. Calculate the single well pumping rate (Q) using the known values of aquifer thickness (B) and the Darcy velocity for regional flow (U) along with the value of Q/BU indicated on the type curve (TCV) with the equation

$$Q = B \cdot U \cdot \text{TCV}$$

4. If the pumping rate is feasible, one well with pumping rate Q is required for cleanup. If the required production is not feasible due to a lack of available drawdown, it will be necessary to continue adding wells (see step 5).

5. Repeat steps (2), (3), and (4) using the two-, three-, or four-well type curves in that order, until a single well pumping rate is calculated that the aquifer can support. The only extra difficulty comes from having to calculate the optimum spacing between wells using the following simple rules

2 wells	$Q/(BU)$
3 wells	$1.26Q/(BU)$
4 wells	$1.2Q/(BU)$

and to account for the interfacing among the pumped wells when checking on the feasibility of the pumping rates. The wells are always located symmetrically around the x-axis, as the type curves show.

Reinjecting the treated water produced by the wells will accelerate the rate of aquifer cleanup. The procedure is essentially the same as that just discussed except the type curves are reversed and the wells are injecting instead of pumping. The authors suggest that the injection wells should be moved slightly upstream of the calculated location to avoid causing parts of the plume to follow a long flow path. Their rule of thumb is to place wells half the distance between the theoretical location and the tail of the plume. The following example taken from Javandel and Tsang (1986) illustrates how the technique is used.

Example 13.1. CAPTURE ZONE

Shown on Figure 13.9 is a plume of trichloroethylene (TCE) present in a shallow confined aquifer having a thickness of 10 m, a hydraulic conductivity of 10^{-4} m/s, an effective porosity of 0.2, and a storativity of 3×10^{-5}. The hydraulic gradient for the regional flow system is 0.002 and the available drawdown for wells in the aquifer is 7m. Given this information, design an optimum collection system.

Values of B and U are required for the calculation. B is given as 10 m, but U needs to be calculated from the Darcy equation:

$$U = K \, dh/dl \quad \text{or} \quad U = 10^{-4} \times (0.002) = 2 \times 10^{-7} \text{ m/s}$$

Now we are ready to work with the type curves following the steps just outlined.

Superposition of the type curve for one well on the plume provides a Q/BU curve of about 2500. With this number and the values of B and U, the single well pumping rate is

$$Q = B \cdot U \cdot \text{TCV} \quad \text{or} \quad 10 \cdot (2 \times 10^{-7}) \cdot 2500 = 5 \times 10^{-3} \text{ m}^3/\text{s}$$

A check is required to determine whether this pumping rate can be supported for the aquifer. The Cooper-Jacob (1946) equation provides the drawdown at the well, assuming $r = 0.2$ m and the pumping period is one year:

$$s = \log \frac{2.25Tt}{r^2 S}$$

where $Q = 5 \times 10^{-3}$ m^3/s, $T = KB = 10^{-3}$ m^2/s, $t = 1$ year or 3.15×10^7 sec, $r = 0.2$ m, and $S = 3 \times 10^{-5}$.

The pumping period represents some preselected planning horizon for cleanup. Substitution of the known values into Cooper-Jacob equation gives a drawdown of 9.85 m. Even without accounting for well loss, the calculated drawdown exceeds the 7 m available. Thus, a multiwell system is necessary.

Superimposing the plume on the two-well type curve provides a Q/BU value of 1200, which in turn gives a Q for each of the two wells of $10 \cdot (2 \times 10^{-7}) \cdot 1200$ or 2.4×10^{-3} m^3/s. The optimum distance wells is $Q/(BU)$ or $2.4 \times 10^{-3}/[10 (2 \times 10^{-7})] = 382$ m. Again we check the predicted drawdown at each well after one year against the available 7 m. Because of symmetry, the drawdown in each well is the same. The total drawdown at one of the wells includes the contribution of that well pumping plus the second one 382 m away, based on the principal of superposition.

The calculated drawdown is 6.57 m, which is less than the available drawdown. However, well loss should be considered, which makes the two-well scheme unacceptable. Moving to a three-well scheme, Q/BU is 800 (Figure 13.9), which translates to a pumping rate of 1.6×10^{-3} m^3/s for each well. Carrying out the drawdown calculation for three wells located $1.26Q/(BU)$ or 320 meters apart provides an estimate of 5.7 m for the center well, which is comfortably less than the available drawdown. Thus, we have been able to ascertain the need for three wells, located 320 m apart, and each pumped at 1.6×10^{-3} m^3/s.

There are assumptions built into the formulation, such as constant aquifer transmissivity, fully penetrating wells, no recharge, and isotropic hydraulic conductivity, which must be satisfied by the field problem or the method will not necessarily yield a correct result. Actual field sites where boundary conditions and site heterogeneity are important issues may require analysis using numerical models as described in the next section.

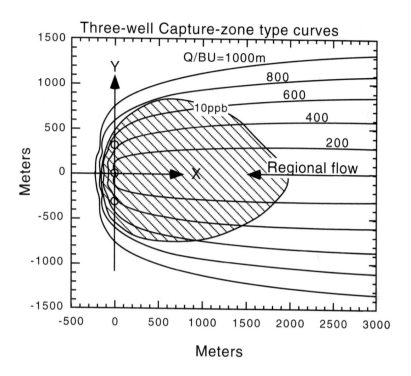

Figure 13.9 The 10-ppb contour line of TCE at the matching position with the capture zone type curve of Q/BU = 800. Source: Javandel and Tsang, 1986.

13.4.2 Analysis of Pumped Systems with Numerical Models

Ground water flow and transport modeling performed during the remedial investigation can be a powerful tool to estimate plume movement and response to various remedial schemes (see Chapter 10). Flow and contaminant transport models should be calibrated to a measured plume of contamination to the extent possible. However, caution should be used when applying models at hazardous waste sites because there can be great uncertainty whenever subsurface transport is modeled, particularly when the results of the model are based on estimated parameters. The purposes of modeling ground water flow for remediation include the following:

1. Predict concentrations of contaminants at receptor points

2. Estimate the effect of source-control actions on remediation

3. Guide the placement of monitoring wells and hydrogeologic characterization when the remedial study is conducted in phases

4. Evaluate expected remedial performance under a variety of alternative designs so that the efficiency and time of cleanup to some specified level can be predicted

The determination of whether or not to use modeling and the level of effort that should be expended is made on the basis of the objectives of the modeling, the ease with which the subsurface can be conceptualized mathematically, and the availability of data. Field data are collected to characterize the variables that govern the hydrologic and contaminant response of the site in question. Estimates based on literature values or professional judgment are frequently used as well.

Models such as the 3-D and RT3D (Clement et al., 1998) can be used to simulate flow patterns and concentration changes resulting from the operation of a pump-and-treat system. Other models are available to analyze contaminant transport such as the 2-D MOC model from Konikow and Bredehoeft (1978) and BIOPLUME III from Rifai et al. (1998). A detailed modeling example for a large pump and treat system in a complex aquifer is described in Section 13.9.

13.4.3 Optimizing Pumping-Injection Systems

Many investigators have used numerical ground water models as a tool in the design of aquifer restoration strategies because they provide a rapid means of predicting or assessing the effects of different remedial alternatives. Andersen et al. (1984) used a finite-difference ground water model as an aid in selecting an appropriate remedial action at the Lipari Landfill in New Jersey. Freeberg et al. (1987) delineated a trichloroethylene plume and used the USGS MOC Model to evaluate different withdrawal schemes at an industrial waste site. Gorelick et al. (1993) developed an entire set of optimization and simulation tools to design efficient and cost-effective capture and containment systems for ground water. However, optimization techniques have suffered because of the ill-posed ground water transport problems, and the inability to handle complex source problems involving NAPL issues.

Satkin and Bedient (1988) used the USGS MOC model to investigate various pumping and injection patterns to remediate a contaminant plume. Seven different well patterns were studied for various combinations of hydraulic gradient, maximum drawdown and aquifer dispersivity. Various cleanup levels were evaluated along with the volume of water circulated and the volume of water requiring treatment. Eight hydrogeologic conditions were modeled for the various remediation schemes. The location of a single well or multiple pumping wells requires that the capture zone encompass the entire plume. Generally, the closer a single well can be to the center of mass of contamination, the faster the cleanup time. Additional wells aligned with the axis of the plume will increase the rate of cleanup over a single well by pumping a greater volume of water.

The key hydrogeologic variables that control the rate of cleanup are well locations, pumping rates, transmissivity, dispersivity and hydraulic gradient. The three-spot, doublet, and double-cell (four wells) well patterns were effective under low hydraulic gradient condi-

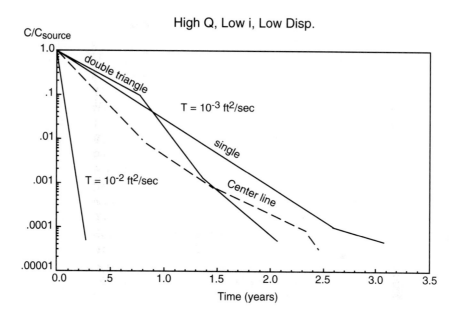

Figure 13.10 Comparison of relative concentrations versus cleanup time for various well patterns for condition A. Source: Satkin and Bedient, 1988.

tions. These well patterns require on-site treatment and reinjection. The three-spot pattern performed best under a high hydraulic gradient. Finally, for a given set of well locations, and maintaining drawdown, dispersivity and hydraulic gradient constant, the cleanup time was found to be inversely related to the pumping rate for selected transmissivities. Figure 13.10 shows typical results for a selected hydrogeologic condition of low gradient and low dispersivity.

13.5 BIOREMEDIATION

The practical application of biodegradation discussed in Chapters 7 and 8 for the remediation of hazardous waste sites is termed **bioremediation**. The process, when carried out *in situ*, or in place, usually involves stimulating the indigenous subsurface microorganisms by the addition of nutrients, such as nitrogen and phosphorus, and an electron acceptor, such as oxygen, to biodegrade the contaminants of concern. The process is not new, in that some of the first systems were installed in the 1970s. Under the proper subsurface conditions, and for petroleum hydrocarbons, microorganisms can biodegrade contaminants to mineral end products such as carbon dioxide and water. Several excellent reviews have been presented in the general literature (NRC, 1993; Norris et al., 1994).

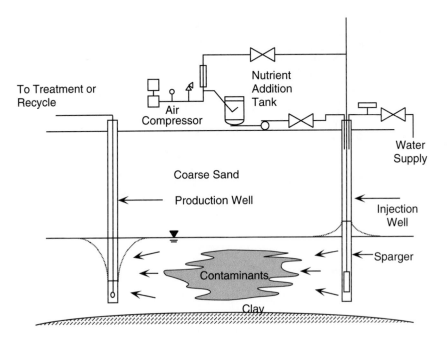

Figure 13.11 Injection system for oxygen.

In contrast with other remedial techniques that transfer the contaminants from one phase in the environment to another, *in situ* bioremediation offers partial or complete destruction of the contaminants (Chapter 7). In some cases, the natural conditions at a site provide all of the necessary materials so that the process can occur without human intervention, which is called **intrinsic bioremediation**. Engineered bioremediation systems usually require some construction of monitoring and delivery systems for the addition of nutrients or electron acceptor (Figure 13.11).

In situ bioremediation process might offer attractive economics for remediation because it precludes the need for excavation and disposal costs associated with other remediation alternatives. The method also offers an advantage where physical limitations due to the presence of structures might inhibit removal of the contaminants, and can be used to treat contaminants, which are both sorbed to the aquifer matrix and dissolved in the ground water simultaneously.

Two essential criteria must be satisfied before bioremediation can be considered a viable remediation alternative for a field site. First, the subsurface geology must have a relatively high hydraulic conductivity ($>10^{-4}$ cm/sec) to allow the transport of the electron acceptor and nutrients through the aquifer. Second, microorganisms must be present in sufficient numbers and types to degrade the contaminants of interest. It is important to keep in mind that any bioremediation project at a field site needs to be preceded by laboratory experiments of microbial stimulation and modeling studies of nutrient delivery and transport to ensure efficient performance of the system. Enhanced aerobic bioremediation for a petroleum spill, for example, is essentially an engineered delivery of nutrients and oxygen to the contaminated zone in an aquifer.

Oxygen sources include air, pure oxygen (gaseous and liquid forms), and hydrogen peroxide. Sparging the ground water with air and pure oxygen can supply only 8 to 40 mg/L of oxygen depending on the temperature of the injection fluid (Lee et al., 1988). Hydrogen peroxide, which dissociates to form water and 1/2 molecule of oxygen, is infinitely soluble in water (Thomas and Ward 1989); however, hydrogen peroxide can be toxic to microorganisms at concentrations as low as 100 ppm. Other limitations have to do with the expense and the stability of hydrogen peroxide.

13.5.1 Engineering Design Issues

The basic steps involved in an in situ biorestoration program (Lee et al., 1988) are:

1. site investigation
2. free product investigation and recovery
3. microbial degradation enhancement study
4. system design and construction
5. operation
6. maintenance

After defining the hydrogeology, recovery of free product, if any, at the site should be completed. LNAPL can be removed using physical recovery techniques such as a dual pump system that produces water and hydrocarbon or a two-pump, two-well system that steepens the hydraulic gradient and recovers the accumulating hydrocarbon. Section 13.7 describes skimmer wells in more detail.

Prior to the initiation of a bioremediation activity, it is important to conduct a feasibility study for the biodegradation of the contaminants present at the site. First, contaminant-degrading microorganisms must be present, and second, the response of these native microorganisms to the proposed treatment method must be evaluated. In addition, the feasibility study is conducted to determine the nutrient requirements of the microorganisms. These laboratory studies provide a reliable basis for performance at the field level only if they are performed under conditions that simulate the field. A number of recent publications are available to help guide the practitioner (NRC, 1993).

The chemistry of a field site will obviously affect the types and amounts of nutrients that are required. Limestone and high mineral content soils, for example, will affect nutrient availability by reacting with phosphorous. Silts and clays at sites may induce nutrient sorption on the soil matrix, and hence decrease the amount of nutrients available for growth. In general, a chemical analysis of the ground water provides little information about the nutrient requirements at a field site; it is mostly the soil composition that is of significance.

Feasibility studies can be completed using several different techniques. Batch culture techniques are used to measure the disappearance of the contaminant; electrolytic respirometer studies are utilized to measure the uptake of oxygen. Studies that measure disappearance of the contaminant or mineralization studies that confirm the breakdown of the contaminant to carbon dioxide and water need to be conducted. Controls to detect abiotic transformation of the pollutants and tests to detect toxic effects of the contaminants on the microflora should be included (Flathman et al. 1984; NRC, 1993; Norris et al., 1994).

For enhanced bioremediation, a system for injection of nutrients into the formation and circulation through the contaminated portion of the aquifer must be designed and constructed (Lee and Ward, 1985). The system usually includes injection and production wells and equipment for the addition and mixing of the nutrient solution (Raymond, 1978). A typical system is shown in Figure 13.11. Placement of injection and production wells may be restricted by the presence of physical structures. Wells should be screened to accommodate seasonal fluctuations in the level of the water table. Nutrients also can be circulated using an infiltration gallery; this method provides an additional advantage of treating the residual gasoline that may be trapped in the pore spaces of the unsaturated zone. Oxygen can be supplied by a number of methods including oxygen in water, pure oxygen, hydrogen peroxide, ozone, or by soil venting.

The performance of the system and proper distribution of the nutrients can be monitored by measuring the organic, inorganic, and bacterial levels in space and time. Carbon dioxide levels are also an indication of microbial activity in the formation. There are a number of field demonstrations of the bioremediation process that have been implemented over the past few years, and several examples are presented in Chapter 8 and in Dupont et al. (1998).

13.5.2 Bioremediation Demonstration Projects

Researchers from Suntech, Inc. are among the earliest pioneers who utilized bioremediation at sites contaminated with gasoline. Classic field experiments are discussed by Raymond et al. (1976) and Raymond (1978). The field study at a site in Ambler, Pennsylvania involved a leak in a gasoline pipeline that had caused the township to abandon its ground water supply wells. The free product was physically removed prior to the initiation of biodegradation studies at the site. Laboratory studies showed that the natural microbial population at the site could use the spilled high-octane gasoline as the sole carbon source if sufficient quantities of the limiting nutrients, in this case, oxygen, nitrogen and phosphate, were supplied. Pilot studies carried out in the field in several wells confirmed the laboratory findings.

Studies began in 1986 at the U.S. Coast Guard Facility in Traverse City, Michigan for fuel hydrocarbons from a large leaking fuel tank. The site was used for six years as a research field site by EPA to evaluate a number of in situ bioremediation technologies (Wilson et al., 1988). Rifai et al. (1988) and Bedient et al. (1992) applied the BIOPLUME II model to demonstrate and quantify that natural biodegradation of BTEX was occurring at the site. Several test areas were used to test enhanced bioremediation through the subsurface injection of oxygen, hydrogen peroxide, phosphates, and nitrates. Natural biodegradation of the off-site plume was quantified based on several wells located down the plume's centerline (Bedient et al., 1992).

Researchers at Stanford University conducted an extensive field demonstration at Moffet Naval Air Station to evaluate the potential of using cometabolism *in situ* bioremediation of chlorinated organics. Chlorinated solvents were added to the site, along with oxygen and methane to stimulate the native microorganisms (Semprini et al., 1990; Roberts et al., 1990). There was a documented loss of contaminants: 95% of vinyl chloride, 85% of trans-DCE, 40% of cis-DCE, and 20% of TCE that had been added to the site. The researchers used a variety of methods to demonstrate biodegradation in the field including evaluation of background conditions and microbial breakdown products, conservative tracer studies, and modeling studies.

Chiang et al. (1989) evaluated the aerobic biodegradation of BTX from a natural gas plant in northern Michigan. They set up an extensive monitoring program to evaluate the effectiveness of intrinsic bioremediation in 1987, and showed that benzene concentrations dropped by 90% and the contaminant plume has shrunk considerably. Laboratory tests confirmed the potential for soil microbes to degrade the fuel contaminants at a high rate in the presence of oxygen. Finally, the BIOPLUME II was used to calibrate to the site data and to predict future conditions at the site. The model worked quite well and matched the rates measured in the field (see Chapter 8).

Since the early nineties, a larger number of successful demonstration projects on active bioremediation at field sites are now available for review. The *Handbook of Bioremediation* by Norris et al. (1994) provides detailed descriptions of the technologies available for handling both contaminated soil and ground water. A recent monograph from Dupont et al. (1998), under the innovative site remediation technology program, presents eight different case studies on bioventing, biosparging, the Raymond process, intrinsic remediation, and land farming. The reader is referred to the above references for more details than can be provided here.

13.6 SOIL VAPOR EXTRACTION SYSTEMS

The unsaturated zone plays a key role in determining the dynamics of subsurface contaminant transport and remediation. Soil vapor extraction (SVE) is an alternative remediation strategy targeting the removal of volatile contaminants from the unsaturated zone, and results in contaminant removal from the vapor, NAPL, and aqueous phases (Rathfelder et al., 1991). Many organic substances have substantial vapor concentrations (i.e., highly volatile) compared to their solubilities. Vapor pressure and Henry's Law constant determine the degree to which the chemical will partition into the gas phase. Volatile contaminants could be more effectively recovered from the unsaturated zone by enhancing air-phase transport as opposed

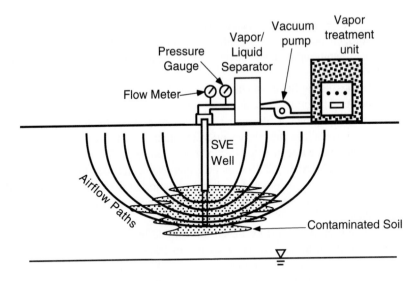

Figure 13.12 Simple vapor extraction system and the resulting pattern airflow.
Source: Johnson et al., 1990.

to water-phase transport (Baehr et al., 1989). In this technique, the soil is decontaminated in place by pulling air through the soil, and the extracted gas may be discharged directly to the atmosphere or sent to an emissions control device (DePaoli et al., 1991). Advective vapor transport is induced by withdrawing air through wells that are screened in the vadose zone. As air is drawn through the pores, it will carry away the existing vapors. Thus, contaminants in the liquid and dissolved phases will volatilize and continue to be swept by the carrier air flow. As the process continues, the residual levels of soil contaminants will be effectively reduced. Figure 13.12 shows a schematic of a typical SVE system.

SVE has been successful for sites contaminated with gasoline and organic solvents that contain a large fraction of volatile components (Hutzler et al., 1989). It is extremely useful in decontaminating highly permeable soils in a relatively short time. Among the advantages of the soil vapor extraction process are that it creates a minimal disturbance of the contaminated soil, it can be constructed from standard equipment, and it is cost effective. The success of the operation depends on the rate of contaminant mass transfer from the non-aqueous and aqueous phases to the vapor phase. The feasibility of the technique is site specific. Variables to be considered include: (1) contaminant characteristics such as: contaminant volatility, boiling point, solubility, octanol/water partition coefficient; and (2) site properties such as: permeability, fraction of organic carbon, and moisture content. The decision on whether to use SVE for site remediation, or to take no action and leave the site to naturally attenuate depends on site conditions, and on the potential health risks associated with exposure.

13.6.1 System Components

A typical soil vapor extraction system such as the one shown in Figure 13.12 consists of:

1. one or more extraction wells
2. one or more air inlet or injection wells (optional)
3. piping or air headers
4. vacuum pumps or air blowers
5. flow meters and controllers
6. vacuum gauges
7. sampling ports
8. air/water separator (optional)
9. vapor treatment (optional)
10. a cap (optional)

Extraction wells are typically designed to fully penetrate the unsaturated zone to the capillary fringe. If the ground water is at a shallow depth or if the contamination is confined to near-surface soils, then the extraction wells may be placed horizontally. Extraction wells usually consist of slotted, plastic pipe placed in permeable packing. The surface of the augered column for vertical wells or the trench for horizontal wells is usually grouted to prevent the direct inflow of air from the surface along the well casing or through the trench.

It may be desirable to also install air inlet or injection wells to control airflow through zones of maximum contamination. They are constructed similarly to the extraction wells. Inlet wells or vents are passive and allow air to be drawn into the ground at specific locations. Injection wells force air into the ground and can be used in closed-loop systems (Payne et al., 1986). The function of inlet and injection wells is to enhance air movement in strategic locations and promote horizontal airflow to the extraction wells.

The pumps or blowers reduce gas pressure in the extraction wells and induce airflow to the wells. The pressure from the outlet side of the pumps or blowers can be used to push the exit gas through a treatment system and back into the ground if injection wells are used. Gas flow meters are installed to measure the volume of extracted air. Pressure losses in the overall system are measured with vacuum gauges. Sampling ports may be installed in the system at each well head, at the blower, and after vapor treatment. In addition, vapor and pressure monitoring probes may be placed to measure soil vapor concentrations and the radius of influence of the vacuum in the extraction wells.

Vapor treatment may not be required if the emission rates of chemicals are low or if they are easily degraded in the atmosphere. Typical treatment systems include liquid/vapor condensation, incineration, catalytic conversion, or granular activated carbon adsorption.

Patterns of air circulation to extraction wells have been studied in the field by direct measurements (Batchelder et al., 1986), and more recently by mathematical and experimental modeling (Johnson et al., 1988, 1990, 1994; Krishnayya et al., 1988). Chapter 9 presented governing equations of flow and transport for the unsaturated zone. Most of the theoretical work to date has considered that any density differences in the vapor can be neglected under the forced convective conditions created by the vacuum extraction.

13.6.2 System Variables

A number of variables characterize the successful design and operation of a vapor extraction system. They may be classified as site conditions, soil properties, chemical characteristics, control variables, and response variables (Anastos et al., 1985; Enviresponse, 1987; Hutzler et al., 1989; Johnson et al., 1994).

The extent to which VOCs are dispersed in the soil, vertically and horizontally, is an important consideration in deciding if vapor extraction is preferable to other methods. The depth to ground water is also important. Where ground water is at depths of more than 40 feet and the contamination extends to the ground water, use of soil vapor extraction systems may be one of the few ways to remove VOCs from the soil (Hutzler et al., 1989; Johnson et al., 1994).

Heterogeneities influence air movement as well as the location of chemical, and the presence of heterogeneities make it more difficult to position extraction and inlet wells. There generally will be significant differences in the air conductivity of the various strata of a stratified soil. A horizontally stratified soil may be favorable for vapor extraction because the relatively impervious strata will limit the rate of vertical inflow from the ground surface and will tend to extend the influence of the applied vacuum horizontally from the point of extraction.

The soil characteristics at a particular site will have a significant effect on the applicability of vapor extraction systems. Air conductivity controls the rate at which the applied vacuum can draw air through the soil. Grain size, moisture content, soil aggregation, and stratification probably are the most important properties (Hutzler et al., 1989, Johnson et al., 1994). The soil moisture content or degree of saturation is also important in that it is easier to draw air through drier soils. The success of the soil vapor extraction in silty or clayey soils may depend on the presence of more conductive strata, as would be expected in alluvial settings, or on relatively low moisture content in the finer-grained soils.

Chemical properties will dictate whether a soil vapor extraction system is feasible. A vapor-phase vacuum extraction system is most effective at removing compounds that exhibit significant volatility at the ambient temperatures in soil. Low molecular weight, volatile compounds are favored, and vapor extraction is likely to be most effective at new sites where the more volatile compounds are still present. Compounds that have been effectively removed by vapor extraction include trichloroethene, trichloroethane, tetrachloroethene, and most gasoline constituents. Compounds that are less applicable to removal include trichlorobenzene, acetone, and heavier petroleum fuels (Payne et al., 1986; Bennedsen et al., 1985; Texas Research Institute, 1980).

Soil vapor extraction processes are flexible in that several variables can be adjusted during design or operation. These variables include the air withdrawal rate, the well spacing and configuration, the control of water infiltration by capping, and the pumping duration. Higher air flow rates tend to increase vapor removal because the zone of influence is increased and air is forced through more of the air-filled pores. More wells will allow better control of airflow but will also increase construction and operation costs. Intermittent operation of the blowers will allow time for chemicals to diffuse from immobile water and air and permit removal at higher concentrations.

Parameters responding to soil vapor extraction system performance include air pressure gradients, VOC concentrations, moisture content, and power usage. The rate of vapor removal is expected to be primarily affected by the chemical's volatility, its sorptive capacity onto soil, the air flow rate, the distribution of air flow, the initial distribution of chemical, soil stratification or aggregation, and the soil moisture content.

13.6.3 Design Issues for Vapor Extraction Systems

Site stratigraphy, site hydrogeology, extent of spill, the chemical and physical characteristics of contaminants are key issues to be addressed prior to choosing SVE as a candidate method for site remediation. Once SVE has been selected as a possible strategy for remediation, the following procedure should be adopted for better design of SVE systems.

1. Run air permeability tests to determine site permeability.
2. Run a feasibility analysis using a screening tool to determine whether SVE is an appropriate remedial strategy for the site.
3. Run pilot tests at the site to determine the physical parameters and confirm the accuracy of the feasibility analysis.
4. Design and test the SVE system using more sophisticated modeling tools.

System design can provide data about the required number of wells, well spacing and locations, air flow rates, applied vacuum, vapor concentrations, amount of mass removed, time required for cleanup, and the residual mass remaining in soil. A detailed case study of SVE for Hill AFB is presented in Section 13.9.3.

13.6.4 Air Sparging and Hydrogen Injection

Air sparging is a relatively new technology that has been implemented at numerous sites around the country. The technique involves the forced entry of air into sparge wells or trenches under sufficient pressure to form bubbles in ground water. The bubbles sweep through the aquifer (1) to strip volatile organics from the soluble phase and from any NAPLs present along the path of bubbles, (2) to add oxygen to the water to spur the *in situ* bioremediation process, and (3) in some cases, to establish large circulation cells to move contaminated water to extraction wells. After bubbles make their way up to the unsaturated zone, an SVE system is often used to remove vapors for treatment prior to release to the atmosphere.

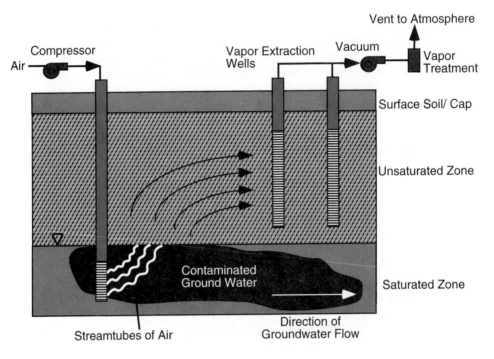

Figure 13.13 Process diagram for air sparging. Source: NRC, 1994.

It was originally assumed that sparged air would travel as bubbles dispersed throughout the contaminated zone, and would provide efficient mass transfer from the NAPL phase into the air. Recent studies indicate that air travels in air stream tubes or filaments (Ahlfield et al., 1993; Goodman et al., 1993). Current indications are that air sparging shows more promise for petroleum sites with LNAPL source zones, where the air brings oxygen that permits aerobic biodegradation to occur (Pankow and Cherry, 1996). Air sparging is more effective at treating dissolved hydrocarbon plumes than for treating source areas (Bass and Brown, 1996), and has been used as an alternative to conventional pump and treat systems (Figure 13.13).

In-situ bioremediation via direct hydrogen addition is an emerging technology designed to enhance the biodegradation of chlorinated solvents (PCE, TCE, and 1,2-DCE) in ground water and in the unsaturated zone. Based on the results of recent research, the role of hydrogen as an electron donor is now widely recognized as the key factor governing the biologically-mediated dechlorination of these common environmental contaminants (Gossett and Zinder, 1996; Carr and Hughes, 1998). Hydrogen can be delivered directly to the subsurface by a variety of means, such as dissolved in a ground water pump-and-reinjection scheme, low volume pulsed biosparging, injection of chemical reactants that produce hydrogen, electrolysis, and other methods (Fisher et al., 1998, Hughes et al., 1997).

Direct hydrogen addition is an extension of natural attenuation processes that occur at many chlorinated solvents sites, that is, hydrogen-based dechlorination where the hydrogen results from naturally-occurring fermentation substrates. The stoichiometry of the reaction (1 mg/L of hydrogen has the potential to dechlorinate 23 mg/L of PCE) and hydrogen's low cost are two strengths of this approach. This process is now being tested at several field sites around the country as part of an Air Force technology development program.

13.7 REMEDIATING NAPL SITES

13.7.1 Proven Technologies for Removing NAPLS

Chapter 11 indicated the difficulties of characterizing and remediating sites with NAPLs in the subsurface. It is now recognized that NAPLs can create a source of contamination for years or decades due to the slow dissolution process. Standard remediation methods of the eighties, such as pump and treat, only addressed the soluble part of the plume, and did little for control of NAPL source areas. A remediation technology is defined as "proven" if (1) it is commonly practiced in the field and (2) if sufficient design methodologies are available so that practitioners can apply the technology and obtain the predicted system response. An emerging technology, on the other hand, is one where some bench-scale or field-scale tests have been conducted, but detailed design procedures are not generally available. This section describes the proven approaches for removal of NAPLs from the subsurface, and Section 13.8 describes some of the more successful emerging methods for site remediation.

13.7.2 General Remediation Strategy for NAPL Sites

As restoration of ground water to drinking water standards may prove infeasible at many NAPL-affected sites, alternative approaches to managing NAPL problems should be considered. The following general management strategy divides a NAPL site into three zones:

1. dissolved phase zone
2. confirmed free-phase NAPL zone
3. potential NAPL zone (either free-phase or residual NAPL)

As shown in Figure 13.14, this classification system is based on the confirmed or suspected presence of NAPL in the aquifer. Areas where site data indicate a low probability of NAPL in the aquifer would be designated as "dissolved phase zones" where conventional remediation technologies could be applied. At many sites, the applicable cleanup standards could be at or near current drinking water standards, and pump-and-treat systems can be used to reach the required concentration levels, assuming that some controls are implemented for the source area.

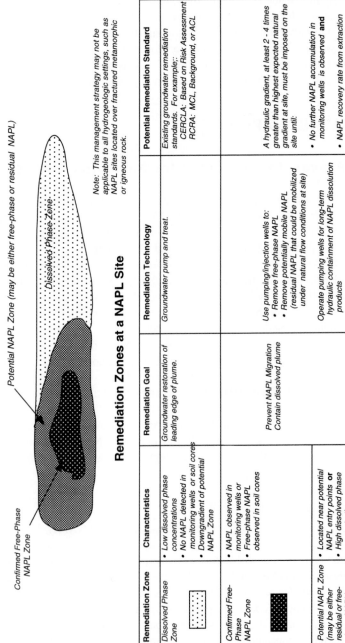

Figure 13.14 *General Management Strategy for NAPL Sites*

In areas where the presence of NAPL is confirmed, due to the presence of free-phase NAPL in monitoring wells, a containment strategy can be applied in place of conventional ground water remediation standards. Containment of NAPL can be achieved by imposing a relatively high hydraulic gradient across the site to remove free-phase material and to ensure that residual NAPL will remain immobilized under natural flow conditions. Some of the containment and barrier methods described in Section 13.3 could then be implemented. Operation of such a system could require a longer-term financial commitment than is currently afforded many sites.

As the presence of NAPL is difficult to confirm in the subsurface, a third zone has been defined for areas where residual and/or free-phase NAPL may be present. For example, the presence of relatively high concentrations (i.e., 1% of solubility) of dissolved organics or proximity to NAPL entry points would be sufficient to designate an area as a potential NAPL zone. The remediation approach for these areas would be identical to confirmed NAPL zones: long-term containment for NAPL and pumping to control off site migration of dissolved constituents.

The remediation goals outlined above can be achieved with existing, proven technologies (e.g., barriers and ground water recovery wells) to provide a significant level of protection to both human and environmental receptors. Implementation of this remediation approach requires modification of current regulatory policies regarding cleanup standards and financial assurance for corrective action programs. Note that the containment period for LNAPL sites is usually shorter than for the containment of DNAPL sites. This is due to more rapid biodegradation of fuel hydrocarbons compared to chlorinated organics, and the relative ease of dealing with floating product near the water table compared to removing DNAPLs deeper in the aquifer (See Figure 13.5 versus Figure 13.6).

13.7.3 Pumping to Remove Continuous-Phase LNAPLs

LNAPLs can be removed from the subsurface by pumping recovery wells screened at the water table or by pumping an interceptor system such as a french drain or interceptor trench (Figure 13.5). The most common approach for maximizing the recovery of LNAPL is to pump the layer relatively slowly in order to keep the LNAPL mass as a continuous flowing mass (Charbeneau et al., 1989; Abdul, 1992). Water pumping is carefully controlled to avoid smearing the LNAPL layer.

Two alternative approaches can be employed: pumping the combined ground water/LNAPL mixture with a single pump, or using two separate pumps working under a control system in order to remove the aqueous phase and nonaqueous phase separately (Blake and Lewis, 1982). For systems with significant accumulations of LNAPL, a two-pump system will provide a more efficient remediation approach. A control system comprised of two water/LNAPL interface probes is used to operate dedicated LNAPL and ground water pumps. The first interface probe is set below the intake of the LNAPL pump and keeps the LNAPL pump operating as long as there is hydrocarbon near the pump intake. The lower interface probe turns the ground water pump off if hydrocarbon level approaches the intake, and on

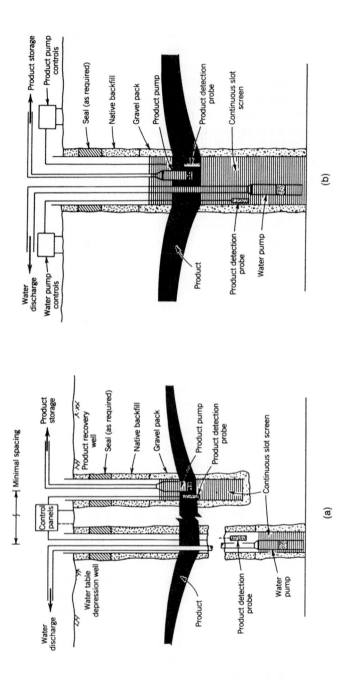

Figure 13.15 Examples of NAPL recovery systems. (a) Two-well, two-pump system. (b) One-well, two-pump system. Source: Blake and Lewis (1982).

again when there is sufficient water above the pump intake (Figure 13.15). An alternate design uses floating "skimmer" pumps and floating interface probes that move up and down on the floating hydrocarbon layer.

Once the LNAPL source area has been controlled, then natural attenuation mechanisms will usually dominate the rest of the plume and the source area, and will limit the overall extent of migration of a typical fuel hydrocarbon plume. Several recent reports from California and Texas discussed in Chapter 12, evaluated hundreds of leaking underground storage tank sites and found the average length of plume to be on the order of 200 ft in the subsurface. This limitation is largely related to the natural processes of dispersion and biodegradation acting on typical hydrocarbon plumes.

13.7.4 Pumping to Remove Continuous-Phase DNAPL

In practice, DNAPL removal is much more difficult than LNAPL removal. Source zones may have buried drums, sludge, or other pipe leaks located primarily in the shallow unsaturated zone, as well as DNAPL below the water table. The DNAPL pools and lenses are much harder to locate and the installation of recovery wells increases the risk of mobilizing DNAPL accumulations (Figure 13.6). Limited field experience indicates that some DNAPL can be mobilized by pumping, and that pumping ground water from the aquifer above the DNAPL recovery will increase yields by creating a water drive for the DNAPL pool. Trenches have been used with some success at a few sites where bedrock forms a clear vertical boundary. A detailed case study is presented in Section 13.9. Emerging and advanced remediation technologies described in Section 13.8 will be required to affect any real improvement for sites contaminated with DNAPL, since these sites are so difficult to cleanup (Pankow and Cherry, 1996).

Fractured sites containing DNAPL present an even more complex problem, since the pure phase product can penetrate deeply into fractures, creating source zones that are impossible to find or clean up in a reasonable time period. (see Figure11.11). A few fractured sites have been addressed using trench technology with some success, since a trench can potentially cut across lateral fractures and cause DNAPL to flow out and be captured by a pumping system.

13.7.5 Bioventing

While soil vapor extraction (SVE) is primarily directed at remediation of unsaturated soils, it can be adapted to the removal of volatile hydrocarbons in LNAPLs from the subsurface. In the case of bioventing just above the water table, the SVE system is operated to deliver oxygen at a slow flow rate to the indigenous microbes, thereby promoting degradation of organics in the pore space. The advantage of bioventing compared to enhanced bioremediation is that oxygen can be more easily transported in air ($280mg/L$ O_2 in air) than in water (10 to 40 mg/L O_2 in water).

First, there will be some transport of volatile organics from contaminated ground water into an air stream being forced across the water table by a soil vapor extraction system.

However, a much more important process occurs when the water table is depressed, for example, by a ground water pumping system, thereby exposing the former saturated zone to the effects of an SVE system. In most cases, such a system will be many times more effective at removing volatile hydrocarbons when compared to conventional ground water pumping systems removing dissolved hydrocarbons. Key design parameters for these applications are presented in Section 13.6.

13.7.6 Low Permeability Enclosures

A low permeability enclosure around a DNAPL source zone will divert much of the ground water flow around the enclosure. Many types of engineered barrier technologies are available and are described elsewhere (Pankow and Cherry, 1996). Each type has its own advantages and disadvantages, depending on the underlying geology of a site, and the relative complexity of the system. Keyed and hanging enclosures are both possible, where the first has the wall set into an aquitard at the bottom of the aquifer, and the second has the wall set deeper than the DNAPL zone (Figure 13.16). Often pumping inside the enclosure is used to cause upward flow at the bottom of the enclosure and to maintain hydraulic control from outside influences.

Figure 13.17 shows a plume of dissolved contamination on the downstream side of an enclosure, for the case of no pumping. Even with pumping inside the enclosure, some contamination may diffuse through the wall and migrate downstream. Enclosures around source zones need not provide zero outward flux in order to effectively isolate the source, but rather the flux must be limited to meet regulatory standards at a specified location downstream. The enclosure also provides a separation of the source zone so that DNAPL removal or soil flushing with surfactants or co-solvents can take place inside the enclosure (see Section 13.9).

13.8 EMERGING REMEDIATION TECHNOLOGIES

13.8.1 Funnel and Gate Systems

The funnel and gate system for the *in situ* treatment of contaminant plumes consists of low permeability cutoff walls, with gaps (gate) that contain reactors that remove contaminants by abiotic or biological processes (Starr and Cherry, 1994). The reactive zone can also be designed to volatilize contaminants (Pankow et al., 1993). These systems have advanced rapidly from pilot scale trials to full-scale systems. Figure 13.18 shows a typical schematic in plan and profile for an aquifer that has a well-defined aquitard at depth. The treatment and gate designs are still the subject of research and demonstrations, and final designs are still being tested for particular geological settings and specific contaminants. Only a limited number of funnel and gate systems have actually been installed.

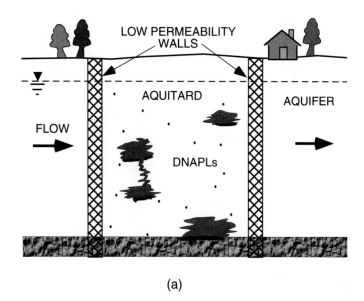

(a)

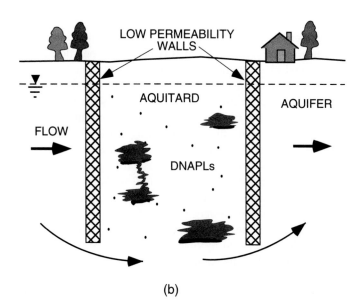

(b)

Figure 13.16 Cutoff wall enclosure: (a) keyed enclosure-groundwater is diverted laterally around the enclosure; and (b) hanging enclosure-groundwater is diverted laterally and vertically (downward) around the enclosure. Source: Pankow and Cherry, 1996.

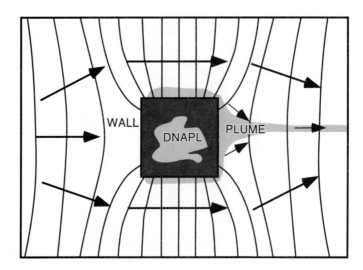

Figure 13.17 A plume of dissolved contamination downgradient of a source-zone enclosure. Dissolved contaminants diffuse through the walls to cause the plume. Source: Devlin and Parker, 1994.

A number of in situ reactive curtains are available for use in funnel and gate systems. These include in situ curtains that modify pH or Eh conditions, dissolve and cause precipitation of a mineral phase, remove materials from solution by sorption, supply nutrients that impact biodegradation, and remove materials via air sparging.

Plume management using in situ reactors has several advantages over traditional pump and treat systems. Most reactors do not require a continuous input of energy and will have fewer mechanical problems than a pumping system. Also, the reactor can be changed out as its capacity is consumed. Finally, discharge of treated water is unnecessary, which creates many regulatory problems with water disposal from pump and treat (Starr and Cherry, 1994).

A funnel and gate system includes cutoff walls and the gate. Issues such as the number of gates, the orientation with ground water flow, and the angle between the sides of the funnel are all important for design. The effect of the gate is related to the residence time and the reaction rate, which in turn depend on gate size and discharge. A number of these variables were analyzed in detail by Starr and Cherry (1994), where they simulated the steady state flow results of various geometries in a homogeneous setting typical of many unconfined sand aquifers.

Two conflicting factors are important in the design of a funnel and gate system. The discharge through a gate should be maximized so that the capture zone (Section 13.4.1) is as wide as possible, but the residence time for treatment should be as long as possible in the gate. These conflicting objectives must be balanced in the overall design in order to maintain high levels of attenuation. Effects of funnel width, gate width, gate hydraulic conductivity, funnel apex angle, orientation to regional flow direction, and retention time are all important

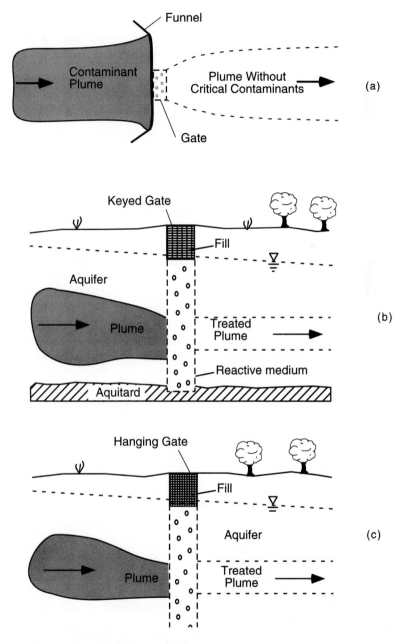

Figure 13.18 Schematic illustration of a funnel-and-gate system: (a) plan view; (b) cross-sectional view, keyed gate; and (C) cross-sectional view, hanging gate. Source: Pankow and Cherry, 1996.

aspects of the design. Starr and Cherry (1994) found that the width of the capture zone is proportional to the discharge through the gate, and the discharge can be increased by increasing the width, length, and K of the gate, or increasing the width of the funnel. Finally, residence times can be increased by making the gates longer in the direction of flow.

Treatment curtains have been recently suggested for the treatment of chlorinated solvents. Gilham and O'Hannesin (1994) describe some interesting laboratory and field studies of zero-valence iron. A substantial rate of abiotic degradation was observed for most of the chlorinated compounds tested, with iron serving as a source of electrons, although the actual degradation mechanisms are uncertain. This method may have limitations for sites with deep plumes or in fractured rock, leaving pump and treat as the only viable option for source or plume control.

13.8.2 Soil Flushing Enhancements

Enhanced pump and treat technologies include circulating steam or water containing chemical additives through a NAPL zone. Several agents can be introduced into a source zone in order to increase the mobility of NAPLs, or to increase the solubility of the NAPL or its dissolution products. The flow of water and chemicals is from injection wells or galleries to withdrawal wells where fluid is pumped into treatment units at the surface. Surfactants and cosolvents, such as ethanol or methanol, are the main types of additive chemicals used for remediation of NAPL sites (Brusseau et al., 1999). Figure 13.19 depicts a typical schematic for an enhanced soil flushing system contained in a NAPL zone at a field site.

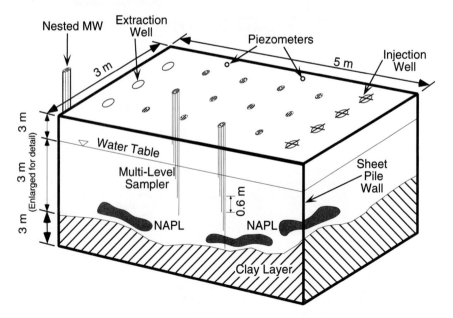

Figure 13.19 Soil Flushing, Hill AFB.

Although several researchers have reported promising results when using surfactants in laboratory trials, using surfactants to restore aquifers to drinking water conditions may be much less successful because of the presence of heterogeneities and low permeability zones in the subsurface (US EPA, 1992; Mackay and Cherry, 1989). A main impediment to the success of the process is inadequate contact of the flushing fluid with DNAPL, which might be trapped in low permeability zones. Another potential drawback to the use of these agents at DNAPL waste sites is that some of them rely on reducing the interfacial tension between the nonaqueous and aqueous phase. This can increase the potential that a residual DNAPL will mobilize downward in the saturated zone, thereby aggravating the remediation problem at a site. Finally, complete capture of the contaminated water and additives must be assured at the withdrawal wells.

Soil flushing still provides one of the only methods by which NAPLs can be solubilized or mobilized for source control. A recent text presents extensive details on the method along with results of numerous studies completed recently on the implementation and costing of surfactants and cosolvents for NAPL remediation (Lowe et al., 1999). These methods offer some promise if source zones are small and can be carefully enclosed with a barrier system to minimize any off site effects. Detailed studies of soil flushing technologies have recently been completed at Hill Air Force Base in Utah, and are described in a case study in Section 13.9.4.

Surfactant-enhanced subsurface remediation is an emerging technology for enhancing pump-and-treat remediation at complex sites. This enhancement can be due to micellar-enhanced aqueous concentrations or to reducing interfacial tensions, and ultra-high solubilization, realized along with middle phase microemulsion systems. This section briefly discusses fundamental surfactant factors critical to successful implementation of this technology (Sabatini et al., 1995; 1999).

Surfactants (surface-active-agents), otherwise known as soaps or detergents, are widely known for their cleansing characteristics, and for their foaming characteristics, which is a result of their accumulation at interfaces. Surfactants are ubiquitous, showing up in our shampoo, toothpaste, mouthwash, whipped cream, mayonnaise, and even in our cell walls. Surfactants are classified by their charge (cationic, anionic, nonionic), their origin (biosurfactants from plant or microbial production versus synthetic surfactants), and their regulatory status (direct or indirect food additive status, acceptable for discharge to wastewater treatment systems or for use in pesticide formulations). Surfactants are also characterized by their hydrophilic-lipophilic balance (HLB); surfactants with a high HLB value are water soluble while oil soluble surfactants have low HLB values.

Above a critical concentration surfactant monomers self-aggregate into micelles, and the surfactant concentration above which micelles form is known as the critical micelle concentration (CMC). The hydrophilic micelle exterior makes them highly soluble in water. Having a hydrophobic (oil like) interior, micelles are sometimes described as dispersed oil drops. When surfactant concentrations exceed the CMC, the incremental surfactant goes almost totally to formation of additional micelles. Surfactant enhanced subsurface remediation is often categorized into two systems; solubilization and mobilization.

Solubilization results from contaminant partitioning into the oil-like core of the micelle, thereby effectively increasing the aqueous solubility of the contaminant. With increasing solubility, the number of water flushes required to achieve a treatment goal decreases. At low surfactant concentrations (sub-CMC), the contaminant is present at its water solubility. Just above the CMC the solubility enhancement is minor, but increases as the surfactant concentration continues to increase above the CMC. The higher the surfactant concentration is above the CMC, the greater the number of micelles and thus the greater the solubility enhancement. Thus, to dramatically improve contaminant extraction, one should operate significantly above the CMC (an order of magnitude or more).

Mobilization refers to bulk oil displacement from the trapped residual oil (as opposed to simply enhancing the solubility). The displacement occurs due to significant reductions in interfacial tension between the NAPL and water phases. It is this interfacial tension that is largely responsible for the NAPL trapping (residual saturation) in the porous media. Significant reductions in the oil-water interfacial tension virtually eliminates the capillary forces which cause the oil to be trapped, thereby allowing the oil to readily flush out with the water. Thus, mobilization of the NAPL is maximized when ultra-low interfacial tensions are achieved.

The minimum interfacial tension occurs in middle phase microemulsion systems. By adjusting the surfactant system, it is possible to transition from normal micelles (aqueous phase), to middle phase microemulsions, to reverse micelles (oil phase inverted micelles). Careful system design will minimize the formation of mesophases in the transition region (e.g., liquid crystals), which may occur instead of the desired middle phase system. Traditionally alcohols have served this purpose while more recently hydrotropes (e.g., naphthalene sulfonates) and cosurfactants (e.g., a second surfactant) have been evaluated. Recent studies in surfactant-enhanced environmental remediation, along with prior research on surfactant enhanced oil recovery have helped advance environmental remediation technologies; (Sabatini et al., 1995; 1999).

Surfactant-enhanced subsurface remediation must be economically viable if it is to be widely implemented. In looking at two cases, Krebs-Yuill et al. (1995) determined that surfactant-enhanced remediation can be more economical than conventional pump-and-treat systems. The two most important conclusions were: (1) surfactant capital costs constitute the single largest cost in a surfactant-enhanced remediation process; and (2) decontamination of the surfactant-stream and surfactant reuse is critical. A subsequent economic study evaluated surfactant-enhanced pump-and-treat for residual zones of two acres or less (Krebbs-Yuill et al., 1996). It was shown that surfactant-enhanced remediation could be economically viable for all sites of less than one acre in size, and for 1-acre sites with residual saturation of 5% or less. For 1/4-acre sites with residual saturations of 5% or less, the cost of solubilization remediation was only 40% of the cost of pump-and-treat.

Given that surfactant reuse is crucial to the economic viability of the system, contaminant-surfactant separation and surfactant reuse needs to be a key consideration in the surfactant selection process. The ultimate goal is a surfactant system that is highly efficient in extracting the contaminant, has favorable phase behavior in the subsurface, and can efficiently be decontaminated and reused. Failure in any of these areas can render the system uneconomical and/or infeasible, illustrating the importance of an integrated design approach. More details can be found in Lowe et al., (1999).

Cosolvents generally rely on a mixture of water and alcohols, such as ethanol and pentanol, to enhance solubilization of NAPL contaminants. In this regard, alcohols are extremely miscible, and may partition into both water and NAPL phases, and create a mixture that enhances solubility of the contaminants present at a site. Some of the most successful cosolvent flushing experiments were completed at Hill AFB in Utah, funded under SERDP/EPA, and are reported in Sillan et al. (1998) and Brusseau et al. (1999). The alcohol mixtures are used to increase the solubility of NAPL compounds so that circulation of the water/chemical mixture through the contaminated zone will remove mass more quickly than conventional pump and treat systems using water alone. Rao et al. (1997) employed a mixture of 70% ethanol, 12% n-pentanol, and 18% water to remove a multicomponent LNAPL from the Hill AFB site. Section 13.9.4 presents more details on the soil flushing experiments performed at Hill AFB in nine side-by-side comparison tests of various remediation technologies.

13.8.3 Thermally Enhanced Recovery

The use of heat to increase the mobility of NAPLs in the subsurface has been established in enhanced oil recovery (EOR) used in the petroleum industry. Specific technologies include hot water flooding or the addition of steam to reduce NAPL density and NAPL viscosity. Use of steam will also condense volatile NAPLs in front of the steam front, thereby increasing NAPL saturation and mobility (EPA, 1992). Although these technologies have removed significant amounts of NAPL in both laboratory and field pilot tests, complete removal was not achieved. Steam injection was one of the technologies tested at the Hill AFB OU1 field site, with mixed results.

13.8.4 AATDF Description

The DoD Advanced Applied Technology Demonstration Facility for Environmental Technologies (AATDF) was established by the U.S. Department of Defense (DoD) following a national competition. The program was initiated on May 1, 1993, when the DoD awarded a $19.3 million grant to a university consortium of environmental research centers led by Rice University and headed by Dr. C. Herb Ward.

The mission of the DoD/AATDF was to enhance the development of innovative technologies for the DoD by bridging the gap between academic research and proven technologies. This was accomplished by selecting the most appropriate peer-reviewed technologies for quantitative demonstrations at DoD sites.

A consortium approach was selected to implement the DoD/AATDF program. The consortium represented a unique mixture of research and engineering talent and state-of-the-science and technology in the hazardous waste remediation field. Members of the consortium included: Stanford University, University of Texas, Rice University, Lamar University, University of Waterloo and Louisiana State University. The U.S. Army Engineer Waterways

Experiment Station managed the AATDF Grant for the DoD. The DoD/AATDF was supported by five state-of-the-art consulting engineering firms: Remediation Technologies, Inc.; Battelle Memorial Institute; Geo Trans., Inc.; Arcadis Geraghty and Miller, Inc.; and Groundwater Services, Inc., along with advisory groups from the DoD, industry, and commercialization interests.

To find the best environmental remediation ideas for further demonstration, a broadly disseminated announcement was sent out to researchers in academia, government, environmental engineering and consulting companies and industry. A total of 170 preproposals were received. A peer review process narrowed the number to 40. Requests were made for full proposals. Further peer review selection resulted in 12 projects for field demonstrations. The technologies chosen targeted the DoD's main problems of soil and ground water remediation. They were aimed at providing more cost-effective solutions to difficult problems, preferably using *in situ* remediation technologies.

The results of the AATDF are being developed as a series of ten monographs (Lewis Publishers) including:

- Surfactants and cosolvents for NAPL Remediation: A Technology Practices Manual (Lowe et al., 1999)
- Sequenced Reactive Barriers for Ground water Remediation
- Modular Remediation Testing System
- Phytoremediation of Hydrocarbon-Contaminated Soil
- Steam and Electro-Heating Remediation of Tight Soils
- Soil Vapor Extraction Using Radio Frequency Heating: Resource Manual and Technology Demonstration
- Laser-Induced Fluorescence for Subsurface Contaminant Monitoring
- Reuse of Surfactants and Cosolvents for NAPL Remediation
- Remediation of Firing-Range Impact Berms
- NAPL Removal: Surfactants, Foams, and Microemulsions

13.8.5 Practicality of Containing NAPLs

Containment alternatives for NAPL sites must address several potential contaminant migration pathways. First, the migration of mobile NAPL must be stopped by (1) pumping continuous-phase NAPL until it is all trapped in the aquifer as a residual phase; (2) operation of some type of NAPL interception system, such as a NAPL interceptor trench (Figure 13.5); and (3) constructing some type of physical barrier, such as a slurry wall (Figure 13.2). Second, the vertical and lateral migration of the dissolution products in the aquifer must be curtailed using hydraulic controls or physical barriers. In some cases, natural attenuation (from dispersion, dilution, chemical degradation, and biological degradation) will stop migration of dissolved contaminants, which may be sufficient to ensure that potential receptors are protected.

At some sites facing long containment periods, the use of physical barriers such as slurry walls or treatment curtains around source areas will be cost-effective additions to the overall remediation scheme. Containment options not only minimize the migration from NAPL source areas, but they provide valuable time during which other more efficient technologies (i.e., soil flushing with surfactants) may be developed and implemented within the source area. A number of case studies showing the use of selected remediation methods are presented below. These examples represent only a limited number of possibilities, and the reader is referred to the voluminous literature that exists on the topic of ground water remediation.

13.9 CASE STUDIES OF REMEDIATION

13.9.1 Case 1: The Pump and Treat System at U.S. Air Force Plant Number 44, Tucson, Arizona – Modeling Study

Trichloroethene (TCE), 1,1-dichloroethene (DCE), and chromium have been detected in the ground water beneath the U.S Air Force Plant No. 44 site in Tucson, Arizona. Activities at this facility include development, manufacturing, testing and maintenance of missile systems from 1952 until the present. The contaminated ground water is in an extensive alluvial aquifer that Tucson uses as its principal aquifer. The Tucson area is one of the largest metropolitan areas in the country that is totally dependent on ground water for drinking water supplies, and the TCE contamination is viewed as a threat to the integrity of the water supply system. The site is listed on the National Priority List and is known as the Tucson Airport Area Superfund Site.

In 1986, prior to the pump and treat remediation system begun at the site, the area of TCE contamination was approximately 5 mi long and 1.6 mi wide. Contours of the dissolved TCE plume from measurements taken in 1986 and are shown in Figure 13.20. The maximum measured TCE concentration in 1986 was 2.7 mg/L, although concentrations as high as 15.9 ppm have been observed. The cleanup standard for TCE in this case is the drinking water standard of 5 µg/L.

TCE is a halogenated aliphatic organic compound that is typically used as an industrial cleaning solvent. In addition, reductive dehalogenation through natural biodegradation may result in production of vinyl chloride, which is a known carcinogen. TCE is denser than water, has low viscosity, is sparingly soluble in water and is fairly volatile. It has a relatively low octanol-water partition coefficient, which means that its movement in the aqueous phase is not retarded to a great degree by the organic materials in the aquifer.

Site Characterization. Results of a subsurface investigation indicate that the subsurface can be divided into four hydrogeologic units:

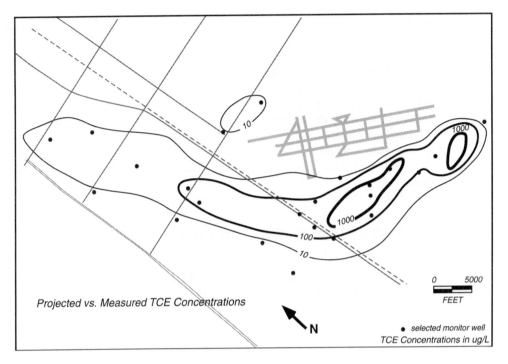

Figure 13.20 TCE Plume, Hughes Plant 44; 1986.

1. An unsaturated zone that extends from the ground surface to the water table, which is at a depth of 110 ft to 130 ft

2. An upper zone extending to a depth of 180 ft to 220 ft

3. An aquitard consisting of 100 ft to 150 ft of low permeability clay

4. A lower zone of unknown thickness

The lower portion of the unsaturated zone consists of a laterally extensive layer of relatively low permeability perching clay, which is 20 ft to 40 ft thick and which partially confines the upper aquifer. The unsaturated, upper and lower zones consist of layers of relatively low conductivity clays and sandy clays, alternating with quite permeable sand and gravel units.

Hydraulic conductivity measurements were obtained in 12 locations in the immediate vicinity of current surface impoundments from pump test data. These data indicate that hydraulic conductivity ranges from 1.5×10^{-4} ft/s to 3.1×10^{-3} ft/s for the upper zone aquifer. For clean sands and gravels, porosity measurements of 26% to 34% have been obtained for this formation. The background hydraulic gradient, calculated from water table elevation data, is estimated to be 0.006 in the north-northwesterly direction. Ground water velocity at the site ranges from 250 to 800 ft/yr, based on an average porosity value of 25%.

Potential sources of subsurface contamination at the site include pits, ponds, trenches, and drainage ditches in which on-site disposal of solvents, wastewater, and sludge is believed to have occurred from approximately 1952 through 1977. Wastes generated during this time period include TCE, paint sludge, acids, cyanides, and alcohols. For the purpose of demonstrating pump and treat remediation in this case study, TCE is considered the contaminant of interest.

Remediation by Pump and Treat. A ground water pump and treat remediation system began operation at the site in April 1987. The pump and treat system consists of 17 extraction wells and 13 recharge wells, and the above-ground treatment plant, which utilizes ion exchange followed by air stripping, vapor phase activated carbon and pressure sand filtration. As one of the largest pump and treat systems in the United States, it was designed to treat 5000 gpm of extracted ground water. Water level elevation and contamination concentration data for the approximately 40 monitoring wells are collected monthly. The location of the extraction, recharge, and monitoring wells are shown in Figure 13.21.

Monthly concentration measurements taken at the extraction and monitoring wells are used to evaluate the remediation process with respect to TCE removal. Measured TCE plumes were contoured yearly, and as can be seen from Figure 13.22, the plume area does

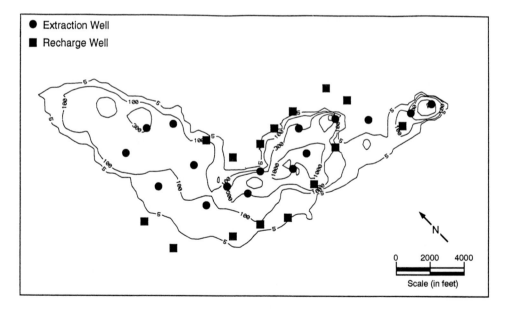

Figure 13.21 Locations of recharge and extraction wells at the Plant 44 site. Source: Burgess, 1993.

not appear to shrink a great deal through the five-year pumping period. However, concentrations do decrease through this period. Dissolved mass of the contaminated plumes may be calculated by integrating concentration contours across the area of the plume, and adjusting for porosity (Figure 13.22). The total TCE mass removed via pumping is approximately 6000 kg over 5 years. The concentration of dissolved TCE in the extracted ground water decreases during remediation, particularly in those wells with initially high TCE concentrations. In the majority of cases, the TCE concentration appears to level out between 3 and 5 years.

Modeling of the Pump and Treat System. The pump and treat system, as it applies to the Tucson site, was evaluated further through modeling with the BIOPLUME II model for transport in the aqueous phase (Burgess et al., 1993). All advection and dispersion were assumed to take place in the high permeability sand and gravel layers, which were assumed continuous in the upper zone. Based on the site characteristics and modeling results, hydraulic conductivities were found to range from 2.39×10^{-4} to 5.55×10^{-3} ft/s.

The initial distribution of potentiometric ground water elevation was determined by contouring water table elevation measurements from December 1986. The model was calibrated by varying the hydraulic conductivity as well as the model boundaries in order to obtain the water table as it existed prior to extraction. Zones of conductivity were chosen based on the shape of the water table and matched the initial field measurements well. The root mean squared (RMS) error of the modeled versus the actual potentiometric head distribution was used to determine the deviation of the simulated run from the actual data. For the flow calibration, the calculated RMS error was 4.25% (a value of less than 10-15% is desirable). The model was validated by modeling the potentiometric elevation after approximately five years of pumping and injection. The RMS error for the simulation versus actual December 1991 measurements was 7.94%, based on comparison of values at 68 locations.

The TCE plume as it appeared in December 1986 is shown as Figure 13.20. The objective of the transport calibration was to match the TCE plume as it appeared in 1986 prior to remediation startup using source locations, flowrates, and TCE concentrations. Source infiltration rates used varied from 0.001 to 0.003 cfs, and TCE concentrations of the infiltrating water varied from 400 to 10,000 ppb. The duration of source infiltration was assumed to be 20 years. Calibration is determined based on comparison of TCE concentrations at monitoring locations as well as plume area and dissolved mass. The simulated plume compares well visually with the 1986 plume. The chemical mass balance (CMB) error for the simulation, which is calculated based upon the difference between the change in dissolved mass inflow minus outflow, is 2.26% after taking into account the mass that moves beyond the model boundary during simulation. (A CMB error of < 5% is desirable).

Results of the Tucson Model. To validate the transport calibration, the December 1986 plume was modeled using the pumping and injection pattern as in the actual remediation operation. All the other aquifer parameters remained the same as in the calibration to pumped water table with the exception of the addition of the initial TCE concentration array.

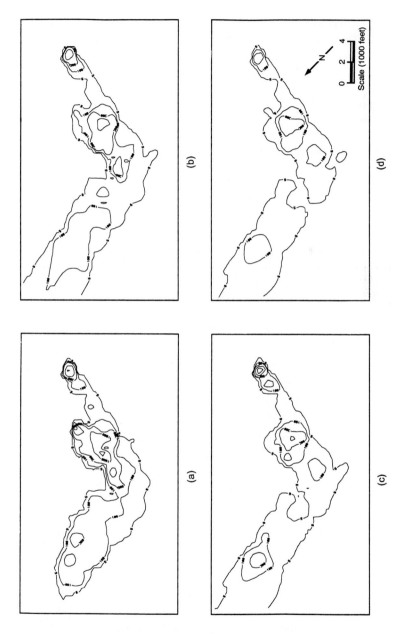

Figure 13.22 TCE plumes during remediation at the Plant 44 site, December 1986 to December 1991. Measured TCE concentrations for (a) December 1986 (ppb), (b) December 1988 (ppb), (c) December 1990 (ppb), and (d) December 1991 (ppb). Source: Burgess, 1993.

The simulation was run for five years in an attempt to predict the TCE plume in December 1991. The simulated plume compared well to the actual remediation. However, the simulated plume appeared to decrease more in area than the actual plume, a fact that may be attributed to the contouring method used. CMB errors for the remediation runs range from 0.52% to 2.36%. Overall, the model predicts that plume remediation is achieved in about 50 years, assuming that NAPLs are not a major factor at this site, which remains for further investigation (Burgess et al., 1993).

13.9.2 Case 2: Conceptual Design For a DNAPL Superfund Site

The presence of dense nonaqueous phase liquids (DNAPL) can greatly complicate ground water remediation efforts due to the downward migration of these heavy oils within an aquifer system and the difficulty of extracting DNAPL using conventional pumping methods. These problems were observed at the Motco Superfund Site near Houston, Texas, where DNAPL is present in a shallow surficial aquifer. To develop an effective scheme for DNAPL management, the aquifer remediation program for this site includes these elements (Connor et al., 1989):

- Detailed stratigraphic interpretation of the aquifer to delineate the zone of DNAPL accumulation

- A pilot recovery test to determine the effectiveness of enhanced oil recovery technologies (EOR) for mobilizing DNAPL

- A combined modeling and field study to evaluate the effect of DNAPL dissolution on future remediation activities at the site

- A conceptual remedial design for extracting mobile DNAPL and for managing residual DNAPL and DNAPL dissolution products

Given the difficulty of achieving conventional ground water clean-up standards in DNAPL-affected portions of an aquifer, an alternative approach for the management of DNAPL sites is proposed below. This approach is based on restoration of ground water quality in areas that are considered to be free of DNAPL as well as long-term containment of DNAPL and DNAPL dissolution products in zones where DNAPL presence is either confirmed or suspected based on evaluation of site data.

Delineation of DNAPL Zones. The Motco Site is a former reclamation facility that operated in the vicinity of La Marque, Texas, during the period of 1958 to 1968. Reclamation efforts involved collection and reprocessing of petrochemical residues within an 11-acre system of unlined pits. Hydrogeologic investigations have shown this area to be underlain by a surface deposit of interbedded sands, silts, and clays designated the Transmissive Zone. The Transmissive Zone, extending from the ground surface to a depth of approximately 50 ft. below grade, is in turn underlain by a stiff, high-plasticity clay layer, termed

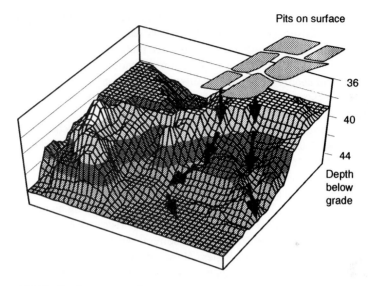

Figure 13.23 Surface map of top of clay unit, showing movement of DNAPLs down topographic valleys in TZ-3 unit.

the UC-1 Clay. DNAPL accumulations have been observed in wells screened in low spots in the shallow transmissive zone immediately atop the underlying clay stratum (see Figure 13.23).

To map the DNAPL zone, 60 boring and well logs at the site were supplemented with an additional 73 cone penetrometer logs (a geotechnical tool) to generate a continuous and laterally extensive stratigraphic record of the shallow aquifer system. The data were used to develop detailed topographic maps of the base of the transmissive zone to find DNAPL accumulation, select locations for soil borings to confirm the presence of DNAPL pools atop this clay surface, and to design a pilot test for recovery of DNAPL and affected ground water. Results of this investigation showed DNAPL to be moving through fractures and other secondary porosity features of the silt stratum, in general accordance with the base topography of the unit.

DNAPL Recovery Pilot Test. To evaluate the feasibility of pumped withdrawal of DNAPL fluids, a pilot test was conducted at the Motco Site in 1989 to compare three recovery technologies: pumping, water-flooding, and vacuum-enhanced recovery. To test the performance of pumping alone, a recovery well was installed in a zone of DNAPL accumulation and equipped with a submersible, positive displacement pump. For the vacuum-enhanced pumping scheme, the downhole pump was augmented by a wellbore vacuum, increasing the available drawdown and maximum yield of the recovery well. For the water-flooding scheme, a freshwater injection well was operated at a distance of 100 ft from a pumping well to increase the hydraulic gradient. A three-week testing program demonstrated that some DNAPL could be removed by pumping alone, but that waterflooding and vacuum-enhanced recovery greatly increased recovery rates.

Results of the pilot test demonstrated that mobile DNAPL could be recovered from the transmissive strata by means of ground water pumping. As evidenced by DNAPL accumulation within nearby observation wells during recovery well operation, hydraulic gradients 40 to 60 times greater than normal are capable of overwhelming density forces and inducing DNAPL flow within the aquifer.

Test results indicate that any of the three pumping schemes should prove effective for ground water/DNAPL recovery from the transmissive zone. However, due to improved well yield and higher induced flow gradients, vacuum-enhanced pumping and water flooding offer significant advantages in terms of the rate and potential degree of DNAPL removal. Over a 100% increase in DNAPL production rate was observed when both enhancements were used (50 - 100 gal DNAPL/day vs. 25-50 gal/day with pumping alone).

DNAPL Dissolution Study. The pilot recovery test demonstrated that the mobile fraction of the DNAPL fluids could be removed from the water-bearing stratum using enhanced oil recovery technologies. However, a significant percentage of the DNAPL mass would remain immobilized within the aquifer matrix, possibly acting as a continued source of organic constituent release to ground water due to dissolution of soluble DNAPL components.

To quantify the effect of DNAPL dissolution on the aquifer remediation program now being planned for the Motco Site, a modeling study and in-situ field test were designed to simulate the performance of the full-scale ground water recovery system. The modeling study employed an existing dissolution relationship (Borden and Kao, 1989) which assumed equilibrium partitioning of soluble organics between water and DNAPL. On the basis of this analysis, a field test was designed to simulate the actual hydraulic conditions that might be expected during a full-scale pumping and waterflooding program for DNAPL-affected areas. One injection well and one production well, spaced 11 feet apart, were used to flush fresh water through the test area during the 30-day test period. As the test progressed, over 11,000 gallons of fresh water were drawn through the test area, resulting in significant reductions in the concentrations of key organic constituents (i.e., > 85%, see Figure 13.24).

At this site, the field dissolution test showed that approximately 50 to 100 pore volumes of fresh water may be required to achieve the current ground water recovery standards (ranging from 2 to 50 mg/L for key indicator constituents in the Class III saline aquifer) in DNAPL-affected areas. These empirical results are in good agreement with modeling predictions, which indicated that roughly a 50 pore-volume flush would be required to adequately reduce dissolution products from the residual DNAPL. As this level of flushing is probably impracticable to achieve at the site, a long-term containment system was specified to protect human health and the environment (Newell et al., 1991).

Long-Term Containment Modeling Study. To assist in the design of a long-term containment system for dissolved constituents at the Motco Site, a modeling study was conducted using the MODFLOW ground water model. To simulate the various transmissive zones and clays at the site, a 3-D model consisting of four different layers was created.

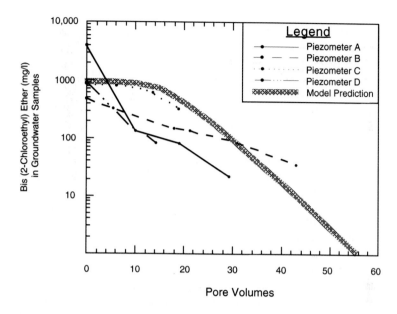

Figure 13.24 Concentration of indicator parameter versus pore volumes flushed during DNAPL dissolution pilot test.

Transmissivity and vertical conductance values were assigned to the 9200 finite difference cells using data from pump tests, slug tests, soil borings, and cone penetrometer surveys. To ensure accurate simulations, the model was calibrated using data from natural flow conditions and from the DNAPL recovery test.

Ground water pumping rates required to achieve hydraulic control of the affected areas at the site were determined for three containment system designs: (1) existing conditions, (2) partial enclosure of affected areas, (3) complete enclosure of affected areas. The existing conditions include a 900-ft long slurry wall currently in place along one side of the site. Complete enclosure of affected areas with a slurry wall reduces pumping rates required to achieve hydraulic control by approximately 10 fold, from 2.0–3.0 gpm to 0.3–0.6 gpm. Lower pumping rates will reduce the cost of treating recovered ground water, and may lead to significant cost savings during operation of the long-term containment system.

13.9.3 Case 3: Modeling a Soil Vapor Extraction Operation at Hill AFB, Utah Using VENT3D

VENT3D, a 3-D vapor flow and multicomponent transport model described in Chapter 9, was used to simulate the performance of a previously reported SVE operation at a jet (JP-4) fuel contaminated site at Hill Air Force Base, Utah, (DePaoli, 1991). Field data were used to obtain the input parameters needed to describe the subsurface air flow and contaminant removal rate. The applicability of the model to this field site is demonstrated by comparing model predictions to field data. The model was then used in a predictive mode to describe the depletion of JP-4 by volatilization during the full-scale vapor extraction operation, and to predict the time frame within which cleanup goals could be achieved. This modeling effort also demonstrates the use of more sophisticated flow and transport models for describing the behavior of contaminants at field sites (El-Beshry et al., 1998; El-Beshry et al., 1999).

VENT3D (Benson, 1994), is a 3-D, finite-difference code for simulating vapor flow and transport of a multi-component mixture. The model computes the movement of compounds in the vapor phase and keeps track of the phase distribution of each compound in the other three phases, NAPL, dissolved, and sorbed using equilibrium partitioning. The model domain is divided into blocks, and each block may be given unique properties such as permeability or contaminant concentrations. Both extraction and injection wells can be simulated. Contaminant components can be present in different proportions and have different physico-chemical properties.

The site selected for this study was a fuel storage area at Hill Air Force Base (HAFB), Utah, where 102,000 L (27,000 gal = 76,500 kg) of jet fuel (JP-4) were spilled onto the ground in 1985, after an automatic filling system malfunctioned and storage tanks overflowed. A field study of in-situ soil venting was performed at Hill AFB by Oak Ridge National Laboratory (ORNL) (DePaoli et al., 1991). A total mass of 48,000 Kg was removed from the site at the end of the 10-months SVE operation. A number of pilot tests and a full-scale SVE study were carried out at the site to demonstrate the clean-up efficiencies attainable using soil venting for remediation of fuel contaminated sites. The vent system consisted of 15 vertical vents in the main contaminated area of the site.

Air permeability was appropriately estimated at 40 darcys for the horizontal permeability and 1 darcy for the vertical permeability, using a software called GASSOLVE (Falta, 1996) and data from the pilot tests conducted at the site. The initial contaminant mass was the only parameter that had to be adjusted to simulate contaminant removals during the early months of the full-scale study. The initial contaminant mass was estimated at 76,500 kg which is equal to the total spill mass. The contaminant distribution followed hydrocarbon concentrations from soil cores. The accuracy of model predictions was tested by simulating the full-scale venting operation using the estimated input parameters. VENT3D predictions were compared with observed data measured during the 10-months venting operation.

Different well configurations with different extraction rates operated during the study. The system was shutdown and restarted several times. Figures 13.25a and 13.25b show the depth averaged vacuum calculated by VENT3D and measured by ORNL from one of the flow tests. It is observed that vacuum values and contour lines are very close, except at the extraction well, where the calculated vacuum is almost half of the measured value. Overall, the model was able to adequately simulate the gas flow field based on the independently determined permeabilities.

Figure 13.26 is a plot of the observed versus calculated mass removals using 76,500 kg as the total initial contaminant mass and subdividing the fuel mixture into 10 compo-

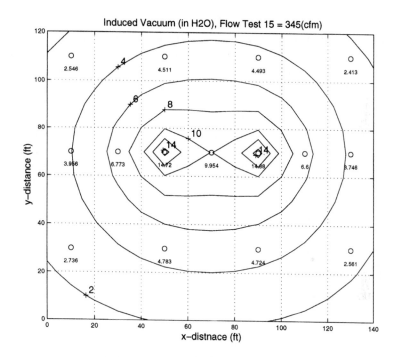

Figure 13.25a VENT3D Depth Averaged Vacuum (in H_2O), Flow Test 15.

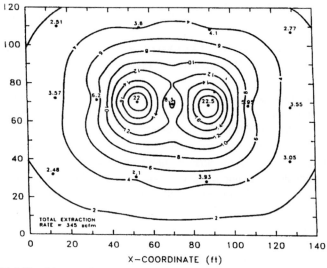

Figure 13.25b Observed Depth Averaged Vacuum (in H_2O), Flow Test 15.

nents. More details of how the field site was modeled are reported in El-Beshry et al. (1998). The initial and final (at the end of the SVE study) contaminant concentration in soil and the initial and final soil gas concentrations as predicted by VENT3D compared well.

One of the significant features of VENT3D is that it can simulate a multicomponent mixture using properties for each constituent. This causes a dilemma for fuel contamination because fuels are made up of too many compounds to account for each separately. In this study, the JP-4 was represented by 10 classes of compounds (C_5-C_{15}), categorized according to the number of carbon atoms. Each class is represented by specific physicochemical properties such as molecular weight, boiling point, vapor pressure, solubility, and octanol/water partition coefficient. Each class was represented by a single compound whose vapor pressure was the median of those in that class. The model was used to examine the effect of changes in chemical composition of jet fuel (JP-4) due to volatilization.

During vapor extraction the composition of the mixture changes, that is, the mixture loses the more volatile compounds at the beginning of the process, thus it becomes more concentrated in the less volatile components and less rich in the more volatile components. Figure 13.27 shows the changes in mass fractions of the classes in the JP-4 fuel mixture during the length of the SVE study as computed by VENT3D. The graph indicates that depletion of lighter compounds (lower carbon number) takes place while the mass fraction of the higher carbon number compounds increase because they volatilize in relatively lesser, and even insignificant, quantities.

VENT3D was successful in simulating the behavior of the SVE system during the 10-month field study. Therefore, the model was used in a predictive manner to evaluate the total time to achieve complete cleanup of the NAPL. After 10 months of operation (October 1989), actual measurements and VENT3D predictions indicated that 64% of the contamination at the site was removed, which was close to the actual removals.

13.9.4 Case 4: Surfactants and Cosolvents For Enhanced NAPL Removal at Hill AFB

Introduction. In a study funded by SERDP and USEPA, nine enhanced aquifer remediation technologies were demonstrated side-by-side at a chemical disposal pit (CDP) site at Hill Air Force Base in Utah. The demonstrations were performed inside 3 x 5 m cells, isolated from the surrounding shallow aquifer by steel sheet piling. The site was originally contaminated with an LNAPL mixture of chlorinated solvents and fuel hydrocarbons. The technologies demonstrated manipulated the solubility, mobility, and volatility of the contaminants in order to enhance the aquifer remediation over a standard "pump-and-treat" system. About 10,000 samples per cell were collected as part of tracer tests, soil flushing demonstrations, and routine characterization efforts.

The purpose of the studies was to evaluate innovative technologies for the removal of non-aqueous phase liquids (NAPL) from the saturated and, in some cases, the unsaturated

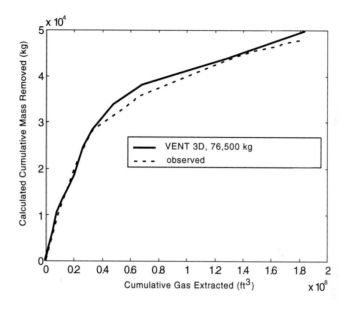

Figure 13.26 Observed and VENT3D Calculated Mass Removals during Full Scale Study at Hill AFB, Utah.

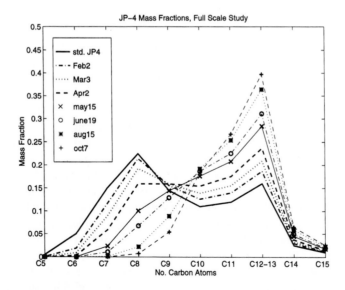

Figure 13.27 Changes in mass fractions of the different components in the JP-4 fuel mixture during the SVE study.

zone. Hill AFB's OU 1 site was chosen because all nine technologies could be demonstrated side-by-side at the location, with similar hydrogeology at a single contaminated site.

The technologies evaluated at Hill AFB included:

- air sparging/soil vapor extraction (Michigan Technological University)
- in-well aeration (University of Arizona)
- cosolvent mobilization (Clemson University)
- complexing sugar flush (University of Arizona)
- surfactant solubilization (University of Oklahoma)
- middle-phase microemulsion (University of Oklahoma)
- steam injection (Tyndall Air Force Base)
- single-phase microemulsion (University of Florida) [AATDF /EPA]
- cosolvent solubilization (University of Florida, 1995)

Site Background. The portion of the base selected for the treatability studies is known as Operable Unit 1 (OU 1), and is located near the northeastern boundary of Hill AFB. The study test cells are adjacent to chemical disposal pits 1 and 2, which had industrial liquid waste disposal sites in operation from 1952 through 1973. Wastes consisted mostly of principally petroleum hydrocarbons and spent solvents, which were periodically burned at the site.

Prior to the beginning of the enhanced remediation demonstrations at Hill AFB, Montgomery Watson, Inc. (1995, 1996) had performed site characterization and evaluation for the remedial investigation. The work included installing monitoring wells, collecting soil cores, performing slug tests, and characterizing the geology of the area. The sedimentary formation which contains the shallow aquifer on base consist of two sedimentary units, an upper sand and gravel unit and an intermediate silty clay.

The saturated portion of the upper sand and gravel phreatic aquifer has a horizontal hydraulic conductivity ranging from 10^{-1} to 10^{-2} cm/sec based on aquifer test data, and from 10^{-2} to 10^{-5} cm/sec based on slug test data. The horizontal hydraulic conductivity of the underlying clay unit ranges from 10^{-4} to 10^{-5} cm/sec based on slug test data

Chlorinated solvents, chlorinated benzenes, pesticides, PCBs, dioxins, and furans have been detected in the LNAPL associated with the chemical disposal pits. The VOC detected at the highest concentration and with the widest distribution is 1,2-DCE. The apparent free phase LNAPL thickness based on monitoring well observations ranges from 0 to 0.3 meters in the area of the proposed treatability studies. This thickness does not include residual LNAPL. High concentrations of fuel hydrocarbons and chlorinated hydrocarbons in the were also found in the subsurface soils at the CDPs.

Test Cell Operation. Each of the nine treatability study test cells has a similar layout of injection and extraction wells, multilevel ground water samplers, piezometers, and monitoring wells. A schematic of the standard test cell is shown in Figure 13.19. During the flushing demonstrations, there was an influent tank farm (consisting of three 75,000 L tanks and three 23,000 L tanks), and an effluent tank farm (consisting of eight 75,000 L tanks and two 23,000 L tanks), along with two 23,000 L water supply tanks and related plumbing. This standard layout was used in all test cells to allow the pre- and post-treatment tracer test configurations. The multilevel samplers were used during the tracer tests and flushing studies to collect ground water and soil gas samples for analysis. The results were used to monitor flow characteristics and composition of the fluids of the tests and to adjust the treatment process, if necessary. Soil samples were collected at selected MLS locations to characterize the pretreatment soil conditions in the test cell.

Test Cell Characterization. The performance of the innovative technologies is evaluated based on the change in the amount of NAPL mass within each of the test cells, and on the amount of mass remaining in the cell after treatment. If properly designed, partitioning tracer studies can give an estimate of the distribution of NAPL within a test cell, as well as the total mass in the cell (Jin et al., 1994). Tracer studies as well as soil borings were performed to estimate the total mass of NAPL pre- and post-remediation and to evaluate the performance of each remediation technology.

Tracer Tests. Partitioning tracer tests (PTTs) were performed in all nine test cells before and after the technology demonstrations. These tests were designed to determine the spatial distribution and the total volume of NAPL within each cell. Laboratory tests were used to evaluate several tracers for use in the field tests, including: ethanol, methanol, hexanol, bromide, 2,2-dimethyl-3-pentanol, n-pentanol, and 6-methyl-2-heptanol.

During the partitioning tracer test, a small volume of solution containing low concentrations of both conservative and partitioning tracers was pumped through the cell. The conservative tracer will pass through the system unaffected by the NAPL content of the cell. The partitioning tracers will partition into the NAPL phase when they encounter it, and partition back out of the NAPL after the main mass of the tracer pulse has passed, resulting in a chromatographic separation between the partitioning and conservative tracers. This chromatographic separation is reflected in concentration breakthrough curves (BTCs) developed for the various sampling points in each cell, and allows NAPL saturations to be computed for each area of the cell (Jin et al., 1994)

Breakthrough curves for the reactive tracers were used to estimate the volume and spatial distribution of NAPL in each test cell. A minimum of three methods are used to calculate the NAPL distribution. First, the integrated mass of NAPL in the swept volume is calculated by the method of moments. Second, an inversion technique is used with a solution to the 1-D advection–dispersion equation utilizing a method of superposition to account for spatial variability along the flow path. The third method will be an inversion technique that incorporates the code developed by Gary Pope at the University of Texas. Calculations can be made for each of the MLS points and the extraction well.

Results. A surfactant solubilization and a surfactant mobilization test were conducted in two different cells at HAFB OU1 by the University of Oklahoma. In the solubilization cell, 10 pore volumes of 4.3 wt% Dowfax 8390 were flushed through the cell. Results indicated that greater than 95% recovery of the surfactant was achieved, along with removal of roughly 50% of the contaminant (obviously additional flushing would have removed more contaminant, but this was the pre-established number of pore volumes to be conducted). The Dowfax 8390 proved to be a very robust system, although not as efficient as the middle phase system (as expected) (Sabatini et al., 1999).

In the mobilization cell a surfactant system of 2.2 wt% AOT, 2.1 wt% Tween 80, and 0.43 wt% calcium chloride was used. In this case 6.6 pore volumes of surfactant removed roughly 85% to 90% of the contaminant. The improved elution was obvious, both visually and by measured concentrations. While this system was more efficient, it required much higher operator skill to both design and implement, especially for this highly hydrophobic oil. At the same time surfactant-enhanced solubilization was much more efficient than water alone, as observed from the pre- and post-surfactant injection periods. For additional details on this field test, refer to Knox et al. (1999).

During the cosolvent flushing tests performed by the University of Florida, a mixture of water and two alcohols was used, including ethanol and n-pentanol to enhance solubiliza-tion. The 10-day cosolvent flood was followed by a 20-day period of water flushing, and one pore volume per day (3.1 L/min) was maintained throughout the tests (Rao et al., 1997; Sillan et al., 1998). Because of more than 60 sampling locations within each cell, a great deal was learned about the distribution of NAPL saturation as cosolvents were flushed through the cell. Both core analyses and pre- and post-partitioning tracer tests were used to evaluate the changes in NAPL saturations during the test. Results were encouraging after the 10-day flush, with typical removal values in the range of 75% to 85%. More details on simi-lar tests in the general literature are summarized in Lowe et al. (1999). Overall, the soil flushing methods show promise for small NAPL source areas, but economic considerations may preclude their use for larger areas. Preliminary results from several of the test cells at

TABLE 13.1   Mass Removal Reported in Hill AFB Field demonstra-tions.

Project	Cell Size	Target Depth	Reported Mass Recovered[a]	Reported Fraction of Initial Mass Recovered[a]
Hill AFB, Utah- Ethanol-OU 1	3 by 5 m	4.6 to 6.1 bgs	Approx. 350 liters of NAPL	>85% Cell-Wide Basis:> 95% in the Central Flood Zone: > 75% in Bottom 0.5 m
Hill AFB, Utah OU 1-Cosolvent Mobilization -Cell No.3	3 by 5 m	5 to 9 m bgs	Not known at this time	Preliminary Estimate 80 to 90% Based on Soil Cores
Hill AFB, Utah- OU 1, Solubilization- Cell No. 5	3 by 5 m	5 to 9 m bgs	Not known at this time	45-55%
Hill AFB, Utah- OU 1, Mobilization- Cell No. 6	4 by 5 m	6 to 9 m bgs	Not known at this time	85-95%
Hill AFB, Utah - OU 1 Surfactant with Cosolvent-Cell No. 8	3 by 5 m	4.9 to 7.9 m bgs	Approx. 350 liters	72% Based on Partitioning Tracer Testing, 64 to 96% Based on Soil Cores
Hill AFB, Utah - OU 2 Micellar Flood	6 by 9 m (1 PV =15,000 gallons)	8 to 15 m bgs	511 gallons (By Partitioning Interwell Tracer Tests)	99% (By Partitioning Interwell Tracer Tests)
Hill AFB, Utah - OU 2 Foam Flood	6 to 10 m	12 to 14 m bgs	36.5 gallons of DNAPL	Approximately 90%

[a] Methods for mass estimates include soil cores, concentrations in produced fluids, and partitioning tracer tests.

Hill AFB are contained in the ACS publication edited by Brusseau et al. (1999). A brief summary of reported mass removals at Hill AFB is shown in Table 13.1.

SUMMARY

Chapter 13 reviews the important concepts of aquifer remediation as applied to contaminated hazardous-waste sites. Many of the flow and transport issues discussed in previous chapters are used here. Various methods of containment, hydraulic control, pump and treat, bioremediation, soil vapor extraction, and NAPL control are presented in detail, along with four complete case studies from the authors' experiences. Modern approaches to site remediation include consideration of two related but distinct problems: (1) source control near the area of greatest contamination and (2) plume control either at some downgradient boundary or for removal of soluble components. Figure 13.1 depicts several of the methods available for site cleanup; earlier pump-and-treat systems for soluble plume removal are being combined with more intensive methods near source areas. Finally, hazardous-waste site remediation is a rapidly evolving field with new technologies merging rapidly. New remediation approaches include funnel and gate systems, treatment walls, air sparging, surfactant flushing, and cosolvent flushing for NAPLs removal. Due to the performance problems of original pump-and-treat systems, new and combined remediation methods are currently being tested at a number of field sites. It is clear that no single method will emerge as superior, due to the heterogeneous nature of field sites, the complexity of the contaminants involved, the NAPL issue, and the expense involved in cleaning up a site.

REFERENCES

Abdul, A. S., "A New Pumping Strategy for Petroleum Product Recovery from Contaminated Hydrogeologic Systems: Laboratory and Field Evaluations," *Ground Water Monitoring Rev.* XIII, 105-114, 1992.

Ahlfeld, D., A. Dahami, E. Hill, J. Lin, and J. Wei, "Laboratory Study of Air Sparging: Air Flow Visualization," *Ground Water Monitoring and Remediation*, 4, 115-126, 1993.

Anastos, G. J., P. J. Marks, M. H. Corbin, and M. F. Coia, "Task 11. In Situ Air Stripping of Soils, Pilot Study, Final Report," Report No. AMXTH-TE-TR-85026. U.S. Army Toxic & Hazardous Material Agency. Aberdeen Proving Grounds. Edgewood, MD, 88 pp., 1985.

Andersen, M. P., "Movement of Contaminants in Groundwater: Groundwater Transport —Advection and Dispersion," *Studies in Geophysics, Groundwater Contamination*, National Academy Press, Washington, D.C., pp. 37-45, 1984.

Annable, M. D.; P. S. C. Rao, K. Hatfield, K.; W. D. Graham, A. L. Wood, *Second Tracer Workshop,* University of Texas, Austin, November 1994.

Ayres, J. E., D. C. Lager, and M. J. Barvenik, "The First EPA Superfund Cutoff Wall: Design and Specifications," *3rd Natl. Symp. on Aquifer Restoration and Ground Water Monitoring*, NWWA, Columbus, OH, p. 13, 1983.

Baehr, A. L., G. E. Hoag, and M. C. Marley, "Removing Volatile Contaminants from the Unsaturated Zone by Inducing Advective Air-Phase Transport," *Contaminant Hydrology,* 4, 1-26, 1989.

Bass, D., and R. Brown, "Air Sparging Case Study Data Base Update," *First International Symposium on In Situ Air Sparging for Site Remediation,* Las Vegas, Nevada, October 26-27, 1996.

Batchelder, G. V., W. A. Panzeri, and H. T. Phillips. "Soil Ventilation for the Removal Of Adsorbed Liquid Hydrocarbons in the Subsurface," *Petroleum Hydrocarbons and Organic Chemicals in Ground Water,* NWWA, Dublin, OH, pp. 672-688, 1986.

Bedient, P. B., G. P. Long, and H. S. Rifai, "Modeling Natural Biodegradation with BIOPLUME II," *5th International Conference, Solving Ground Water Problems with Models,* Dallas, Texas, pp. 699-714, February 11-13, 1992.

Bedient, P. B., A. W. Holder, C. G. Enfield and A. L. Wood, "Field Testing of Innovative Subsurface Remediation and Characterization Technologies," *American Chemical Society Symposium Series Volume Based on Field Testing of Physical, Chemical, and Characterization Technologies,* Brusseau, M., et al., Eds., in press, 1999.

Bennedsen, M. B., J. P. Scott, and J. D. Hartley. "Use of Vapor Extraction Systems for In Situ Removal of Volatile Organic Compounds from Soil." *National Conference on Hazardous Wastes and Hazardous Materials,* HMCRI, pp. 92-95, 1985.

Benson, D., "User's Manual to VENT3D: A Three-Dimensional Multi-Compound, Multi-Phase Partitioning Vapor Transport Model," 1994.

Blake, S. B., and R. W. Lewis, "Underground Oil Recovery," *Proceedings,* Second National Symposium on Aquifer Restoration and Ground Water Monitoring, D. M. Nielson, ed., NWWA, Dublin, OH, pp. 69-75, 1982.

Borden, R. C., P. B. Bedient, and J. T. Wilson, "Numerical Model of Organics Transport and Biodegradation from a UST Release," Seventh Annual Meeting, Society of Environmental Toxicology and Chemistry (SETAC), Alexandria, VA, November 2-5, 1986.

Borden, R. C., and C. Kao, "Water Flushing or Trapped Residual Hydrocarbon: Mathematical Model Development and Laboratory Validation," *Petroleum Hydrocarbons and Organic Chemicals in Ground Water,* NWWA, 175-189, Houston, TX, 1989.

Brusseau, Mark M., M. Annable, J. Gierke and D. Sabatini, Eds., *Innovative Subsurface Remediation: Field Testing of Physical, Chemical and Characterization Technologies,* ACS Symposium Series, in press, 1999.

Burgess, K. S., H. S. Rifai, and P. B. Bedient, "Flow and Transport Modeling of a Heterogeneous Field Site Contaminated with Dense Chlorinated Solvent Waste," *Petroleum Hydrocarbons and Organic Chemicals in Ground Water,* NWWA, Houston, TX, 1993.

Canter, L. W. and R. C. Knox, *Ground Water Pollution Control,* Chelsea, MI, Lewis Publishers, Inc., 526 pp., 1986.

Carr, C., and J. B. Hughes, "High-Rate Dechlorination of PCE: Comparison of Lactate, Methanol and Hydrogen as Electron Donors," *Environmental Science and Technology,* 30(12): 1817-1824, 1998.

Charbeneau, R. J., N. Wanukule, C. Y. Chiang, J. P. Nevin and C. L. Klein, "A Two-Layer Model to Simulate Floating Free Product Recovery: Formulation and Applications," *Petroleum Hydrocarbons and Organic Chemicals in Ground Water,* NWWA, Houston, TX, pp. 333-345, 1989.

Chiang, C. Y., J. P. Salanitro, E. Y. Chai, J. D. Colthart, and C. L. Klein, 1989, "Aerobic Biodegradation of Benzene, Toluene, and Xylene in a Sandy Aquifer - Data Analysis and Computer Modeling," *Ground Water,* 6:823-834.

Clement, T. P., Y. Sun, B. S. Hooker, and J. N. Petersen, "Modeling Multispecies Reactive Transport in Ground Water." *Ground Water Monitoring & Remediation*, 18 (2): 79-92, 1998.

Connor, J. A., Newell, C. J., and Wilson, D. K., "Assessment, Field Testing, and Conceptual Design for Managing Dense Nonaqueous Phase Liquids (DNAPL) at a Superfund Site, *Petroleum Hydrocarbons and Organic Chemicals in Ground Water*, NWWA, Houston, TX, 1989.

DePaoli, D. W., S. E. Herbes, J. H. Wilson, D. K. Solomon, H. L. Jennings, T. D. Hylton and J. E. Nyquist, "Field Demonstration of In Situ Venting at Hill Air Force Base JP-4 Jet Fuel Spill Site," 1991.

Dupont, R. Ryan, et al., *Innovative Site Remediation Technology: Bioremediation Design and Application*, American Academy of Environmental Engineers, Vol. 1, 1998

Ehrenfeld, J. and J. Bass, *Evaluation of Remedial Action Unit Operations at Hazardous Waste Disposal Sites*, Park Ridge, NJ, Noyes Publications, 434 pp., 1984.

El-Beshry, Manar Z., J. S. Gierke and P. B. Bedient, "Application of a Multicomponent, 3-Dimensional, Vapor Transport Model for Simulating Data from a Full-Scale SVE System for Removing Jet Fuel," *Petroleum Hydrocarbons NWWA Conference*, Houston, TX, 1998.

El-Beshry, Manar Z., John S. Gierke and P. B. Bedient, "Comparison of Predictions of a 3-Dimensional Numerical Simulator to Data From a Full-Scale Soil Vapor Extraction System at a Jet-Fuel Contaminated Site," *ASCE Journal of Environmental Engineering*, accepted, 1999.

Envirespose, Inc. "Demonstration Test Plan, In-Situ Vacuum Extraction Technology, Terra Vac Inc., SITE Program, Groveland Wells Superfund Site, Groveland, MA." EERU Contract No. 68-03-3255, Work Assignment 1-R18, Envirespose No. 3-70-06340098. Edison, NJ, 1987.

Falta, R. W., "A Program for Analyzing Transient and Steady-State Soil Gas Pump Tests," *Ground Water*, 34(4), pp. 750-755, 1996

Fetter, C. W., *Applied Hydrogeology,* New York, MacMillan Publishing Co., 3rd Ed., 1994.

Fisher, R.T., C. J. Newell, J. B. Hughes, P. E. Haas, and P. C. Johnson, "Direct Hydrogen Addition and Pulse Biosparging for the In-Situ Biodegradation of Chlorinated Solvents," *Petroleum Hydrocarbon and Organic Chemicals in Ground Water Conference*, NWWA, Houston, Texas, 1998.

Flathman, P. E., J. R. Quince, and L. S. Bottomley, "Biological treatment of ethylene glycol-contaminated ground water at Naval Engineering Center in Lakehurst, New Jersey," *Proceedings,* 4th Natl. Symp. on Aquifer Restoration and Ground Water Monitoring, Nielsen, D. M. and M. Curl, Eds., 111, NWWA, Worthington, OH, 1984.

Freeberg, K. M., P. B. Bedient, and J. A. Conner, "Modeling of TCE Contamination and Recovery in a Shallow Sand Aquifer," *Ground Water*, 25:70-80, 1987.

Gillham, R. W. and S. F. O'Hannesin, "Enchanced Degradation of Halogenated Aliphatics by Zero-Valent Iron," *Ground Water,* 32, 958-967, 1994.

Goodman, I., R. E. Hinchee, R. L. Johnson, P. C. Johnson, and D. B. McWhorter, "An Overview of In Situ Air Sparging," *Ground Water Monitoring and Remediation*, 4, 127-135, 1993.

Gorelick, S. M., R. A. Freeze, D. Donohue, J. Keely, *Groundwater Contamination: Optimal Capture and Containment*, Bacon Raton, FL, Lewis Publishers, 1993.

Gossett, J. M., and S. H. Zinder, "Microbiological Aspects Relevant to Natural Attenuation of Chlorinated Ethenes," *Proceedings,* Symposium on Natural Attenuation of Chlorinated Organics in Ground Water Dallas, Texas, EPA/540/R-96/509, 1996.

Hughes, J. B., C. J. Newell, and R. T. Fisher, "Process for In-Situ Biodegradation of Chlorinated Aliphatic Hydrocarbons by Subsurface Hydrogen Injection," U.S. Patent No. 5,602,296, February 11, 1997.

Hutzler, N. J., B. E. Murphy, and J. S. Gierke, "State of Technology Review Soil Vapor Extraction Systems." Cooperative Agreement No. CR-814319-01-1. Risk Reduction Engineering Lab. Cincinnati, OH, U.S. Environmental Protection Agency, 1989.

Jin, M.; M. Delshad, D. C. McKinney, G. A. Pope, K. Sepehrnoori, C. Tilburg, R. E. Jackson, *American Institute of Hydrology Conference,* 1994.

Javandel, I. and C. F. Tsang, "Capture-Zone Type Curves: A Tool for Aquifer Cleanup," *Ground Water,* 24(5):616-625, 1986.

Johnson, A. I., R. K. Frobel, N. J. Cavalli and C. B. Pettersson, Eds., *Hydraulic Barriers in Soil and Rock,* Philadelphia, PA, American Society for Testing and Materials, 1985.

Johnson, P. C., C. C. Stanely, M. W. Kemblowski, D. L. Byers, and J. D. Colthart, "A Practical Approach to the Design, Operation, and Monitoring of In-Situ Soil-Venting Systems," *Ground Water Monitoring Review,* 10:2:159-178, 1990a.

Johnson, P. C., M. W. Kemblowski, and J. D. Colthart, "Quantitative Analysis for the Cleanup of Hydrocarbon-Contaminated Soils by In-Situ Venting," *Ground Water,* 28:3:413-429, 1990b.

Johnson, P. C., M. W. Kemblowski, and J. D. Colthart. "Practical screening models for soil venting applications," *Petroleum Hydrocarbons and Organic Chemicals in Ground Water,* NWWA, Dublin, OH, pp. 521-546, 1988.

Johnson, P. C., A. Baehr, R. A. Brown, R. Hinchee, and G. Hoag, *Innovative Site Remediation Technology: Vacuum Vapor Extraction,* American Academy of Environmental Engineers, 1994.

Knox, R. C., D. A. Sabatini, J. H. Harwell, R. E. Brown, C. C. West, F. Blaha, and S. Griffin, "Surfactant remediation field demonstration using a vertical circulation well," *Ground Water* 35(6), 948-953.

Knox, R. C., B. J. Shiau, D. A. Sabatini, and J. H. Harwell, "Field Demonstration of Surfactant Enhanced Solubilization and Mobilization at Hill Air Force Base, UT," Brusseau, M., et al., Eds., *Innovative Subsurface Remediation: Field Testing of Physical, Chemical and Characterization Technologies,* ACS Symposium Series, American Chemical Society, In Press.

Konikow, L. F. and J. D. Bredehoeft, "Computer Model of Two-Dimensional Solute Transport and Dispersion in Ground Water, Automated Data Processing and Computations," Techniques of Water Resources Investigations of the U.S. Geological Survey, Washington, DC, 1978.

Krebbs-Yuill, B., J. H. Harwell, D. A. Sabatini, and R. C. Knox, "Economic considerations in surfactant-enhanced pump-and-treat," *Surfactant Enhanced Subsurface Remediation: Emerging Technologies* (ed. by D. A. Sabatini, R. C. Knox & J. H. Harwell), ACS Symposium Series 594, 265-278, American Chemical Society, Washington, DC , 1995,.

Krebbs-Yuill, B., J. Harwell, D. Sabatini, G. Quinton, and S. Shoemaker, "Economic study of surfactant-enhanced pump-and-treat remediation," 69th Annual WEF Conference, Dallas, Texas, October 5-9, 1996.

Krishnayya, A. V., M. J. O'Connor, J. G. Agar, and R. D. King, "Vapor extraction systems factors affecting their design and performance," *Petroleum Hydrocarbons and Organic Chemicals in Ground Water,* NWWA, Dublin, OH, pp. 547-569, 1988.

Lee, M. D, et al., "Biorestoration of Aquifers Contaminated with Organic Compounds," NCGWR, R. S. Kerr Environmental Research Laboratory, Ada OK, U. S. Environmental Protection Agency, 18:1:29-89, 1988.

Lee, M. D., and C. H. Ward, "Biological Methods for the Restoration of Contaminated Aquifers," *Environ. Toxicol. Chem.,* 4:743, 1985.

Lowe, Donald F., Carroll L. Oubre, and C. Herb Ward, Eds., *Surfactants and Cosolvents for NAPL Remediation: A Technology Practices Manual*, New York, Lewis Publishers, 1999.

Lynch, E. R., S. W. Anagnost, G. A. Swenson, and R. K. Goldman, "Design and evaluation of in-place containment structures utilizing ground-water cutoff walls," *Proceedings*, Fourth National Symposium and Exposition on Aquifer Restoration and Ground Water Monitoring, 1-7, National Water Well Association, Dublin, OH, 1984.

Mackay, D. M. and J. A. Cherry, "Groundwater contamination: pump-and-treat remediation," *Environ. Sci. Technol.*, 23:6:630-636, 1989.

McDonald, M. G. and A. W. Harbaugh, "A modular three-dimensional finite-difference groundwater flow model," U.S. Geological Survey, Open File Report 83-875, 1984.

Mercer, J. W., D. C. Skipp, and D. Giffin, *Basics of Pump-and-Treat Ground-Water Remediation Technology*, Robert S. Kerr Environmental Research Laboratory, U.S. Environmental Protection Agency, Ada, OK, EPA-600/8-90/003, March 1990.

Mercer, J. W., and R. M. Cohen, "A Review of Immiscible Fluids in the Subsurface," *Journal Of Contaminant Hydrology*, 6:107-163, 1990.

Montgomery-Watson, *Phase I Work Plan for Eight Treatability Studies at Operable Unit 1*. Prepared for Hill AFB, 1995.

Montgomery-Watson and Dynamac, *Phase II Work Plan for Eight Treatability Studies at Operable Unit 1*. Prepared for Hill AFB, 1996.

National Research Council, *In Situ Bioremediation*, Washington, DC, National Academy Press, 1996.

National Research Council, *In Situ Bioremediation*, Washington, DC, National Academy Press, 1993.

National Research Council, *Alternatives for Ground Water Cleanup*, Washington, DC, National Academy Press, 1994.

National Research Council, *Innovations in Ground Water and Soil Cleanup: From Concept to Commercialization*, Washington, DC, National Academy Press, 1997.

Need, E. A., and M. J. Costello, "Hydrogeologic Aspects of Slurry Wall Isolation Systems in Areas of High Downward Gradients," *Proceedings*, 4th Nat. Symp. on Aquifer Restoration and Ground Water Monitoring, D. M. Nielsen and M. Curl, eds., Columbus, OH, May 1984, National Water Well Association, Worthington, OH, p. 18, 1984.

Newell, C. J., J. A. Connor, D. K. Wilson, and T. E. McHugh, "Impact of Dissolution of Dense Non-Aqueous Phase Liquids (DNAPLs) on Groundwater Remediation," *Petroleum Hydrocarbons and Organic Chemicals in Ground Water*, NWWA, Houston, TX, pp. 301-315, 1991.

Norris, et al., *Handbook of Bioremediation*, New York, Lewis Publishers, 1994.

Pankow, J. F., and J. A. Cherry, *Dense Chlorinated Solvents and other DNAPLs in Groundwater*, Portland, OR, Waterloo Press, 1996.

Pankow, J. F., R. L. Johnson, and J. A. Cherry, "Air Sparging in Gate Wells in Cutoff Walls and Trenches for Control of Plumes of Volatile Organic Compounds," *Ground Water*, 654-663, 1993.

Payne, F. C., C. P. Cubbage, G. L. Kilmer, and L. H. Fish, "In Situ Removal of Purgeable Organic Compounds from Vadose Zone Soils," Purdue Industrial Waste Conference, 1986.

Rao, P. S. C., et al., "Field-Scale Evaluation on In Situ Cosolvent Flushing for Enchanced Aquifer Remediation," *Water Resour. Res.*, 33(12), 2673-2686, 1997.

Rathfelder, K., Yeh, W. W. G., and D. Mackay, "Mathematical Simulation of Soil Vapor Extraction Systems: Model Development and Numerical Examples." J. of *Contaminant Hydrology*, 8, 263-297, 1991.

Raymond, R. L., V. W. Jamison, and J. O. Hudson, "Beneficial stimulation of bacterial activity in groundwaters containing petroleum products," AIChE Symp. Ser., 73, 390, 1976.

Raymond, R. I., "Environmental bioreclamation," presented at 1978 Mid-Continent Conf. and Exhibition on Control of Chemicals and Oil Spills, Detroit, Mich., September, 1978.

Rifai, H. S., C. J. Newell, J. R. Gonzalez, et al., "BIOPLUME III Natural Attenuation DSS User's Manual," US Air Force Center for Environmental Excellence, San Antonio, TX, 1997.

Rifai, H. S., P. B. Bedient, J. T. Wilson, K. M. Miller, and J. M. Armstrong, "Biodegradation modeling at a jet fuel spill site," ASCE *J. Environmental Engr. Div.* 114:1007-1019, 1988.

Roberts, P. V., G. D. Hopkins, D. M. Mackay, and L. Semprini, "A Field Evaluation of In-Situ Biodegradation of Chlorinated Ethenes: Part I, Methodology and Field Site Characterization," *Ground Water*, 28(4):591-604, 1990.

Sabatini, D. A., J. H. Harwell, M. Hasegawa, and R. C. Knox, "Membrane processes and surfactant-enhanced subsurface remediation: Results of a field demonstration," *J. Membrane Science,* accepted 1998.

Sabatini, D. A., R. C. Knox, and J. H. Harwell, (Eds), *Surfactant Enhanced Subsurface Remediation: Emerging Technologies*, ACS Symposium Series 594, American Chemical Society, Washington, D.C., 1995.

Sabatini, D. A., J. H. Harwell, and R. C. Knox, "Surfactant Selection Criteria for Enhanced Subsurface Remediation," Brusseau, M., et al., Eds., *Innovative Subsurface Remediation: Field Testing of Physical, Chemical and Characterization Technologies*, ACS Symposium Series, in press, 1999.

Satkin, R. L., and P. B. Bedient, "Effectiveness of various aquifer restoration schemes under variable hydrogeologic conditions," *Ground Water,* 26, no. 4:488-98, 1988.

Semprini, L., P. V. Roberts, G. D. Hopkins, and P. L. McCarty, "A field evaluation of in situ biodegradation of chlorinated ethenes: Part 2, results of biostimulation and biotransformation experiments," *Ground Water,* 28, no. 5:715-27, 1990.

Sillan, R. K., M. D. Annable, P. Suresh, C. Rao, et al., "Evaluation of In Situ Cosolvent Flushing Dynamics Using a Network of Spatially Distributed Multilevel Samplers," *Water Resources Research,* 34(9), pp. 2191-2202, September 1998.

Starr, R. C., and J. A. Cherry, "In Situ Remediation of Contaminated Ground Water: The Funnel-and-Gate System," *Ground Water,* 32, 465-476, 1994.

Tallard, G., "Slurry trenches for containing hazardous wastes," *Civil Engineering ASCE* 41, 1985.

Texas Research Institute, "Examination of Venting for Removal of Gasoline Vapors from Gasoline Vapors from Contaminated Soil," American Petroleum Institute, 1980 (Reprinted 1986).

Thomas, J. M., and C. H. Ward, *In situ biorestoration of organic contaminants in the subsurface, Environmental Science and Technology* 23, no. 7:760-66, 1989.

Thomas, J. M., M. D. Lee, P. B. Bedient, R. C. Borden, L. W. Canter, and C. H. Ward, "Leaking Underground Storage Tanks: Remediation with Emphasis on In Situ Biorestoration," NCGWR, Robert S. Kerr Environmental Research Laboratory, U.S. Environmental Protection Agency, Ada, OK, EPA/600/2-87/008, 1987.

Threlfall, D., and M. J. Dowiak, "Remedial Options for Ground Water Protection at Abandoned Solid Waste Disposal Facilities," U.S. Environmental Protection Agency National Conference on Management of Uncontrolled Hazardous Waste Sites, Washington, D.C., 1980.

U.S. Environmental Protection Agency, *Evaluation of Ground-Water Extraction Remedies*, Volume 1 Summary Report, Office of Emergency and Remedial Response, EPA/540/2-89/054, Washington, D.C., 1989.

U.S. Environmental Protection Agency, *Evaluation of Ground-Water Extraction Remedies: Phase II*, Volume 1 Summary Report, EPA OERR 9355.4-05, Washington, D.C., 1992.

Wilson, J. T, L. E. Leach, M. Henson, and J. N. Jones, "In Situ Biorestoration as a Ground Water Remediation Technique," *Ground Water Monitoring Review*, 6:4 Fall, 1986.

Wilson, D. J., A. N. Clarke, and J. H. Clarke, "Soil Clean-up by in situ aeration, I. Mathematical Modeling," *Sep. Science Tech.*, 23:991-1037, 1988.

CHAPTER 14

LEGAL PROTECTION OF GROUND WATER

JAMES B. BLACKBURN

The protection of ground water in the United States is accomplished through a set of statutes passed at different times. These statutes are not comprehensive; instead, they cover specific types of problems that cause ground water contamination. These statutes reflect the political issues of the time of their passage and incorporate different relationships between the executive and legislative branches.

This chapter will present: (1) the governmental institutions that address ground water contamination; (2) the major requirements of the various acts; and (3) case studies associated in the various programs. It is the goal of this chapter that both the substance and the process of ground water protection will be addressed and made understandable.

14.1 THE PROCESS OF GROUND WATER PROTECTION

Several federal statutes protect ground water: the Safe Drinking Water Act of 1974, the Resource Conservation and Recovery Act of 1976 (RCRA), the Comprehensive Environmental Response, Compensation and Liability Act of 1980 (CERCLA), the Hazardous and Solid Waste Amendments of 1984 (HSWA) and the Superfund Amendments and Reauthorization Act of 1986 (SARA).

These federal statutes are implemented under the auspices of the U.S. Environmental Protection Agency (EPA). EPA publishes regulations in the Federal Register through a process known as informal rule-making. Regulations are published as "draft" regulations and are commented upon by the regulated public, environmental groups, and other interested parties. After consideration of these comments, EPA will promulgate "final" regulations in the *Federal Register*. Each year, the rules of the agency are codified in a single document titled *Code of Federal Regulations* (CFR). The final regulations of the EPA are just as binding as are the terms of the statutes.

EPA is part of the executive branch of government that is headed by the President of the United States. A dynamic exists between the executive branch and legislative branch (the House of Representatives and the Senate). In essence, the Congress writes the policy of the United States in the form of statutes, and the executive branch (i.e., EPA) implements that policy through rule-making.

A key issue is the extent of the discretion that is delegated to EPA by Congress. In the early days of ground water regulation, EPA was granted a great degree of discretion by Congress. However, a major disagreement emerged between EPA and Congress in the early days of the Reagan Administration. Conflicts emerged over the implementation of the newly-passed CERCLA/Superfund program as well as RCRA. These conflicts culminated with the criminal indictment of Rita LaVelle for perjury and the exit of Ann Burford as the Administrator of EPA.

Since that time, Congress has taken substantial discretion away from EPA with regard to the implementation of ground water protection. Stated otherwise, Congress has been much more explicit in its policy statement, leaving less policy discretion in EPA headquarters. This dispute between EPA and Congress is important because it was the driving force in the 1984 HSWA amendments that in turn substantially altered U.S. ground water policy. This dispute also will have a bearing on future initiatives by Congress in the ground water arena.

A second institutional issue of importance is the role between the states and EPA. Just as there is a dynamic between Congress and the EPA, there is also a dynamic between the states and EPA. Under the United States Constitution, states are the repository of governmental power whereas the federal government has limited power. Federal environmental control is undertaken pursuant to the commerce clause of the Constitution.

The states have a very strong role in ground water protection. First, all laws about ground water supply and allocation arise under state rather than federal law. Second, each state has property rights and tort concepts that apply to ground water. For example, if your neighbor contaminated your ground water, there may be rights that you as a landowner can assert in state court. These rights are in addition to, and distinct from, federal environmental law. These will not be covered in this chapter.

Every state has one or more administrative agencies that are the state counterpart to EPA. Ground water protection programs of the federal government are implemented in whole or in part by these state agencies. As a general rule, the state program must be as strong as the federal program. It can, however, be more stringent. The state program may be designated through a process called delegation to act on behalf of EPA. If delegation occurs, then a separate regulatory program will not exist at EPA for that state for those matters that have been delegated.

Confusion sometimes exists when some portions of a program have been delegated and some have not. For example, when HSWA was passed in 1984, it substantially changed the RCRA program. Most states had already been delegated the RCRA program. For that reason, the HSWA program was implemented by EPA until the state could pass regulations sufficiently strong to allow delegation of the new HSWA programs. As of 1991, most of the HSWA requirements have been delegated to the states.

In this chapter, ground water law will be presented from the standpoint of the requirements of federal law and EPA regulations. This should define the "bottom line" of ground water protection throughout the United States. It is important to remember that each state may have variations from this "bottom line" and these state requirements should always be consulted to be confident about the status of regulation in any particular state.

Finally, it is important to note that this ground water system is constantly being reviewed, criticized, interpreted, and reinterpreted by EPA, Congress, and the court system. Given that Superfund site clean-ups may cost hundreds of millions of dollars and ground water contamination can paralyze a community with fear, it is inevitable that changes and fine-tuning will occur in this system.

14.2 THE SAFE DRINKING WATER ACT OF 1974

The Safe Drinking Water Act (SDWA) of 1974, passed because of concerns regarding the safety of public water supplies, set forth two large initiatives. First, the EPA was empowered to develop drinking water standards throughout the United States for public water supply systems. Second, the EPA was given responsibility for implementing a broad-scale ground water protection program called the Underground Injection Control (UIC) program.

Of the two major programs, only the UIC program protects ground water. The drinking water standards govern the quality of water delivered to the consumer but does not regulate sources of ground water contamination. Stated otherwise, the drinking water program prevents the delivery of contaminated water to the ultimate consumer but does not prevent the occurrence of contamination. That responsibility is vested in the UIC program.

The SDWA was passed before Congress determined that the federal government would directly regulate ground water protection activities. For this reason, the UIC program gives the states a major role in the implementation of this act. Under the SDWA, EPA was empowered to develop general regulations for underground injection control. Then, each state is required to adopt rules and regulations implementing the UIC program, including the development of a state permit program. EPA is authorized to implement a program in any state that does not have its own program.

The UIC program regulates underground injection of fluids into wells. A well is defined as a hole in the ground that is deeper than it is wide or long. A fluid is defined to include liquids, semi-solid material and other nonliquid substances. According to the SDWA, a state must have a regulatory program to prevent underground injection, that endangers drinking water sources. A drinking water source is considered to be endangered if underground injection results in the placement of any contaminant into an underground source of drinking water and such contaminant results in a violation of the national primary drinking water standards.

Under the regulations promulgated by EPA to implement the SDWA, five classes of underground injection wells have been identified.

- Class I wells inject hazardous waste or industrial or municipal waste below the lowermost underground source of drinking water (USDW).
- Class II wells inject fluids brought to the surface in association with oil and gas production or injected as part of a secondary and tertiary recovery process.
- Class III wells inject fluids for the extraction of minerals, including the Frasch method of mining sulfur.
- Class IV wells inject hazardous waste into or above an underground source of drinking water.
- Class V wells are those that are not included in classes I- IV. Class V wells include air conditioning return flow, community cesspools (not single family), cooling water, drainage wells, dry wells, recharge wells, saltwater barrier wells, backfill wells, community septic system wells (not single family), subsidence control wells, radioactive waste wells, geothermal injection wells, conventional mine solution wells, brine extraction wells, injection wells for experimental technologies and injection wells used for the in situ extraction of lignite, coal, tar sands and oil shale.

As a general premise, all of the above underground injection wells may be permitted by the state except for Class IV wells, that are prohibited (40 CFR 144.13). The state is not required to allow underground injection; however, if it chooses to allow underground injection, this injection must be accomplished in accordance with the EPA regulations appearing at 40 CFR Part 146.

Underground injection of waste is only one part of the activities regulated by the UIC program. Although passed in 1974, the regulations implementing this act were not promulgated by EPA until 1980 at the same time that the RCRA regulations were promulgated.

The definition of hazardous waste used for Class I and Class IV wells is the same for the SDWA as it is for the RCRA program. For a discussion of what a hazardous waste, see the discussion under RCRA.

A substantial amount of controversy has been generated by the oil and gas lobby over the potential effect of the UIC regulations on the extraction of oil and gas, leading to the establishment of a separate Class II well for oil and gas exploration and production. Brine waste is generated in the production of oil and gas, and water often is injected into the ground to "enhance" production in depleted reservoirs. Permits are not necessary for individual wells but can be obtained for entire fields. The oil and gas lobby was so strong that Section 1425 was added to the SDWA in 1980 to allow an optional approach to regulating underground injection associated with oil and gas production.

Underground injection is accomplished by injecting fluids at high pressure into a well. The regulations established by EPA require that these wells be cased and that the casing be cemented into the geologic formation. The space between the well and the casing—called the annulus—must be filled with a fluid and a positive annulus pressure must be maintained such that if a leak occurs, the leak will be from the annulus into the well rather than from the well outward.

A substantial amount of site-specific geologic and construction data is required to obtain a permit for underground injection of hazardous waste. First, the injection of hazardous waste must be below the lowermost source of drinking water. Second, the injection must be into a formation that is suitably permeable and confined by impermeable layers. Third, the confining zone must be free from faults, fractures and punctures (wells). Corrective action may be required to plug abandoned wells that could allow the upward migration of hazardous waste (40 CFR 146.7). And fourth, the well must exhibit mechanical integrity. Mechanical integrity means that there is no significant leak in the casing, tubing or packer and there is no significant fluid movement into an underground source of drinking water through vertical movement adjacent to the well (40 CFR 146.8).

One of the major differences between the UIC program and the RCRA program is that ground water monitoring is not required for the UIC program. Instead, the UIC program depends upon remote sensing and integrity analyses to determine whether the fluid is actually staying where it is supposed to stay. In this manner, the UIC program differs substantially in philosophy and in specific regulatory provisions from the RCRA program.

Substantial disagreement exists among experts as to the desirability of underground injection of wastes. Underground injection generally does not require pretreatment and results in the long-term presence of hazardous waste and other wastes in the receiving formation. As such, underground injection is not destruction but simply land disposal and storage. The continuation of the practice of underground injection was in question after the passage of the Hazardous and Solid Waste Amendments of 1984, with the ban on land disposal of hazardous waste. Underground injection is subject to the land ban, but EPA, particularly region 6, has "no migration" of the waste for 10,000 years, thereby triggering an exemption to the land ban. For more on the land ban, see the section on HSWA.

The UIC program covers more than waste disposal. Many economic activities may threaten ground water through mining activities or nonwaste-related activities. To the extent that they involve injection of fluids through a well, such activities are regulated under the SDWA if underground sources of drinking water are potentially affected.

14.3 THE RESOURCE CONSERVATION AND RECOVERY ACT OF 1976

The Resource Conservation and Recovery Act (RCRA) was passed in 1976. RCRA is the centerpiece of United States efforts to protect ground water and to regulate solid waste and hazardous waste. Although RCRA was passed in 1976, regulations implementing the hazardous waste requirements of RCRA were not promulgated by EPA until November, 1980. Comprehensive regulation of hazardous waste did not exist prior to November of 1980.

A recurring theme of United States hazardous waste laws is to make the generator of hazardous waste responsible for the ultimate fate of that waste. As will be seen, RCRA set in motion a comprehensive system for tracking hazardous waste. The point here, however, is that a uniform system of regulation did not exist prior to late 1980 and many ground water problems were in existence at the time RCRA became effective. In all of these ground water protection statutes and their amendments, Congress is continually trying to bring all ground water contamination sources under either the RCRA or CERCLA programs.

The RCRA forever changed the solid waste disposal practices of the United States and is an extremely powerful piece of legislation. However, it is important to note that it is part of a comprehensive approach to solid waste management with references to solid waste in the definitions and provisions of RCRA. The regulation of municipal solid waste disposal is undertaken pursuant to Subtitle D of RCRA whereas the disposal of hazardous waste is regulated under Subtitle C of RCRA. For purposes of this subpart, the manifest system of RCRA will be discussed first, followed by a discussion of hazardous waste permitting under RCRA and then permitting of sanitary landfills under Subtitle D.

RCRA has been amended several times since its initial passage. The most far-reaching of these amendments have come from the Hazardous and Solid Waste Amendments of 1984 (HSWA). To the extent possible, the HSWA changes will be treated in a separate section because these amendments significantly altered the requirements for hazardous waste disposal in the U.S. In some instances, however, the HSWA changes will be mentioned in the discussion of RCRA. All of these changes have a significant impact upon what is legal at what point in time. Stated otherwise, an act that was legal in 1990 may not be legal in 1991 as new provisions become applicable.

14.3.1 Goals and Objectives of RCRA

RCRA is a far-reaching act that does more than control the handling and disposal of hazardous waste. Section 1003(b) states:

(b) NATIONAL POLICY. The Congress hereby declares it to be the national policy of the United States that, wherever feasible, the generation of hazardous waste is to be reduced or eliminated as expeditiously as possible. Waste that is nevertheless generated should be treated, stored, or disposed of so as to minimize the present and future threat to human health and the environment.

The objectives of RCRA are set forth in Section 1003(a) and include the following:

(a) OBJECTIVES. The objectives of this Act are to promote the protection of health and the environment and to conserve valuable material and energy resources by:

(3) prohibiting future open dumping on the land and requiring the conversion of open dumps to facilities which do not pose a danger to the environment or to health;

(4) assuring that hazardous waste management practices are conducted in a manner which protects human health and the environment;

(5) requiring that hazardous waste be properly managed in the first instance thereby reducing the need for corrective action at a future date;

(6) minimizing the generation of hazardous waste and the land disposal of hazardous waste by encouraging process substitution, materials recovery, properly conducted recycling and reuse, and treatment.

Additionally, Congress made specific findings with regard to solid waste, environment and health, materials, and energy in Section 1002 of the Act. The bottom line is that the generation of hazardous waste is to be reduced over time, proper recycling should be encouraged, and destruction and detoxification of hazardous waste should be encouraged. The details of the realization of these lofty goals are contained in the specific requirements of the various programs.

14.3.2 The RCRA Manifest Program

Within the RCRA structure, standards are set out for facilities that generate hazardous waste, transporters of hazardous waste, and facilities that store, treat or dispose of hazardous waste. Section 3002(a)(5) of RCRA requires that a manifest system be established "... to assure that all such hazardous waste generated is designated for treatment, storage, or disposal in, and arrives at treatment, storage and disposal facilities ... for which a permit has been issued..." In other words, the manifest program is to track the hazardous waste from the generator through the transporter to the treatment, storage and disposal (TSD) facility.

Essentially, the manifest is a set of papers. The intent of the manifest program is to create a "paper trail" to follow the waste from "cradle to grave." The generator initiates the manifest and gives the manifest to a transporter who must follow the manifest's instructions on the delivery of the hazardous waste to a TSD facility. The generator retains a copy of the manifest when the waste is picked up and gives the manifest to the transporter. The transporter delivers the waste to the site identified on the manifest and passes on the manifest, retaining a copy for her records. The TSD facility must be permitted to receive the waste. Upon receipt of the waste, the TSD facility retains a copy and returns the manifest to the generator, thereby completing the cycle. If the manifest is not returned within 35 days, the generator is responsible for finding the missing hazardous waste and must submit an exception report to EPA if the waste is not found within 45 days.

RCRA and the manifest program have divided the world of hazardous waste into parts. There are generators, transporters, and TSD facilities. Each generator and transporter have an identification number and each TSD facility must be permitted. RCRA is clear that the generator is responsible for determining where the waste is sent, thereby removing transporters and disposers from their pre-1980 "turn-key" role. Today, a prudent generator will perform an extensive investigation of the disposal company taking the waste in order that clean-up liability and environmental damage liability will not be realized under other statutes, such as CERCLA.

14.3.3 Generator Responsibility

It is the responsibility of the generator to determine whether its waste is hazardous. The definition of hazardous waste under RCRA is very complex and full of loopholes. A hazardous waste is a solid waste that can cause or increase mortality or serious irreversible or incapacitating reversible illness or pose a substantial present or potential hazard to human or the environment when improperly treated, stored, transported, or disposed of, or otherwise managed (RCRA section 1004(5)).

As a practical matter, many wastes can be excluded as being hazardous by definition, including waste from oil and gas exploration and production. If a waste is not excluded, it may be listed as a hazardous waste by source or by name. If a waste is not excluded but not listed, it must be tested to determine if it is (1) ignitable; (2) reactive; (3) corrosive, and (4) toxic. If the waste meets any one of those four tests, it is a RCRA hazardous waste.

A manifest is not required for all hazardous waste disposal. If a generator is disposing of hazardous waste on-site, no manifest is required. If fewer than 100 kilograms of hazardous waste are generated per month and that waste is not acutely hazardous, no manifest is required and that waste may be disposed of in facilities not permitted for hazardous waste disposal. Similarly, in some situations, hazardous wastes that are being recycled may be excluded from the manifest requirements. Otherwise, the generator is required to initiate a manifest. In addition to manifesting, the generator must prepare the hazardous waste for shipment. The waste must be packaged, labeled, marked, and/or placarded prior to shipment in order that the hazardous waste will be properly identified. A generator must not accumulate hazardous waste on-site awaiting shipment for too long a time or in too great a quantity. Otherwise, the generator may be deemed to be a storage facility subject to permitting requirements. A generator normally is not required to obtain a hazardous waste permit. Finally, extensive recordkeeping is required of the generator and a biennial report must be submitted to the EPA.

Throughout the requirements applicable to generators, provisions of the regulations inquire as to the waste reduction accomplished by the generator. For example, the biennial report requests a comparison of the volume of hazardous waste generated in the prior reporting period to the volume generated this reporting period. This and many other provisions press the generator to reduce the volume of hazardous waste.

On the other hand, regulatory changes may substantially increase the amount of hazardous waste. For example, EPA adopted a new procedure for testing for the toxicity requirement in 1990. The toxicity characteristic leaching procedure (TCLP) increased substantially the volume of hazardous waste generated in the United States and made many facilities RCRA hazardous waste generators overnight.

14.3.4 Transporter Requirements

The requirements applicable to transporters are very straightforward. Transporters must have an EPA identification number and must follow the Department of Transportation regulations for transporting hazardous materials as set forth in 49 CFR Subchapter C. Transporters must sign for the hazardous waste when they pick it up and must follow the instructions of the manifest. It is illegal for a transporter to pick up hazardous waste without a manifest unless the generator generates fewer than 100 kilograms per month. Under the RCRA scheme, the transporter simply provides a service of transportation and is removed from major decision-making with regard to the place and type of disposal activity.

14.3.5 TSD Facility Requirements

All TSD facilities must be permitted in order to receive manifested hazardous wastes. The receiving facility must verify that the amount and type of waste received matches the amount and type of waste manifested. The receiving facility must sign the manifest, leaving a signed copy with the transporter, retaining a signed copy for its own records and sending the original back to the generator within 30 days. The owner or operator of a TSD facility must retain manifests for three years and must keep an operating record identifying the disposition of each waste shipment. Each TSD facility is required to submit a biennial report.

A waste analysis plan must be developed by TSD facilities to insure that the waste delivered indeed matches that which was manifested (40 CFR 265.13(b)). An attempt must be made to reconcile manifest discrepancies. If the discrepancy is not resolved within 15 days, then the TSD facility must report the discrepancy to the Regional Administrator of the EPA and identify the manifest at issue and attempts to resolve the discrepancy.

The manifest program was intended to make illegal disposal of hazardous waste very difficult. As will be seen in the next section, RCRA imposed very strict standards on facilities that treat, store, and dispose of hazardous waste. However, if hazardous waste is simply thrown in an abandoned pit or upon the side of the road, the most stringent permitting program will fail to protect ground water. Therefore, the manifest was viewed as Step 1 in the national strategy under RCRA to protect ground water.

14.3.6 The RCRA Hazardous Waste Permitting Program

Subtitle C of RCRA created a program for the permitting of facilities that treat, store, or dispose of hazardous waste in Section 3005(a). Under this section, facilities in existence on November 19, 1980, were to be treated differently from facilities constructed after that date. Facilities in existence as of November 19, 1980, were eligible for "interim status," which allowed these facilities to continue operation until a permit application could be filed and a final permit issued. Therefore, a distinction exists between interim status facilities and final permitted facilities or new facility permits.

The rationale for this distinction is valid and created one of the most interesting of all permitting systems in federal environmental law. Unlike air and water pollution, hazardous waste deposited into the ground is not going to disappear if the dumping activity ceases. Indeed, the United States is full of sites that continue to contaminate ground water decades after the disposal activity ceased. On the other hand, EPA had no records of the location of hazardous waste disposal activities around the country in the late 1970s. For these two reasons, existing facilities that were storing, treating or disposing of hazardous waste were given "interim status" if they would identify themselves and adhere to minimal regulations.

Essentially, interim status allowed existing sites to continue operation until the magnitude of the contamination problem was assessed and the safety the operations evaluated. Interim status also gave the United States time to develop other technologies for hazardous waste disposal. In the sections that follow, interim status is described first, followed by final permitting.

14.3.7 Interim Status

The RCRA permitting concept essentially turned the traditional permitting concepts around. Instead of environmental controls being required when the permit is issued, "interim status" simply brings the industry into the permitting program. The important environmental controls occur when the "interim status" facility moves to final permitted status after several years of ground water data collection. Stated otherwise, the controls are on the back end of the RCRA interim status program, not the front end.

All interim status facilities had to file a Part B application to matriculate from interim status to final permitted status. Most of these Part B applications were filed between 1985 and 1987. In order to receive a final permit, very stringent environmental performance standards have to be met. A large number of interim status facilities, perhaps up to 75%, are not safe enough to be granted final permits. These facilities must undertake "closure" activities. A significant amount of environmental clean-up occurs at the "closure" stage.

Once a TSD facility qualifies for interim status, the EPA regulations at 40 CFR Part 265 become applicable. These regulations apply to treatment, storage, and disposal facilities, and contain specific requirements with regard to activities such as tanks, surface impoundments, waste piles, land treatment, landfills, incinerators, thermal treatment and chemical, physical and biological treatment. However, there are number of requirements that apply to all TSD facilities.

14.3.8 Ground Water Requirements

If land disposal alternatives such as surface impoundments, landfills or land treatment facilities were used to manage hazardous waste and were granted interim status, then ground water monitoring was required to be implemented within one year. This ground water monitoring program must be carried out during the life of the facility and during the post-closure care period for these disposal facilities. The ground water monitoring regulations are found at 40 CFR 265.90-94.

An upgradient well is required to test the uppermost aquifer for background levels that will be used for comparison purposes with downgradient wells. With downgradient, at least three wells are required although more may be necessary to immediately detect any statistically significant concentrations of hazardous waste or hazardous waste constituents in the uppermost aquifer (40 CFR 265.91). The number, location, and depths will vary to reflect the geometric and geologic complexity of the site.

If there are multiple land disposal units on site, then the "waste management area" must be adequately monitored. The boundaries of the waste management area will be determined on a case-by-case basis, but once determined, at least one upgradient and at least three downgradient wells must be present at the boundaries of the waste management area to immediately detect leakage of contaminants. All ground water monitoring wells must be cased to maintain the integrity of the monitoring well bore hole.

Once these ground water monitoring wells are located and completed, the owner or operator must develop and follow a ground water sampling plan. This plan will identify how samples are collected, preserved and shipped, as well as how the samples are analyzed and chain of custody of the samples (40 CFR 265.92). These wells must be sampled for EPA interim drinking water standards in Appendix III as well as parameters for ground water quality such as chloride, iron, manganese, phenols, sodium and sulfate. Further, monitoring is required of ground water contamination indicators such as pH, specific conductance, total organic carbon (TOC) and total organic halogen (TOH). Background levels must be established for each of these parameters. The sampling frequency is more intense in the first year, with quality parameters being measured annually thereafter and contamination indicators being measured at least semi-annually thereafter. The ground water elevation must be determined each time the well is sampled.

Further, the owner or operator must prepare a ground water quality assessment program that includes a more comprehensive ground water monitoring program. This ground water quality assessment program must be capable of determining whether hazardous constituents have entered the ground water, the rate and extent of contaminant migration, and the concentrations of hazardous waste or hazardous waste constituents in the ground water. For the ground water contaminants, pH, specific conductance, TOC and TOH, the Students t-test must be utilized to determine whether statistically significant increases have occurred over the monitored background (upgradient) concentrations.

Within 15 days of notifying EPA, the facility must develop a plan certified by a qualified geologist or geotechnical engineer for a ground water assessment program. This assessment plan must include number, location, and depth of wells, including the development of new wells. Sampling must be increased to include all hazardous waste and hazardous waste constituents at the facility. Further, evaluation procedures must be specified and schedules set forth identifying the implementation of the program over time.

The importance of ground water monitoring to the RCRA scheme cannot be overemphasized. Interim status facilities were allowed to continue in operation but only long enough to determine the ground water problems and issues associated with the facility. If the facility has no major ground water problems, then the facility may be granted final permitted status. If, however, the ground water contamination is severe enough, the owner or operator may have to close the facility and undertake corrective action to remediate the ground water contamination.

It should be noted, however, that the EPA regulations do not require immediate cleanup or corrective action in the case where contamination of the ground water is found. As long as the facility is active, ground water contamination can be identified, studied, and evaluated for a substantial amount of time. Indeed, a shortcoming of the RCRA structure is that the ground water analysis may take an extremely long time to be completed, with substantial discretionary authority being given to the agency to allow continued study prior to action.

14.3.9 Closure and Post-Closure Care Requirements

Perhaps no provisions distinguish RCRA from other statutes as do the requirements for closure, post-closure care and corrective action. These requirements reflect the fact that contamination of soil and ground water is not dissipated as are air and water pollution. Even though the hazardous waste storage, treatment, and disposal may be completed, the impacts of that activity remain after cessation of the TSD activity.

Closure plans are required of all facilities having interim status. A performance standard is established for closure that has three parts. First, all facilities must be closed in a manner that minimizes the need for further maintenance. Second, facilities must be closed in a manner that controls, minimizes or eliminates—to the extent to protect human health and the environment—post-closure escape of hazardous waste, hazardous constituents, leachate, contaminated run-off, or hazardous waste decomposition products into the ground or surface waters or into the air. And third, the closure must meet requirements specific to various types of facilities. As can be seen, the key terms are: controls, minimizes or eliminates. The closure requirement, therefore, will vary upon the facts of a particular situation.

A closure plan must be prepared that identifies how long the facility will continue to operate and how the waste on site will be handled after closure. Obviously, waste will have to be removed from treatment and storage facilities and the closure plan requires an identification of how such removal is to be accomplished. In the case of land disposal facilities, waste may be left on-site and contained or removed from the site. These plans are to be maintained during the life of the interim status facility and shown to the Regional Administrator upon request. If changes occur in the operation of the facility, then the closure plan must be amended.

14.3.10 Permitted Facility Requirements

Interim status facilities matriculate to final permitted status over time. Initially, the time for submitting a Part B application for final permitted status was unclear. However, the Hazardous and Solid Waste Amendments of 1984 specified that interim status would expire for land disposal facilities that failed to submit part B applications within 12 months of the passage of HSWA. In addition to submitting a Part B application, the land disposal facilities had to certify that they were in compliance with the ground water monitoring and financial responsibility requirements of interim status regulations.

Once the Part B application has been submitted, the agency conducts a review to determine whether the final RCRA permit should be issued or denied. If the determination is made that the permit should be issued, then a detailed permit will be issued that identifies the terms and conditions under which that facility must operate. This permit review process includes substantial detail as well as steps where the agency staff reviewing an application will send notices of deficiency (NODs) to the applicant. There are different types of deficiencies, including administrative and technical ones. Administrative completeness is first determined to insure that the applicant has answered all of the questions and blanks in the application. The second NOD is a technical one concerned with the substance of the permit application. Here, the applicant is told of problems in the application as submitted and the need for new or reviewed information to support a determination to issue the permit.

An important part of the permit process is the RCRA facility assessment (RFA). The RFA is a study of existing (e.g., interim status) facilities to determine the status of their RCRA compliance including the results of their ground water monitoring and evaluation. If substantial ground water contamination exists, then a major hurdle will exist in moving to final permitted status.

General standards exist that are applicable to facilities that have been permitted to store, treat, and dispose of hazardous waste. These regulations are found at 40 CFR Part 264. The facility must comply with these regulations as well as the requirements of the permit. These standards include requirements for good housekeeping to minimize the potential for ground water contamination as well as specific aspects associated with closure and post-closure care. Specific standards are identified for various types of disposal activities, including incinerators (40 CFR Part 264, Subpart O) and landfills (40 CFR Part 264, Subpart N) as well as several other storage or disposal alternatives.

These standards include design requirements as well as operating requirements. For example, in the landfill section, elements associated with landfill design are specified to protect the ground water. Here, a liner is required that has been designed to prevent migration of the waste from the landfill to the surrounding soil, ground water, and surface water. This liner system is required to contain a top liner, a composite bottom liner, a leachate collection, and removal system and a leak detection system (40 CFR 264.301). The permit will contain sufficient provisions to implement these and other requirements.

As will be shown in the section discussing the Hazardous and Solid Waste Amendments of 1984, many disposal options have been eliminated or substantially restricted by the ban on the land disposal of hazardous wastes. Therefore, a significant portion of the interim status facilities never received final permitted status and instead went straight to closure and post-closure care. Also, many interim status disposal facilities identified ground water contamination and went to closure, post-closure care, and remediation.

These facility standards have been adopted by most states in the United States. In such a situation, RCRA provides that the federal program may be delegated to the state for implementation if the state program is "consistent" with the federal program (40 CFR 271.4). Therefore, as a practical matter, much of actual business of protecting ground water under RCRA is undertaken by state agencies implementing a state program that is consistent with the RCRA requirements and EPA guidelines rather than by the Environmental Protection Agency itself.

14.4 THE HAZARDOUS AND SOLID WASTE AMENDMENT OF 1984 (HSWA)

RCRA was amended in 1984 by a Congress that was unhappy with EPA's early implementation of the act. The head of EPA during the early days of RCRA and CERCLA implementation substantially reduced EPA's budget and cut its personnel from 11,000 to 6,000.

Congress was upset over the EPA's decision to allow the disposal of free liquid hazardous waste in land disposal facilities. This was not a result Congress intended in the initial passage of RCRA and Congress no longer trusted the EPA to implement general policy directives. With the passage of the Hazardous and Solid Waste Amendments of 1984 (HSWA), Congress signaled a major change of national environmental policy. No longer was Congress willing to let EPA be in charge of hazardous waste policy. Congress took policy control over hazardous waste back from the executive branch.

The changes of HSWA were swift and far-reaching. First, a ban on the land disposal of hazardous waste was implemented. Second, the small generator exemption was substantially reduced. Third, underground storage tanks became regulated. And fourth, an overlooked area of hazardous waste disposal—solid waste management units or SWMUs ("smoos")—became regulated.

14.4.1 The Land Ban

Section 101(a)(7) of HSWA created a new section 1002(b)(7) of RCRA that states:

> (b) ENVIRONMENT AND HEALTH.—The Congress finds with respect to the environment and health, that:

> > (7) certain classes of land disposal facilities are not capable of assuring long-term containment of certain hazardous wastes, and to avoid substantial risk to human health and the environment, reliance on land disposal should be minimized or

eliminated, and land disposal, particularly landfill and surface impoundment, should be the least favored method for managing hazardous wastes.

In order to implement this Congressional finding, Congress enacted certain prohibitions on land disposal. Over time, successive prohibitions would apply. Land disposal was defined for purposes of the land ban in a new subsection 3004(k) to include "... any placement of such hazardous waste in a landfill, surface impoundment, waste pile, injection well, land treatment facility, salt dome formation, salt bed formation or underground mine or cave."

Initially, the disposal of free liquids into salt domes was prohibited. Six months after the date of enactment of HSWA, a prohibition against the disposal of bulk or non-containerized liquid hazardous waste into landfills took effect. More generally, the placement of any noncontainerized liquids into a hazardous waste landfill was prohibited in Section 3004(c)(3), as amended.

The prohibition against the land disposal of liquids was a priority of Congress due to the high potential for ground water contamination associated with free liquid hazardous waste. However, Congress went much further in HSWA than simply banning the disposal of free liquid hazardous waste in landfills. The HSWA land ban also included a prohibition of varying types of land disposal activities at varying time increments.

For example, the land disposal of certain types of solvents and dioxin-containing material was banned 24 months after the passage of HSWA (except for deep well injection). The land disposal of certain heavy metals, liquid hazardous waste with a very low pH, liquid hazardous waste containing polychlorinated biphenyls greater than 50 ppm and organic halogenated compounds greater than 1000 mg/kg was banned within 32 months after passage of HSWA.

All other types of hazardous waste proposed for land disposal were to be analyzed and evaluated by the Administrator, with certain of the wastes to be analyzed within 48 months of the passage of HSWA and all wastes to be analyzed within 66 months of the passage of HSWA. This requirement came to be divided into thirds, with the first third of EPA hazardous wastes evaluated in 48 months, the second third evaluated within 55 months and the third evaluated within 66 months.

The goal of this evaluation was to determine whether one or more types of land disposal should be banned. If EPA failed to act within a specified time frame, then the ban was automatically imposed. This is the so-called "hammer provision," a self enforcing provision. If EPA failed to act (which was common during the Reagan Administration), then the prohibition would automatically take place.

This land ban was not absolute. In many cases, treatment could be undertaken that would alter the hazardous waste to such an extent that land disposal was allowed. The goal of this new Section 3004(m) was to either substantially diminish the toxicity of the waste or substantially reduce the likelihood of migration to drinking water sources. Subsequent EPA rules have identified some treatment standards that allow land disposal, but these requirements can be rather difficult and expensive in certain situations and unavailable in other

These EPA regulations required that regulated tank owners test the integrity of these tanks. The existence of any releases had to be reported and corrective action had to be undertaken in response to releases. In some cases, the sites had to be closed in accordance with general closure requirements.

In essence, the site of an underground storage tank became regulated in a manner similar to SWMU or even an existing disposal site. The leakage of contaminants had to be identified, the extent of the damage to soil and ground water had to be assessed, and the problem remediated.

Further, EPA was required to promulgate standards for new underground storage tank construction under Section 9003(e) of RCRA. These "New Tank Performance Standards" shall include requirements for the "design, construction, installation, release detection, and compatibility standards." In the resulting regulations, EPA opted for noncorroding tank shells and/or leachate collection systems, making the design of underground storage tanks similar in many ways to landfill design requirements.

14.4.5 HSWA Impacts

HSWA forever changed the relationship of Congress and EPA. Not only did Congress reassert control of the nation's hazardous waste program, it did so decisively. EPA was forced into responding to a series of HSWA deadlines. When EPA failed to meet statutory deadlines, the regulatory hammer fell, eliminating the activity. If a mistake was to be made, Congress had decided the mistake would be in regulating too much rather than too little.

HSWA also marked a new, get-tough attitude on underground contamination. Leak-prone land disposal methods were banned and old hazardous waste disposal sites were brought into the corrective action/remediation program. Underground storage tanks were regulated, analyzed, and remediated. Congress had declared a national war on ground water contamination with the passage of HSWA.

14.5 CERCLA

The Comprehensive Environmental Response, Compensation and Liability Act of 1980, known as CERCLA, was passed to provide the legal and regulatory basis to clean-up releases of hazardous substances as well as to introduce a concept of hazardous substance reporting. During the decades preceding the passage of RCRA and CERCLA, hazardous substances had been dumped around the United States in thousands of places. No permits were required in many cases. When permits were required, the state of the art was simply not sufficient to contain the waste and protect ground water. By the time CERCLA was passed, Congress knew that a major problem existed in the United States with regard to past disposal practices and ongoing releases.

The concept of clean-up that Congress adopted consisted of several parts. First, CERCLA had a companion piece of legislation called the Superfund Tax Act, which created an excise tax on oil and certain hazardous substances. This tax was paid into a fund, which was initially bankrolled by Congress. This fund was called "the Superfund" and was to be used to study and clean up non-RCRA sites where hazardous substance releases were occurring. As the companion to the Superfund Tax Act, CERCLA provided controls on the use of Superfund monies. CERCLA required EPA to establish rules for the expenditure of Superfund money and established liability provisions to insure that the parties responsible for the release ultimately paid for the clean-up. CERCLA also created a reporting requirement for past disposal operations and for current releases.

From a conceptual standpoint, CERCLA is quite different than RCRA and HSWA. CERCLA is not a true regulatory act. Instead, CERCLA created a process for identifying releases and cleaning up sites that pose a hazard to health and the environment. No permits are required. No application is made. Instead, the EPA identifies the site and prepares a clean up plan. Then, after the clean-up takes place, the potentially responsible parties (PRPs) are sued by the federal government to reimburse the Superfund for the money spent to cleanup the problem they created. In this respect, CERCLA is unique among environmental laws.

CERCLA is a harsh statute. CERCLA imposes statutory strict liability for clean-up costs upon generators, transporters, and owners responsible for releases. Conceptually, CERCLA can be viewed in three parts. The first part concerns the identification, analysis, and remediation of releases. The second part concerns the rules of liability associated with the remediation of these releases. And the third part addresses the more general reporting requirements that are created by CERCLA.

The common thread through all parts of CERCLA is the focus upon releases. Releases are to be reported and releases are to be remediated. As will be seen, the concept of release is very broad, covering an extremely wide range of actions. In virtually all cases, these releases either have affected or have the potential to affect ground water. For the most part, the release of concern will involve the leaching of chemicals from an old disposal site into the ground water. For the student of ground water, knowledge of the CERCLA process is essential.

The Superfund process and its harsh liability provisions have forever changed the real estate industry in the United States. Because an owner may be liable for the clean-up of a release under CERCLA, prospective property owners have become concerned about purchasing clean-up liability. Banks, savings and loans, and large institutional real estate investors are now on notice that the purchase of real estate may be accompanied by liability. The owners of shopping centers and commercial buildings are now on notice that they may be liable for the release of hazardous substances by their tenants.

This liability was initiated by the CERCLA provisions and enhanced and amplified by the Superfund Amendment and Reauthorization Act of 1986 (SARA), which reauthorized CERCLA. SARA created a defense for real estate purchasers if they have "no reason to know" about hazardous substances on the property. This "no reason to know" defense can be perfected by conducting an environmental audit of property prior to purchase. These environmental audits are now routinely required throughout the United States for property transactions and represent a major consulting practice for engineers and scientists around the country.

Finally, the 1986 SARA amendments created a new reporting requirement under the Title III provisions. The so-called SARA Title III program required that certain industries report all of their releases of hazardous substances, both permitted and unpermitted, to EPA. This SARA Title III report would include an inventory of hazardous substances in the wastewater, air emissions, underground injection, and land disposal. Never before had such a compilation been required. No legal provision stands for the power of information more than does SARA Title III.

Because of the concise reporting format, the SARA Title III information can be accessed and compared across industrial sectors and across the United States. Lists of the "Toxic 500" companies or of the most toxic counties in the United States could be compiled from the data sets and become public. No other act created information more readily accessible for media use than did SARA Title III. And the results have been phenomenal. Substantial competition exists today among industries **not** to be number one, or even in the top fifty, of the "Toxic 500" companies. As a result, substantial waste reduction has occurred in many industries originally identified as the most toxic in the United States.

CERCLA and SARA have left an incredible legacy in the decade of the 1980s. Extensive liability has been brought to generators and owners. Remediation of releases will continue well into the twenty-first century. Reporting of hazardous substance releases is pervasive. And the public is more concerned than ever about ground water contamination, Superfund site clean-up and their safety. Bankers are worried about chemicals compromising their real estate loans and companies are scrambling to escape the Toxic 500 list. CERCLA and SARA are worth a little time.

14.5.1 The National Contingency Plan

The overall process for identifying and cleaning up Superfund sites is contained in a set of regulations titled the "National Contingency Plan." These regulations are found at 40 CFR Part 300. Essentially, there are criteria for placing sites on the Superfund list. Then, there are criteria for studying and evaluating the site. And then there are criteria for cleaning up the site. No action may qualify for the use of Superfund monies unless the procedures outlined in the National Contingency Plan are followed.

The National Priority List. 40 CFR 300.425 sets forth the process for establishing remedial priorities. The structure of CERCLA is such that the focus of the statute is upon the reporting and remediation of "releases" of hazardous substances. Section 101(22) of CERCLA defines release as:

> ... any spilling, leaking, pumping, pouring, emitting, emptying, discharging, injecting, escaping, leaching, dumping or disposing into the environment (including the abandonment or discarding of barrels, containers, and other closed receptacles containing any hazardous substance or pollutant or contaminant)... [with certain exceptions].

As a practical matter, there are hundreds of thousands of releases of hazardous substances throughout the United States that are theoretically in competition for the Superfund remediation money and agency priority action. Congress needed a manner to discriminate among these candidate sites to insure that the Superfund money was spent properly. Therefore, Congress directed EPA to create a National Priorities List to guide the expenditure of these Superfund monies.

Under Section 105(a)(8)(B) of CERCLA, Congress stated that the President of the United States ". . . shall list as part of the [national contingency] plan national priorities among the known releases or threatened releases throughout the United States and shall revise the list no less often than annually." In Section 105(a)(8)(A) of CERCLA, Congress states:

> Criteria and priorities under this paragraph shall be based upon relative risk or danger to the public health or welfare or the environment ... taking into account ... the population at risk, the hazard potential of the hazardous substances at such facilities, the potential for contamination of drinking water supplies, the potential for direct human contact, the potential for destruction of sensitive ecosystems, the damage to natural resources which may affect the human food chain and which is associated with any release or threatened release, the contamination or potential contamination of the ambient air which is associated with the release or threatened release, State preparedness to assume State costs and responsibilities, and other appropriate factors.

Under the directive of this section, EPA has established a so-called National Priorities List (NPL). Only the releases included on the NPL shall be eligible for Superfund-financed remedial activities. On the other hand, removal actions that are not financed by the fund are not limited to NPL sites.

EPA has developed a methodology for determining eligibility for the NPL. This methodology is extremely complex, taking up more than 100 pages in the *Code of Federal Regulations*. This Hazard Ranking System (HRS) is found in Appendix A to 40 CFR Part 300 and has resulted in the listing of NPL sites plus NPL federal facility sites. These are the so-called Superfund sites.

Releases are added to the NPL by action of the so-called lead agency, which is usually the EPA or the state agency working with EPA. It is the responsibility of the lead agency to apply the HRS methodology to a particular release and to submit the results of this analysis to EPA. If EPA concurs in the HRS scoring and if the HRS score is sufficiently high (e.g., greater than 28.5), then a site shall be added to the NPL. The NPL shall be updated annually and new sites must be published in the Federal Register for public comment prior to being added to the NPL. Releases may be deleted from the NPL where no further response is appropriate. A release may be deleted if (a) responsible parties have undertaken appropriate response action, (b) fund-financed response under CERCLA has been implemented and no addition action by responsible parties is appropriate, or (c) investigations indicate the release poses no significant threat to public health or the environment and remedial responses are not appropriate. Notices of intent to delete must also be published in the Federal Register.

14.5.2 The RI/FS Process

A tremendous amount of time and effort goes into the analysis of a Superfund site and the selection of a clean-up remedy. The EPA regulations set out procedures that must be followed to move forward with the clean-up. There are two distinct steps in the process. First, there are the remedial investigations (RI) where data is compiled and site characterization is achieved. Then there is the feasibility study (FS) where various clean-up alternatives are evaluated to determine whether they meet the goals of EPA and the needs of the public. Within this process, interaction with the affected community must occur and ultimately a remedy must be selected. All of this must be undertaken under the umbrella of the ultimate goal of adequately protecting the public and the environment.

The importance of this RI/FS process cannot be overstated. Remedies for various Superfund sites can be extremely costly, ranging well into the tens if not hundreds of millions of dollars. The future of the citizens living next to a facility may hinge on remedy selection as well. To what level will clean-up occur? Will there be air pollution residuals? Will ground water will be cleaned up or contained or left contaminated in place? All of these issues and many more are decided in the RI/FS process leading to remedy selection.

14.5.3 EPA Program Goals

The purpose of the remedy selection process is to implement remedies that eliminate, reduce or control risks to human health and the environment (40 CFR 300.430(a)(1). It is important to note at the outset that risk analysis is a major aspect of the remedy selection process. The purpose of this process is not only to eliminate risks but also to reduce and control risks. Therefore, the role of risk assessment and risk management is extremely important. The EPA has a program goal that shapes the overall direction of the remedy selection process:

> The national goal of the remedy selection process is to select remedies
> that are protective of human health and the environment, that maintain
> protection over time and that minimize untreated waste. 40 CFR
> 300.430(a)(i).

To implement this program goal, EPA has identified a number of expectations, which shall be considered in developing the appropriate response alternatives. These are:

1. Treatment is expected to be used to address the principle threats of a site where practicable, including particular liquids, high concentration toxic areas, and for highly mobile compounds.

2. Engineering controls such as containment are expected to be used for waste that poses a relatively low long-term threat or where treatment is impracticable.

3. Combinations of clean-up controls are expected to be used where principle threats may be addressed by treatment and lesser threats addressed by containment or institutional controls.

4. Institutional controls such as water use limitations and deed restrictions limiting property use are expected to be used in association with engineering controls and not as the sole remedy unless active measures are determined not to be feasible in the remedy selection process.

5. Innovative technology (such as bioremediation) is expected to be used when it can be shown that it will result in equal or superior treatment, performs better from an environmental impact standpoint, or costs less for the same level of performance as other alternatives.

6. Ground water is expected to return to beneficial uses wherever practicable within site-specific reasonable time frames. When beneficial use restoration is not practicable, EPA expects to prevent plume migration and exposure to the contaminated ground water and to evaluate further risk reduction.

From the foregoing goals and expectations, it is clear that absolute clean-up and zero risk are not requirements of the national contingency plan. Instead, the analysis and management of the risk are the critical elements. A clear bias exists for treatment rather than containment, although containment is acceptable in certain situations, as are land use and water use controls. Therefore, the choice of remedies is highly dependent upon the specifics of the site and the analysis of the risk.

14.5.4 Scoping

The first step in the RI/FS process is to determine how to proceed with the study. This step is called scoping and sets the protocol for site investigation.

Existing information is evaluated in the scoping step to determine the extent to which additional data must be collected. Of primary importance is the determination of future data collection efforts to be undertaken in the RI step. The type of data collection, the quality, and the quantity of data must all be determined in advance of the RI. This process is expected to result in a sampling and analysis plan with both field protocols and quality assurance/quality control (QA/QC) components. Also, the type of protective equipment necessary for workers needs to be determined at this juncture.

During scoping, a preliminary assessment is made of the range of potential clean-up alternatives to guide future deliberations. If natural resource damage has been identified or is anticipated, preliminary contact must be made with the state and federal resource agencies that are authorized to act as natural resource trustees to insure protection of the natural environment in the remedy selection process. And finally, applicable or relevant and appropriate requirements (ARARs) must be determined. ARARs are regulatory requirements from other federal or state laws that apply to a particular site cleanup. ARARs have a major role in determining the acceptability of a particular remedial alternative. If no ARAR exists (or if the ARAR allows relative risk assessment), then risk analysis is used to determine appropriate clean-up levels.

14.5.5 Community Relations

Interface with the affected community is initiated prior to undertaking any field work. Interviews should be conducted with public officials, community residents and public interest groups to discover their concerns and to set up a system for informing them of the progress of the RI/FS process. A community relations plan (CRP) is to be developed that identifies opportunities for citizens to participate in the decision-making process, and a local information repository must be set up so that the local affected public may review the documents utilized by EPA.

14.5.6 Remedial Investigation (RI)

The purpose of the RI is to collect data to adequately characterize the site for the purpose of developing and evaluating effective remedial alternatives. Information regarding the risk to the public and the environment posed by a particular site will be generated by the RI. That is the central focus of the RI.

The nature and character of the threat posed by the hazardous substances and the particular conditions of the release at the site will be determined in the RI. The data collection effort of the RI should generate information relevant to the following concerns:

1. physical characteristics of the site (soils, geology, hydrogeology, meteorology, ecology)
2. characteristics of the surface and ground water
3. characteristics of the waste, including quantities, state, concentration, toxicity, bioaccumulation tendencies, persistence and mobility
4. extent to which the source can be identified and characterized
5. actual and potential exposure pathways through environmental media
6. actual and potential exposure pathways to the body
7. other factors such as sensitive populations

14.5.7 Source Control Actions

Source control actions are to be evaluated by the lead agency. Source control actions include first and foremost a range of alternatives that utilize treatment to reduce the toxicity, mobility or volume of hazardous substances. Here the goal is removal and/or destruction of the hazardous substance, thereby eliminating or minimizing the long-term need for management. The lead agency is authorized to vary from total treatment to partial treatment. Alternatives other than treatment are also developed, such as containment or land use controls, including evacuation, to achieve protection of human health and the environment.

Where ground water response actions are required, a number of alternatives that produce site specific remediation levels over different periods of time shall be developed. Further, the agency is required to develop one or more innovative alternatives if such alternatives can generate comparable or better results than other alternatives.

The detailed analysis of alternatives is accomplished in a comparative manner by utilizing nine evaluation criteria:

1. overall protection of human health and the environment

2. compliance with ARARs (or with criteria for waiver)

3. long-term effectiveness and permanence, including consideration of residual risk resulting from remaining, untreated waste and adequacy and reliability of controls

4. reduction of toxicity, mobility, or volume through treatment or recycling including the type of waste remaining after the clean-up

5. short-term effectiveness, focusing upon risks to the community, to workers, and to the environment during the clean-up including the length of such exposures

6. implementability (i.e., the technical and administrative feasibility of implementing the alternative as well as the availability of off-site treatment, storage and disposal sites)

7. cost, including capital costs, annual operation and maintenance, and net present value of capital

8. state acceptance, including state's preferred alternative and state ARARs

9. community acceptance, including a determination of community concerns with alternatives and preferences

14.5.8 Remedy Selection

The decision-maker must select a remedy based upon the above nine factors. However, each of these factors is not equally weighted. To be eligible for selection, each alternative must achieve overall protection of human health, and the environment and must comply with applicable ARARs unless they are waived. These are the two threshold requirements. An alternative cannot be considered if it does not meet these two requirements.

All alternatives meeting the threshold requirements are then reviewed against the five primary balancing requirements. These five balancing requirements are long-term effectiveness and permanence, reduction of toxicity, mobility and volume through treatment, short-term effectiveness, implementability, and cost. The final two criteria—state and community acceptance—are modifying criteria.

Remedy selection is a two-step process. First, a proposed plan is put forth. Here, the agency identifies the alternative that best meets the evaluation criteria and proposes this alternative to the public for review and comment. The selected alternative must be protective of human health and the environment, meet ARARs, be cost-effective, and utilize permanent solutions to the maximum extent practicable.

This proposed plan is then circulated to the public for review and comment. The availability of the plan and a summary must be published in a newspaper of general circulation. An administrative record of all pertinent documents, studies, and analyses, including those developed during the RI/FS process, must be made available to the public for review and inspection. Then, the public must be given time to submit comments in writing. The agency must provide the opportunity for a public meeting during the public comment period, and a transcript must be made of the public meeting. A written summary – called a responsiveness summary – must be prepared by the agency and carried forward to the final decision. If significant new information is identified during this public comment process, then the lead agency must evaluate it and incorporate it into the analysis.

The second step in remedy selection is to reconsider the proposed plan, factoring in additional information provided by the state and the public. These comments may prompt the lead agency to modify its proposed plan. The final remedy selection shall be made and documented in a record of decision (ROD). This ROD shall document all facts, analysis of facts, and site specific policy determinations considered in the course of carrying out the alternative selection. Specific findings of how the evaluation criteria are met must be included in the agency ROD.

14.5.9 The Remedial Design/Remedial Action (RD/RA) Stage

After the remedy is selected, the clean-up occurs. The selected alternative must be designed in sufficient detail to be implemented, and then the actual clean-up must take place. The RD/RA process must follow the ROD. Specifically, the attainment of specific clean-up levels and/or ARARs must be monitored to determine that the alternative has performed to the extent specified in the ROD. Specific attention must be focused upon the QA/QC process as was the case in the RI/FS stage. If the need arises to alter the clean-up alternative adopted in the ROD, the ROD must be amended through formal procedures. Such procedures involve public notice and formal amendment, including formal review and comment and potentially public meetings. A strong preference exists to maintain the integrity of the ROD.

When the RA is completed, a determination is made that the remedy is operational and functional. At that time, the site enters the operation and maintenance (O&M) phase. A site is operational and functional either one year after the completion of the construction or when the remedy is determined to be properly functioning. When ground water remediation is involved, the operation of the treatment for a period of up to ten years is considered to be part of the remedial action.

14.5.10 Liability Under CERCLA

The concept of liability under CERCLA is one of the harshest ever adopted by the United States Congress. Strict liability exists under CERCLA for clean-up costs incurred by the federal government acting pursuant to the national contingency plan. Strict liability also exists for damages to the environment occurring as a result of the release. Section 107 of CERCLA contains the liability provisions. Section 107(a) states:

(a) Notwithstanding any other provision or rule of law, and subject only to the defenses set forth in subsection (b) of this section:

1. the owner and operator of a vessel or a facility,
2. any person who at the time of disposal of any hazardous substance owned or operated any facility at which such hazardous substances were disposed of,
3. any person who by contract, agreement or otherwise arranged for disposal or treatment or arranged with a transporter for transport for disposal or treatment, of hazardous substances owned or possessed by such person, by any other party or entity, at any facility or incineration vessel owned or operated by another party or entity and containing such substances, and
4. any person who accepts or accepted any hazardous substances for transport to disposal or treatment facilities, incineration vessels or site selected by such person, from which there is a release or threatened release which causes the incurrence of response costs, of a hazardous substance, shall be liable for:

(A) all costs of removal or remedial action incurred by the United States Government or a state or an Indian tribe not inconsistent with the national contingency plan,
(B) any other necessary costs of response incurred by any other person consistent with the national contingency plan,
(C) damages for injury to, destruction of, or loss of natural resources, including the reasonable costs of assessing such injury, destruction, or loss resulting from such release; and
(D) the costs of any health assessment or health effects study carried out under section 104(i).

This Section 107(a) creates liability in the current owner and operator of the facility that is the site of the release, the past owner and operator of the facility that was associated with the release, the generator of the hazardous substance that is being released and the transporter delivering the hazardous substance to the release site. It should be noted that any of these parties are liable for *all* costs identified in (A)-(D) above. This liability is known as joint and several. In this manner, a single generator can be liable for an entire clean-up even though that generator may not have generated all of the hazardous substances being released from a site.

If a party did not generate or transport hazardous substances to a particular release site, a defense exists. If the hazardous substance that is present at the release site could not be the defendants', then a defense exists. If a person is sued for owning a site and never owned it, a defense exists. However, for someone correctly identified as a generator, transporter or owner/operator contributing to a release at a facility, the defenses are limited.

The defenses to liability under subsection (a) are very few and very narrow. If the release of hazardous substance and the damages relating therefrom were caused by either (1) an act of God or (2) an act of war, then no liability will exist. An act of God is defined to include severe natural disasters, the effects of which could not have been prevented or avoided by the exercise of due care or foresight. As a practical matter, the defenses of acts of God and war are of very limited utility.

Because the defenses are so limited, the liability concept is considered to be statutory strict liability. Reasonable care is not a defense except in very specific situations such as third party liability or in the utilization of the act of God defense. By and large, if a defendant generated the waste, transported the waste, currently owns and/or operates the facility and formerly owned and/or operated the facility, liability exists.

A third aspect exists to the liability under CERCLA. Under Section 107(c)(3), a potentially responsible party (PRP) may be liable for punitive damages in the amount of three times the costs actually incurred by the Fund. Punitive damages become applicable if that PRP is requested by the President (e.g., EPA) to provide removal or remedial actions under Sections 104 and 106 of CERCLA and fails to do so. In this manner, a PRP may be liable for the costs of cleanup and for three times that amount. The clear intention of this punitive damages section was to force PRPs to cooperate with the government at an early stage in CERCLA process.

As a practical matter, PRPs are contacted in writing by the EPA at a relatively early stage in the process and asked to cooperate with the various investigations, including the provision of documents and access. The President, acting through the Regional Administrator of EPA, has the authority to request individual PRPs to undertake certain removal and remedial actions under either Section 104 or 106 of CERCLA. If the PRP lacks just cause for refusing such a request (e.g., lacks a defense), then the punitive damages apply. As a practical matter, most PRP's are very hesitant to refuse voluntary cooperation and risk the imposition of punitive damages.

PRP's take a very active role in site clean-up selection by undertaking their own RI/FS process under EPA supervision. In this manner, the PRPs have control of the national contingency plan process while at the same time avoiding the potential punitive damage assessment. All of the PRP studies are undertaken with EPA oversight and ultimate control.

14.6 SUPERFUND AMENDMENT AND REAUTHORIZATION ACT OF 1986 (SARA)

The Superfund Amendment and Reauthorization Act of 1986 (SARA) is notable for several provisions. First, Congress left the major liability requirements of CERCLA unchanged, meaning that the relatively harsh clean-up liability was acceptable from a congressional point of view. Second, additional monies were placed into the Superfund to aid in the cleanup of the ever increasing number of abandoned hazardous waste disposal sites. However, the two most important requirements related to the liability for innocent purchasers and the disclosure of annual releases of hazardous substances.

14.6.1 Limited CERCLA Liability Through Environmental Audits

Under CERCLA, the current landowner may be liable for the clean-up of hazardous substances even if that landowner did not cause the contamination. This liability provision is particularly important to banks and lending institutions because these institutions lend money and use property as collateral for those loans. If the borrower does not pay back the money and the bank or savings and loan takes over the property used as collateral, the bank or savings and loan becomes the current property owner. In this manner, both new owners and foreclosing owners may be liable under CERCLA.

Although SARA generally left the CERCLA liability provisions unchanged, a provision was added that allows "innocent" purchasers to limit their liability under CERCLA. Under the SARA amendment, a so-called due diligence defense was added to allow new purchasers to limit their liability. If, when the property was purchased, the buyer had "no reason to know" about the contamination of the property, then a defense to liability exists.

SARA sets out the considerations that a judge should take into account in determining whether or not the buyer had "no reason to know" about the contamination (CERCLA Section 9601 (35) (A)). According to §9601 (35) (B), in order to establish "no reason to know," the defendant must establish that an inquiry was undertaken into previous ownership and uses of the property in an attempt to determine whether there might be a reason to anticipate contamination. Further, this section states that the court shall consider any specialized knowledge of the purchaser, the purchase price, commonly known or easily obtained information about the contamination, the obviousness of the problem, and the ability to detect the problem by inspection.

This provision has totally changed the commercial real estate market. After the passage of SARA, virtually all lenders and smart buyers began requiring studies of proposed land purchases to determine whether there was "reason to know" about contamination. These studies have evolved into a nationwide consulting practice called Phase I, II, and III environmental audits.

Phase I audits typically entail a visual inspection of the property, a review of the prior ownership and use, a review of agency records and known contamination sites, a review of aerial photographs, and perhaps interviews with neighbors and/or past employees. The purpose of this initial review is to determine whether or not the purchaser has reason to know that contamination exists on the property. If no problems are detected, the audit is concluded and the land purchase goes forward with the written documentation of the Phase I audit ready to be used as a defense.

If problems are detected, then a Phase II study is initiated to determine the extent of the problem. Phase II typically involves soil testing and ground water monitoring to determine the extent of soil and ground water contamination. Phase II will include a detailed analysis of the extent of contamination, including plumes of contamination and delineation of affected soils.

Phase III is the remediation effort. Depending upon how the audit is conducted, the design of the remediation effort may be included in either the Phase II or Phase III analysis. Generally, a buyer would require the information on the cost of remediation in order to make an informed decision about the extent of the risk that she will be encountering if she goes ahead and purchases the property.

Oftentimes, the detection of soil or ground water contamination will stop the transaction from occurring. Many buyers and lenders require full clean-up and certification of closure prior to even considering lending money on contaminated property. More sophisticated lenders and buyers have developed criteria to assist them in understanding these risks and working with them. However, the important point is that ground water monitoring, soil contamination, and remediation are now common issues in the real estate community. Such was not the case prior to the passage of CERCLA and SARA.

14.6.2 SARA Title III

The other major change introduced by SARA is the reporting requirement under Title III. Here, facilities that exceeded certain size thresholds in the handling and release of hazardous substances must submit an annual report to EPA identifying the total poundage of releases of hazardous substances, both permitted and unpermitted, into the environment.

The hazardous substance releases required to be submitted include permitted and accidental wastewater discharges, permitted RCRA land disposal., permitted underground injection allowed under the Safe Drinking Water Act, and permitted stack and fugitive air emissions. These submissions are on a facility by facility basis and covered virtually all major industrial facilities in the United States.

SUMMARY

The changes that occurred in ground water protection in the 1980s were staggering. RCRA and the Safe Drinking Water Act became effective in November of 1980, CERCLA was passed in 1980, HSWA was passed in 1984 and SARA was passed in 1986. The United States went from a country that had no uniform hazardous waste requirements to one with a comprehensive system of ground water protection. The 1990s has been a period of reflection and evaluation of the changes that were initiated in the 1980s.

One area of change during the 1990s involves the generation of hazardous wastes and the release of hazardous substances. Simply stated, the costs of waste generation and disposal are extremely high and the negative publicity associated with hazardous wastes and substances is great. For many good reasons, the trend of the 1990s has been to minimize the production of hazardous wastes and to reduce substantially the release of hazardous substances into the environment. Ground water protection of the future will certainly entail the reduction of the contamination potential by reducing the volume of waste generated.

In thinking about the future of ground water protection, it is important to keep in mind that Congress has continually revised and expanded its view of the scope of environmental law and ground water protection. The federal law has expanded from RCRA manifesting and permitting and CERCLA clean-up litigation to land bans under HSWA and environmental audits and Title III reporting under SARA. Ground water protection practices include monitoring, modeling, and permitting but are much broader than hydrogeology. Full disclosure of contamination may ultimately prove to be one of the most important ground water protection and waste minimization tools. Therefore, while it is important to understand the site specific requirements, it is also important not to lose sight of the larger societal goals of ultimately eliminating the source of the contamination.

On the other hand, the costs of remediation of existing contamination are extremely high. It is reasonable to question the overall cost to society of the gains to public health associated with many of these clean-up activities and to assess the risks associated with leaving contaminants in the ground. In many respects, the major ground water protection debate of the 1990s may be between proponents of extensive remediation and proponents of encapsulation and monitoring. The use of risk assessment concepts and techniques will likely become more prevalent as clean-up negotiations concentrate upon relative benefits associated with extensive clean-up costs.

The use of risk assessment will raise ethical and professional questions. Who is competent to assess the risk to the public? What type of credentials should be required? And who is going to assess the risk of risk assessors?

These laws have created a framework within which professionals must work into the twenty-first century. These laws were designed to protect the public health and regulate sources of contamination. It is difficult to clearly define the balance between protecting the public and fairly regulating sources of contamination. In many respects, correctly balancing these concerns will be the ultimate task in the regulation and protection of ground water.

REFERENCES

Code of Federal Regulation (CFR).

H O M E W O R K

Chapter 2

2-1. A sample of silty sand in its natural condition had a volume of 220 cm^3 and weighed 481.2 g. After saturating the sample with water it weighed 546.9 g. The sample was then drained by gravity until it reached a constant weight of 445.7g. Finally the sample was oven dried at 105 °C after which it weighed 432.8 g. Note that the volume of the voids in the sample under natural conditions is the volume of water in the sample at saturation. Assuming the density of water is 1 g/cm^3, compute the following:

(a) water content (mass basis) under natural conditions, defined as the ratio of the mass of water to the mass of the sample under natural conditions.

(b) volumetric water content under natural conditions, defined as the ratio of the volume of water to the volume of the sample under natural conditions.

(c) saturation ratio under natural conditions, defined as the fraction of voids filled with water under natural conditions.

(d) porosity, defined as the ratio of the volume of voids to the volume of the sample under natural conditions.

(e) specific yield , defined as the ratio of the volume of water drained from the saturated sample due to gravity to the volume of the saturated sample.

(f) specific retention, defined as the ratio of the volume of water a sample can retain against gravity to the volume of the saturated sample, also equal to the difference between porosity and specific yield.

(g) dry bulk density, defined as the mass of the soil particles divided by the volume of the sample under natural conditions.

2-2. Three piezometers, A, B, and C are located 1000 m apart (in a straight line) in an unconfined aquifer. Fill in the blank spaces in the table below. Calculate the pressure head and elevation head at the base of the piezometer.

Piezometer	A	B	C
Ground surface (msl)(m)	450	435	430
Depth of piezometer (m)	___	___	70
Depth to water (m)	27	___	50
Pressure head (m)	53	___	___
Elevation head (msl)(m)	___	335	___
Total head (msl)(m)	___	400	___
Hydraulic gradient (m/m)		___	___

2-3. Compute the discharge velocity, seepage velocity, and flow rate for water flowing through a sand column with the following characteristics

$$K = 10^{-4} \text{ cm/s} \qquad \frac{dh}{dl} = 0.01$$

$$\text{Area} = 75 \text{ cm}^2 \qquad n = 0.20$$

2-4. The average water table elevation has dropped 5 ft due to the removal of 100,000 ac-ft from an unconfined aquifer over an area of 75 mi^2. Determine the storage coefficient for the aquifer.

2-5. A confined aquifer is 50 m thick and 0.5 km wide. Two observation wells are located 1.4 km apart in the direction of flow. The head in well 1 is 50.0 m and in well 2 the head is 42 m. The hydraulic conductivity K is 0.7 m/day.
(a) What is the total daily flow of water through the aquifer?
(b) What is the height of the piezometric surface 0.5 km from well 1 and 0.9 km from well 2?

2-6. Three piezometers arranged in an aquifer as an equilateral triangle with sides of 1000 m. A is located to the east of Well B and Well C which are aligned in a north-south direction. The water surface elevations are measured for the three wells are as follows: A = 150m, B = 100m and C = 200m. Find the direction and two dimensional rate of flow within the triangle using graphical methods. The hydraulic conductivity of the aquifer is 5×10^{-7} cm/s.

2-7. Answer the following questions with reference to Figure 2.11(b) for a flow net under a dam with a sheet pile. Note that the numbers beside the equipotentials are labels only and not representative of head values.
(a) What are the values of equipotentials 17, 9, 2, and 0?
(b) What is the rate of seepage under the dam if the dam is 120 ft long and the hydraulic conductivity is 5 m/d?
(c) What is the rate of seepage under the dam if the upstream water level drops to 12 ft?

2-8. Refer to Figure 5.18 which shows the potentiometric map for a shallow sand aquifer. The hydraulic conductivity of the unit is estimated to be 1.5×10^{-2} cm^2/s
(a) Which well would you expect to be most contaminated?
(b) What is the groundwater velocity and seepage velocity across the plume?
(c) Estimate how long the source has been contaminating the aquifer. You may ignore the effects of dispersion, diffusion and adsorption.
(d) Estimate the rate of flow across the plume.
(e) How would you explain contamination upgradient of the source?

2-9. Two observation wells 1700 m apart have been constructed in a confined variable 587 hydraulic conductivity in the direction (see Figure P2.9). The flow rate is 0.008 m^3/h per unit width of the confined aquifer. Well 1 is drilled in Soil A with hydraulic conductivity 13 m/d, and Well 2 is drilled in Soil C with hydraulic conductivity 9 m/d. The soil zone B is between the wells, 600 m from Well 1 and 300 m from Well 2. The potentiometric surface is 6 m above the upper confining unit in Well 1 and 2.5 m above the upper confining unit in Well 2. Evaluate the hydraulic conductivity of Soil B.

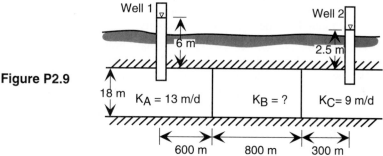

Figure P2.9

2-10. Three observation wells separated by 1000 m are drilled in a line in a confined aquifer with variable hydraulic conductivity in the x direction. The water surface elevation in Well 1 is 60 m and 52 m in Well 3. The hydraulic conductivity of the aquifer between Wells 1 and 2 is K_A, and between Wells 2 and 3 the hydraulic conductivity is K_B. Determine the water surface elevation in Well 2 for the following conditions:
   (a) $K_A = 10$ m/d, $K_B = 20$ m/d
   (b) $K_A = 10$ m/d, $K_B = 50$ m/d
   (c) $K_A = 50$ m/d, $K_B = 10$ m/d

2-11. Two piezometers are located 1000 ft apart with the bottom located at depths of 50 ft and 350 ft, respectively, in a 400 ft thick unconfined aquifer. The depth to the water table is 50 ft in the deeper piezometer and 40 ft in the shallow one. Assume that hydraulic conductivity is 0.0002 ft/s.
   (a) Use the Dupuit equation to calculate the height of the water table midway between the piezometers.
   (b) Find the quantity of seepage through a section 25 ft wide.

2-12. Three geologic formations overlie one another with the characteristics listed below. A constant velocity vertical flow field exists across the three formations. The hydraulic head is 33 ft at the top of the formations (top of formation no. 1) and 21 ft at the bottom (bottom of formation no. 3). Calculate the hydraulic head at the two internal boundaries, that is, at the top and bottom of formation no. 2. Assume:
$$b_1 = 50 \text{ ft} \qquad K_1 = 0.0002 \text{ ft/s}$$
$$b_2 = 20 \text{ ft} \qquad K_2 = 0.000005 \text{ ft/s}$$
$$b_3 = 210 \text{ ft} \qquad K_3 = 0.001 \text{ ft/s}$$

2-13. A formation is composed of four horizontal, homogeneous, and isotropic strata overlying one another. The hydraulic conductivity in the top layer is 1×10^{-3} cm/s, 1×10^{-6} cm/s in the second layer, 1×10^{-2} cm/s in the third layer, and 1×10^{-4} cm/s in the bottom layer. Calculate the effective horizontal and vertical hydraulic conductivities for the entire formation if each layer is 3 m thick. Give an example of soil types that might make up this formation.

2-14. A soil sample 6 in. in diameter and 1 ft long is placed in a falling head permeameter. The falling head tube diameter is 1 in. and the initial head is 6 in. The head falls 1 in. over a two hour period. Calculate the hydraulic conductivity.

2-15. A constant head permeameter containing fine grained sand has a length of 12 cm, and an area of 30 cm². For a head of 10 cm, a total of 100 ml of water is collected in 25 min. Find the hydraulic conductivity.

2-16. Two observation wells, 450 m apart, have been constructed in a confined aquifer with a hydraulic conductivity of 5×10^{-4} cm/s and a porosity of 0.35. The average thickness of the aquifer between the wells is 45 m. Well 1 (water surface elevation of 95 m) lies to the east of Well 2 (water surface elevation of 94.6 m). A stream lies 900 m to the west of Well 2.
   (a) Determine the flow rate per unit width of the aquifer.
   (b) Calculate how long it would take groundwater contaminants to travel from Well 1 to the stream.
   (c) Calculate the level of the potentiometric surface at a distance 600 m to the east of Well 1.

2-17. A conservative compound is discharged into a pond with water surface elevation of 100 m. The compound moves from the pond to a river (water surface elevation 99.3 m) 1.2 km away through a confined aquifer 12 m thick. The aquifer has a transmissivity of 0.05 m²/s and a porosity of 0.30. Ignoring the effects of dispersion (see Chapter 6) and adsorption to the soil, and assuming immediate and complete mixing, how long would it take for the contaminant to reach the river? How would your answer differ if the aquifer was unconfined?

2-18. The base of a proposed landfill for paper-mill sludge is in a glacial till, 30 ft above an aquifer. The vertical hydraulic conductivity of the till is 1×10^{-7} cm/s, the vertical hydraulic gradient is 0.075, and the effective porosity is 0.30. If the leachate (contaminated fluid) drains from the landfill into the till, how many years would pass before the leachate reached the aquifer below? If the vertical hydraulic conductivity 3×10^{-6} cm/s, what would the travel time be?

2-19. A 3 m thick aquitard ($K_2 = 0.5$ m/d) separates an unconfined aquifer ($K_1 = 15$ m/d) from a leaky confined aquifer ($K_3 = 10$ m/d). The water table is above the potentiometric surface for the leaky confined aquifer. Three observation wells are drilled- one in the unconfined aquifer, one in the aquitard, and one in the leaky confined aquifer. The head in the leaky confined aquifer is 23 m and in the unconfined aquifer the head is 25 m. Using Darcy's Law calculate the head in the well at the top of the leaky confined aquifer (the base of the aquitard). Assume steady state conditions. The datum is at the base of the aquitard layer.

2-20. Two parallel rivers are separated by 1.5 km. The water surface elevations of the rivers are 60 m and 45 m and the datum is defined as the base of the river beds. A confined aquifer extends between the two rivers from elevation 0 m to elevation 30 m, and has a transmissivity of 210 m²/d. The hydraulic conductivity of an unconfined aquifer on top of this formation is 10 m/d.
   (a) Determine the combined flow rate between the two rivers.
   (b) Determine the shortest time of travel for a contaminant to move from one to the other. Neglect dispersion effects and assume both aquifers have a porosity of 0.25.

2-21. A confined aquifer (hydraulic conductivity 1 m/d) flows into an unconfined aquifer (hydraulic conductivity 2 m/d) and then enters a shallow lake (as shown in Figure P2.21). The elevation of the lower confining unit for both aquifers is 130 m. The elevation of the base of the upper confining unit is 138 m. The upper confining unit is 2 m thick and extends across both aquifers. The thickness of the confined aquifer is 8 m. If the potentiometric surface at A is at an elevation of 140 m (h_A), find the elevation of the lake water surface (h_c).

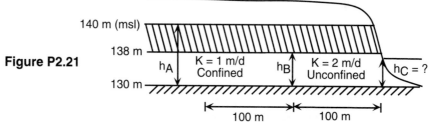

Figure P2.21

2-22. Two rivers are 1000 m apart. The water surface elevation of the first river is 30 m, and 25 m for the second river. The area between the rivers receives a recharge of 10 cm/y (after runoff). If the hydraulic conductivity is 0.8 m/d, find the location and elevation of the water divide and the daily seepage into each river. Sketch a flow net for the aquifer in the problem above.

2-23. A landfill liner is laid at elevation 50 ft msl (mean sea level) on top of a good unit. A clean sand unit extends from elevation 50 ft to elevation 75 ft, and another clay unit extends up to the surface located at elevation 100 ft. The landfill can be represented by a square with length of 500 ft on a side and a vertical depth of 50 ft from the surface. The landfill has a 3 ft thick clay liner with $K = 10^{-7}$ cm/s around the sides and bottom, as shown in Figure P2.23. The regional ground water level for the confined sand ($K = 10^{-2}$ cm/s) is located at depth of 10 ft below the surface. How much water will have to be continuously pumped from the landfill to keep the potentiometric surface at 60 ft elevation (msl) within the landfill? Assume mostly horizontal flow.

Figure P2.23

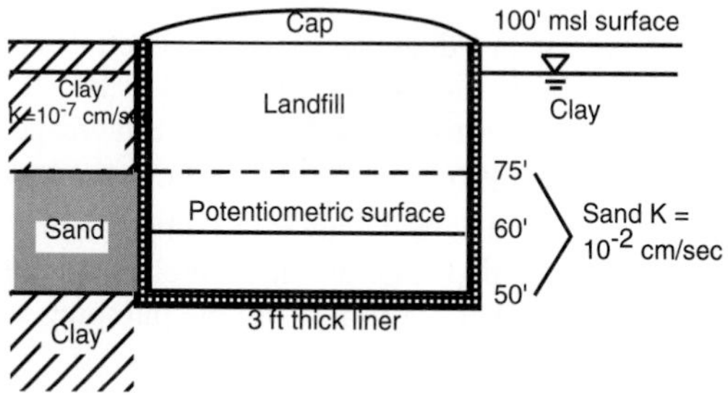

2-24. Repeat Problem 2.23 for the case where the clean sand unit extends below the landfill to an elevation of 25 ft msl. Assume water can flow through the sides and bottom of the clay liner

2-25. Repeat Example 2.3 for the case where net recharge $W = 10$ cm/yr. Repeat the example for the case where $W = 0$.

2-26. Compute the flow rate through Figure 2.13 if the total head drop is 10 ft and $K = 1$ ft/day

2-27. A confined aquifer slopes gradually from 20 m to 10 m in thickness over a length of 1 km. The slope of the potentiometric surface is 0.5 m/km and the hydraulic conductivity of the aquifer is 50 m/d. For a sloping aquifer, the continuity equation yields the following relation:

$$Q = \frac{(\phi_1 - \phi_2)/L}{\int \dfrac{dx}{T(x)}}$$

What is the flow rate through a 100 m wide section of the aquifer?

2-28. Sketch a quantitative flow net for the following confined a total flow per unit width if the hydraulic conductivity is 20 m/d.

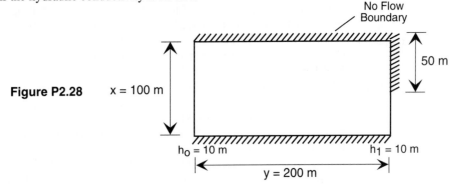

Figure P2.28   x = 100 m

Chapter 3

3-1. A well with a diameter of 18 in. penetrates an unconfined aquifer that is 100 ft thick. Two observation wells are located at 100 ft and 235 ft from the well, and the measured drawdowns are 22.2 ft and 21 ft, respectively. Flow is steady and the hydraulic conductivity is 1320 gpd/ft². What is the rate of discharge from the well?

3-2. A well of 0.5 m diameter is pumped from confined aquifer at 0.08 m³/s. The drawdown recorded at Observation Well 1 (15 m from the pumping well) is 3.8m; at Observation Well 2 (50 m from the pumping well) the drawdown is 2.8m. What is the drawdown at the pumping well?

3-2. A single well pumps 1000 m³/d in a confined aquifer of thickness 10 m and porosity 0.3. At the radius of influence of the well (1000 m) the head is 20 m. Assuming steady state conditions calculate the seepage velocity towards the well at a radius of 100 m, and a radius of 500 m.

3-3. (a) A well in a confined aquifer of thickness B pumps continuously at a rate Q. Using Darcy's Law in radial coordinates and the fact that the seepage velocity, $v_s = dr/dt$, show that the travel time for contaminants to move to the well of radius r_w, from a point on the radius of influence, R, is

$$t = (\pi Bn/Q)(R^2 - r_w^2)$$

(b) A fully penetrating well of 0.8 m diameter and with a radius of influence of 100 m, is drilled in a confined aquifer 15 m thick. The aquifer has a transmissivity of 50 m²/d and a porosity of 0.3. At what rate should the well be pumped if the time of travel for a contaminant to reach the well from the radius of influence is to be not less than 200 days. If the potentiometric surface was 15 m above the upper confining layer before pumping began, what is the steady state drawdown in the well?

3-5. A confined aquifer extends 3.5 km between the West River and the East River. The water surface elevations of the rivers are 230 m and 228.5 m respectively. The radius of influence of a fully penetrating pumping well located halfway between the rivers is 90 m. The well has a diameter of 0.5 m and pumps at a rate of 750 L/min. The elevation of the upper confining unit is 227 m and the aquifer is 25 m thick. The transmissivity of the aquifer is 8 m²/d. Determine the steady state head 20 m to the east of the well.

3-6. In a fully penetrating well, the equilibrium drawdown is 30 ft with a constant pumping rate of 20 gpm. The aquifer is unconfined and the saturated thickness is 100 ft. What is the steady-state drawdown measured in the well when the pumping rate is 10 gpm? Assume radius of influence remains constant.

3-7. A fully penetrating well in an unconfined aquifer is pumped continuously so that the steady state drawdown is 15 m. The water table is at a height of 55 m from the bottom of the aquifer which has a hydraulic conductivity of 20 m/d. The diameter of the well is 0.25 m.
(a) If the pumping has no effect on the water table at a distance of 1.2 km, determine the pumping rate.
(b) Determine the drawdown in an observation well located 600 m from the pumping well.
(c) Determine the travel time from the observation well to the pumping well if the aquifer has a porosity of 0.4.

3-8. A fully penetrating well of radius r_w is located in the center of a circular confined aquifer of radius r_a and thickness B. The hydraulic conductivity of the aquifer varies with radius such that $K = K_1$ for $r_1 \geq r \geq r_w$ and $K = K_2$ for $r_a \geq r \geq r_1$ If the piezometric head is maintained at h_w at $r = r_w$ and h_a at $r = r_a$ at what rate would the well be pumping?

3-9. Two wells are located 100 m apart in a confined aquifer with transmissivity $T = 2 \times 10^{-4}$ m²/s and storativity $S = 7 \times 10^{-5}$. One well is pumped at a rate of 6.6 m³/hr and the other at a rate of 10.0 m³/hr. Plot drawdown as a function of distance along the line joining the wells at 1 hr after the pumping starts.

3-10. A Hvorslev slug test was performed in a confined aquifer with a piezometer screened over of 20 ft and a radius of 1 in. The radius of the rod was 0.68 in. The following recovery data for the well were observed. Given that the static water level is 7.58 ft and $H_o = 6.88$ ft, calculate the hydraulic conductivity.

TIME(s)	20	45	75	101	138	164	199
h (ft)	6.94	7.00	7.21	7.27	7.34	7.38	7.40

3-11. A well casing with a radius of 6 in. is installed through a confining layer into a formation with a thickness of 10 ft. A screen with a radius of 3 in. is installed in the casing. A slug of water is injected, raising the water level by 0.5 ft. Given the following recorded data for head decline, find the values of T, K, and S for this aquifer.

TIME(s)	5	10	30	50	80	120	200
h (ft)	0.47	0.42	0.32	0.26	0.10	0.05	0.01

3-12. A small municipal well was pumped for 2 hr at a rate of 15.75 L/s. An observation well was located 50 ft from the pumping well and the following data were recorded. Using the Theis method outlined in Example 3.3, compute T and S.

TIME (min)	DRAWDOWN (ft)	TIME (min)	DRAWDOWN (ft)
1	1.5	15	14.9
2	4.0	20	17.0
3	6.2	40	21.4
5	8.5	60	23.1
7	10.0	90	26.0
9	12.0	120	28.0
12	13.7		

3-13. A well in a confined aquifer is pumped at a rate of 833 L/min for a period of over 8 hr. Time-drawdown data for an observation well located 250 m away are given below. The aquifer is 5 m thick. Use the Cooper-Jacob method to find value K, and S for this aquifer.

TIME (hr)	DRAWDOWN (m)	TIME (hr)	DRAWDOWN (m)
0.050	0.091	1.170	1.860
0.083	0.214	1.333	1.920
0.133	0.397	1.500	2.040
0.200	0.640	1.670	2.130
0.333	0.976	2.170	2.290
0.400	1.100	2.670	2.530
0.500	1.250	3.333	2.590
0.630	1.430	4.333	2.810
0.780	1.560	5.333	2.960
0.830	1.620	6.333	3.110
1.000	1.740	8.333	3.320

3-14. Drawdown, s, was observed in a well located 100 ft from a pumping well that was pumped at a rate of 1.11 cfs for a 30 hr period. Use the Cooper-Jacob method to compute T and S for this aquifer.

Time(hr)	1	2	3	4	5	6	8	10	12	18	24	30
S(ft)	0.6	1.4	2.4	2.9	3.3	4.0	5.2	6.5	7.5	9.1	10.5	11.5

3-15. Repeat Problem 3.14 using the Theis method.

3-16. The drawdown in three observation wells was recorded after 24 hours of pumping from a well at 2300 m³/d and the results are shown below. Calculate the transmissivity and storage coefficient of the aquifer using the Theis Method. You will need to plot drawdown versus r^2/t at a point in time for the three different radii and match the curves as before. Based on your estimate of the storativity, do you think the aquifer is confined or unconfined?

Well Number	Distance from Well (m)	Drawdown (m)
1	100	1.5
2	200	1.25
3	300	1.10

3-17. A well injects water into an aquifer at $Q = 1.0$ cfs. A river running north/south lies 300 ft west of the well. The confined aquifer with thickness of 10 ft has $T = 3200$ sq ft/day and $S = 0.005$. Observation wells are located 10, 50, 150, 300 and 450 ft west of the well.
   (a) Compute the head buildup along the x-axis at the observation well locations after 6 hr of injection.
   (b) Compute the Darcy velocity along the x-axis using simple graphical methods at the various well locations.

3-18. Use the Theis Method equations for the functions u and $W(u)$ to characterize the expected behavior of an areally infinite, homogeneous, horizontal, isotropic, confined aquifer. The aquifer has a transmissivity of 500 m²/d and a storativity of 1×10^{-5}. The well is pumped continuously at 2500 m³/d.
   (a) What will be the drawdown 75 m away from the pumping well at 1, 10, 100, 1000, and 10,000 minutes after pumping begins?
   (b) Estimate when the system will reach steady state.
   (c) Estimate the steady state drawdown in the well.
   (d) What will be the drawdown after one day at distances of 2, 5, 10, 50, 200, and 1000 m from the pumping well? Estimate the distance at which the pumping will have no effect on the potentiometric surface after one day of pumping.

3-19. A well at distance d from an impermeable boundary pumps at a flow rate Q. The head at any point (x, y) is given by the following expression:

$$h(x, y) = \frac{Q}{2\pi kb} \ln(r_1 r_2) + C$$

where C is a constant, r_1 is the straight line distance from the well to point (x, y), and r_2 is the straight line distance from the image well to the point (x, y). The y-axis lies along the impermeable boundary. Use Darcy's Law to show that the discharge across the y-axis is zero.

3-20. A well is to be placed in an unconfined aquifer at a distance x from a stream. The well will be required to pump at a constant rate of 1.3×10^{-3} m³/s. The aquifer has an average thickness of 10m and hydraulic conductivity of 1×10^{-2} cm/s. Regulations stipulate that the drawdown at a radius of 15 m from the well may not exceed 0.6 m.. Calculate x such that it is the smallest distance that satisfies the requirements.

3-21. A fully penetrating well pumps from a confined aquifer of thickness 20 m and hydraulic conductivity 10 m/d. There is no water table above the confined aquifer. The radius of the well is 0.25 m, and the recorded drawdown in the well is 0.5 m. Assume that the radius of influence of the well is 1250 m.

(a) Calculate the pumping rate if the well is 100 m from a stream.

(b) Calculate the pumping rate if the well is 100 m from an impermeable boundary.

3-22. An excavation site is to be dewatered by using four pumping wells located at the corners of a square with sides of 500 m. The wells are fully penetrating and have diameters of 0.5 m. What is the required flow rate in each well if the objective is to lower the original water table ($h_0 = 100$ m) by 5 m everywhere in the square site? Note that the maximum drawdown may not occur in the center of the square. The hydraulic conductivity of the aquifer is 1.5 m/d and the radius of influence for each well is 1000 m.

3-23. (a) Three fully penetrating wells in a confined aquifer form an equilateral triangle of side a. Two of the wells are a distance d from a long river. Each well has a radius r_w,. and pumps at a rate Q. At steady state the wells have a radius of influence of R and the water table is at an elevation of h_0. If the aquifer has a conductivity of K, derive an expression for the drawdown in the center of the triangle.

3- What is the drawdown in the center of the triangle if the parameters are: $a = 70$ m, d $= 100$ m, $K = 1.5$ m/d, $Q = 700$ m³/d, $R = 600$ m, $h_0 = 50$m

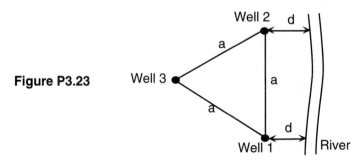

Figure P3.23

3-24. Walton (1960) gave data for an aquifer test in a well confined by a leaky aquitard 14 ft thick. Drawdown was measured in an observation well 96 ft away from a pumping well which was pumping at 25 gpm. For the following data, use Figure 3.13 to determine T, S and K'.

TIME (min)	DRAWDOWN (ft)	TIME (min)	DRAWDOWN (ft)
5	0.76	493	5.96
28	3.30	669	6.11
41	3.59	958	6.27
60	4.08	1129	6.40
75	4.39	1185	6.42
244	5.47		

3-25. An interceptor well fully penetrates a confined aquifer with a hydraulic conductivity of 0.5 cm/s. Before pumping began the aquifer had a hydraulic gradient of 0.001 and a saturated thickness of 27 m. The interceptor well pumps at a rate of 60 L/s. Define the capture zone of the interceptor well by calculating the maximum width and the distance to the stagnation point. Sketch the shape of the groundwater divide using at least ten points.

Chapter 6

6-1. Chloride was injected as a continuous source into a 1-D column 50 cm long at a seepage velocity of 10^{-3} cm/sec. The concentration measured after 1800 seconds from the beginning of the test was 0.3 of the initial concentration, and after 2700 seconds it reached 0.4 of the initial concentration. Find the coefficient of dispersion and longitudinal dispersivity.

6-2. Chloride has been injected into a 1-D column continuously. If the system has a Darcy velocity of 5.18×10^{-3} in/day, the porosity of the medium is 0.3, and the longitudinal dispersivity is 5 m,
(a) What is C/C_0 at 0.3 m from the point of injection after 5 days?
(b) Repeat (a) with a longitudinal dispersivity of 20 m.
(c) Comment on the difference in results.

6-3. The estimated mass from an instantaneous spill of benzene was 107 kg per m^2 of the 1-D aquifer. The aquifer has a seepage velocity of 0.03 in/day and a longitudinal dispersion coefficient of 9×10^{-4} m^2/day.
(a) Calculate the maximum concentration at $t = 1$ year.
(b) Calculate the benzene concentrations at $t = 1$ year, at one standard deviation on either side of the center mass of the plume.
(c) Plot the breakthrough curve vs. time at $x = (vt)$ ($t = 1$ year).
(d) Plot the breakthrough curve vs. distance at $t = 1$ year.
(e) Discuss the difference.

6-4. Match the breakthrough curves given in the diagram with the proper description given below. Curves represent responses to the injection of a tracer in l-D soil columns. Choose the best match for each case or indicate none of the above (NA).

   (a) Curve for a l-D continuous injection where the constituents get sorbed to the medium.

   (b) Curve for a l-D continuous injection where plug flow is observed.

   (c) Curve for an instantaneous source with longitudinal dispersion.

   (d) Curve for an instantaneous source with no dispersion

   (e) Curve for a l-D continuous injection with longitudinal dispersion

   (f) Curve for a l-D continuous injection with longitudinal dispersion and biodegradation.

   (g) Curve for a l-D continuous injection in which a fracture existed along the soil column.

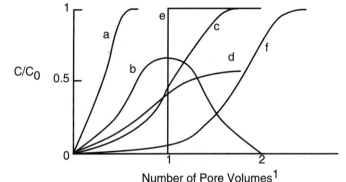

Figure P6.4

[1]A pore volume in a column is the volume of water that will completely fill all of the voids in the column.

6-5. Sketch (on the same graph) C/C_0 as a function of time for transport in a sand column from an instantaneous source for each of the following cases:

   (a) Advection only

   (b) Advection with low dispersion.

   (c) Advection with high dispersion.

   (d) Advection with high dispersion with biodegradation.

   (e) Advection with high dispersion with retardation.

6-6. A continuous source has been leaking contaminant for 2 years into a 1-D aquifer. The steady state dilution attenuation factor DAF for the aquifer is 100. DAF = Concentration at source/concentration at receptor well. Source concentration = 1200 mg/L

   (a) What is the concentration of benzene at a receptor well after 2 years.

   (b) What is the concentration of benzene at a receptor well in 2 years, if there is first order decay at a rate of 0.01 (1/day).

6-7. An instantaneous release of biodegradable organics occurs in a 1-D aquifer. Assume that the mass spilled is 1.0 kg over a 10 m^2 area normal to the flow direction, α_x = 1.0 m, the seepage velocity is 1.0 m/day and the half life of the decaying contaminant is 33 years. Compute the maximum concentration at 100 m from the source.

6-8. For a 2-D aquifer, calculate the maximum concentration of a spike source of Tritium, H-3 (half life = 12.26 years) at 100 m from a well injecting 1.0 kg of mass over 10 m of well screen. The plume velocity is 0.5 m/day, α_x = 1.0 m, α_y = 0.1 m.

6-9. An accidental spill from a point source introduced 10 kg of contaminant mass to an aquifer. The seepage velocity in the aquifer is 0.1 ft/day in the x direction. The longitudinal dispersion coefficient D_L = 0.01 ft^2/day, the lateral and vertical dispersion coefficient, $D_y = D_z$ = 0.001 ft^2/day.

    (a) Calculate the maximum concentration at x = 100 ft and t = 5 years.

    (b) Calculate the concentration at point x = 200 ft, y = 5 ft, z = 2 ft, 5 years after the spill.

6-10. Domenico & Schwartz, 1998, developed a model for a planar source that accounts for the source geometry with longitudinal, lateral and vertical spreading. The steady state model was applied at the plane of symmetry where y = z = 0 (see Figure 6.8).

The model is to be applied to the case of a continuous source that has been leaking contaminant into an aquifer for 15 years. The source had a width Y and a depth Z of 6 m, the initial concentration of the source was 10 mg/L, the seepage velocity is 0.057 m/day, and the longitudinal, transverse and vertical dispersivities were estimated at 1 m, 0.1 m, 0.01 m respectively. Calculate the present contaminant concentration at x = 200 m from source, using the Domenico model.

6-11. A slug of contaminant was injected into a well for a tracer test (2-D). If the initial contaminant concentration is 1000 mg/L, the background seepage velocity in the aquifer is 0.022 m/day, the well radius is 0.05 m, the longitudinal dispersion coefficient is 0.034 m^2/day, and the transverse dispersion coefficient is 0.01 of the longitudinal dispersion coefficient.

    (a) What is the maximum concentration reached after 24 hours?

    (b) Plot the concentration vs. distance at t = 24 hours.

6-12. An underground storage tank (volume = 1.0 m^3) spills its contents of 1.0 kg of TCE in a 10 m thick sand aquifer. The seepage velocity is 1.0 m/day in the x direction. The longitudinal dispersivity is 1.0 m, the transverse and vertical dispersivities are 0.1 m.

    (a) Calculate the maximum concentration at a distance of x = 500 m. Note: y, z=0 for maximum concentration.

    (b) If the contaminant was uniformly spilled over the 10 m thickness of the aquifer, what is the maximum concentration at x = 500 m, y, z = 0, with vertical dispersion = 0.

    (c) Comment on the results.

6-13. A finite source of chloride is released at x = 0 into a 1-D aquifer over a 1 year period. The plume moves at a seepage velocity of 0.2 m/day, α_x = 2 m. Assume that the solution can be found by using an imaginary negative concentration source beginning at the end of the release period. Develop the equation for concentration $C(x,t)$ if C_0 = 1000 mg/L. Find the maximum concentration at x = 100 m.

6-14. The concentration of organic waste in a landfill is 100 mg/L. The pit is placed in a clay layer, $K = 10^{-6}$ cm/sec underlain by a sand layer, $K = 2 \times 10^{-2}$ cm/sec. The two units are separated by a thin impermeable silty layer. The top surface of the clay layer is at elevation 9.15 m above MSL for which the water table is at 8.5 m above MSL. The top surface of the sand layer is at elevation 6.1 m, for which the piezometric surface is 7.6m above MSL. The pit bottom lies at elevation 8.4 m above MSL. The slope of the piezometric surface is 0.01. The porosity of the 2 layers is 0.25, and the longitudinal dispersivity is estimated at 0.3 m. An observation well is located 300 m from the pit. (See Figure P6.14.)

   (a) Calculate the seepage velocity for the clay layer. How long does it take the contaminant to reach the sand layer.

   (b) Calculate the seepage velocity for the sand layer. What is the contamination level in the well after 15 years from the beginning of the release, assuming a 1-D model.

   (c) What would happen to the concentration in the well if lateral dispersion exists in the sand aquifer in addition to longitudinal dispersion.

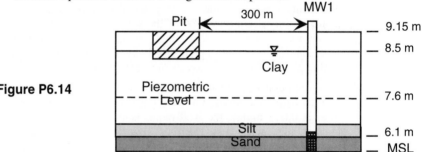

Figure P6.14

6-15. From example 6.4, multiply the vertical scale of Figure 6.10a times 2 and repeat the problem.

6-16. Prove that the plume described in Eq. (6.27) takes the form of a two dimensional Gaussian (normal) distribution as described below, and evaluate α_x and α_y

$$P = [1/(2\pi\sigma_x\sigma_y)]\exp(-[(x-x_0)^2/(2\sigma_x^2)] - [(y-y_0)^2/(2\sigma_y^2)])$$

6-17. A well 300 ft west of a river (which runs north/south) injects waste chloride at a rate of 30,000 ft³/day into a confined aquifer. The head in the aquifer and river prior to pumping was 100 ft. Aquifer characteristics include $T = 1,000$ ft²/ day, thickness of 20 ft, and $n = 0.25$. A farmer's well pumps water supply from the same aquifer 300 ft east of the river (on the other side) at 20,000 ft³/day. Both wells have a radius of influence of 1000 ft.

   (a) Compute the heads and velocities at 100 and 200 ft from the pumping well.

   (b) Will chloride arrive at the pumping well?

   (c) Find the average seepage velocity from the injection well to the river along the shortest line of travel. Use any convenient approximation method.

6-18. A tank of TCE located directly below a water table is known to be continuously leaking at concentration of 10,000 μg/L of TCE. The source can be assumed to be a vertical plane 5 m wide and 3 m deep located just below the water table. Dispersivity in the x, y, and z directions can be assumed to be 10 m, 3 m, and 0.3 m. Hydraulic gradient of the water table is 0.001 and the porosity is 0.3. The hydraulic conductivity K ranges from 2.0×10^{-2} to 5.0×10^{-2} cm/sec.

What is the highest concentration predicted to occur at a receptor located at $x = 100$ m, $y = 5$ m, and $z = 3$ m, where x is longitudinal, y is transverse, and z is vertical? Evaluate the results at $t = 1$ year, 3 years and 6 years. What level of remediation would be required to keep the receptor level below 5 µg/L for the range of K values indicated at $t = 6$ yr?

6-19. (a) From the chloride data presented in Figure 6.12b of a 2-D experiment at the Borden landfill, estimate the average seepage velocity in the aquifer, where porosity averages 0.3. Explain how you would compute the longitudinal and transverse dispersivity for the site from the field data (do not perform this calculation). What equation would you use?

(b) Adsorption of carbon tetrachloride was tested at the site and retardation is defined as the ratio of velocity of a natural tracer (chloride) to that of the retarding chemical. Roughly estimate the retardation factor of carbon tetrachloride (CTET) from the data in Figure 7.3b. All contaminants originated from the source location (0,0) at time zero.

6-20. Refer to the figure from the Borden Landfill natural gradient test. Assume that day 1 represents the input of chloride into the aquifer with $C_0 = 892$ mg/L over a 20 m² area. The plumes of chloride in 2-D for day 85, 462 and 647 are plotted on Figure 6.12b. Note that the latter two plumes overlap each other.

(a) Roughly sketch the longitudinal distribution of chloride concentration for day 85, 462, and 647 on a single graph of concentration vs. distance measured from the peak conc. of each curve.

(b) Use the 2-D equation for a pulse input to compute α_L and α_T (dispersivity) based only on the observed peak conc. for day 647 (Eq. 6.27). Use seepage $V = 30$ m/yr, $C_0 = 892$ mg/L, $area = 20$ m², and $t = 647$ days. Assume that the ratio of α_L to α_T is 10/1.

6.21 A landfill next to a river has been leaking chromium continuously for 20 years, creating a plume of contamination. The gradient of ground water flow is towards the river, as shown in the figure below. Well concentration data is provided along with water level readings. Assume that chromium acts as a conservative tracer in this aquifer where longitudinal dispersivity =1.0 m. Landfill, ground water, and river data are provided in the following table and Figure P6.21. $K = 10^{-3}$ cm/sec; n = 0.4; b = 20 ft; Q(river) = 200 cfs; Concentration of Cr at point A (upstream) = 0 mg/L.

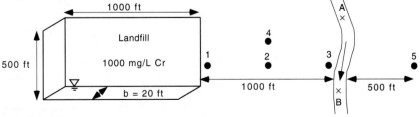

Figure P6.21

Well	Water elevation (ft)	Cr Concentration (mg/L)
1	100	1000
2	90	no data
3	80	no data
4	90	0
5	100	0

(a) Find the predicted concentration of Cr in well 3 (at t = 20 years).

3- Find the concentration of Cr in the river at point B (immediately downstream) Consider the flow from both sides of the river.

6-22. A well fully penetrates an aquifer which has a uniform depth of 10 m. 100 grams of benzene is spilled into the well and is immediately dissolved and mixed into the water in the well. The seepage velocity = 30 m/yr in the x direction, the longitudinal dispersivity = 1.0 m, and the transverse dispersivity is 0.1 m.

Using the following aquifer characteristics, calculate the retardation factor R for benzene in this aquifer. Bulk density = 1.8 g/cm^3, porosity = 0.3, organic carbon fraction = 1%, K_{ow} for benzene = 135 L/kg

(a) Which equation should you use for calculating benzene concentrations downgradient of the well (1-D, 2-D, or 3-D; spike or continuous)

(b) What is the maximum benzene concentration at t = 1 year? Where is this maximum located?

(c) What is the benzene concentration at t = 1 year, 3 meters away from the center of mass in the x direction?

(d) What is the benzene concentration at t = 1 year, 3 meters away from the center of mass in the y direction?

(e) Comment on how the dispersivity affects the concentration of benzene 3 m away in the x and y directions.

6-23. Repeat Example 6.1a from Chapter 6, using a retardation factor $(R = 2.5)$ for benzene.

6-24. Repeat Example 6.2 from Chapter 6 for benzene (with a retardation factor, R = 2) for a 10,000 µg/L spill.

6-25. Bromide (Br⁻), a common field tracer, is injected continuously at a concentration of 500 mg/L and a flowrate of 5 L/min from a well (6 inches in diameter) into a confined aquifer with a hydraulic conductivity of 2×10^{-4} cm/s and a gradient of 0.009. The porosity is 0.3 and α_x = 1 m, α_y = 0.1m A receptor well is located 2 meters downgradient of the injection well. You may neglect the z-direction as the well is assumed to be fully penetrating the aquifer.

(a) Plot out the Br⁻ concentration versus time for the receptor well.

(b) For t = 24 hours, plot the concentration as a function of distance.

6-26. Chromium is a common contaminant associated with metal plating operations. Chromium was continuously released from a small metal shop for 5 years at a concentration of 5000 mg/L into an aquifer with a porosity of 0.3, α_x = 1 m, and α_y = 0.1 m. the aquifer is a fine sand $(2.4 \times 10^{-3}$ cm/s). Groundwater flow is to the south with a gradient of 0.01. A nearby resident placed a shallow well (fully screened) for watering a garden 1000 feet south and 50 feet east of the discharge location. The EPA MCL for chromium is 0.1 mg/L. Assume that there is no degradation. Calcu-

late the maximum possible concentration in the well if the depth of the source zone
was 1 foot and the width of the source zone was

(a) 6 inches   (b)   12 inches   (c)   36 inches

6-27. Several drums of radioactive waste leaked into an aquifer. with $\alpha_x = 1$ m, $\alpha_y = 0.1$m,
and $\alpha_y = 0.04$m. The drums contained 1000 ci Sr–90 and 300 ci Cs–137 (see table
4.5) The linear groundwater velocity is 10 cm/day. Sr–90 has a half life of 28 years,
and Cs–137 has a half life of 33 years. A river is located 1000 feet downgradient of
the drums. Calculate the time it takes for Sr–90 and Cs–137 to reach the river and determine what the maximum concentration will be at a point near the river bank.

6-28. A tracer study is to be performed at a field site to determine hydraulic conductivity.
Slug tests indicate that the site has a conductivity between 10^{-3} and 10^{-4} cm/s. The
aquifer is confined with a thickness of 15 ft. Bromide has been selected for the tracer
(field detection limit of 0.1 mg Br⁻/L using the Phenol Red colorimetric method).
The tracer is injected at a concentration of 1000 mg/L for 12 hours into a fully
screened well with a 6 inch diameter and then monitored at various receptor wells to
determine hydraulic conductivity and dispersivity. The tracer test needs to be finished
within 3 weeks.

(a) Choose the location for five monitoring wells around the injection well. Since
this is for design purposes, assume porosity of 0.3, $\alpha_x = 1$ m, and $\alpha_y = 0.1$ m.

(b) Design a sampling schedule for the test taking into account the cost associated
with taking a round of samples and the resolution necessary to determine the hydraulic conductivity and dispersivity. Remember that you do not know the exact
hydraulic conductivity and dispersivity beforehand.

Chapter 8

8-1. Example 8.2 in the text presents a biodegrading plume (assume that it is all benzene)
which then receives 20 and 40 mg/L of oxygen into the aquifer. Answer the following questions regarding the benzene plume.

(a) What is the average seepage velocity in the plume with the pump/treat system
on? What is the flow rate across the plume assumed to be 2500 ft wide?

(b) Each well in the pump and treat system is pumping 1 gpm. How does this
combined flow compare to the average flow across the plume without pumping?

(c) What mass of oxygen in Kg is transported into the plume over the two year period assuming a concentration of 8.0 mg/L in the groundwater.

(d) If there is 15 inches of rainfall per year, with an O_2 concentration of 8.0 mg/L,
what mass of additional benzene will be degraded over that contained in Fig. 8.6.

(e) Why does the plume shape change in Fig. 8.6 after biodegradation?

8-2. Set up a BIOPLUME II or III model for the input data given in example 8.2

(a) Change pump locations by 2 cells

(b) Change pump rates by a factor of 2

(c) Change O_2 concentrations by a factor of 2

(d) Change the gradient across the plume by a factor of 2

(e) Compare your results with example 8.2 and discuss.

Chapter 11

11-1. A contaminated site has been surveyed and a contaminated region 100 ft × 150 ft × 15 ft deep was delineated. The average concentration of total petroleum hydrocarbons (TPH) on soil is 10,000 mg/Kg .

  (a) What is the total mass of contaminants at the site in kilograms? Assume the density of the soil is about 128 lb per cubic foot (specific gravity = 2).

  (b) Using the results from (a), estimate the total volume of petroleum hydrocarbons released assuming 50% of the hydrocarbons have been lost to volatilization, biodegradation, and dissolution (report the answer in gallons). Assume that the hydrocarbon released at the site was gasoline with a specific gravity of 0.8, and that the density of the gasoline did not change over time in the soil.

  (c) Estimate the residual saturation of the hydrocarbon-soil system. Assume a soil porosity of 0.35.

11-2. A sampling program at a Superfund site indicated the following DNAPL zones:
  - A "pool" of free-phase DNAPL in a stratigraphic depression in an unfractured clay. The pool is 200 ft² in area and averages 5 ft in thickness.
  - A zone of residual DNAPL extending directly underneath an old pit 100 ft² in area. The residual zone extends through the 5 ft thick unsaturated zone and 15 ft through the saturated zone until it reaches the DNAPL pool.

  Other Data: Laboratory tests of mgs of hydrocarbons on the soil and engineering judgment provided the following saturation data:
  Residual saturation in the unsaturated zone: 0.10
  Residual saturation in the saturated zone: 0.35
  Saturation in the free-phase zone: 0.70

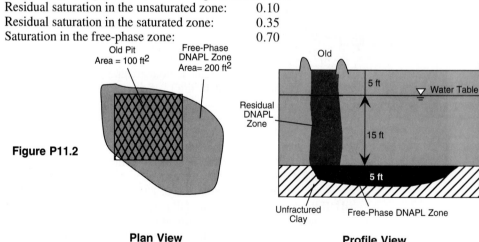

Figure P11.2

Plan View   **Profile View**

  (a) What is the estimated total volume of DNAPL at the site?
  (b) How much is pumpable from a theoretical basis?
  (Assume a typical porosity value of 0.3. This should be considered an upper range estimate of the total recoverable volume. Actual volumes are usually much lower).

11-3. A source zone contains about 2000 drums of residual DNAPL comprised of TCE (Trichloroethylene). The porosity is 0.4 and the total mass of DNAPL is 1.3×10^5 kg. The average down gradient dissolved hydrocarbon concentration is 100 mg/L. If there is no adsorption, biodegradation, or natural attenuation of any kind, what is a ballpark estimate for the maximum length of contaminant plume that would result?

> **Hint:** Do not use the advection dispersion equation. Assume the entire depth and width of the aquifer downstream of the source contains dissolved hydrocarbons at 100 mg/L. Calculate the maximum length of the plume when all of the DNAPL is dissolved into the aquifer. Note that the result from this approach may be much greater than the longest plumes observed in the field (a couple of miles) as no attenuation effects are considered.

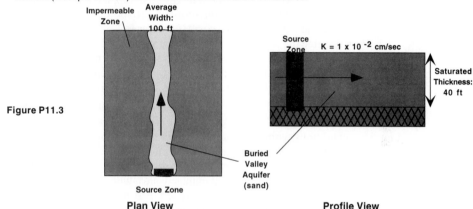

Figure P11.3

Plan View   Profile View

11-4. Gasoline is found in a monitoring well with a specific gravity of 0.8. If a total of 6 ft of gasoline is found in the well, what is the estimated actual thickness of the LNAPL in the formation?

11-5. A large gasoline release completely displaces the water in an shallow sandy aquifer at an old refinery. A large recovery trench is installed to recovery the free-product gasoline.

Using Darcy's law, what is the estimated recovery rate of LNAPL in gpm (gallons per minute)?

Note that hydraulic conductivity can be converted to intrinsic permeability by using 1 cm/sec ~ 1×10^3 darcies = 10^{-5} cm^2. Use values in units of cm^2 for intrinsic permeability and poise (not centipoise; 1 cp = 0.01 poise) for dynamic viscosity in Eq. 11.9.

Profile View

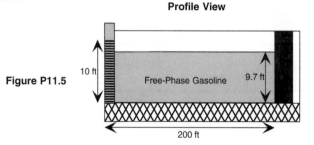

Figure P11.5

Trench Length: 100 ft.

Hydraulic Conductivity of Sand:
1x 10^{-2} cm/sec

Density of Gasoline: 0.8 fm/cm^3

Dynamic viscosity: 0.45 centipoise

11-6. Assume that Figure 11.14 represents the residual saturation curve for the system for this system (even though gasoline is not a DNAPL). If there is 20% of water in the system shown in Problem 11-5 (therefore saturation of gasoline = 0.8),

(a) What would the relative permeability be?

(b) What percentage reduction in gasoline recovery would there be?

(c) Would there be any water recovery?

(d) When the NAPL reaches residual saturation, what is the relative permeability for NAPL and for water?

11-7. Using the capillary number relationship (Eq. 11.13), estimate the hydraulic gradient required to initiate movement of gasoline trapped at residual saturation in a gravel aquifer with a hydraulic conductivity of 1×10^{-1} cm/sec.

• Assume the dynamic viscosity of water is 1 cp, or 0.01 g/cm-sec.

• Assume the interfacial tension for gasoline is 50 dyne/cm

• (1 dyne = 1 gm cm/sec^2). Use the capillary number curve for sandstone in Fig. 11.16 as representative data for this system.

Is your answer the same as is shown if Fig. 11.16?

11-8. A contaminated area in the saturated zone has approximately 250 kg of gasoline trapped as a residual NAPL. If you needed to remediate this area back to background conditions within a 6 month timeframe, how could one use in-situ biodegradation to reach the 6 month cleanup objective?

• Assume that you can design a groundwater injection/extraction system that will flush the contaminated area with oxygenated (but otherwise untreated) water. Therefore the only removal mechanism will be the in-situ biodegradation, and the flushing zone will serve as an underground bio-reactor.

• Assume the groundwater Darcy velocity is 5 m/day and the oxygen/hydrocarbon consumption ratio by the native microorganisms is 2 mg O_2/mg NAPL. See Example 11.7 for any other required data.

• Note that the solubility of oxygen in water at 20 °C is 9.2 mg/L when the water is in equilibrium with air (21% O_2) and proportionally higher when in contact with pure oxygen)

Is it possible to dissolve this much oxygen into the reinjection stream using air? Using pure oxygen?

11-9. A DNAPL mixture is estimated to consist of 110,000 mg/kg 1,2 dichloroethane, 5,000 mg/kg trichloroethene, and the rest long chained alkanes such as decane. What is the effective solubility of these chemicals when water is in contact with this DNAPL?

Chemical	Molecular Weight (g/mole)	Solubility (mg/L)
1,2 DCA	72	8,690
TCE	131	1,000
Decane	142	Insoluble

INDEX